NEW CONCISE

PROJECT MATHS 4

FOR LEAVING CERT HIGHER LEVEL

GEORGE HUMPHREY, BRENDAN GUILDEA, GEOFFREY REEVES
LOUISE BOYLAN

GILL & MACMILLAN

Gill & Macmillan
Hume Avenue
Park West
Dublin 12
with associated companies throughout the world
www.gillmacmillan.ie

© George Humphrey, Brendan Guildea, Geoffrey Reeves and
Louise Boylan 2012

978 07171 5031 1

Print origination by MPS Limited

The paper used in this book is made from the wood pulp of managed forests. For every tree felled, at least one tree is planted, thereby renewing natural resources.

Any links to external websites should not be construed as an endorsement by Gill & Macmillan of the content or views of the linked materials.

For permission to reproduce photographs, the authors and publisher gratefully acknowledge the following:

© Alamy: 417, 431, 441B, 443; © Getty Images: 367, 441T, 446, 447.

The authors and publisher have made every effort to trace all copyright holders, but if any has been inadvertently overlooked we would be pleased to make the necessary arrangement at the first opportunity.

Contents

Acknowledgments

The authors would like to thank Sorcha Forde, David Grimes, Elaine Guildea, Jessica Hayden, Colman Humphrey, Allison Lynch and Gráinne McKnight who helped with the proofreading, checked the answers and made many valuable suggestions that are included in the final text.

The authors also wish to express their thanks to the staff of Gill & Macmillan, and special thanks to Kristin Jensen, for her advice, guidance and untiring assistance in the preparation and presentation of the book.

Preface

New Concise Project Maths 4 is one of two books covering the new Leaving Certificate Higher Level course for students taking the 2014 exam and onwards. The second book is *New Concise Project Maths 5*.

New Concise Project Maths 4 incorporates the approach to the teaching of mathematics envisaged in **Project Maths**. It reflects the greater emphasis on the understanding of mathematical concepts, developing problem-solving skills and relating mathematics to everyday events.

The authors strongly sympathise with the main aims and objectives of the new Project Maths syllabus and examination. In the worked examples, a numbered, step by step approach is used throughout the book to help with problem solving. There is a comprehensive range of carefully graded exercises to reflect the new exam. Exam style context questions are included to enhance students' understanding of everyday practical applications of mathematics. The emphasis is on a clear and practical presentation of the material. Simple and concise language is used throughout, instead of technical language, which is not required in the exam.

Additional teachers resources, including a **Digital Flipbook**, are provided online at www.gillmacmillan.ie.

An excellent resource for teachers and students is the dynamic software package GeoGebra. The package is of particular use for co-ordinate geometry, geometry and graphing functions. It can be accessed at www.geogebra.org.

George Humphrey
Brendan Guildea
Geoffrey Reeves
Louise Boylan
April 2012

Simplifying algebraic expressions and fractions

Special factors

1. $a^2 - b^2 = (a - b)(a + b)$ Difference of two squares
2. $a^3 - b^3 = (a - b)(a^2 + ab + b^2)$ Difference of two cubes
3. $a^3 + b^3 = (a + b)(a^2 - ab + b^2)$ Sum of two cubes

Special expansions

1. $(a + b)^2 = a^2 + 2ab + b^2$ 2. $(a - b)^2 = a^2 - 2ab + b^2$
3. $(a + b)^3 = a^3 + 3a^2b + 3ab^2 + b^3$ 4. $(a - b)^3 = a^3 - 3a^2b + 3ab^2 - b^3$

These factors and expansions occur frequently and should be memorised.

EXAMPLE

Factorise: (i) $6a^2b - 9ab^2$ (ii) $25x^2 - 16y^2$ (iii) $8x^3 - 27y^3$ (iv) $1 + 1{,}000p^3$

Solution:

(i) $6a^2b - 9ab^2$
$= 3ab(2a - 3b)$
(HCF is $3ab$)

(ii) $25x^2 - 16y^2$
$= (5x)^2 - (4y)^2$
$= (5x - 4y)(5x + 4y)$

(iii) $8x^3 - 27y^3$
$= (2x)^3 - (3y)^3$
$= (2x - 3y)[(2x)^2 + (2x)(3y) + (3y)^2]$
$= (2x - 3y)(4x^2 + 6xy + 9y^2)$

(iv) $1 + 1{,}000p^3$
$= (1)^3 + (10p)^3$
$= (1 + 10p)[(1)^2 - (1)(10p) + (10p)^2]$
$= (1 + 10p)(1 - 10p + 100p^2)$

Note: $xy + x = x(y + 1)$ not $x(y + 0)$
because $(x)(1) = x$ but $(x)(0) = 0$.
It is useful to remember that factorisation is just the reverse process to multiplying out.

Factors by grouping

On our course, an expression consisting of four terms with no common factor can be factorised with the following steps.

1. Group into pairs with a common factor.
2. Take out the common factor in each pair separately.
3. Take out the new common factor.

EXAMPLE 1

Factorise $6pq + rs - 2sq - 3rp$.

Solution:

There are no common factors in the first two pairs or in the last two pairs.

Therefore, we have to rearrange the terms.

$$6pq + rs - 2sq - 3rp$$ (rearrange order of the terms so that they are grouped
$$= 6pq - 3rp + rs - 2sq$$ into pairs with a common factor)
$$= 3p(2q - r) + s(r - 2q)$$ (take out the common factor in each pair)
$$= 3p(2q - r) - s(2q - r)$$ $(s(r - 2q) = -s(2q - r))$
$$= (2q - r)(3p - s)$$ (take out the common factor $(2q - r)$)

Note: This expression could also have been rearranged into pairs with common factors in other ways before factorising, such as:

$$6pq - 2sq - 3rp + rs \quad \text{or} \quad 6pq - 3rp - 2sq + rs$$

Multiplication and division of algebraic fractions

Operations with algebraic fractions follow the same rules as in arithmetic. Before attempting to simplify when multiplying or dividing algebraic fractions, factorise where possible and divide the top and bottom by common factors. The contents of a bracket should be considered as a single term.

EXAMPLE 2

Simplify $\dfrac{4x^2 - 10x}{9x^2 + 6x} \div \dfrac{2x - 5}{3x + 2}$.

Solution:

$\dfrac{4x^2 - 10x}{9x^2 + 6x} \div \dfrac{2x - 5}{3x + 2}$

$= \dfrac{4x^2 - 10x}{9x^2 + 6x} \times \dfrac{3x + 2}{2x - 5}$ (turn the fraction we divide by upside down and multiply)

$= \dfrac{2x(2x - 5)(3x + 2)}{3x(3x + 2)(2x - 5)}$ (factorise the top and bottom)

$= \dfrac{2}{3}$ (divide the top and bottom by the common factors, x, $(3x + 2)$ and $(2x - 5)$)

Addition and subtraction of algebraic fractions

To add or subtract algebraic fractions, do the following.

1. Factorise denominators (if necessary).
2. Find the LCM of the denominators.
3. Express each fraction in terms of this LCM and simplify.

EXAMPLE 3

Express the following as one fraction in its lowest terms:
$\dfrac{3}{x + 5} - \dfrac{2}{x + 3} + \dfrac{5x + 19}{x^2 + 8x + 15}$.

Solution:

$\dfrac{3}{x + 5} - \dfrac{2}{x + 3} + \dfrac{5x + 19}{x^2 + 8x + 15}$

$= \dfrac{3}{(x + 5)} - \dfrac{2}{(x + 3)} + \dfrac{5x + 19}{(x + 5)(x + 3)}$ (factorise the denominators; their LCM is $(x + 5)(x + 3)$)

$$= \frac{3(x + 3) - 2(x + 5) + (5x + 19)}{(x + 5)(x + 3)}$$ (each fraction expressed in terms of this LCM)

$$= \frac{3x + 9 - 2x - 10 + 5x + 19}{(x + 5)(x + 3)}$$ (remove brackets on top)

$$= \frac{6x + 18}{(x + 5)(x + 3)}$$ (simplify the top)

$$= \frac{6(x + 3)}{(x + 5)(x + 3)}$$ (factorise the top)

$$= \frac{6}{x + 5}$$ (divide the top and bottom by $(x + 3)$)

EXAMPLE 4

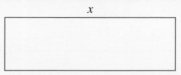

Given that the rectangle has length x and perimeter 8, write down the area of the rectangle in terms of x.

Solution:

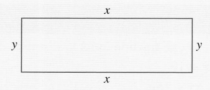

Let y = width of the rectangle as in the diagram.

Perimeter = 8	Area = xy
$\therefore x + y + x + y = 8$	$= x(4 - x)$
$2x + 2y = 8$	$= 4x - x^2$
$x + y = 4$	
$y = 4 - x$	

EXAMPLE 5

Simplify:

(i) $\dfrac{1 - \dfrac{3}{x}}{x - \dfrac{9}{x}}, \quad x \neq 0, 3$ (ii) $\dfrac{3x - 5}{x - 2} + \dfrac{1}{2 - x}, \quad x \neq 2$

Solution:

(i) $\dfrac{1 - \dfrac{3}{x}}{x - \dfrac{9}{x}}$

$= \dfrac{x - 3}{x^2 - 9}$ (multiply the top and bottom by x)

$= \dfrac{(x - 3)}{(x - 3)(x + 3)}$ (factorise the bottom)

$= \dfrac{1}{x + 3}$ (divide the top and bottom by $(x - 3)$)

(ii) $\dfrac{3x - 5}{x - 2} + \dfrac{1}{2 - x}$

$= \dfrac{3x - 5}{x - 2} - \dfrac{1}{x - 2}$ (as the denominators differ only in sign)

$= \dfrac{3x - 5 - 1}{x - 2}$ (same denominator)

$= \dfrac{3x - 6}{x - 2}$

$= \dfrac{3(x - 2)}{(x - 2)}$ (factorise the top)

$= 3$ (divide the top and bottom by $(x - 2)$)

Exercise 1.1

1. Verify the following (show your work).

   (i) $(x + y)(x - y) = x^2 - y^2$

   (ii) $(x + y)(x^2 - xy + y^2) = x^3 + y^3$

   (iii) $(x - y)(x^2 + xy + y^2) = x^3 - y^3$

   (iv) $(r + 1)^3 - (r - 1)^3 = 6r^2 + 2$

Simplify each of the following in questions 2–5.

2. $4x(3x^2 + 5x + 6) - 2(10x^2 + 12x)$

3. $(x + 2)^2 + (x - 2)^2 - 8$

4. $(a + b)^2 - (a - b)^2 - 4ab$

5. $(2a + b)^2 - 4a(a + b)$

Factorise each of the following in questions 6–20.

6. $x^2 + 3x$

7. $3xy - 6y^2$

8. $a^2b + ab^2$

9. $9x^2 - 16y^2$

10. $121p^2 - q^2$

11. $1 - 25a^2$

12. $x^2 - 2x - 8$

13. $3x^2 + 13x - 10$

14. $6x^2 - 11x + 3$

15. $27a^3 + 8b^3$

16. $1 - 64x^3$

17. $125 - 8p^3$

18. $1 + 125x^3$

19. $216 - x^3$

20. $1,000x^3 + y^3$

Simplify each of the following in questions 21–27.

21. $\dfrac{a^2 - 16}{a - 4}$

22. $\dfrac{x^2 + 5x}{x^2 + 7x + 10}$

23. $\dfrac{a^3 + b^3}{a^2 - ab + b^2}$

24. $\dfrac{x^2 + x - 2}{x^2 - x} \times \dfrac{x^2 - 3x}{x^2 - x - 6}$

25. $\dfrac{a^2 - 4}{a - 2} \times \dfrac{a^2 - a - 20}{a^2 - 3a - 10}$

26. $\dfrac{x^2 + 8x + 15}{x^2 - 9} \div \dfrac{xy + 5y}{x^2 - 3x}$

27. $\dfrac{3a^2}{5b^2} \div \sqrt{\dfrac{9a^2}{100b^2}}$

28. Factorise and hence evaluate each of the following. Show your work in each case.

    (i) $2,014^2 - 2,012^2$ (ii) $12^3 + 8^3$ (iii) $9^3 - 5^3$

29. Factorise each of the following.

    (i) $ax + ay + bx + by$

    (ii) $am - an + 4m - 4n$

    (iii) $x^2 - 3x + xy - 3y$

    (iv) $ab + ac - 2b - 2c$

    (v) $p(x - y) + 2(y - x)$

    (vi) $px + qx - p - q$

    (vii) $3b - 2a^2 - 2ab + 3a$

    (viii) $an - 5b - 5a + bn$

    (ix) $p^2 - p(2q - 1) - 2q$

    (x) $a^2 + 3b - a(3 + b)$

30. The length of one side of a rectangle is $x + 4$.
The area of the rectangle is $x^2 + 16x + 48$.
Find an expression in x for the length of the other side.

31. A square is divided into four sections, as shown.

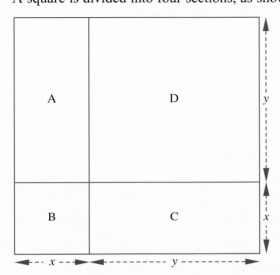

   (i) Find in terms of x and y the area of: (a) A (b) B (c) C (d) D
   (ii) Hence or otherwise, write down the area of A + B + C + D in terms of x and y.

32. Simplify and factorise fully.
   (i) $(2x - 1)^2 - (x - 1)^2$
   (ii) $(2x + a)(4x - 2a) - (3y + a)(6y - 2a)$
   (iii) $(3 - 4x)^2 - (3 - 5x)^2$
   (iv) $(7x - 2)(7x + 2) - (5y - 2)(5y + 2)$
   (v) $(x + 2)^3 - (x - 2)^3$
   (vi) $(x + a)^3 + (x - a)^3$

33. Use factors to simplify the following as far as possible.
   (i) $\dfrac{3x^2 - 19x - 14}{x^2 - 49}$
   (ii) $\dfrac{2x^2 + 4x - 30}{x - 3}$
   (iii) $\dfrac{x^3 + 7x^2 + 12x}{x^2 + 2x - 3}$
   (iv) $\dfrac{3x^2 + x - 4}{9x^2 - 16}$
   (v) $\dfrac{n^3 + 8}{n + 2}$

34. Express the following in its simplest form.
   (i) $\dfrac{1}{x - 1} + \dfrac{1}{x + 1}$
   (ii) $\dfrac{1}{x - 1} - \dfrac{1}{x + 1}$
   (iii) $\dfrac{3}{x + 1} - \dfrac{2}{x + 4}$
   (iv) $\dfrac{6}{x} + \dfrac{6}{x + 2}$
   (v) $\dfrac{1}{2x - 3} - \dfrac{1}{x + 3}$
   (vi) $\dfrac{1}{2x - 3} - \dfrac{1}{2x + 3}$

35. Show that:

(i) $\dfrac{1}{r-1} - \dfrac{1}{r+1} = \dfrac{2}{r^2-1}$, $r \neq \pm 1$ (ii) $n + \dfrac{n(n-1)}{2} = \dfrac{n(n+1)}{2}$

(iii) $\dfrac{1}{k} - \dfrac{1}{k+2} = \dfrac{2}{k(k+2)}$, $k \neq 0, -2$ (iv) $\dfrac{1}{n+2} - \dfrac{1}{n+3} = \dfrac{1}{(n+2)(n+3)}$, $n \neq -2, -3$

(v) $\dfrac{1}{2r-1} - \dfrac{1}{2r+1} = \dfrac{2}{(2r-1)(2r+1)}$, $r \neq \pm\dfrac{1}{2}$

36. Evaluate the following.

(i) $\dfrac{1}{1+\dfrac{1}{3}}$ (ii) $\dfrac{1}{1+\dfrac{1}{1+\dfrac{1}{3}}}$ (iii) $\dfrac{1}{1+\dfrac{1}{1+\dfrac{1}{1+\dfrac{1}{3}}}}$

(iv) Can you predict the next answer in the sequence if the pattern in the question is continued?

37. Simplify the following.

(i) $\dfrac{1}{1+\dfrac{1}{x}}$ (ii) $\dfrac{1}{1+\dfrac{1}{1+\dfrac{1}{x}}}$ (iii) $\dfrac{1}{1+\dfrac{1}{1+\dfrac{1}{1+\dfrac{1}{x}}}}$

(iv) Can you predict the next answer in the sequence if the pattern in the question is continued?

38. Express each of the following as one fraction in its lowest terms.

(i) $\dfrac{5x-6}{x^2+x-6} - \dfrac{3}{x+3}$ (ii) $\dfrac{2x}{x^2-1} - \dfrac{1}{x-1}$

(iii) $\dfrac{5}{2x-3} - \dfrac{3}{2x^2-3x} - \dfrac{1}{x}$ (iv) $\dfrac{a}{ab+b^2} - \dfrac{b}{a^2+ab}$

(v) $\dfrac{1}{x-1} + x - 1 - \dfrac{1}{1-x}$ (vi) $\dfrac{1+\dfrac{2}{x}-\dfrac{3}{x^2}}{1+\dfrac{3}{x}-\dfrac{4}{x^2}}$

39. Show that each of the following reduces to a constant and find that constant.

(i) $\dfrac{x-2}{x-3}+\dfrac{1}{3-x}$

(ii) $\dfrac{5x-3}{3x-2}-\dfrac{x-1}{2-3x}$

(iii) $\dfrac{1}{1-x}+\dfrac{x}{x-1}$

(iv) $\dfrac{3}{1+x^p}+\dfrac{3}{1+x^{-p}}$

(v) $\dfrac{x-2}{x^2+2x}+\dfrac{3}{x^2+3x}-\dfrac{x+4}{x^2+5x+6}$

40. Simplify each of the following.

(i) $\dfrac{x+y}{\dfrac{1}{x}+\dfrac{1}{y}}$

(ii) $\dfrac{\dfrac{a}{b}-\dfrac{b}{a}}{b^{-1}-a^{-1}}$

(iii) $\left(x+\dfrac{1}{x}\right)^2-\left(x-\dfrac{1}{x}\right)^2$

(iv) $\dfrac{x-\dfrac{2}{x+1}}{\dfrac{2x}{x+1}-1}$

(v) $\dfrac{x^2+4}{x^2-4}-\dfrac{x}{x+2}$

41. Let $f(x)=x^2-7x+12$.

Show that if $f(x+1)\neq 0$, then $\dfrac{f(x)}{f(x+1)}$ simplifies to $\dfrac{x-4}{x-2}$.

42. Simplify $\dfrac{(a^2-b^2)^4(a^4-b^4)}{(a^2+b^2)(a+b)^5}$.

43. If $x=2p+1$ and $y=2p-1$, write $(x+y)^2-(x-y)^2$ in the form $k^2(kp-1)(kp+1)$ where $k\in\mathbb{N}$.

44. If $x=\dfrac{6t}{1+t^2}$ and $y=\dfrac{2(1-t^2)}{1+t^2}$, find the value of $\dfrac{x^2}{9}+\dfrac{y^2}{4}$.

45. Let $f(x)=\dfrac{x^3-1}{x^2-1}$, $x\neq\pm1$, and $g(x)=\dfrac{x^2+x+1}{x^2-x-2}$, $x\neq -1, 2$.

If $f(x)\div g(x)=ax+b$, find the value of a and b.

46. If $f(x)=\dfrac{1}{x}$, show that $f(p)-f(q)=f\left(\dfrac{pq}{q-p}\right)$.

Changing the subject of a formula

When we rearrange a formula so that one of the variables is given in terms of the others, we are said to be **changing the subject of the formula**. The rules in changing the subject of a formula are the same as when solving an equation. That is, we can:

1. **Add** or **subtract** the same quantity to both sides.
    (In practice this involves moving a term from one side to another and changing its sign.)
2. **Multiply** or **divide** both sides by the same quantity.
3. **Square** both sides, **cube** both sides, etc.
4. Take the **square root** of both sides, take the **cube root** of both sides, etc.

Note: Whatever letter comes after the word 'express' is to be on its own.

 EXAMPLE 1

If $m = \dfrac{y_2 - y_1}{x_2 - x_1}$, express y_2 in terms of the other variables.

Solution:

$$m = \frac{y_2 - y_1}{x_2 - x_1}$$
$$m(x_2 - x_1) = y_2 - y_1 \qquad \text{(multiply both sides by } x_2 - x_1\text{)}$$
$$m(x_2 - x_1) + y_1 = y_2 \qquad \text{(add } y_1 \text{ to both sides)}$$

 EXAMPLE 2

If $v = u + at$, express t in terms of the other variables.

Solution:

$$v = u + at$$
$$v - u = at \qquad \text{(subtract } u \text{ from both sides)}$$
$$\frac{v - u}{a} = t \qquad \text{(divide both sides by } a\text{)}$$

Note: Three common errors made when manipulating formulae are:

1. $\dfrac{1}{a} + \dfrac{1}{b} \neq \dfrac{1}{a + b}$

2. $\dfrac{a}{b + c} \neq \dfrac{a}{b} + \dfrac{a}{c}$

3. $a\left(\dfrac{b}{c}\right) = \dfrac{ab}{c}$, not $\dfrac{ab}{ac}$

Verify 1, 2 and 3 by putting $a = 8$, $b = 2$, $c = 4$ into each.

EXAMPLE 3

(i) If $\dfrac{1}{b} + \dfrac{1}{a} = \dfrac{1}{c}$, express c in terms of a and b.

(ii) If $\sqrt[3]{\dfrac{3p-2}{2p+1}} = q$, express p in terms of q.

Solution:

(i) $\quad \dfrac{1}{b} + \dfrac{1}{a} = \dfrac{1}{c}$

$\quad ac + bc = ab$ (multiply each term by abc to remove fractions)

$\quad c(a + b) = ab$ (take out the common factor c on the left-hand side)

$\quad c = \dfrac{ab}{a+b}$ (divide both sides by $(a+b)$)

(ii) $\quad \sqrt[3]{\dfrac{3p-2}{2p+1}} = q$

$\quad \left(\dfrac{3p-2}{2p+1}\right)^{\frac{1}{3}} = q$ (replace $\sqrt[3]{\ }$ with $(\ )^{\frac{1}{3}}$)

$\quad \left[\left(\dfrac{3p-2}{2p+1}\right)^{\frac{1}{3}}\right]^3 = (q)^3$ (cube both sides)

$\quad \dfrac{3p-2}{2p+1} = q^3$ $\left[\left(x^{\frac{1}{3}}\right)^3 = x^{\frac{1}{3}\times3} = x^1 = x\right]$

$\quad 3p - 2 = (2p+1)q^3$ (multiply both sides by $(2p+1)$)

$\quad 3p - 2 = 2pq^3 + q^3$ (remove brackets)

$\quad 3p - 2pq^3 = q^3 + 2$ (put terms with p on the left-hand side)

$\quad p(3 - 2q^3) = q^3 + 2$ (take out the common factor p on the left-hand side)

$\quad p = \dfrac{q^3 + 2}{3 - 2q^3}$ (divde both sides by $(3 - 2q^3)$)

Exercise 1.2

1. If $\dfrac{2a-b}{3} = c$, express a in terms of b and c.

2. If $p - \dfrac{t}{q} = r$, express q in terms of p, t and r.

3. If $\dfrac{a}{b} = \dfrac{b}{c} + d$, express c in terms of a, b and d.

4. If $r = \dfrac{q^2 - pr}{q+p}$, express p in terms of q and r.

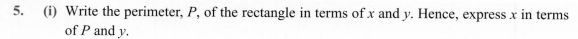
5. (i) Write the perimeter, P, of the rectangle in terms of x and y. Hence, express x in terms of P and y.

   (ii) A cube has side of length K. Write the surface area, A, of the cube in terms of K. Hence, express K in terms of A.

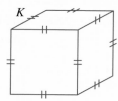

6. In a triangle with sides a, b, c, where $s = \dfrac{a + b + c}{2}$, express b in terms of the other variables.

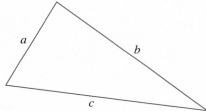

7. Given a trapezium with sides a and b as in the diagram and given that the area of the trapezium, A, is given by $A = \left(\dfrac{a + b}{2}\right)h$, express b in terms of A, a and h.

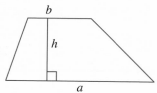

8. If $x = \dfrac{2t - 1}{t - 1}$, express t in terms of x.

9. (i) Given $x = t + 2$ and $y = 3t$, express: (a) t in terms of x (b) t in terms of y.
   (ii) Hence, equating both values for t, write down an equation in x and y.

10. Given that μ is the mean of p, q, r and s, express q in terms of the other variables.

11. A cone has a radius r cm, vertical height h cm and slant height $10\sqrt{3}$ cm.
    Using the theorem of Pythagoras, express r in terms of h.

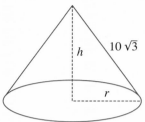

12. If $a^2 = b^2 + c^2 - 2bc \cos A$, express $\cos A$ in terms of a, b and c.

13. k is a circle with centre O, as in the diagram.
    A, B, C and D are points on k such that $ABCD$ is a rectangle.
    $|OA| = r$ cm, $|AB| = 2x$ cm and $|AD| = 2y$ cm.
    Using the theorem of Pythagoras, express y in terms of x and r.

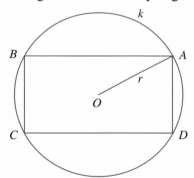

14. (i) Write down the formula for the circumference of a circle.
    (ii) A solid cylinder has a height h and radius r. Write down
         the formula for the volume of a cylinder.
   (iii) Given that the height of the cylinder added to the
         circumference of its base is equal to 3 metres, express the
         volume of the cylinder in terms of r and π.

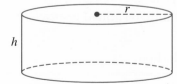

15. (i) If $m^2 = \dfrac{1}{h^2} - 8p$, express h in terms of p and m.
    (ii) Hence, determine the values of h when $m = 9$ and $p = -7$.

16. $y = ax - 2a^2$ and $x = 2 + 3a$.

    (i) Express y in terms of a.

    (ii) Evaluate y when $a = -2$.

17.   (i) If $q^2x = p + 2q^2$, express x in terms of p and q.

    (ii) If $y = q(x - 4)$, show that $y = \dfrac{p - 2q^2}{q}$.

18. If $\sqrt{\dfrac{y + 1}{y - 1}} = x$, express y in terms of x.

19. If $\dfrac{1}{u} + \dfrac{1}{v} = \dfrac{1}{f}$, express f in terms of u and v.

20. If $t = k\sqrt{\dfrac{l}{g}}$, express l in terms of t, k and g.

21. If $\dfrac{p}{2} = \sqrt{\dfrac{1}{x^2 - 1}}$, express x^2 in terms of p.

22.   (i) If $px - b = a - qx$, express x in terms of a, b, p and q.

    (ii) Hence, if $\sqrt{2p} = 4a$ and $q = -8b^2$, show that $8x = \dfrac{1}{a - b}$.

23. If $\sqrt[3]{x + 1} = y$, express x in terms of y.

Undetermined coefficients

When two expressions in x (or any other variable) are equal to one another for all values of x, we can equate the coefficients of the same powers of x in the two expressions. This is known as the **principle of undetermined coefficients**.

Method:

1. Remove all fractions and brackets.
2. Form equations by equating coefficients of like terms.
3. Solve the equations to find the coefficients.

EXAMPLE 1

Find the real numbers k and q such that $(x + 5)^2 + k = x^2 + 2qx + 11$.

Solution:

Expand the left-hand side and equate the coefficients:
$$(x + 5)^2 + k = x^2 + 2qx + 11$$
$$x^2 + 10x + 25 + k = x^2 + 2qx + 11$$

Equating coefficients of like terms:
$$10 = 2q \quad \text{and} \quad 25 + k = 11$$
$$5 = q \quad \text{and} \quad k = -14$$

EXAMPLE 2

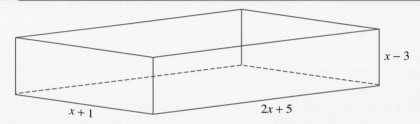

The dimensions of the open rectangular box are given in the diagram, where $x > 3$.

(i) The volume, V, is given by the expression $V = px^3 + qx^2 + rx + s$ where $p, q, r, s \in \mathbb{Z}$. Find the value for p, q, r, s.

(ii) The total external surface area, A, is given by $A = ax^2 + bx + c$ where $a, b, c \in \mathbb{Z}$. Find the value of a, b, c.

Solution:

(i)   Volume $= V = lbh$
$$= (2x + 5)(x + 1)(x - 3)$$
$$= (2x + 5)(x^2 - 2x - 3)$$
$$= 2x(x^2 - 2x - 3) + 5(x^2 - 2x - 3)$$
$$= 2x^3 - 4x^2 - 6x + 5x^2 - 10x - 15$$
$$px^3 + qx^2 + rx + s = 2x^3 + x^2 - 16x - 15$$
$$\therefore p = 2 \quad q = 1 \quad r = -16 \quad s = -15$$

(ii) **Note:** An open box has five sides.

Surface area $= A = 2(x + 1)(x - 3) + 2(2x + 5)(x - 3) + 1(x + 1)(2x + 5)$
$$= 2(x^2 - 2x - 3) + 2(2x^2 - x - 15) + 1(2x^2 + 7x + 5)$$
$$= 2x^2 - 4x - 6 + 4x^2 - 2x - 30 + 2x^2 + 7x + 5$$
$$ax^2 + bx + c = 8x^2 + x - 31$$
$$\therefore a = 8 \quad b = 1 \quad c = -31$$

EXAMPLE 3

$(2x + p)(x^2 + qx - 5) = 2x^3 + 5x^2 - 13x + 5$ for all values of x. If $p, q \in \mathbb{R}$, find the value of p and the value of q.

Solution:

$(2x + p)(x^2 + qx - 5) = 2x^3 + 5x^2 - 13x + 5$

Expand the left-hand side and equate the coefficients.

$2x(x^2 + qx - 5) + p(x^2 + qx - 5) = 2x^3 + 5x^2 - 13x + 5$

$2x^3 + 2qx^2 - 10x + px^2 + pqx - 5p = 2x^3 + 5x^2 - 13x + 5$

$2x^3 + (2q + p)x^2 + (-10 + pq)x - 5p = 2x^3 + 5x^2 - 13x + 5$

Equating coefficients of like terms gives:

$\quad\quad 2q + p = 5 \quad \text{①} \quad\quad\quad\quad -10 + pq = -13 \quad \text{②} \quad\quad\quad\quad -5p = 5 \quad \text{③}$

$\quad\quad\quad -5p = 5 \quad \text{③} \quad\quad\quad\quad\quad\quad\quad\quad\quad\quad\quad\quad\quad\quad\quad\quad 2q + p = 5 \quad \text{①}$

$\quad\quad\quad\quad 5p = -5$

$\quad\quad\quad\quad\quad p = -1 \quad\quad\quad\quad\quad\quad\quad\quad\quad\quad\quad\quad\quad\quad\quad\quad\quad\quad 2q - 1 = 5$

Substitute $p = -1$ into ① or ②. $\quad\quad\quad\quad\quad\quad\quad\quad\quad\quad\quad\quad\quad\quad 2q = 6$

$\quad\quad\quad\quad\quad\quad\quad\quad\quad\quad\quad\quad\quad\quad\quad\quad\quad\quad\quad\quad\quad\quad\quad\quad\quad q = 3$

Note: $p = -1$ and $q = 3$ will satisfy $-10 + pq = -13$ ②

EXAMPLE 4

If $(ax + k)(x^2 - px + 1) = ax^3 + bx + c$, for all x, show that $c^2 = a(a - b)$.

Solution:

Expand the left-hand side and equate the coefficients.

$\quad\quad\quad (ax + k)(x^2 - px + 1) = ax^3 + bx + c$

$ax^3 - apx^2 + ax + kx^2 - kpx + k = ax^3 + 0x^2 + bx + c \quad\quad \text{(put in } 0x^2)$

$ax^3 + (-ap + k)x^2 + (a - kp)x + k = ax^3 + 0x^2 + bx + c$

Equating coefficients of like terms:

(basic idea is to remove the constants **not** in the answer required)

$\quad\quad -ap + k = 0 \quad \text{①} \quad\quad\quad\quad a - kp = b \quad \text{②} \quad\quad\quad\quad k = c \quad \text{③}$

From ③, $k = c$. Replace k with c in ① and ②, as k is not in the answer required.

$\quad\quad\quad -ap + k = 0 \quad \text{①} \quad\quad\quad\quad\quad\quad\quad\quad\quad\quad a - kp = b \quad \text{②}$

$\quad\quad\quad\quad -ap + c = 0 \quad \text{④} \quad\quad\quad\quad\quad\quad\quad\quad\quad\quad a - cp = b \quad \text{⑤}$

What we do next is get p on its own from ④ and put this in ⑤.

This removes p, which is not in the answer.

$$-ap + c = 0 \quad ④$$
$$-ap = -c$$
$$ap = c$$
$$p = \frac{c}{a}$$

$$a - cp = b \quad ⑤$$
$$\downarrow$$
$$a - c\left(\frac{c}{a}\right) = b$$
$$a - \frac{c^2}{a} = b$$
$$a^2 - c^2 = ab$$
$$-c^2 = ab - a^2$$
$$c^2 = a^2 - ab$$
$$c^2 = a(a - b)$$

Exercise 1.3

1. If $3ax + 5aby = 12x + 40y$ for all values of x and y, find the value of a and b.

2. (i) $a(2x + 3) + b(x - 4) = 4x + 17$ for all values of x. Write two equations in a and b.
   (ii) Hence or otherwise, find the value of a and the value of b.

3. Find the real numbers a and b such that $x^2 + 4x - 6 = (x + a)^2 + b$ for all $x \in \mathbb{R}$.

4. $3(x^2 + 2x) + 7 = p(x^2 + 2) + qx(x - 3) + r$ for all values of x. Find the value of p, the value of q and the value of r.

5. $2x(x + 3) = a(x^2 + 1) + b(x^2 - x) + c$ for all values of x. Find the value of a, the value of b and the value of c.

6. (i) Express $x^2 + 10x + 32$ in the form $(x + a)^2 + b$ where $a, b \in \mathbb{N}$.
   (ii) $x^2 - 6x + t = (x + k)^2$ where t and k are constants. Find the value of k and the value of t.

7. $(x + 2)(x^2 + px + q) = x^3 + 5x^2 + 2x - 8$ for all values of x. Find the value of p and the value of q.

8. $(x + a)(2x^2 + bx + 1) = 2x^3 + x^2 - 14x + 3$ for all values of x. Find the value of a and the value of b.

9. $p(x + 1)(x + 2) + q(x + 1) + r = 3x^2 + 5x + 7$ for all values of x. Find the value of p, the value of q and the value of r.

10. If $2x^2 + 5x + 6 = p(x + q)^2 + r$ for all values of x, find the value of p, q and r.

11. $ax^2 + 2abx + ab^2 + c = 3(x - 2)^2 + 5$, where $a, b, c \in \mathbb{Z}$. Find the value of a, b and c.

12. If $a(x + b)^2 + c = 2x^2 + 12x + 23$ for all values of x, find the value of a, b and c.

13. Given that $ax^3 + bx^2 + 1 = (ax + 1)(x - 1)^2$ for all values of x, find the value of a and the value of b.

14. (i) Write down the factors of $x^3 - p^3$.
    (ii) Hence, if $x^2 + bx + c$ is a factor of $x^3 - p^3$, show that **(a)** $b = p$ **(b)** $c = p^2$.

15. For all $x \in \mathbb{R}$, $(x - t)^2(x + w) = x^3 + 3px - t^2$ where $w, t, p \in \mathbb{R}$. Find the value of w, t and p.

16. If $n^2 - 4 = a(n - 1)(n - 2) + b(n - 1) + c$ for all values of n, find the value of a, the value of b and the value of c.

17. $(2x + k)(px + q) = x(2px + 2q - p) + r$ for all values of x. Show that: **(i)** $k = -1$ **(ii)** $q + r = 0$

18. $(4x + r)(x^2 + s) = 4x^3 + px^2 + qx + 2$ for all values of x. Show that $pq = 8$.

19. $(ax + k)(x^2 - px + 1) = ax^3 + bx + c$ for all values of x. Show that:
    (i) $k = c$ **(ii)** $c = ap$ **(iii)** $b = a(1 - p^2)$

20. (i) Show that $(a + b)^3 = a^3 + 3a^2b + 3ab^2 + b^3$.
    (ii) If $x^3 + px^2 + qx + r = (x + h)^3$ for all values of x, show that: **(a)** $p^2 = 3q$ **(b)** $q^3 = 27r^2$.

21. A large window consists of six square panels of glass, as shown. Each pane is x m by x m and all the dividing wood is y m wide.

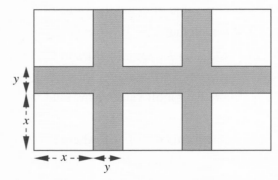

(i) Given that the total area of the whole window can be written in the form $px^2 + qxy + ry^2$ where p, q and $r \in \mathbb{N}$, find the values for p, q and r.
(ii) Show that the total area of the dividing wood is $7xy + 2y^2$.

22. A picture is enclosed in a frame, as shown. The frame is a uniform 1 cm in width all around the picture.

The height of the picture and frame is h cm, as shown. The width of the picture and frame exceeds the height by 4 cm. The area of the picture is given by $(h^2 + q)$ cm^2, where $q \in \mathbb{Z}$. Find the value of q.

23. A rectangle is 3 m longer than it is wide. The diagonal is 11 m. If x is the width of the rectangle, then:
    (i) Write down the length of the rectangle in terms of x.
    (ii) Using the theorem of Pythagoras, an equation $x^2 + px + q = 0$ is found where $p, q \in \mathbb{Z}$. Find the value of p and the value of q.

24. The dimensions of the solid cuboid are given in the diagram, where $x > 2$.

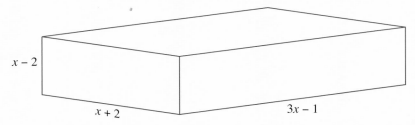

    (i) The volume, V, is given by $V = px^3 + qx^2 + rx + s$ where $p, q, r, s \in \mathbb{Z}$. Find the value for p, q, r and s.
    (ii) The total surface area is given by $A = ax^2 + bx + c$ where $a, b, c \in \mathbb{Z}$. Find the value of a, b and c.

25. A rectangle measuring $\dfrac{3}{x}$ by y has an area of $\dfrac{18}{x^2 + x}$ square units.

    Write y in the form $\dfrac{c}{x + p}$ where $c, p \in \mathbb{N}$.

26. $(x + p)(x - p)(ax + w) = ax^3 + bx^2 + cx + d$ for all values of x.
    Show by comparing coefficients that $bc = ad$.

Surds

Properties of surds:

1. $\sqrt{ab} = \sqrt{a}\sqrt{b}$	**2.** $\sqrt{\dfrac{a}{b}} = \dfrac{\sqrt{a}}{\sqrt{b}}$	**3.** $\sqrt{a}\sqrt{a} = a$

Simplification of surds

The key idea is to find the largest possible perfect square number greater than 1 that will divide evenly into the number under the square root and use property 1.

The perfect squares greater than 1 are 4, 9, 16, 25, 36, 49, 64, 81, 100, . . . etc.

EXAMPLE 1

Write each of the following in the form of $a\sqrt{b}$, where b is prime.

(i) $\sqrt{32}$ **(ii)** $\sqrt{45}$ **(iii)** $\sqrt{75}$

Express the following in the form $\dfrac{a}{b}$, $a, b \in \mathbb{N}$: **(iv)** $\sqrt{\dfrac{9}{4}}$ **(v)** $\sqrt{2\dfrac{7}{9}}$

(vi) Express $\dfrac{10}{\sqrt{2}}$ in the form $k\sqrt{2}$.

Solution:

(i) $\sqrt{32} = \sqrt{16 \times 2} = \sqrt{16}\sqrt{2} = 4\sqrt{2}$

(ii) $\sqrt{45} = \sqrt{9 \times 5} = \sqrt{9}\sqrt{5} = 3\sqrt{5}$

(iii) $\sqrt{75} = \sqrt{25 \times 3} = \sqrt{25}\sqrt{3} = 5\sqrt{3}$

(iv) $\sqrt{\dfrac{9}{4}} = \dfrac{\sqrt{9}}{\sqrt{4}} = \dfrac{3}{2}$

(v) $\sqrt{2\dfrac{7}{9}} = \sqrt{\dfrac{25}{9}} = \dfrac{\sqrt{25}}{\sqrt{9}} = \dfrac{5}{3}$

(vi) $\dfrac{10}{\sqrt{2}} = \dfrac{10}{\sqrt{2}} \times \dfrac{\sqrt{2}}{\sqrt{2}}$ (multiply the top and bottom by $\sqrt{2}$)

$= \dfrac{10\sqrt{2}}{2} = 5\sqrt{2}$

Note: The process of removing a surd from the denominator of an expression is called **rationalising the denominator**.

Addition and subtraction

Only like surds can be added or subtracted. Express each surd in its simplest form and add or subtract like surds.

 EXAMPLE 2

(i) Express $\sqrt{18} + \sqrt{50} - \sqrt{8}$ in the form $a\sqrt{b}$, where b is prime.

(ii) $\sqrt{20} - \sqrt{5} + \sqrt{45} = k\sqrt{5}$. Find the value of k.

Solution:

(i) $\sqrt{18} + \sqrt{50} - \sqrt{8}$
$= 3\sqrt{2} + 5\sqrt{2} - 2\sqrt{2}$
$= 8\sqrt{2} - 2\sqrt{2}$
$= 6\sqrt{2}$

(ii) $\sqrt{20} - \sqrt{5} + \sqrt{45}$
$= 2\sqrt{5} - \sqrt{5} + 3\sqrt{5}$
$= 5\sqrt{5} - \sqrt{5}$
$= 4\sqrt{5} = k\sqrt{5}$
$\therefore k = 4$

Conjugate surds

$a + \sqrt{b}$ is a compound surd. Its conjugate is $a - \sqrt{b}$ or $-a + \sqrt{b}$.

$\sqrt{a} - \sqrt{b}$ is a compound surd. Its conjugate is $\sqrt{a} + \sqrt{b}$ or $-\sqrt{a} - \sqrt{b}$.

They have the same components, with one of the signs changed.

The product of a surd and its conjugate is always a rational number.

Think of the difference of two squares: $(a - b)(a + b) = a^2 - b^2$, which is rational.

 EXAMPLE 3

Show that $\dfrac{-1 + \sqrt{3}}{1 + \sqrt{3}} = 2 - \sqrt{3}$.

Solution:

$\dfrac{-1 + \sqrt{3}}{1 + \sqrt{3}} = \dfrac{-1 + \sqrt{3}}{1 + \sqrt{3}} \times \dfrac{1 - \sqrt{3}}{1 - \sqrt{3}}$ (multiply the top and bottom by $1 - \sqrt{3}$, the conjugate surd of $1 + \sqrt{3}$)

$= \dfrac{-1 + \sqrt{3} + \sqrt{3} - 3}{1 - \sqrt{3} + \sqrt{3} - 3}$ (multiply the top by the top and the bottom by the bottom)

$= \dfrac{-4 + 2\sqrt{3}}{-2}$ (simplify the top and bottom)

$= 2 - \sqrt{3}$ (divide each part on top by -2)

Note: We could have also multiplied the top and bottom by $-1 + \sqrt{3}$, also the conjugate surd of $1 + \sqrt{3}$.

EXAMPLE 4

In the diagram, the rectangle $QRST$ has sides $|TQ| = 3 + \sqrt{2}$ cm and $|TS| = 3 - \sqrt{2}$ cm.

(i) Find the length of the perimeter, P, of the rectangle where $P \in \mathbb{N}$.

(ii) Find the area of the rectangle, A, where $A \in \mathbb{N}$.

(iii) Find the length of the diagonal $|SQ| = \sqrt{k}$ where $k \in \mathbb{N}$.

Solution:

(i)

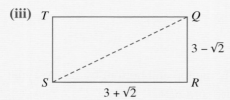

Perimeter $= (3 + \sqrt{2}) + (3 - \sqrt{2}) + (3 + \sqrt{2}) + (3 - \sqrt{2})$

$\qquad\qquad = 3 + \sqrt{2} + 3 - \sqrt{2} + 3 + \sqrt{2} + 3 - \sqrt{2}$

$\qquad\qquad = 12$ cm

(ii) Area $= lb = (3 + \sqrt{2})(3 - \sqrt{2})$

$\qquad\qquad = 3(3 - \sqrt{2}) + \sqrt{2}(3 - \sqrt{2})$

$\qquad\qquad = 9 - 3\sqrt{2} + 3\sqrt{2} - 2$

$\qquad\qquad = 7$ cm^2

(iii)

Using the theorem of Pythagoras:

$|SQ|^2 = |SR|^2 + |RQ|^2$

$|SQ|^2 = (3 + \sqrt{2})^2 + (3 - \sqrt{2})^2$

$|SQ|^2 = (3 + \sqrt{2})(3 + \sqrt{2}) + (3 - \sqrt{2})(3 - \sqrt{2})$

$|SQ|^2 = 9 + 6\sqrt{2} + 2 + 9 - 6\sqrt{2} + 2$

$|SQ|^2 = 22$

$|SQ| = \sqrt{22}$ cm

EXAMPLE 5

If $x = \sqrt{a} + \dfrac{1}{\sqrt{a}}$ and $y = \sqrt{a} - \dfrac{1}{\sqrt{a}}$, $a > 0$, find the value of $\sqrt{x^2 - y^2}$.

Solution:

Method 1

$x^2 = \left(\sqrt{a} + \dfrac{1}{\sqrt{a}}\right)\left(\sqrt{a} + \dfrac{1}{\sqrt{a}}\right)$ $\qquad$ $y^2 = \left(\sqrt{a} - \dfrac{1}{\sqrt{a}}\right)\left(\sqrt{a} - \dfrac{1}{\sqrt{a}}\right)$

$x^2 = \sqrt{a}\left(\sqrt{a} + \dfrac{1}{\sqrt{a}}\right) + \dfrac{1}{\sqrt{a}}\left(\sqrt{a} + \dfrac{1}{\sqrt{a}}\right)$ $\qquad$ $y^2 = \sqrt{a}\left(\sqrt{a} - \dfrac{1}{\sqrt{a}}\right) - \dfrac{1}{\sqrt{a}}\left(\sqrt{a} - \dfrac{1}{\sqrt{a}}\right)$

$x^2 = a + 1 + 1 + \dfrac{1}{a}$ $\qquad$ $y^2 = a - 1 - 1 + \dfrac{1}{a}$

$x^2 = a + 2 + \dfrac{1}{a}$ $\qquad$ $y^2 = a - 2 + \dfrac{1}{a}$

$\therefore \sqrt{x^2 - y^2} = \sqrt{a + 2 + \dfrac{1}{a} - \left(a - 2 + \dfrac{1}{a}\right)}$

$\qquad\qquad = \sqrt{a + 2 + \dfrac{1}{a} - a + 2 - \dfrac{1}{a}}$

$\qquad\qquad = \sqrt{4} = 2$

Method 2 Use the difference of two squares.

$x^2 - y^2 = (x - y)(x + y)$

$\qquad = \left[\left(\sqrt{a} + \dfrac{1}{\sqrt{a}}\right) - \left(\sqrt{a} - \dfrac{1}{\sqrt{a}}\right)\right]\left[\left(\sqrt{a} + \dfrac{1}{\sqrt{a}}\right) + \left(\sqrt{a} - \dfrac{1}{\sqrt{a}}\right)\right]$

$\qquad = \left(\sqrt{a} + \dfrac{1}{\sqrt{a}} - \sqrt{a} + \dfrac{1}{\sqrt{a}}\right)\left(\sqrt{a} + \dfrac{1}{\sqrt{a}} + \sqrt{a} - \dfrac{1}{\sqrt{a}}\right)$

$\qquad = \left(\dfrac{2}{\sqrt{a}}\right)(2\sqrt{a}) = 4$ $\qquad\qquad\qquad$ $\left(\dfrac{1}{\sqrt{a}} + \dfrac{1}{\sqrt{a}} = 2\dfrac{1}{\sqrt{a}} = \dfrac{2}{\sqrt{a}}\right)$

$\therefore \sqrt{x^2 - y^2} = \sqrt{4} = 2$

Exercise 1.4

1. Express each of the following in the form $a\sqrt{b}$, where b is prime.

   (i) $\sqrt{12}$ $\qquad$ (ii) $\sqrt{18}$ $\qquad$ (iii) $\sqrt{20}$ $\qquad$ (iv) $\sqrt{72}$

   (v) $\sqrt{48}$ $\qquad$ (vi) $\sqrt{45}$ $\qquad$ (vii) $\sqrt{125}$ $\qquad$ (viii) $\sqrt{63}$

   (ix) $\sqrt{500}$ $\qquad$ (x) $\frac{1}{2}\sqrt{80}$ $\qquad$ (xi) $\frac{1}{3}\sqrt{108}$ $\qquad$ (xii) $\frac{3}{5}\sqrt{75}$

2. Express each of the following in the form $\dfrac{p}{q}$, where $p, q \in \mathbb{N}$.

   (i) $\sqrt{\dfrac{4}{9}}$

   (ii) $\sqrt{\dfrac{36}{49}}$

   (iii) $\sqrt{\dfrac{100}{81}}$

   (iv) $\sqrt{2\frac{1}{4}}$

   (v) $\sqrt{1\frac{9}{16}}$

   (vi) $\sqrt{4\frac{21}{25}}$

3. Express each of the following in the form $a\sqrt{b}$, where b is prime.

   (i) $\dfrac{12}{\sqrt{3}}$

   (ii) $\dfrac{6}{\sqrt{2}}$

   (iii) $\dfrac{15}{\sqrt{5}}$

   (iv) $\dfrac{28}{\sqrt{7}}$

   (v) $\dfrac{12}{\sqrt{18}}$

   (vi) $\dfrac{60}{\sqrt{80}}$

4. Express each of the following in the form $\dfrac{a\sqrt{b}}{c}$, where b is prime.

   (i) $\dfrac{5}{\sqrt{2}}$

   (ii) $\dfrac{4}{\sqrt{3}}$

   (iii) $\dfrac{6}{\sqrt{8}}$

   (iv) $\dfrac{15}{2\sqrt{5}}$

   (v) $\dfrac{8}{\sqrt{18}}$

   (vi) $\dfrac{25}{\sqrt{45}}$

5. In each case, find the value of x.

   (i) $\dfrac{5x}{3\sqrt{5}} = 2\sqrt{5}$

   (ii) $\dfrac{8}{\sqrt{3}} \div \dfrac{2}{\sqrt{3}} = x$

   (iii) $\dfrac{\sqrt{11}}{3} + \dfrac{\sqrt{11}}{3} = \dfrac{x}{3}$

6. In each of the following, find the odd one out and justify your answer.

   (i) $3\sqrt{2}, \sqrt{12}, \sqrt{18}$

   (ii) $4\sqrt{3}, \sqrt{12}, \sqrt{48}$

   (iii) $\sqrt{3}, \dfrac{3}{\sqrt{3}}, \dfrac{1}{\sqrt{3}}$

   (iv) $\sqrt{20}, \sqrt{10}, 2\sqrt{5}$

   (v) $5\sqrt{2}, \sqrt{50}, 2\sqrt{5}$

   (vi) $6\sqrt{2}, \dfrac{12}{\sqrt{2}}, \sqrt{12}$

7. Evaluate each of the following and write each answer in the form $p\sqrt{2}$ where $p \in \mathbb{Q}$.

   (i) $\sqrt{2} + 2\sqrt{2} + 3\sqrt{2}$

   (ii) $\sqrt{2} - 2\sqrt{2} + 3\sqrt{2}$

   (iii) $\sqrt{2} \times 2\sqrt{2} \times 3\sqrt{2}$

   (iv) $\sqrt{2} \div 2\sqrt{2} \div 3\sqrt{2}$

8. Find k in each of the following, where $k \in \mathbb{Z}$.

   (i) $\left(2 - \sqrt{5}\right)\left(2 + \sqrt{5}\right) = k$

   (ii) $\left(10 - \sqrt{2}\right)\left(10 + \sqrt{2}\right) = k$

   (iii) $(-5 - \sqrt{7})(-5 + \sqrt{7}) = k$

   (iv) $(2\sqrt{3} - 11)(2\sqrt{3} + 11) = k$

9. Show that:

   (i) $\dfrac{1}{\sqrt{2} + 1} = \sqrt{2} - 1$

   (ii) $\dfrac{\sqrt{3} + \sqrt{2}}{\sqrt{3} - \sqrt{2}} = 5 + 2\sqrt{6}$

   (iii) $\dfrac{1}{\sqrt{3} - 1} + \dfrac{1}{\sqrt{3} + 1} = \sqrt{3}$

   (iv) $\dfrac{\sqrt{5} - 1}{3 - \sqrt{5}} = \dfrac{1 + \sqrt{5}}{2}$

10. $\sqrt{50} - \sqrt{200} + \sqrt{98} = k\sqrt{2}$. Find the value of k^2.

11. Express $(2 - \sqrt{3})^2$ in the form $a + b\sqrt{c}$, where $a, b, c \in \mathbb{Z}$.

12. Express $(7 + \sqrt{5})^2 - (7 - \sqrt{5})^2$ in the form $k\sqrt{5}$, $k \in \mathbb{N}$.

13. Express $\dfrac{1}{3\sqrt{5}} - \dfrac{1}{2\sqrt{20}}$ in the form $k\sqrt{5}$, $k \in \mathbb{Q}$.

14. Express the following in the form $a\sqrt{3} - b$, where $a, b \in \mathbb{N}$.

    (i) $\dfrac{1 - \sqrt{3}}{1 + \sqrt{3}}$

    (ii) $\dfrac{1 - \sqrt{2}}{1 + \sqrt{2}}$

15. Find the natural number b such that $\dfrac{-4}{\sqrt{5} - 3} = \sqrt{5} + b$.

16. Express the area of the triangle given in the diagram in the form $a + b\sqrt{2}$ where $a, b \in \mathbb{Q}$.

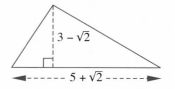

17. Given the area of a square with side of length x cm equals 8 cm^2, write x in the form $k\sqrt{k}$ where $k \in \mathbb{N}$.

18. In the right-angled triangle ABC, use the theorem of Pythagoras to find the value of k where $k \in \mathbb{N}$.

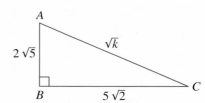

19. The diagram shows a rectangular box. Rectangle $ABCD$ is the top of the box and rectangle $EFGH$ is the base of the box. $|AF| = a - \sqrt{a}$, $|FG| = a + \sqrt{a}$ and $|AG| = \sqrt{24}$. Use the theorem of Pythagoras to solve for a.

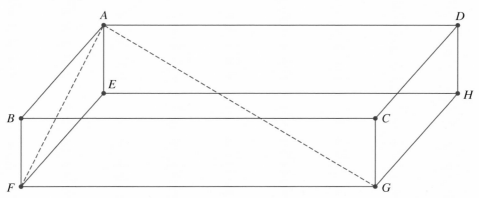

20. Simplify $\left(x^2 + \sqrt{2} + \dfrac{1}{x^2}\right)\left(x^2 - \sqrt{2} + \dfrac{1}{x^2}\right)$ and express your answer in the form $x^n + \dfrac{1}{x^n}$ where n is a whole number.

21. (i) Express $\dfrac{1}{a} - \dfrac{1}{b}$ as a single fraction.

    (ii) Hence or otherwise, express $\dfrac{1}{a} - \dfrac{1}{b}$ in the form $-k\sqrt{k}$, when $a = 1 - \sqrt{2}$ and $b = 1 + \sqrt{2}$.

22. $17\left(1 - \dfrac{1}{17^2}\right)^{\frac{1}{2}} = n\sqrt{2}$. Find the value of n.

Quadratic equations

Any equation of the form $ax^2 + bx + c = 0$, $a \neq 0$, is called a **quadratic equation**. To solve a quadratic equation we either:

> **1.** Factorise and let each factor $= 0$
>
> or
>
> **2.** Use the formula $x = \dfrac{-b \pm \sqrt{b^2 - 4ac}}{2a}$

EXAMPLE

(i) Solve $6x^2 - 11x - 10 = 0$.

(ii) Solve $x^2 + 4x - 1 = 0$, giving your solutions in surd form.

Solution:

(i) $6x^2 - 11x - 10 = 0$

$(3x + 2)(2x - 5) = 0$ (factorise the left-hand side)

$3x + 2 = 0$ or $2x - 5 = 0$ (let each factor $= 0$)

$3x = -2$ or $2x = 5$

$x = -\dfrac{2}{3}$ or $x = \dfrac{5}{2}$ (solve each simple equation)

(ii) $x^2 + 4x - 1 = 0$ (answers in surd form $\therefore$ use formula)

$x = \dfrac{-b \pm \sqrt{b^2 - 4ac}}{2a}$

$x = \dfrac{-4 \pm \sqrt{(4)^2 - 4(1)(-1)}}{2(1)}$

$x = \dfrac{-4 \pm \sqrt{16 + 4}}{2}$

$x = \dfrac{-4 \pm \sqrt{20}}{2}$

$x = \dfrac{-4 \pm 2\sqrt{5}}{2}$

$x = -2 \pm \sqrt{5}$

$\therefore x = -2 + \sqrt{5}$ or $x = -2 - \sqrt{5}$

$$x^2 + 4x - 1 = 0$$
$$a = 1, \, b = 4, \, c = -1$$

$$\sqrt{20}$$
$$= \sqrt{4 \times 5}$$
$$= \sqrt{4}\sqrt{5}$$
$$= 2\sqrt{5}$$

Exercise 2.1

Solve the equations in questions 1–12.

1. $2x^2 + 5x - 12 = 0$
2. $x^2 - 3x = 0$
3. $x^2 - 4 = 0$
4. $3x^2 + 14x + 8 = 0$
5. $5x^2 + 14x - 3 = 0$
6. $x^2 - 6x + 9 = 0$
7. $2x^2 = 3x$
8. $6x^2 - x = 2$
9. $9x^2 - 12x + 4 = 0$
10. $8x^2 = 9 - 6x$
11. $15x^2 + x - 6 = 0$
12. $4x^2 - 25 = 0$

Solve the equations in questions 13–18, giving your solutions in surd form.

13. $x^2 + 6x + 4 = 0$
14. $x^2 - 4x + 1 = 0$
15. $x^2 - 8x + 13 = 0$
16. $x^2 - 2x - 2 = 0$
17. $x^2 - 4x - 14 = 0$
18. $x^2 + 10x - 23 = 0$

Using quadratic equations to solve problems

Use the following steps to solve problems.

1. Draw a diagram, if possible.
2. Write the problem in the form of an algebraic equation.
3. Manipulate the equation to form a quadratic equation.
4. Solve the quadratic equation.

EXAMPLE

The length of a rectangle is 3 cm longer than its width. If the area of the rectangle is 18 cm^2, calculate the dimensions of the rectangle.

Solution:

Draw a diagram, letting:

> Width $= x$
> Length $= x + 3$

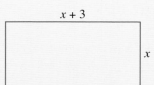

$$\text{Length} \times \text{Width} = \text{Area}$$
$$(x + 3)(x) = \text{Area}$$
$$x^2 + 3x = 18$$
$$x^2 + 3x - 18 = 0$$
$$(x + 6)(x - 3) = 0$$
$$x = -6, \quad x = 3$$

Reject the $x = -6$ value as you cannot have a negative dimension.

$\therefore x = 3$

Width $= 3$ cm and length $= 6$ cm

Exercise 2.2

1. The length of a rectangular garden is 6 m more than the width. If the area of the garden is 27 m^2, calculate the dimensions of the garden.

2. A window has a height that is $\frac{4}{3}$ times longer than its width. If the area of the window is 192 m^2, what are the dimensions of the window?

3. The length of a rectangle is 8 cm less than twice its width. If the area of the rectangle is 120 cm^2, what is the length of the diagonal, leaving your answer in surd form?

4. In a right-angled triangle, the length of the hypotenuse is 10 cm. Of the two shorter sides, one side is 2 cm longer than the other side.

   (i) Find the lengths of the two shorter sides.

   (ii) Hence, find the area of the triangle.

5. A garden measuring 12 m by 16 m is to have a pedestrian pathway installed all around it, increasing the total area to 285 m^2.

   What will be the width of the pathway?

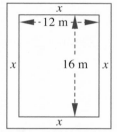

6. A rectangular garden is 30 m long and 20 m wide. A path of uniform width is set around the edge that reduces its area to 375 m^2. What is the width of the path?

7. A rectangular garden measures 20 m by 30 m. A pathway is laid around the garden that reduces its area by 264 m^2. How wide is the pathway?

8. The sum of the areas of two circles is 106π cm^2 and the radius of the larger circle is 4 cm longer than the radius of the smaller circle. Find the lengths of the radii.

9. 132 chocolates are equally divided among a number of people at a party. If the number of chocolates that each receives is one more than the number of people, find how many people were at the party.

10. You have to make an open square-bottomed box with a height of 3 cm and a volume of 75 cm^3. To do this, you will take a square piece of cardboard, cutting 3 cm squares from each corner, scoring between the corners and folding up the edges. Find the dimensions of the cardboard.

11. A rectangular piece of cardboard is 2 cm longer than it is wide. From each of its corners, a square piece 2 cm on a side is cut out. The flaps are then turned up to form an open box that has a volume of 70 cm^3. Calculate the dimensions of the cardboard.

12. A ball is thrown vertically upwards. The height, h metres, of the ball t seconds after it is thrown is given by $h = 7t - t^2$. Find the two times when the height of the ball is 10 m.

13. A ball is thrown vertically upwards. The height, h metres, of the ball t seconds after it is thrown is given by $h = 20t - 5t^2$. Find the two times when the height of the ball is 15 m.

14. A ball is thrown vertically upwards. The height, h metres, of the ball t seconds after it is thrown is given by $h = 36t - 6t^2$. Find the two times, correct to two decimal places, when the height of the ball is 18 m.

15. Find two non-zero consecutive integers such that their product is 3 less than three times their sum.

16. Two consecutive positive odd numbers are squared and the results are added to give 290. Write down an equation to represent this information and hence find the two numbers.

17. The product of two positive consecutive odd integers is 1 less than six times their sum. Find the integers.

18. Find three consecutive integers such that the product of the first and the second is equal to the product of -6 and the third. Answer in the form a, b, c and d, e, f (smallest to largest).

Equations involving fractions

> ### EXAMPLE 1
>
> Solve for x: $\dfrac{10}{x + 3} - \dfrac{2}{x} = 1$.
>
> **Solution:**
>
> $$x(x + 3)\left(\frac{10}{x + 3}\right) - x(x + 3)\left(\frac{2}{x}\right) = x(x + 3)(1) \qquad \text{(multiply each part by } x(x + 3)\text{)}$$
>
> $$(x)(10) - (x + 3)(2) = (x + 3)(x) \qquad \text{(simplify)}$$
>
> $$10x - 2x - 6 = x^2 + 3x \qquad \text{(remove the brackets)}$$
>
> $$x^2 + 3x + 2x - 10x + 6 = 0 \qquad \text{(bring all terms to one side)}$$
>
> $$x^2 - 5x + 6 = 0$$
>
> $$(x - 2)(x - 3) = 0 \qquad \text{(factorise the left side)}$$
>
> $$x - 2 = 0 \quad \text{or} \quad x - 3 = 0 \qquad \text{(let each factor equal zero)}$$
>
> $$x = 2 \quad \text{or} \quad x = 3 \qquad \text{(solve each simple equation)}$$

Exercise 2.3

In questions 1–9, write the equations in the form $ax^2 + bx + c = 0$ and hence solve each equation.

1. $1 - \dfrac{5}{x} + \dfrac{6}{x^2} = 0$

2. $3 + \dfrac{2}{x - 2} = \dfrac{1}{x}$

3. $\dfrac{1}{2} = \dfrac{1}{x - 1} - \dfrac{1}{x}$

4. $\dfrac{1}{2} - \dfrac{1}{x} = \dfrac{1}{x + 3}$

5. $\dfrac{4x - 5}{x - 2} + \dfrac{5}{x + 2} = 8$

6. $\dfrac{2}{9} = \dfrac{1}{x - 5} - \dfrac{1}{x + 1}$

7. $\dfrac{10}{x - 1} = \dfrac{7}{2} - \dfrac{12}{x + 2}$

8. $\dfrac{1}{2} = \dfrac{1}{x} + \dfrac{1}{x + 3}$

9. $\dfrac{5}{2} = \dfrac{1}{x - 1} + \dfrac{3}{x + 2}$

10. Solve $\dfrac{m}{x - m} - \dfrac{2m}{x + 2m} = \dfrac{1}{10}$ for x in terms of m.

11. Solve $\dfrac{1}{4} - \dfrac{1}{x + 2} = \dfrac{1}{x - 2}$, giving your answer in the form $a \pm b\sqrt{c}$.

12. Solve $\dfrac{2}{x} - \dfrac{1}{x + 1} = \dfrac{1}{3}$, giving your answer in the form $a \pm b\sqrt{c}$.

13. The perimeter of a triangle is $\dfrac{17x}{24}$ and the lengths of two of the sides are $\dfrac{3x}{8}$ and $\dfrac{2x - 5}{12}$. Find the length of the third side in terms of x.

14. The perimeter of a rectangle is $\dfrac{14x}{15}$ and the measure of each length is $\dfrac{x + 2}{3}$. Find the measure of each width in terms of x.

15. The numerator of a fraction is 8 less than the denominator of the fraction.

    (i) If the numerator is x, write the denominator in terms of x.

    (ii) If this fraction can be broken down to be $\frac{3}{5}$, write an equation to represent this information and hence solve for x.

    (iii) Write down the fraction.

16. A teacher is organising a day trip to a museum. The total cost of entry for the students to the museum is €72.

    (i) By letting x equal the number of students in the class, write an expression to represent the cost of the trip per student.

    (ii) If two students decided not to go to the museum, the total cost of entry would be €70. Write an expression for the new cost per student.

    (iii) The cost of entry per student in this case would be increased by €1. Write an equation to represent the above information and hence solve this equation to find the number of students who were originally meant to go on the trip.

17. To promote a school play, a class undertook to make 100 posters, with each pupil making the same number of posters.

   (i) If there were x pupils in the class, express the number of posters made by each in terms of x.

   (ii) On the day they were making the posters, five pupils were absent and each pupil present had to make one extra poster. Express the number of posters now made by each student in terms of x.

   (iii) Calculate the number of students normally in the class.

18. Jane rode her bicycle for x km at 10 km/hr and then rode $(x + 4)$ km further at 8 km/hr.

   (i) Represent, in terms of x, the total time that she rode.

   (ii) If she rode for 2 hours 18 minutes, find the total distance she travelled.

19. An airplane flies 520 km against the wind and 680 km with the wind in a total time of 4 hours. The speed of the airplane in still air is 300 km/hr. Calculate the speed of the wind.

20. A boat travels at a speed of 20 km/hr in still water. It travels 48 km upstream and then returns to the starting point in a total of 5 hours. Find the speed of the current in km/hr.

21. A jogger and a walker both cover a distance of 5 km. The runner is travelling 1·5 times faster than the walker and finishes in 25 minutes less time. How fast is each going in km/hr?

22. 140 students taking part in a drill display were arranged in rows containing equal numbers of students. To facilitate four new students, one extra student was added to each row. It was found that two fewer rows were required. How many students were originally in each row?

23. A number of people share equally in a prize of €300. The following week, 10 people more share equally in the prize of €300. Each share in the second week was €2·50 less than each share in the first week. Find how many people shared in the prize the first week.

24. 72 people attended the first night of a concert. They were seated in rows, each of which contained x people. The following evening, 80 people attended the concert and they were seated in rows containing $(x + 2)$ people. If on the second night there was one less row needed than on the first night, calculate the number of rows needed on each night.

25. For a concert, the choreographer divided a group of 90 dancers into an equal number of rows. Each row had the same number of dancers. It was then decided to put three fewer dancers into each row and as a result five more rows were needed. How many dancers were in each row originally?

26. Paving slabs are to be laid end to end in a single line along a straight path which is 60 m long. The paver has two different types of slabs that he can choose from. One type of slab is 1 m longer than the other type. If he uses the longer slabs, he will require five fewer slabs than if he used the shorter ones. Calculate how many of the shorter slabs he would need if he decided to pave the path with them.

Solving quadratic equations using substitution

In some questions we can use the roots of one quadratic equation to help us solve another quadratic equation by using a substitution.

EXAMPLE 2

Solve the equation $x - 11 + \dfrac{24}{x} = 0$.

Hence, solve $(y^2 - 2y) - 11 + \dfrac{24}{(y^2 - 2y)} = 0$.

Solution:

$$x - 11 + \frac{24}{x} = 0$$

$x^2 - 11x + 24 = 0$	(multiply both sides by x)
$(x - 3)(x - 8) = 0$	(factorise the left-hand side)
$x - 3 = 0$ or $x - 8 = 0$	(let each factor $= 0$)
$x = 3$ or $x = 8$	(solve each simple equation)

$$\text{let } x = y^2 - 2y \qquad \text{(this is the substitution)}$$

$x = 3$	or	$x = 8$
$y^2 - 2y = 3$		$y^2 - 2y = 8$
$y^2 - 2y - 3 = 0$		$y^2 - 2y - 8 = 0$
$(y + 1)(y - 3) = 0$		$(y + 2)(y - 4) = 0$
$y + 1 = 0$ or $y - 3 = 0$		$y + 2 = 0$ or $y - 4 = 0$
$y = -1$ or $y = 3$		$y = -2$ or $y = 4$

$$\therefore y = -2, -1, 3, 4$$

Exercise 2.4

1. Solve $x^2 - x - 20 = 0$. Hence, solve $\left(2k + \dfrac{2}{k}\right)^2 - \left(2k + \dfrac{2}{k}\right) - 20 = 0$.

2. Solve $3x^2 + 16x - 12 = 0$. Hence, solve $3\left(y - \dfrac{7}{y}\right)^2 + 16\left(y - \dfrac{7}{y}\right) - 12 = 0$.

3. Solve $x^2 - 2x - 24 = 0$. Hence, solve $\left(x + \dfrac{4}{x}\right)^2 - 2\left(x + \dfrac{4}{x}\right) - 24 = 0$.

4. Solve $x^2 - 6x + 8 = 0$. Hence, solve $\left(x + \dfrac{1}{x}\right)^2 - 6\left(x + \dfrac{1}{x}\right) + 8 = 0$.

5. Solve $x^2 + 3x - 54 = 0$. Hence, solve $\left(y + \dfrac{8}{y}\right)^2 + 3\left(y + \dfrac{8}{y}\right) - 54 = 0$.

6. Solve the equation $x - 11 + \dfrac{24}{x} = 0$. Hence, solve $(x^2 - 2x) - 11 + \dfrac{24}{(x^2 - 2x)} = 0$.

7. Solve $x^2 - 9x + 20 = 0$. Hence, solve $y - 9\sqrt{y} + 20 = 0$.

8. Solve $x^2 - 7x = 0$. Hence, solve $(x^3 - 1)^2 - 7(x^3 - 1) = 0$.

9. Solve $x^2 - 5x - 14 = 0$. Hence, solve $(x^3 - 1)^2 - 5(x^3 - 1) - 14 = 0$.

10. Solve: **(i)** $x^4 - 13x^2 + 36 = 0$ **(ii)** $x^4 - 17x^2 + 16 = 0$

Modulus and irrational equations

Modulus equations

The modulus of x, written $|x|$, is defined as its positive or absolute value.
For example, $|5| = 5$ and $|-2| = 2$.

A modulus equation is one where the variable is contained within a modulus.
For example, $|x - 1| = 4$, is a modulus equation.

Note: If $|x| = 3$, then $x = 3$ or $x = -3$.

Modulus equations are solved with the following steps.

> 1. Arrange to have the modulus part by itself on one side of the equation.
> 2. Square both sides (this removes the modulus bars).
> 3. Solve the resultant equation.

Note: If there are two modulus parts, arrange to have one modulus part on each side.

EXAMPLE 1

Solve $2|x - 2| - |x + 3| = 0$.

Solution:

$2|x - 2| - |x + 3| = 0$

$\qquad 2|x - 2| = |x + 3|$ (one modulus on each side)

$\qquad (2|x - 2|)^2 = (|x + 3|)^2$ (square both sides)

$\qquad 4(x^2 - 4x + 4) = x^2 + 6x + 9$ $((ab)^2 = a^2 b^2)$

$\qquad 4x^2 - 16x + 16 = x^2 + 6x + 9$ (remove brackets)

$\qquad 3x^2 - 22x + 7 = 0$ (write in the form $ax^2 + bx + c = 0$)

$\qquad (3x - 1)(x - 7) = 0$ (factorise the left-hand side)

$\qquad 3x - 1 = 0 \quad$ or $\quad x - 7 = 0$ (let each factor $= 0$)

$\qquad 3x = 1 \quad$ or $\quad x = 7$

$\qquad x = \frac{1}{3} \quad$ or $\quad x = 7$ (solve each simple equation)

Irrational equations

An irrational equation is one where the variable is contained under a square root.

For example, $\sqrt{x + 2} = x - 4$ is an irrational equation.

Irrational equations are solved with the following steps.

1. Arrange to have the surd (root) part on its own on one side.
2. Square both sides (removes square root symbol).
3. Solve the resultant equation.
4. Test every solution in the **original** equation.

EXAMPLE 2

Solve $x = \sqrt{19 - 2x} + 2$.

Solution:

$$x = \sqrt{19 - 2x} + 2$$
$$(x - 2) = \left(\sqrt{19 - 2x}\right) \qquad \text{(rearrange with surd part on its own)}$$
$$(x - 2)^2 = \left(\sqrt{19 - 2x}\right)^2 \qquad \text{(square both sides)}$$
$$x^2 - 4x + 4 = 19 - 2x \qquad \text{(remove brackets)}$$
$$x^2 - 2x - 15 = 0 \qquad \text{(write in the form } ax^2 + bx + c = 0)$$
$$(x + 3)(x - 5) = 0 \qquad \text{(factorise the left-hand side)}$$
$$x + 3 = 0 \quad \text{or} \quad x - 5 = 0 \qquad \text{(let each factor = 0)}$$
$$x = -3 \quad \text{or} \quad x = 5 \qquad \text{(solve each simple equation)}$$

Check $x = -3$: $\quad -3 = \sqrt{19 - 2(-3)} + 2 = \sqrt{25} + 2 = 5 + 2 = 7 \qquad$ **False**

Check $x = 5$: $\qquad 5 = \sqrt{19 - 2(5)} + 2 = \sqrt{9} + 2 = 3 + 2 = 5 \qquad$ **True**

$\therefore \qquad x = 5$ is the only solution.

Note: Squaring both sides introduced a new root, called an extraneous root, $x = -3$. This does not satisfy the original equation and hence is rejected.

Note: The square root of a number is defined as the positive square root. For example, $\sqrt{16} = 4$, not ± 4.

Exercise 2.5

In questions 1–30, solve the equations.

1. $|x - 1| = 4$
2. $|x - 2| = 3$
3. $|x + 3| = 5$
4. $|2x - 1| = 3$
5. $|3x - 1| - 4 = 0$
6. $2|x - 1| = 3$
7. $|x + 1| = |x - 2|$
8. $|2x + 1| = |x - 1|$
9. $|2x - 1| - x = 0$
10. $|4 - 3x| - |2x - 1| = 0$
11. $|3x - 1| - |1 - 2x| = 0$
12. $2|x - 1| = |x + 1|$
13. $2|x + 1| - |x + 3| = 0$
14. $3|x + 1| = |2x - 1|$
15. $|2 - x| = \frac{1}{2}|x|$

16. $\left|\dfrac{x-2}{3}\right| = 1$ **17.** $\left|\dfrac{3x+1}{x-1}\right| = 2$ **18.** $\left|\dfrac{2x+1}{x+2}\right| = \dfrac{1}{2}$

19. $x = \sqrt{5x-4}$ **20.** $x = \sqrt{x+6}$ **21.** $x + 6 = 5\sqrt{x}$

22. $x - 2 = \sqrt{2x-1}$ **23.** $2x - 1 = \sqrt{8x+1}$ **24.** $2x - 7 = \sqrt{x^2 - 3x - 1}$

25. $x = \sqrt{3x-5} + 1$ **26.** $x - \sqrt{x+3} = 3$ **27.** $x + 1 = 3\sqrt{x-1}$

28. $\dfrac{|x+5|}{\sqrt{13}} = \sqrt{13}$ **29.** $\dfrac{|3x-1|}{\sqrt{x^2+1}} = \sqrt{8}$ **30.** $\dfrac{5|x-1|}{\sqrt{x^2+1}} = \sqrt{10}$

Completing the square

Completing the square means taking any quadratic polynomial in the form $px^2 + qx + r$ and expressing it in the form $p(x + a)^2 + b$ for some a and b.

> **To complete the square:**
> 1. Halve the coefficient of the x term.
> 2. Square this value and then add and subtract this value to the expression.
> 3. Factorise the portion which is a perfect square and tidy up the constants.

Note:

> The minimum value of an expression in the form $p(x + a)^2 + b$ is b.
> This occurs when $x + a = 0$ $(x = -a)$.
> The maximum value of an expression in the form $b - p(x + a)^2$ is b.
> This occurs when $x + a = 0$ $(x = -a)$.

EXAMPLE 1

  (i) Express $x^2 - 6x + 4$ in the form $(x + a)^2 + b$.

 (ii) Hence or otherwise:

    (a) Find the minimum value of $x^2 - 6x + 4$.

    (b) Solve the equation $x^2 - 6x + 4 = 0$, writing your answer in the form $p \pm \sqrt{q}$ where $p, q \in \mathbb{N}$.

Solution:

(i) $x^2 - 6x + 4$ (half the coefficient of $x = -3$)

     $= x^2 - 6x + 9 + 4 - 9$ (add and subtract $(-3)^2 = 9$)

     $= (x - 3)(x - 3) - 5$ $(x^2 - 6x + 9 = (x - 3)(x - 3))$

     $= (x - 3)^2 - 5$ (in the form $(x + a)^2 - b$)

(ii) (a) The minimum value of $(x - 3)^2 - 5$ occurs when $(x - 3) = 0$.

$$x - 3 = 0$$
$$x = 3$$

$\therefore$ Minimum value $= (3 - 3)^2 - 5 = 0 - 5 = -5$.

(b) $x^2 - 6x + 4 = 0$

$(x - 3)^2 - 5 = 0$	$(x^2 - 6x + 4 = (x - 3)^2 - 5)$
$(x - 3)^2 = 5$	(add 5 to both sides)
$x - 3 = \pm\sqrt{5}$	(take the square root of both sides)
$x = 3 \pm \sqrt{5}$	(add 3 to both sides now in the form $p \pm \sqrt{q}$)

EXAMPLE 2

Express $-x^2 + 4x + 5$ in the form $a^2 - (x + b)^2$.

Solution:

$$-x^2 + 4x + 5$$

$= -1(x^2 - 4x - 5)$	(factor out -1, half the coefficient of $x = -2$)
$= -1(x^2 - 4x + 4 - 5 - 4)$	(add and subtract 4 inside the brackets)
$= -1[(x - 2)^2 - 9]$	$(x^2 - 4x + 4 = (x - 2)^2)$
$= -(x - 2)^2 + 9$	(remove the brackets)
$= 9 - (x - 2)^2$	
$= 3^2 - (x - 2)^2$	(in the form $a^2 - (x + b)^2$)

Exercise 2.6

Express questions 1–9 in the form $(ax + b)^2$ where $a, b \in \mathbb{Z}$.

1. $x^2 + 2x + 1$
2. $x^2 + 6x + 9$
3. $x^2 - 8x + 16$
4. $x^2 - 10x + 25$
5. $x^2 + 4x + 4$
6. $x^2 - 16x + 64$
7. $4x^2 - 4x + 1$
8. $4x^2 - 20x + 25$
9. $9x^2 + 12x + 4$

Express questions 10–15 in the form $(x + b)^2 + c$. Hence or otherwise, find the value of x that gives a minimum value for each expression and find that minimum value.

10. $x^2 - 6x + 11$
11. $x^2 + 2x + 6$
12. $x^2 + 8x + 14$
13. $x^2 - 10x + 19$
14. $x^2 + 12x + 3$
15. $x^2 - 4x + 7$

Express questions 16–24 in the form $(x + a)^2 - b = 0$. Hence or otherwise, solve for x, writing your answers in the form $p + q\sqrt{r}$ where p, q and $r \in \mathbb{Z}$.

16. $x^2 - 6x + 7 = 0$
17. $x^2 - 10x + 22 = 0$
18. $x^2 + 2x - 6 = 0$
19. $x^2 + 4x - 1 = 0$
20. $3 - 4x - x^2 = 0$
21. $2 - 2x - x^2 = 0$
22. $4 + 2x - x^2 = 0$
23. $x^2 + 12x + 16 = 0$
24. $x^2 - 8x + 4 = 0$

In questions 25–30, rewrite the expression in the form $c^2 - (ax + b)^2$. Hence or otherwise, find the value of x that gives a maximum value for the expression and find that maximum value.

25. $-x^2 + 6x - 5$ 26. $8 - 2x - x^2$ 27. $-x^2 - 10x - 9$

28. $16 - 6x - x^2$ 29. $8x - x^2$ 30. $45 - 4x - x^2$

31. Let $f(x) = 2x^2 + 12x + 50$. Express $f(x)$ in the form $2[(x + a)^2 + b^2]$. Hence, find the minimum value of $f(x)$.

32. Let $f(x) = 3x^2 - 30x + 69$. Express $f(x)$ in the form $[(x - a)^2 - b]$. Hence: (i) find the minimum value of $f(x)$ (ii) solve the equation $f(x) = 0$.

Graph of a quadratic equation

- The graph of a quadratic equation $y = ax^2 + bx + c$, where a, b and c are real numbers, is a parabola. This is a smooth curve, which is symmetrical around an axis of symmetry.
- The values where the graph crosses the x-axis are the roots of the equation.

If a is positive, the graph has a $\cup$ shape and two real roots.	If a is negative, then the graph is a $\cap$ shape and two real roots.	If the graph only touches the x-axis at one point, the two real roots are equal.

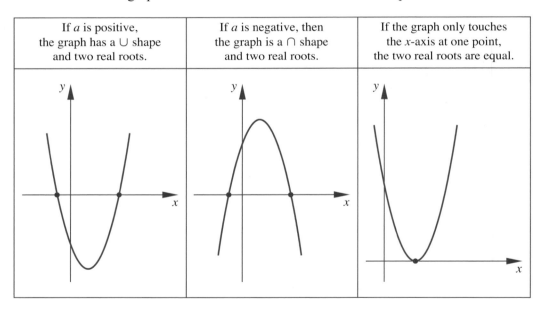

Note: On the x-axis, $y = 0$ and on the y-axis, $x = 0$.

EXAMPLE 1

(i) Sketch the graph of the function $y = x^2 + x - 6$.

(ii) Sketch the graph of the function $y = -x^2 + 6x - 9$.

Solution:

(i) To find where the graph crosses the x-axis, let $y = 0$.

$$x^2 + x - 6 = 0$$
$$(x + 3)(x - 2) = 0$$
$$x = -3 \quad \text{and} \quad x = 2$$

Thus, this graph crosses the x-axis at -3 and 2.

To find where the graph crosses the y-axis, let $x = 0$.

$$y = x^2 + x - 6$$
$$y = (0)^2 + (0) - 6$$
$$y = -6$$

Thus, this graph crosses the y-axis at -6.

Since it was a positive x^2 term, the graph is a $\cup$ shape.

(ii) To find where the graph crosses the x-axis, let $y = 0$.

$$-x^2 + 6x - 9 = 0$$
$$x^2 - 6x + 9 = 0$$
$$(x - 3)(x - 3) = 0$$
$$x = 3 \quad \text{and} \quad x = 3$$

Since the roots are equal, this graph touches the x-axis at 3 only.

To find where the graph crosses the y-axis, let $x = 0$.

$$y = -x^2 + 6x - 9$$
$$y = (0)^2 + (0) - 9$$
$$y = -9$$

Thus, this graph crosses the y-axis at -9.

Since it was a negative x^2 term, the graph is a $\cap$ shape.

Therefore, the sketch is:

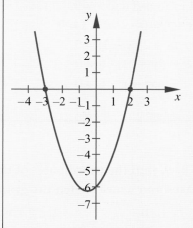

Therefore, the sketch is:

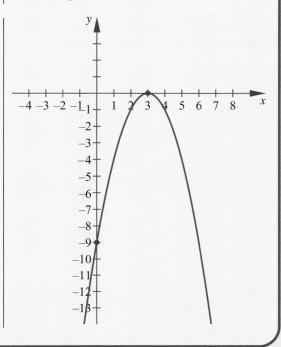

EXAMPLE 2

Find a quadratic equation with roots **(i)** -2 and 3 **(ii)** $\frac{2}{3}$ and $-\frac{1}{5}$.
Write your answers in the form $ax^2 + bx + c = 0$, $a, b, c \in \mathbb{Z}$.

Solution:

(i) Roots -2 and 3.

Let $x = -2$ and $x = 3$.

$x + 2 = 0 \qquad x - 3 = 0$

$(x + 2)(x - 3) = 0$

$x^2 - 3x + 2x - 6 = 0$

$x^2 - x - 6 = 0$

(ii) Roots $\frac{2}{3}$ and $-\frac{1}{5}$.

Let $x = \frac{2}{3}$ and $x = -\frac{1}{5}$.

$3x = 2 \quad$ and $\quad 5x = -1$

$3x - 2 = 0 \quad 5x + 1 = 0$

$(3x - 2)(5x + 1) = 0$

$15x^2 + 3x - 10x - 2 = 0$

$15x^2 - 7x - 2 = 0$

Exercise 2.7

In questions 1–9, find the coordinates of the points where the quadratic function crosses the x and y-axes and hence sketch the graph.

1. $y = x^2 + 7x + 10$
2. $y = x^2 + 3x - 4$
3. $y = 2x^2 - 18$
4. $y = -x^2 + 7x - 10$
5. $y = -3x^2 - 7x + 10$
6. $y = 2x^2 + 3x - 14$
7. $y = x^2 - 8x + 16$
8. $y = -x^2 + 9x - 14$
9. $y = -2x^2 + 6x + 8$

In questions 10–15, construct a quadratic equation with the given roots. In each case, write your answer in the form $ax^2 + bx + c = 0$, where $a, b, c \in \mathbb{Z}$.

10. $-2, 5$
11. $-3, -4$
12. $\frac{1}{2}, 3$
13. $\frac{1}{3}, -\frac{1}{2}$
14. $-\frac{1}{3}, \frac{5}{2}$
15. $-\frac{1}{2}, \frac{2}{5}$

Express each of the following functions in questions 16–19 in the form $f(x) = ax^2 + bx + c$, where a, b and $c \in \mathbb{Z}$.

16.

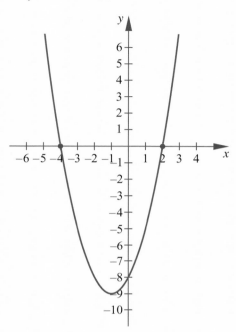

17.

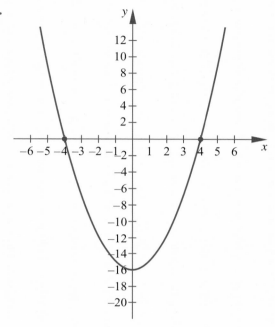

18.

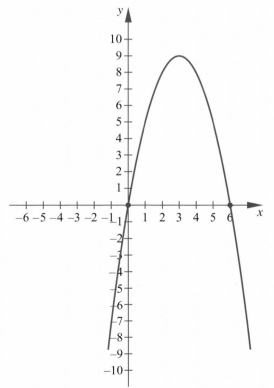

19.

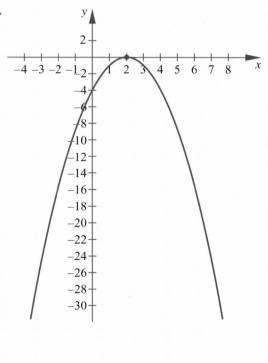

20. The diagram shows a graph of the function
$f(x) = x^2 + ax - 8$.
The graph cuts the x-axis at p and 4.
Calculate the value of a and the value of p.

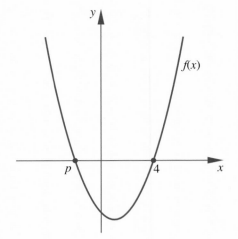

21. The diagram shows a graph of the function
$f(x) = x^2 - 6x + a$.
The graph cuts the x-axis at -1 and p.
Calculate the value of a and the value of p.

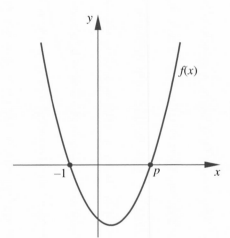

22. A satellite dish is parabolic in shape. The
equation of the parabola is $y = \dfrac{x^2}{128}$.
What is the depth of the dish at the centre if
the diameter of the dish is 64 cm?

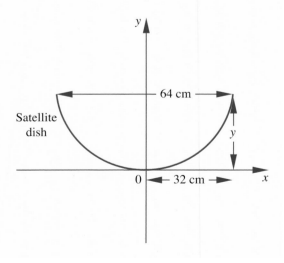

23. Two flagpoles are 32 m high. A rope is strung between the tops of the poles.

    The lowest point of the rope is 7 m from the ground.

    If the rope has the parabolic shape $y = x^2$, how far apart are the poles?

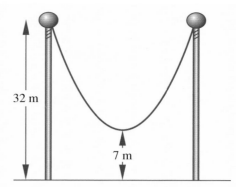

32 m

7 m

24. The bow of a boat is parabolic in shape. This parabola is expressed by $y = -x^2 + 6x - 8$.

    If the length of the bow is 9 m, calculate its width, w m, at the widest point, as indicated in the diagram.

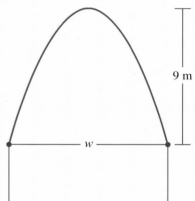

9 m

w

25. A suspension bridge is hanging between two cliffs, each of height 155 m. The shape of the bridge is parabolic and can be expressed by $y = \dfrac{x^2}{25}$.
    If the lowest point of the bridge is 146 m above the ground (as in the diagram), find the distance, w m, between the cliffs.

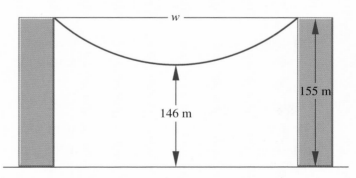

w

155 m

146 m

26. A farmer has 100 m of fencing and wants to fence off a rectangular field that borders a straight river. He needs no fence along the river.

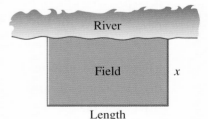

River

Field

x

Length

   (i) By letting the width be x, find an expression for the length.

   (ii) Find the area of the field in terms of x.

   (iii) Graph the area against the width (in units of 10) for $0 \le x \le 50$.

   (iv) Using the graph, determine the length and width which will yield a maximum area for the field.

27. The perimeter of a sector of a circle of radius r is 8 metres.

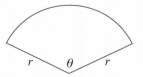

    (i) Express θ in terms of r where θ is the angle of the sector in radians, as shown.

    (ii) Hence, show that the area, A, is given by $A = (4r - r^2)$ m^2.

    (iii) Graph the area of the sector against the radius for $0 \leq r \leq 4$.

    (iv) Use your graph to determine the maximum area of the sector and the corresponding radius.

28. The diagram shows a sector of a circle of radius r cm. The perimeter of the sector is 100 cm.

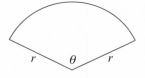

    (i) Express θ in terms of r where θ is the angle of the sector in radians, as shown.

    (ii) Show that the area, A, of the sector is given by $A = (50r - r^2)$ m^2.

    (iii) Graph A against r for r being all multiples of 5 from 0 to 50 inclusive and hence find the maximum value for the area.

    (iv) Hence, find the value of r and θ, in radians, which give this maximum value.

29. In the diagram, $PQ \perp QR$. The lengths of the sides can vary, but in each case $PQ \perp QR$ and $|PQ| + |QR| = 20$ cm. Let $|PQ| = x$ cm.

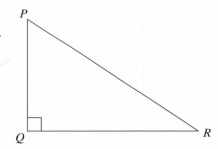

    (i) Find an expression for the area of $\triangle PQR$ in terms of x.

    (ii) Graph the area against x for the even values of $0 \leq x \leq 20$ and use the graph to determine the maximum possible area for $\triangle PQR$.

30. A and B are real numbers such that $A + B = 5$.

    (i) Express their product in terms of A only.

    (ii) Graph the product against A and find the value of A that maximises the product.

31. ABC is a right-angled isosceles triangle, where $|AC| = |BC|$ and $|AB| = 8$ cm. $PQRS$ is a rectangle inscribed in the triangle, as shown.

$|PQ| = x$ cm and $|QR| = y$ cm.

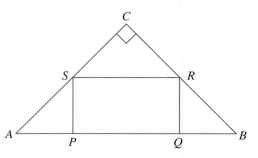

    (i) Express y in terms of x.

    (ii) Determine the area of $PQRS$ in terms of x.

    (iii) Graph the area against x and determine the maximum area.

    (iv) Hence, find the values of x and y that give this maximum area.

Factor theorem

A polynomial in x is a collection of powers of x added together.
For example, $2x^2 - 3x + 5$ and $5x^3 + 6x^2 - x + 4$ are polynomials.

Note: 1. There cannot be negative or fractional powers in a polynomial.

      2. A polynomial is often denoted as $f(x)$.

Factor theorem

If an algebraic expression is divided by one of its factors, then the remainder is zero. The expression $(x - k)$ is a factor of a polynomial $f(x)$ if the remainder when we divide $f(x)$ by $(x - k)$ is zero.

Generalising this:

> **1.** If $f(k) = 0$, then $(x - k)$ is a factor of $f(x)$.
>
> **2.** If $(x - k)$ is a factor of $f(x)$, then $f(k) = 0$.

The factor theorem can be extended:

> **1.** If $f\left(\dfrac{b}{a}\right) = 0$, then $(ax - b)$ is a factor of $f(x)$.
>
> **2.** If $(ax - b)$ is a factor of $f(x)$, then $f\left(\dfrac{b}{a}\right) = 0$.

The factor theorem can be used to factorise polynomials or to find unknown coefficients in a polynomial.
Here are some examples:

Factor	Put factor = 0 and solve	Factor theorem
$x + 4$	$x = -4$	$f(-4) = 0$
$x - 3$	$x = 3$	$f(3) = 0$
$2x + 1$	$x = -\frac{1}{2}$	$f(-\frac{1}{2}) = 0$

Note: If $(x + a)$ and $(x + b)$ are both factors of a polynomial $f(x)$, then so is their product, $(x + a)(x + b)$.

    Thus, $(x + a)(x + b) = x^2 + (a + b)x + ab$ is also a factor.

EXAMPLE 1

If $(2x - 1)$ is a factor of the polynomial $f(x) = 2x^3 - 5x^2 - kx + 3$, find the value of k.
Hence, find the other two factors.

Solution:
$f(x) = 2x^3 - 5x^2 - kx + 3$
If $(2x - 1)$ is a factor, then $f\left(\frac{1}{2}\right) = 0$.

$$f\left(\tfrac{1}{2}\right) = 0$$
$$2\left(\tfrac{1}{2}\right)^3 - 5\left(\tfrac{1}{2}\right)^2 - k\left(\tfrac{1}{2}\right) + 3 = 0 \quad \left(\text{replace } x \text{ with } \tfrac{1}{2}\right)$$
$$2\left(\tfrac{1}{8}\right) - 5\left(\tfrac{1}{4}\right) - k\left(\tfrac{1}{2}\right) + 3 = 0$$
$$\tfrac{1}{4} - \tfrac{5}{4} - \tfrac{1}{2}k + 3 = 0$$
$$1 - 5 - 2k + 12 = 0 \quad \text{(multiply each part by 4)}$$
$$-2k + 8 = 0$$
$$-2k = -8$$
$$k = 4$$

Now divide $2x^3 - 5x^2 - 4x + 3$ by $(2x - 1)$.

$$
\begin{array}{r}
x^2 - 2x - 3 \\
2x - 1 \overline{\smash{)}2x^3 - 5x^2 - 4x + 3} \\
\underline{2x^3 - x^2} \\
-4x^2 - 4x \\
\underline{-4x^2 + 2x} \\
-6x + 3 \\
\underline{-6x + 3} \\
0
\end{array}
$$

Now factorise $x^2 - 2x - 3$.
$$x^2 - 2x - 3$$
$$= (x + 1)(x - 3)$$
Thus, the other two factors are
$$(x + 1) \text{ and } (x - 3).$$

EXAMPLE 2

Let $f(x) = 2x^3 + mx^2 + nx + 2$ where m and n are constants.
Given that $x - 1$ and $x + 2$ are factors of $f(x)$, find the value of m and the value of n.

Solution:
$$f(x) = 2x^3 + mx^2 + nx + 2$$

If $(x - 1)$ is a factor, then $f(1) = 0$.
$$f(1) = 0$$
$$2(1)^3 + m(1)^2 + n(1) + 2 = 0$$
$$2 + m + n + 2 = 0$$
$$m + n = -4 \quad ①$$

If $(x + 2)$ is a factor, then $f(-2) = 0$.
$$f(-2) = 0$$
$$2(-2)^3 + m(-2)^2 + n(-2) + 2 = 0$$
$$-16 + 4m - 2n + 2 = 0$$
$$4m - 2n = 14$$
$$2m - n = 7 \quad ②$$

We now solve the simultaneous equations ① and ②:

$$m + n = -4 \qquad ①$$
$$\underline{2m - n = 7 \qquad ②}$$
$$3m = 3 \quad \text{(add)}$$
$$m = 1$$

$$m + n = -4 \qquad ①$$
$$1 + n = -4$$
$$n = -5$$

Thus, $m = 1$ and $n = -5$.

Exercise 2.8

1. Verify that $(x - 1)$ is a factor of $x^3 + 2x^2 - x - 2$ and find the other two factors.

2. Verify that $(x + 3)$ is a factor of $x^3 + 9x^2 + 23x + 15$ and find the other two factors.

3. Verify that $(2x - 1)$ is a factor of $6x^3 + 7x^2 - 9x + 2$ and find the other two factors.

4. Verify that $(2x - 3)$ is a factor of $2x^3 - 15x^2 + 34x - 24$ and find the other two factors.

5. Verify that $(x - 1)$ is a factor of $x^3 - (2k + 1)x^2 + (k^2 + 2k)x - k^2$.

6. If $(x + 2)$ is a factor of the polynomial $f(x) = 6x^3 + kx^2 + 11x - 6$, find the value of k. Hence, find the other two factors.

7. If $(2x + 1)$ is a factor of the polynomial $f(x) = 2x^3 + 7x^2 + kx + 2$, find the value of k. Hence, find the other two factors.

8. If $(2x - 1)$ is a factor of the polynomial $f(x) = 2x^3 - 5x^2 - kx + 3$, find the value of k. Hence, find the other two factors of $f(x)$.

9. Show that $2x - \sqrt{3}$ is a factor of $4x^2 - 2(1 + \sqrt{3})x + \sqrt{3}$ and find the other factor.

10. Let $f(x) = px^3 + 3x^2 - 9x + q$ where p and q are constants. Given that $(x + 1)$ and $(x - 2)$ are factors of $f(x)$, find the value of p and the value of q.

11. Let $p(x) = 2x^3 - ax^2 - bx + 42$ where a and b are constants. Given that $(x - 2)$ and $(x + 3)$ are factors of $p(x)$, find the value of a and the value of b.

12. Let $f(x) = 2x^3 + ax^2 + bx - 6$ where a and b are constants. Given that $f(-2) = 0$ and $f\left(\frac{1}{2}\right) = 0$, find the value of a and the value of b.

13. Let $f(x) = x^3 - (h + 2)x + 2k$ and $p(x) = 2x^3 + hx^2 - 4x - k$. Given that $(x + 3)$ is a common factor of $f(x)$ and $p(x)$, find the value of h and the value of k.

14. Factorise $x^2 + x - 6$. Let $f(x) = px^3 + x^2 - 20x + q$ where p and q are constants. Given that $x^2 + x - 6$ is a factor of $f(x)$, find the value of p and the value of q.

15. Given that $px^3 + 8x^2 + qx + 6$ is exactly divisible by $x^2 - 2x - 3$, find the value of p and the value of q.

16. If $(x - 2)^2$ is a factor of $x^3 + px + q$, find the value of p and the value of q.

Further factor theorem problems

EXAMPLE

$x^2 - px + q$ is a factor of $x^3 + 3px^2 + 3qx + r$.

(i) Show that $q = -2p^2$.

(ii) Show that $r = -8p^3$.

Solution:

Method 1: Equating the coefficients

Let $(x + k)$ be the second factor.

Thus,
$$(x + k)(x^2 - px + q) = x^3 + 3px^2 + 3qx + r$$
$$x^3 - px^2 + qx + kx^2 - kpx + qk = x^3 + 3px^2 + 3qx + r$$
$$x^3 + (-p + k)x^2 + (q - kp)x + qk = x^3 + 3px^2 + 3qx + r$$

Equating coefficients of like terms:
$$-p + k = 3p \quad ① \qquad q - kp = 3q \quad ② \qquad qk = r \quad ③$$

(Basic idea is to remove the constant, k, which is not in the solution required.)
$$-p + k = 3p \quad ① \qquad \text{(get } k \text{ on its own from } ①)$$
$$k = 4p \qquad (k \text{ on its own})$$

Put $k = 4p$ into ② and ③.

(i) $q - kp = 3q$ ②

$q - (4p)p = 3q$
$q - 4p^2 = 3q$
$-4p^2 = 2q$
$-2p^2 = q$

(ii) $qk = r$ ③

$q(4p) = r$
$4pq = r$
$4p(-2p^2) = r \quad \left(\begin{array}{c} q = -2p^2 \\ \text{from (i)} \end{array} \right)$
$-8p^3 = r$

Method 2: Using long division

$$
\begin{array}{r}
x + 4p \\
x^2 - px + q \overline{\smash{\big)}\ x^3 + 3px^2 + 3qx + r} \\
\underline{x^3 - px^2 + qx} \\
4px^2 + 2qx + r \\
\underline{4px^2 - 4p^2x + 4pq} \\
(2q + 4p^2)x + (r - 4pq)
\end{array}
$$

Since $(x^2 - px + q)$ is a factor, the remainder must equal 0.

Thus, $2q + 4p^2 = 0$ ①

$2q = -4p^2$

$q = -2p^2$

Put this into ②.

or $r - 4pq = 0$ ②

$r - 4p(-2p^2) = 0$

$r + 8p^3 = 0$

$r = -8p^3$

Exercise 2.9

1. Given that $x^2 - ax - 3$ is a factor of $x^3 - 5x^2 + bx + 9$ where $a, b \in \mathbb{R}$, find the value of a and the value of b.

2. $(x - a)^2$ is a factor of $x^3 + 3px + q$. Show that:
   (i) $p = -a^2$ (ii) $q = 2a^3$

3. $x^2 + bx + c$ is a factor of $x^3 - p$. Show that:
   (i) $c = b^2$ (ii) $bc = p$ (iii) $b^3 = p$ (iv) $c^3 = p^2$

4. $x^2 - px + 1$ is a factor of $ax^3 + bx + c$ where $a \neq 0$. Show that:
   (i) $p = \dfrac{c}{a}$ (ii) $c^2 = a(a - b)$

5. Two roots of the equation $ax^3 + bx^2 + cx + d = 0$ are p and $-p$. Show that $bc = ad$.

6. $x^2 - t$ is a factor of $x^3 - px^2 - qx + r$.
   (i) Show that $pq = r$.
   (ii) Express the roots of $x^3 - px^2 - qx + r = 0$ in terms of p and q.

7. $(x - p)^2$ is a factor of $x^3 + qx + r$.
   (i) Show that $27r^2 + 4q^3 = 0$.
   (ii) Express the roots of $3x^2 + q = 0$ in terms of p.

8. If $x^2 + ax - 2$ is a factor of $x^3 + (2a - 1)x^2 - b$, find two pairs of values of a and b.

9. $(x - a)^2$ is a factor of $2x^3 - 5ax^2 + 8abx - 36a$, where $a \neq 0$. Find the possible values of a and b.

Solving cubic equations

Any equation of the form $ax^3 + bx^2 + cx + d = 0$, $a \neq 0$, is called a cubic equation.

A cubic equation is solved with the following steps.

1. Find the first root, k, by trial and error, i.e. try $f(1), f(-1), f(2), f(-2)$, etc. (Only try numbers that divide evenly into the constant in the equation.)

2. If $x = k$ is a root, then $(x - k)$ is a factor.

3. Divide $f(x)$ by $(x - k)$, which always gives a quadratic expression.

4. Let the (given cubic) = (linear factor)(quadratic factor).
   Then let (linear factor)(quadratic factor) = 0 and solve by factors or formula.

Note: Each cubic equation we are asked to solve must have at least one integer root.

Graph of a cubic equation

The curve below is the graph of a typical cubic function: $y = x^3 + 5x^2 + 2x - 8$.

The roots of the equation $f(x) = 0$ represent the x-values of the points at which the curve intersects the x-axis.

Roots are $-4, -2, 1$.

Note: When $x = -4, -2$ or 1, $y = 0$.

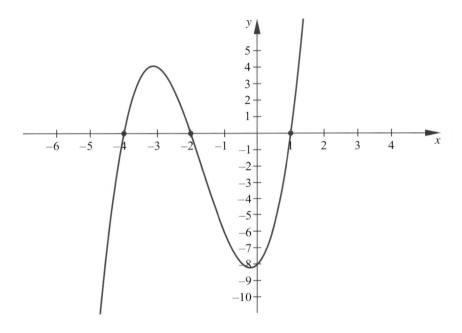

The following three curves illustrate the graph of a cubic function $f(x)$, where $f(x) = 0$ has:

(i) Three real roots	(ii) Three real roots, two of which are equal	(iii) One real root
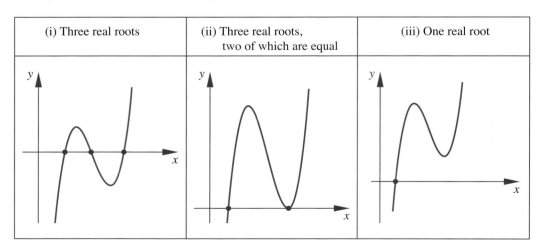		

EXAMPLE 1

Solve the equation $2x^3 + x^2 - 13x + 6 = 0$.

Solution:

Let $f(x) = 2x^3 + x^2 - 13x + 6$.

1. The first root will be a factor of 6.

   $\therefore$ We need try only those values which are factors of 6, i.e. $\pm 1, \pm 2, \pm 3, \pm 6$.

   $$f(1) = 2(1)^3 + (1)^2 - 13(1) + 6 = 2 + 1 - 13 + 6 = -4 \neq 0$$
   $$f(-1) = 2(-1)^3 + (-1)^2 - 13(-1) + 6 = -2 + 1 + 13 + 6 = 18 \neq 0$$
   $$f(2) = 2(2)^3 + (2)^2 - 13(2) + 6 = 16 + 4 - 26 + 6 = 0$$

   $\therefore x = 2$ is a root.

2. $\therefore x - 2$ is a factor.

3. Divide $(2x^3 + x^2 - 13x + 6)$ by $(x - 2)$.

$$
\begin{array}{r}
2x^2 + 5x - 3 \\
x - 2 \enclose{longdiv}{2x^3 + x^2 - 13x + 6} \\
\underline{2x^3 - 4x^2} \\
5x^2 - 13x \\
\underline{5x^2 - 10x} \\
-3x + 6 \\
\underline{-3x + 6} \\
0
\end{array}
$$

4. $2x^3 + x^2 - 13x + 6 = 0$

   $(x - 2)(2x^2 + 5x - 3) = 0$

   Let $x - 2 = 0$ or $2x^2 + 5x - 3 = 0$

   $x = 2$ or $(2x - 1)(x + 3) = 0$

   $2x - 1 = 0$ or $x + 3 = 0$

   $x = \frac{1}{2}$ or $x = -3$

   Thus, the three roots of the equation

   $$2x^3 + x^2 - 13x + 6 = 0$$

   are $-3, \frac{1}{2}$ and 2.

Rough graph of $f(x) = 2x^3 + x^2 - 13x + 6$:

Note: If we draw the graph of

$$f(x) = 2x^3 + x^2 - 13x + 6$$

we can see that the roots of the equation $f(x) = 0$ occur where the graph of $f(x)$ cuts the x-axis, i.e. at $-3, \frac{1}{2}$ and 2.

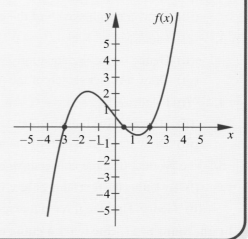

EXAMPLE 2

Find a cubic equation with roots **(i)** -1, 2 and 4   **(ii)** -2, $\frac{1}{2}$ and $\frac{2}{3}$.
Write your answers in the form $ax^3 + bx^2 + cx + d = 0$, where $a, b, c, d \in \mathbb{Z}$.

Solution:

(i) Roots -1, 2 and 4.

Let $x = -1$, $x = 2$ and $x = 4$.

$x + 1 = 0$ $x - 2 = 0$ $x - 4 = 0$

$(x + 1)(x - 2)(x - 4) = 0$

$(x + 1)(x^2 - 4x - 2x + 8) = 0$

$(x + 1)(x^2 - 6x + 8) = 0$

$x^3 - 6x^2 + 8x + x^2 - 6x + 8 = 0$

$x^3 - 5x^2 + 2x + 8 = 0$

(ii) Roots -2, $\frac{1}{2}$ and $\frac{2}{3}$.

Let $x = -2$, $x = \frac{1}{2}$ and $x = \frac{2}{3}$.

So, $x = -2$ $2x = 1$ and $3x = 2$

$x + 2 = 0$ $2x - 1 = 0$ $3x - 2 = 0$

$(x + 2)(2x - 1)(3x - 2) = 0$

$(x + 2)(6x^2 - 4x - 3x + 2) = 0$

$(x + 2)(6x^2 - 7x + 2) = 0$

$6x^3 - 7x^2 + 2x + 12x^2 - 14x + 4 = 0$

$6x^3 + 5x^2 - 12x + 4 = 0$

Exercise 2.10

1. **(i)** Find the three linear factors of $x^3 - x^2 - 14x + 24$.
   (ii) Hence, solve the equation $x^3 - x^2 - 14x + 24 = 0$.
   (iii) Draw a rough sketch of the graph of $f(x) = x^3 - x^2 - 14x + 24$.

2. **(i)** Find the three linear factors of $2x^3 - 4x^2 - 22x + 24$.
   (ii) Hence, solve the equation $2x^3 - 4x^2 - 22x + 24 = 0$.
   (iii) Draw a rough sketch of the graph $f(x) = 2x^3 - 4x^2 - 22x + 24$.

3. **(i)** Factorise $2x^3 - x^2 - 2x + 1$.
   (ii) Hence, solve the equation $2x^3 + 1 = x^2 + 2x$.
   (iii) Draw a rough sketch of the graph of $f(x) = 2x^3 - x^2 - 2x + 1$.

4. **(i)** Factorise $2x^3 - 3x^2 - 3x + 2$.
   (ii) Hence, solve the equation $2x^3 + 2 = 3x^2 + 3x$.
   (iii) Draw a rough sketch of the graph of $f(x) = 2x^3 - 3x^2 - 3x + 2$.

5. The product of three consecutive even numbers is 192.

   (i) By letting the first number be x, derive a cubic expression for the product of the three numbers.

   (ii) Hence, find the three numbers and verify your answer.

In questions 6–11, construct a cubic equation with the given roots. Write your answer in the form $ax^3 + bx^2 + cx + d = 0$, where $a, b, c \in \mathbb{Z}$.

6. $-2, 2, 5$ 7. $-4, -3, 1$ 8. $\frac{1}{2}, 2, 3$

9. $\frac{1}{5}, \frac{1}{3}, -\frac{1}{2}$ 10. $-\frac{1}{3}, \frac{1}{4}, \frac{5}{2}$ 11. $-\frac{1}{2}, \frac{2}{3}, \frac{2}{5}$

Express each of the following functions in questions 12–15 in the form
$f(x) = x^3 + ax^2 + bx + c$ where a, b and $c \in \mathbb{Z}$.

12.

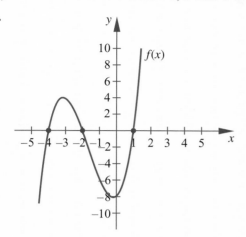

13.

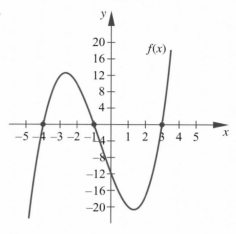

14.

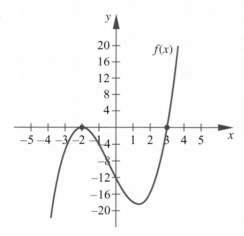

15.

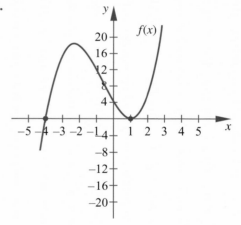

16. The diagram shows a graph of the function
$f(x) = x^3 - 4x^2 + ax + 30$.
The graph cuts the x-axis at p, q and 5.
Calculate the value of a, the value of p and the
value of q.

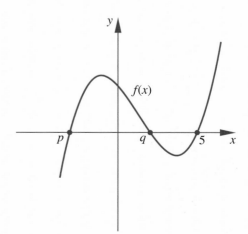

17. The diagram shows a graph of the function
$f(x) = x^3 + ax^2 - 36x + 32$.
The graph cuts the x-axis at p, q and 1.
Calculate the value of a, the value of p and the
value of q.

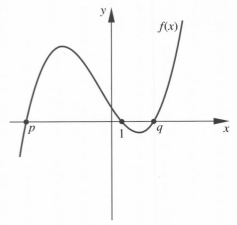

18. Show that $x = \frac{1}{2}$ is a root of the equation $2x^3 - 5x^2 - 4x + 3 = 0$ and find the other two roots.

19. Show that $x = 2$ is a root of the equation $x^3 + 4x^2 - 11x - 2 = 0$ and find the other two roots,
giving your answer in the form $a \pm b\sqrt{b}$.

20. (i) If $x = -\frac{1}{2}$ is one root of the equation $2x^3 - 9x^2 + kx + 6 = 0$, find the value of k.
    (ii) Find the other two roots of the equation.

21. (i) Let $p(x) = ax^3 - 5x^2 - bx + 18$. If -2 and 3 are roots of the equation $p(x) = 0$, find the
    value of a and the value of b.
    (ii) If $p(k) = 0$, $k \neq -2$, 3, find the value of k.

22. If k is a root of the equation $3x^3 + (k + 3)x^2 + (7 - k - 4k^2)x - 4 = 0$, find the values of k.

23. Find the values of the constants p, q and r for which $(x - 4)(x - 2)(x + p) = x^3 - 7x^2 + qx + r$ for
all values of $x \in \mathbb{R}$. Using these values of q and r, solve the equation $x^3 - 7x^2 + qx + r = 0$.

24. Verify that $-4p$ is a root of the equation $x^3 + 3px^2 - 6p^2x - 8p^3 = 0$. Hence or otherwise,
find the three roots of $x^3 + 3px^2 - 6p^2x - 8p^3 = 0$ in terms of p.

25. A rectangular box is designed such that its length is twice its height and its width is 1 cm
greater than the height.
    (i) Find the volume of the box in terms of its height, h, where $h \in \mathbb{N}$.
    (ii) If the volume of the box is 300 cm^3, find the value of h.
    (iii) Hence, find the length and width of the box.

26. A closed cylindrical can has a radius which is 2 cm greater than its height.
    (i) Find the volume of the can in terms of the height, h.
    (ii) If the volume of the can is 75π cm^3, find the value of h.
    (iii) Hence, find the radius, r.

27. A solid cone has a slant length of $2\sqrt{13}$ cm.
    (i) Express r^2 in terms of h, where r is the radius and h is the vertical height of the cone.
    (ii) If the volume of the cone is found to be 32π cm^3, calculate the values of h.

SIMULTANEOUS EQUATIONS

Simultaneous linear equations

Simultaneous linear equations in two variables are solved with the following steps.

1. Write both equations in the form $ax + by = k$ and label the equations ① and ②.
2. Multiply one or both of the equations by a number in order to make the coefficients of x or y the same, but of opposite sign.
3. Add to remove the variable with equal coefficients but of opposite sign.
4. Solve the resultant equation to find the value of the remaining unknown (x or y).
5. Substitute this value in equation ① or ② to find the value of the other unknown.

Solution containing fractions

If the answer at step 4 is a fraction, the substitution might be difficult. In such cases, we repeat steps 1 to 4 for the other variable.

EXAMPLE 1

Solve the simultaneous equations for x and y:

$$\frac{x + 1}{2} - \frac{y + 3}{3} = 4, \qquad x + \frac{y - 3}{2} = \frac{1}{2}.$$

Solution:

Write each equation in the form $ax + by = k$ and label the equations ① and ②.

$$\frac{x + 1}{2} - \frac{y + 3}{3} = 4 \qquad\qquad x + \frac{y - 3}{2} = \frac{1}{2}$$

$$\frac{6(x + 1)}{2} - \frac{6(y + 3)}{3} = 6(4) \qquad\qquad 2(x) + \frac{2(y - 3)}{2} = 2\left(\tfrac{1}{2}\right)$$

(multiply each part by 6) $\qquad\qquad$ (multiply each part by 2)

$$3(x + 1) - 2(y + 3) = 24 \qquad\qquad 2x + (y - 3) = 1$$
$$3x + 3 - 2y - 6 = 24 \qquad\qquad 2x + y - 3 = 1$$
$$3x - 2y = 27 \quad ① \qquad\qquad 2x + y = 4 \quad ②$$

Now solve between equations ① and ②:

$$3x - 2y = 27 \quad ①$$
$$\underline{4x + 2y = 8} \quad ② \times 2$$
$$7x = 35 \quad \text{(add)}$$
$$x = 5$$

(substitute $x = 5$ into ① or ②)

$$2x + y = 4 \quad ②$$
$$2(5) + y = 4$$
$$10 + y = 4$$
$$y = -6$$

Thus, $x = 5$ and $y = -6$.

EXAMPLE 2

McCool the DJ is asked to play at a disco for three hours. She knows each song is about four minutes long. In addition, she knows from experience she needs to play two slow songs for every three fast songs.

(i) Write down the total number of songs McCool expects to play.

(ii) Write down two equations with two unknowns to represent the situation.

(iii) By eliminating one of the variables, solve for the number of slow songs McCool will play.

Solution:

(i) 3 hours = 3 × 60 minutes = 180 minutes

$$\therefore \frac{180}{4} = 45 \text{ songs}$$

(ii) Let x = the number of slow songs played
y = the number of fast songs played

$$\therefore x + y = 45 \text{ and } 3x = 2y.$$

(iii) $x + y = 45$ ① and $3x = 2y$
$$3x - 2y = 0 \quad ②$$

Solve between ① and ②.

$$3x - 2y = 0 \quad ②$$
$$\underline{2x + 2y = 90} \quad ① \times 2$$
$$5x = 90$$
$$x = 18$$

$$x + y = 45 \quad ①$$
$$18 + y = 45$$
$$y = 45 - 18$$
$$y = 27$$

Thus, 18 slow (and 27 fast) songs are required by McCool.

Simultaneous linear equations in three variables are solved with the following steps.

1. Write all three equations in the form $ax + by + cz = k$ and label the equations ①, ② and ③.
2. Select one pair of equations and eliminate one of the variables; call this equation ④.
3. Select another pair of equations and eliminate the same variable; call this equation ⑤.
4. Solve the equations ④ and ⑤.
5. Put the answers from step 4 into ① or ② or ③ to find the value of the third variable.

EXAMPLE 3

Solve for x, y and z:

$x + 2y + z = 3$
$5x - 3y + 2z = 19$
$3x + 2y - 3z = -5$

Solution:

All three equations are in the form $ax + by + cz = k$.
Label the equations ①, ② and ③.

$$x + 2y + z = 3 \quad ①$$
$$5x - 3y + 2z = 19 \quad ②$$
$$3x + 2y - 3z = -5 \quad ③$$

Eliminate z from two different pairs of equations.

$-2x - 4y - 2z = -6$ ① $\times -2$	$3x + 6y + 3z = 9$ ① $\times 3$
$5x - 3y + 2z = 19$ ②	$3x + 2y - 3z = -5$ ③
$3x - 7y = 13$ ④ (add)	$6x + 8y = 4$ ⑤

Now solve between equations ④ and ⑤ to find the values of x and y.

$-6x + 14y = -26$ ④ $\times -2$	$3x - 7y = 13$ ④
$6x + 8y = 4$ ⑤	$3x - 7(-1) = 13$
$22y = -22$	$3x + 7 = 13$
$y = -1$	$3x = 6$
(put $y = -1$ into ④ or ⑤)	$x = 2$

Now put $x = 2$ and $y = -1$ into ① or ② or ③ to find the value of z.

$$x + 2y + z = 3 \quad ①$$
$$(2) + 2(-1) + z = 3 \quad \text{(put in } x = 2 \text{ and } y = -1)$$
$$2 - 2 + z = 3$$
$$z = 3$$

Thus, $x = 2$, $y = -1$ and $z = 3$.

Note: Any of the variables x, y or z could have been eliminated at the beginning.

If one equation contains only two unknowns, then the other two equations should be used to obtain a second equation in the same two unknowns, e.g. solve:

$3x + 2y - z = 3$ ① $5x - 3y + 2z = 3$ ② $5x + 3z = 14$ ③

Here, from equations ① and ②, y should be eliminated to obtain an equation in x and z, which should then be taken with equation ③.

EXAMPLE 4

St Mels Community College ran a disco for students.

The disco was organised by a committee of students from St Mels and the committee did not have to pay for admission. Otherwise, students from St Mels paid €10 each for admission while students from elsewhere paid €20 each for admission.

The total number of students at the disco was 486. When the admission money was counted it amounted to €7,620.

It was noted that twice the number of paying St Mels students plus the number of committee members equalled the number of admissions from elsewhere.

(i) Write down three equations to describe the situation.
(ii) Hence, solve the three equations.

Solution:

(i) Let x = the number of students on the committee
y = the number of paying students from St Mels
z = the number of paying students from elsewhere

$$x + y + z = 486 \qquad ①$$
$$(0)(x) + (10)(y) + (20)(z) = 7,620$$
$$10y + 20z = 7,620 \qquad ②$$
$$2y + x = z \qquad ③$$

(ii) $x + y + z = 486 \qquad ①$

$10y + 20z = 7,620 \implies y + 2z = 762 \quad ②$

$2y + x = z \implies x + 2y - z = 0 \quad ③$

Now combine ① and ③ to eliminate x.

$$\begin{array}{ll} x + y + z = 486 & ① \\ -x - 2y + z = 0 & ③ \times -1 \\ \hline -y + 2z = 486 & ④ \end{array}$$

Now combine ② and ④ to get:

$$\begin{array}{l} y + 2z = 762 \\ -y + 2z = 486 \\ \hline 4z = 1,248 \\ z = 312 \end{array}$$

Now substitute $z = 312$ into ② (or ④).

$$y + 2z = 762 \quad ②$$
$$y + 2(312) = 762$$
$$y + 624 = 762$$
$$y = 138$$

Finally, substitute $z = 312$ and $y = 138$ into ①

to get
$$x + y + z = 486$$
$$x + 138 + 312 = 486$$
$$x + 450 = 486$$
$$x = 36$$

Answer: 36 committee members; 138 St Mels students; 312 from elsewhere.

Exercise 3.1

Solve questions 1–3, without using a calculator, for x and y.

1. $3x + 2y = 9$
   $x - y = -2$

2. $\dfrac{x}{4} - \dfrac{y}{3} = \dfrac{5}{6}$
   $2x - 6 = 3y$

3. $\dfrac{x}{5} - \dfrac{y}{4} = 0$
   $3x + \dfrac{y}{2} = 17$

4. The combined cost of a television and a DVD player is €1,460. The television costs €330 more than the DVD player.

   (i) Use two equations in x and y to represent the situation.

   (ii) Hence, find the cost of the television and the cost of the DVD player.

5. Two rectangles, H and K as in the diagram, have perimeters of 29 cm and 48 cm, respectively.

   (i) Write down an expression in x and y for the perimeter of (a) H (b) K.

   (ii) Hence, solve for the value of x and the value of y.

   (iii) Write down the area of (a) H (b) K.

6. Two numbers have a difference of 13. Twice the bigger number added to 19 times the smaller number makes 110.

   (i) If x is the bigger number and y is the smaller number, write down two equations in x and y.

   (ii) Hence, solve for the two numbers.

7. Carol's farmyard contains both chickens and pigs. Carol knows there are 26 heads and 74 legs.

   (i) Using guesswork, can you find how many chickens and how many pigs are in Carol's farmyard? Describe what you tried to do.

   (ii) Let $x =$ the number of chickens and $y =$ the number of pigs. Write down two equations to represent the above information.

   (iii) Hence, solve for x and y.

8. Let the cost of a meal for an adult be €x and the cost of a meal for a child be €y. The cost of a meal for three adults and two children amounts to €125. The cost of a meal for two adults and three children amounts to €115.

   (i) Write down two equations in x and y to represent this information.

   (ii) Solve these equations to find the cost of an adult's meal and the cost of a child's meal.

9. 400 people attend a cinema, with adults paying €9·75 each and children paying €4·75 each. If each adult had been charged €8·25 and each child charged €6·25, an extra €78 would have been taken in.

   (i) Use two simultaneous equations to represent the situation.

   (ii) Use your equations found in **(i)** to find how many adults attended.

10. Sam had a total of 36 currency notes, some of which were €20 notes and the rest were €50 notes. The total value of the notes was €1,410.

    (i) Express the situation in the form of two simultaneous equations.

    (ii) Hence, find the number of €20 notes and the number of €50 notes.

11. A builders' supplier sells two types of copper pipes. One has a narrow diameter and costs €x per length. The other has a wider diameter and costs €y per length. Tony buys 14 lengths of the narrow diameter pipes and 10 lengths of the wider diameter pipes at a cost of €555. Gerry buys 12 lengths of the narrow diameter pipes and five lengths of the wider diameter pipes at a cost of €390.

    (i) Write two equations to represent the above information.

    (ii) Solve these equations to find the cost of a length of each type of copper pipe.

Solve questions 12–17, without using a calculator, for x and y.

12. $x = 5 - y$

    $\dfrac{4x}{3} + 8 = \dfrac{y}{2}$

13. $3x - 2y = 19$

    $\dfrac{x}{3} + \dfrac{y}{2} = 5$

14. $2x + y = 3(y - x) + 7$

    $\dfrac{x}{3} = 2 - \dfrac{y}{4}$

15. $\dfrac{2x - 5}{3} + \dfrac{y}{5} = 6$

    $\dfrac{3x}{10} + 2 = \dfrac{3y - 5}{2}$

16. $\dfrac{3x}{5} - \dfrac{y}{4} = 8$

    $\dfrac{2x}{3} = 13 - \dfrac{3y}{4}$

17. $2x + 3y = -2$

    $3x + 7y = -6$

18. **(i)** The lines $2x - y + 3 = 0$ and $4x - y + k = 0$ intersect at a point. Find, in terms of k, the coordinates of the point of intersection of the lines.

    (ii) The lines $kx + 3y + 4 = 0$ and $kx + 2y + 1 = 0$ intersect at a point. Find, in terms of k, the coordinates of the point of intersection of the lines.

(iii) The lines $5x + ky - k = 0$ and $4x + ky - 1 = 0$ intersect at a point. Find, in terms of k, the coordinates of the point of intersection of the lines.

(iv) The lines $kx + y = 10$ and $x + ky = 10k$ intersect at a point. Find the coordinates of the point of intersection of the lines.

Solve questions 19–24, without using a calculator, for x, y and z.

19. $3x + 5y - z = -3$
$2x + y - 3z = -9$
$x + 3y + 2z = 7$

20. $x + y - z = 0$
$x - y + z = 4$
$x - y - z = -8$

21. $2x + y - z = -3$
$x + 3y + 2z = 1$
$3x - y = 9$

22. $x + 2y - z = -1$
$2x + y + 3z = 14$
$3x - y - z = -14$

23. $x + y + z = 1$
$2x - 3y - 2z = -9$
$2x - 3z = -16$

24. $x + \dfrac{y}{3} + \dfrac{z}{3} = 0$
$x - y + z = 2$
$x - \frac{3}{2}y - \frac{1}{2}z = 4\frac{1}{2}$

25. At Olly's Café, a salad plus a pizza plus a latte cost €14·80. Three lattes and a pizza cost €12·60. Three salads cost €1·20 more than two pizzas and one latte. By forming a system of equations, find the cost of each of the three items.

26. If the curve $y = ax^2 + bx + c$ contains the points $(0, 5)$, $(1, 4)$ and $(-1, 10)$, find the value of a, the value of b and the value of c.

27. $f(x) = px^2 + qx + r$. If $f(-2) = 7$, $f(1) = -2$ and $f(2) = 3$, find the value of p, the value of q and the value of r.

28. The circle $x^2 + y^2 + ax + by + c = 0$ passes through the points $(0, 1)$, $(9, -2)$ and $(8, 5)$. Find the values of a, b and c.

29. Solve the following simultaneous equations.

(i) $2x + 3y = x + y + z = 3x + 2y - 4z - 9 = 0$

(ii) $x + y = -2$, $y - z = -5$, $x + 2z = 1$

30. A school has 82 students in classes P, Q and R. There are x students in class P, y students in class Q and z students in class R. One-sixth of class P, one-third of class Q and half of class R study mathematics.

One-tenth of class P, three-eighths of class Q and one-quarter of class R study chemistry. 27 students study mathematics and 19 study chemistry.

(i) Show how the information given leads to the following system of equations:

$x + \quad y + \quad z = 82$
$x + \quad 2y + \quad 3z = 162$
$4x + 15y + 10z = 760$

(ii) Find the number of students in each of the three classes.

31. You are given three triangles, A, B and C, with dimensions as shown. The perimeters of A, B and C are respectively 12, 19 and 23 cm.

A 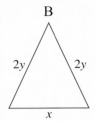 B 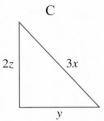 C

(i) Write the information as three simultaneous equations.

(ii) Hence, solve for x, y and z.

32. Lily opened a coin box containing 52 coins. The box had x 50c coins, y 20c coins and z 10c coins. The total amount was €14·30.

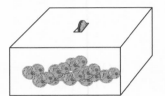

(i) Write down two equations in x, y and z to represent the situation.

(ii) Lily observed that if there had been y 50c coins, z 20c coins and x 10c coins, the total amount would also have been €14·30. Represent her observation in terms of an equation in x, y and z.

(iii) Hence, solve the system of equations for x, y and z.

33. An examination paper consists of 30 questions. Four marks are given for each correct answer, two marks are deducted for each incorrect answer and one mark is given for no answer.

Sean had x answers correct, y answers incorrect and the remaining z questions with no answer. His total score for the examination was 54 marks.

Eileen had $(x - 1)$ answers correct, $(y - 3)$ answers incorrect and the remaining $2z$ questions with no answer.

(i) Represent the information with three simultaneous equations.

(ii) Solve your equations for x, y and z.

(iii) Hence, calculate Eileen's score.

34. (i) Solve the following simultaneous equations.

$$3x + y + z = 16$$
$$2x - y + 3z = 24$$
$$x - y - z = 0$$

   (ii) Hence or otherwise, solve:
$$3a^2 + (b - 2) + (2c - 1) = 16$$
$$2a^2 - (b - 2) + 3(2c - 1) = 24$$
$$a^2 - (b - 2) - (2c - 1) = 0$$

35. Solve the simultaneous equations
$$2a + b - c = 3$$
$$3a + 2b + 2c = 13$$
$$a - 3b + c = -6$$

and deduce the solutions of the following simultaneous equations:
$$\frac{2}{h + 3} + \frac{1}{j - 2} - \frac{1}{1 - k} = 3$$
$$\frac{3}{h + 3} + \frac{2}{j - 2} + \frac{2}{1 - k} = 13$$
$$\frac{1}{h + 3} - \frac{3}{j - 2} + \frac{1}{1 - k} = -6$$

36. Let $P(n)$ denote the product
$$P(n) = \left(1 - \frac{1}{2^2}\right)\left(1 - \frac{1}{3^2}\right)\left(1 - \frac{1}{4^2}\right) \cdots \left(1 - \frac{1}{n^2}\right).$$

   (i) Given that $P(2) = \dfrac{a}{4}$, $P(3) = \dfrac{b}{6}$ and $P(4) = \dfrac{c}{8}$, find a, b and c.

   (ii) Evaluate $P(5)$.

   (iii) Hence or otherwise, write down a formula for $P(n)$ as a rational number in terms of n.

Simultaneous equations, one linear and one quadratic

An equation where the highest exponent of each term is 1 is called an equation of degree 1. It is usually called a **linear** equation.

Examples

> $5x - 3 = 0$ is a linear equation in x.
> $4y + 9 = 0$ is a linear equation in y.
> $2x + y - 10 = 0$ is a linear equation in x and y.
> $3x + 2y + 5z - 19 = 0$ is a linear equation in x, y and z.

An equation where the highest exponent, or the sum of the exponents, of any term is 2 is called an equation of degree 2. It is usually called a **quadratic** equation.

Examples

> $x^2 - 2x - 8 = 0$ is a quadratic equation in x.
> $x^2 + y^2 - 20 = 0$ is a quadratic equation in x and y.
> $x^2 - xy + y^2 - 1 = 0$ is a quadratic equation in x and y.

Exercise 3.2

In questions 1–15, write degree 1 or degree 2 in the box provided beside each equation. The first three are done for you.

1. $x = 3y - 2y^2$ degree 2
2. $x = -4y$ degree 1
3. $x + y = xy$ degree 2
4. $2x - 2y + 9 = 0$
5. $\frac{1}{2}x + \frac{1}{2}y = 1$
6. $x^2 + y^2 = 25$
7. $xy = 50$
8. $xy - y - 10 = 0$
9. $x^2 - y^2 - 20 = 0$
10. $x + y = 3$
11. $(x + 2y)(x + 5) = 2$
12. $x^2 + 2x + 3y = 14$
13. $y = mx + c$ where $m, c \in \mathbb{R}$
14. $x^2 + y^2 + 4x - 6y - 1 = 0$
15. $2x^2 - 3xy + 3y^2 = 0$

The **method of substitution** is used to solve between a linear equation and a quadratic equation. The method involves three steps.

1. From the linear equation, express one variable in terms of the other.
2. Substitute this into the quadratic equation and solve.
3. Substitute separately the value(s) obtained in step 2 into the linear equation in step 1 to find the corresponding value(s) of the other variable.

EXAMPLE 1

The line $y = -2x - 1$ intersects the parabola $y = 5 - 3x - 2x^2$. Find the coordinates of the points of intersection.

Solution:

$y = -2x - 1$ and $y = 5 - 3x - 2x^2$

$$y = y$$
$$-2x - 1 = 5 - 3x - 2x^2$$
$$2x^2 + x - 6 = 0$$
$$(2x - 3)(x + 2) = 0$$
$$2x - 3 = 0 \quad \text{or} \quad x + 2 = 0$$
$$x = \tfrac{3}{2} \quad \text{or} \quad x = -2$$

Substitute separately $x = \tfrac{3}{2}$ and $x = -2$ into the linear equation.

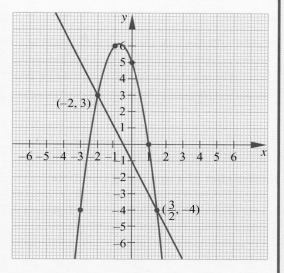

$$y = -2x - 1$$

$x = \tfrac{3}{2}$	$x = -2$
$y = -2\left(\tfrac{3}{2}\right) - 1$	$y = -2(-2) - 1$
$y = -3 - 1$	$y = 4 - 1$
$y = -4$	$y = 3$
$x = \tfrac{3}{2}, y = -4$	$x = -2, y = 3$
Point $\left(\tfrac{3}{2}, -4\right)$	Point $(-2, 3)$

The quadratic equation $ax^2 + bx + c = 0$ has two solutions (roots).

The solutions are given by the quadratic formula $x = \dfrac{-b \pm \sqrt{b^2 - 4ac}}{2a}$.

The nature of the roots depend on the value of $b^2 - 4ac$, which is often called the **discriminant** of the equation.

1. If $b^2 - 4ac > 0$, then there are two distinct real solutions.
2. If $b^2 - 4ac = 0$, then there are two equal real solutions.
3. If $b^2 - 4ac < 0$, then there are two distinct complex solutions.

When we solve a linear and quadratic equation, our work will give us one of the three situations described in the diagrams below.

Intersection of a line and a parabola.

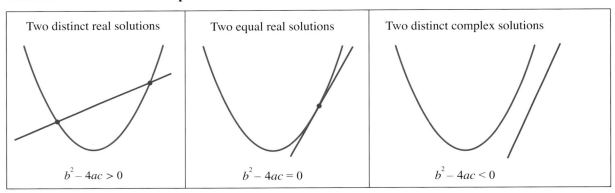

Intersection of a line and a circle.

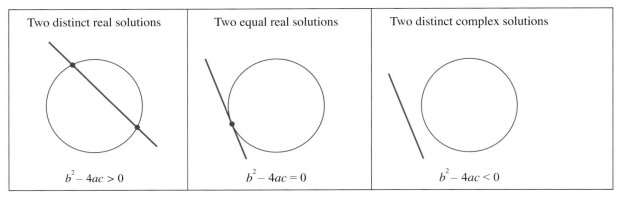

Note: Complex solutions are also called **non-real solutions**.

EXAMPLE 2

Solve for x and y: $2x - y + 1 = 0$ and $y^2 = 2x^2 + x$.

Solution:

$$2x - y + 1 = 0 \qquad \text{(get } y \text{ on its own from the linear equation)}$$
$$-y = -2x - 1$$
$$y = (2x + 1) \qquad \text{(multiply both sides by } -1\text{)}$$

$$y^2 = 2x^2 + x$$

$$(2x + 1)^2 = 2x^2 + x \qquad \text{(substitute } (2x + 1) \text{ for } y\text{)}$$
$$4x^2 + 4x + 1 = 2x^2 + x \qquad \text{(remove brackets)}$$
$$4x^2 + 4x + 1 - 2x^2 - x = 0 \qquad \text{(everything to the left)}$$
$$2x^2 + 3x + 1 = 0 \qquad \text{(simplify)}$$
$$(2x + 1)(x + 1) = 0 \qquad \text{(factorise the left-hand side)}$$
$$2x + 1 = 0 \quad \text{or} \quad x + 1 = 0 \qquad \text{(let each factor} = 0\text{)}$$
$$2x = -1 \quad \text{or} \quad x = -1$$
$$x = -\tfrac{1}{2} \quad \text{or} \quad x = -1$$

Substitute separately $x = -\frac{1}{2}$ and $x = -1$ into the linear equation:

$$y = 2x + 1$$

$x = -\frac{1}{2}$	$x = -1$
$y = 2\left(-\frac{1}{2}\right) + 1$	$y = 2(-1) + 1$
$y = -1 + 1$	$y = -2 + 1$
$y = 0$	$y = -1$
$x = -\frac{1}{2}, y = 0$	$x = -1, \quad y = -1$

Thus, there are two solutions: $x = -\frac{1}{2}, y = 0$ or $x = -1, y = -1$.

Alternatively, $\left(-\frac{1}{2}, 0\right)$ or $(-1, -1)$.

EXAMPLE 3

A plane is travelling along the line $x - y + 4 = 0$.

Ahead lies a large cloud of ash from a volcanic eruption that can be represented by the ellipse $9x^2 + y^2 = 9$.

Show that if the plane maintains its path, it does not pass through the cloud of ash.

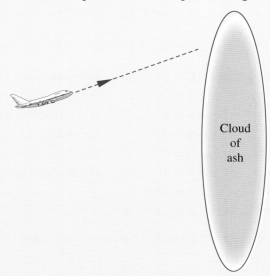

Cloud
of
ash

Solution:

$x - y + 4 = 0$ and $9x^2 + y^2 = 9$

$x - y + 4 = 0$ $9x^2 + y^2 = 9$

    $-y = -x - 4$

      $y = x + 4$ $9x^2 + (x + 4)^2 = 9$

(y on its own) $9x^2 + x^2 + 8x + 16 = 9$

                         $10x^2 + 8x + 7 = 0$

$10x^2 + 8x + 7 = 0$ does not factorise easily. Therefore, we consider the value of $b^2 - 4ac$.

$b^2 - 4ac = (8)^2 - 4(10)(7)$ ($a = 10$, $b = 8$ and $c = 7$)

           $= 64 - 280$

           $= -216 < 0$

As $b^2 - 4ac < 0$, there are no real solutions.

Hence, $x - y + 4 = 0$ and $9x^2 + y^2 = 9$ do **not** intersect.

We conclude that the plane will not pass through the cloud of ash if it maintains its path. (This question depends on the cloud of ash also maintaining its position.)

Exercise 3.3

Solve the following pairs of simultaneous equations in questions 1–19.

1. $y = x^2$
   $2x + y = 3$

2. $y = x^2 - 4x + 6$
   $y = 3x - 4$

3. $x - y + 8 = 0$
   $x^2 + xy + 8 = 0$

4. $y = 2x - 5$
   $x^2 + xy = 2$

5. $3x - y = 8$
   $x^2 + y^2 = 10$

6. $x + y = 1$
   $x^2 + y^2 = 25$

7. $x - y = 0$
   $(x + 2)^2 + y^2 = 10$

8. $x - y = 1$
   $xy = 42$

9. $x^2 + y^2 - 4x + 2 = 0$
   $x + y - 4 = 0$

10. $x^2 - 3y^2 = 13$
    $y = x - 3$

11. $y = 2x - 1$
    $3x^2 - 2xy + y^2 = 9$

12. $x - 3y = 1$
    $x^2 + xy = 0$

13. $x^2 + y^2 - 6x + 4y - 27 = 0$
    $3x - y - 11 = 0$

14. $x + y - 6 = 0$
    $x^2 + 2y^2 - 24 = 0$

15. $2x + y = 3$
    $x^2 + xy + y^2 = 3$

16. $x^2 + 2xy - 8 = 0$
    $1 = \dfrac{2}{x} - \dfrac{2y}{x}$ when $x \neq 0$

17. $\dfrac{x}{y} + 1 = \dfrac{10}{y}$ when $y \neq 0$
    $x^2 - y^2 = 40$

18. $x^2 + 4y^2 + x + 2y = 58$
    $5x - 2y + 2 = 0$

19. $2x + 3y + 4 = 0$
    $(x + 3y)(2x - y) = 4$

20. Show that the pairs of lines and curves have no point of intersection.

    (i) $x - y + 4 = 0$
        $x^2 + y^2 = 6$

    (ii) $3x^2 + y^2 = 1$
         $2x - y + 3 = 0$

    (iii) $3x - 2y = 1$
          $x^2 - xy = 8$

    (iv) $2x - y + 7 = 0$
         $x^2 + y^2 + 2x + 16 = 0$

21. A spacecraft is travelling along the line $2x + y + 6 = 0$. Ahead lies a large asteroid field in the shape of an ellipse represented by the equation $4x^2 + 9y^2 = 36$.

    It is not safe to travel through such an asteroid field. Should the spacecraft alter its course? Justify your answer.

Asteroid field

22. As part of an army exercise, a rocket is fired at a balloon of gas. When passing through the balloon, the rocket will cause the gas to ignite. If the rocket only touches the balloon or misses it entirely, the gas will not ignite.

Rocket

The balloon is represented by the equation $x^2 + y^2 = 20$ and the path of the rocket by $x - 2y + 10 = 0$. Investigate whether the gas will ignite or not.

23. The path of *Voyager 2* as it leaves our solar system is described by $5x + y + 10 = 0$. A new comet, ELEI, is discovered. This comet's path relative to *Voyager 2* is given by $8x = y^2 + 2y + 1$. Will *Voyager 2* cross the path of the comet ELEI? Justify your answer.

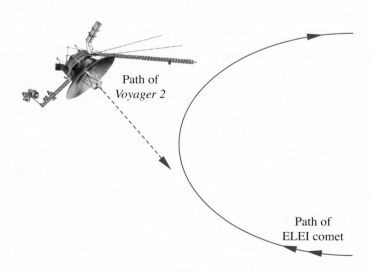

Path of
Voyager 2

Path of
ELEI comet

24. The diagram shows the path of a ski-jumper as she leaves the ramp and the landing hill.

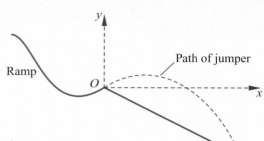

The path of the jumper is given by $y = 0{\cdot}6x - \dfrac{x^2}{40}$.

The landing hill is given by $y = -\dfrac{x}{2}$.

The origin, O, is where she leaves the ramp and L is the point where she lands. All dimensions are in metres. Calculate $|OL|$, the length of the jump, correct to two decimal places.

25. During a match, Pat kicks a football onto the roof of the stand. The stand and the path of the ball are at right angles to each other.

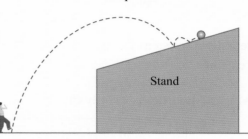

The path of the ball is given by $y = 2{\cdot}5x - \dfrac{x^2}{15}$.

The roof of the stand is given by $y = \dfrac{x}{2} + \dfrac{48}{5}$,

where $18 \le x \le 40$. All dimensions are in metres. The origin is where Pat kicks the ball from.

  (i) Find the height of the ball when it hits the roof of the stand for the first time.

  (ii) If there was no stand, how far from Pat would the ball hit the ground for the first time?

26. The diagram shows the line l and the curve p.
The equation of l is $x - y - 1 = 0$.
The equation of p is $x - y^2 + 1 = 0$.
The real solution(s) of the equation $x - 1 = \sqrt{x + 1}$
can be found by finding the points of intersection of l
and p, at A only, B only or A and B.
Determine which **one** of the three possibilities is
correct. Justify your answer.

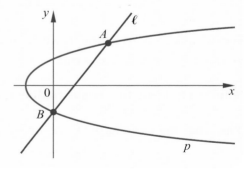

CHAPTER 4

INEQUALITIES

Inequalities

The four inequality symbols

1. $>$ means 'greater than'	**2.** $\geq$ means 'greater than or equal to'
3. $<$ means 'less than'	**4.** $\leq$ means 'less than or equal to'

Algebraic expressions that are linked by one of the four inequality symbols are called **inequalities**. For example, $3x - 1 \leq 11$ and $-3 < 2x - 1 \leq 7$ are inequalities.

Solving inequalities is exactly the same as solving equations, with the following exception

> Multiplying or dividing both sides of an inequality by a
> **negative** number **reverses** the direction of the inequality symbol.
> That is:
>
> $>$ changes to $<$ $\geq$ changes to $\leq$
>
> $<$ changes to $>$ $\leq$ changes to $\geq$

For example, $5 > -3$ is true. If we multiply both sides by -1 and reverse the inequality symbol, it gives $-5 < 3$, which is also true.

Solving an inequality means finding the values of x that make the inequality true.

The following rules apply to graphing inequalities on a number line

> Number line for $x \in \mathbb{N}$ or $x \in \mathbb{Z}$, use **dots**.
> Number line for $x \in \mathbb{R}$, use a **full** heavy line.

Note: Inequalities can be turned around. For example:

$$5 \leq x \text{ means the same as } x \geq 5$$
$$8 \geq x \geq 3 \text{ means the same as } 3 \leq x \leq 8$$

Single variable linear inequalities

EXAMPLE 1

Find the solution set of $14 - 3x \geq 2$, $x \in \mathbb{N}$ and graph your solution on the number line.

Solution:

$14 - 3x \geq 2$

$\quad -3x \geq -12$ (subtract 14 from both sides)

$\quad 3x \leq 12$ (multiply both sides by -1 and reverse the inequality symbol)

$\quad x \leq 4$ (divide both sides by 3)

As $x \in \mathbb{N}$, this is the set of natural numbers less than or equal to 4.

Thus, the values of x are 1, 2, 3 and 4.

Number line:

As $x \in \mathbb{N}$, dots are used on the number line.

EXAMPLE 2

Solve the inequality $-6 \leq 5x - 1 < 9$, $x \in \mathbb{R}$. Graph your solution on a number line.

Solution:

Method 1: Do the same to all three parts.

$-6 \leq 5x - 1 < 9$

$\quad -5 \leq 5x < 10$ (add 1 to each part)

$\quad -1 \leq x < 2$ (divide each part by 5)

Method 2: Write the double inequality as two separate inequalities.

2nd inequality

$$-6 \leq 5x - 1 < 9$$

1st inequality

$-6 \leq 5x - 1$	and	$5x - 1 < 9$
$-6 \leq 5x - 1$		$5x - 1 < 9$
$-5 \leq 5x$		$5x < 10$
$-1 \leq x$		$x < 2$

$\quad\quad -1 \leq x < 2$ (combining solutions)

Number line:

A circle is put around 2 to indicate that 2 is **not** included in the solution.

As $x \in \mathbb{R}$, we use **full heavy shading** on the number line.

EXAMPLE 3

(i) Find the solution set E of $5 - 2x < 13$, $x \in \mathbb{R}$.

(ii) Find the solution set H of $\dfrac{2x}{5} + \dfrac{x}{3} \le \dfrac{22}{15}$, $x \in \mathbb{R}$.

(iii) Find $E \cap H$ and graph your solution on the number line.

Solution:

We solve each inequality separately and then combine their solutions.

(i) $5 - 2x < 13$

$\qquad -2x < 8$

$\qquad\ \ 2x > -8$

$\qquad\ \ \ \ x > -4$

(ii) $\qquad\qquad \dfrac{2x}{5} + \dfrac{x}{3} \le \dfrac{22}{15}$

$\qquad 15\left(\dfrac{2x}{5}\right) + 15\left(\dfrac{x}{3}\right) \le 15\left(\dfrac{22}{15}\right)$

$\qquad\qquad\qquad 6x + 5x \le 22$

$\qquad\qquad\qquad\quad\ 11x \le 22$

$\qquad\qquad\qquad\qquad\ x \le 2$

(iii) Combining the two inequalities:

$$E \cap H: -4 < x \le -2$$

Number line:

A circle is put around -4 to indicate that -4 is **not** part of the solution.

As $x \in \mathbb{R}$, we use **full heavy shading** on the number line.

Exercise 4.1

Solve each inequality in questions 1–16 and graph your solution on the number line.

1. $2x + 1 \le 7$, where $x \in \mathbb{N}$

2. $3x + 2 \le 17$, where $x \in \mathbb{N}$

3. $5x - 8 \le 3x - 6$, where $x \in \mathbb{R}$

4. $2x - 3 \le 4x - 9$, where $x \in \mathbb{N}$

5. $2(x + 4) < 2 - x$, where $x \in \mathbb{R}$

6. $9(x + 1) \ge 1 + 2(5x + 6)$, where $x \in \mathbb{Z}$

7. $3(x - 4) > 5(2x - 3) + 17$, where $x \in \mathbb{R}$

8. $3(3x + 2) + 16 > 5(3x - 1) - 3$, where $x \in \mathbb{R}$

9. $\dfrac{x + 2}{4} - \dfrac{x - 2}{2} < 3$, where $x \in \mathbb{R}$

10. $\frac{2}{5}(x - 1) - \frac{3}{2}(1 - x) \le \frac{19}{10}$, where $x \in \mathbb{R}$

11. $-1 \leq 2x + 3 \leq 11$, where $x \in \mathbb{Z}$

12. $-13 < 4x - 1 \leq 19$, where $x \in \mathbb{R}$

13. $-1 < 6x + 5 \leq 17$, where $x \in \mathbb{Z}$

14. $-33 \leq 7x - 5 \leq -12$, where $x \in \mathbb{R}$

15. $2 > -2x > -8$, where $x \in \mathbb{Z}$

16. $-9 < 1 - 5x < 1$, where $x \in \mathbb{R}$

17.   (i) Find the solution set E of $2x + 7 \leq 19$, where $x \in \mathbb{R}$.

    (ii) Find the solution set H of $3 - 2x < 11$, where $x \in \mathbb{R}$.

    (iii) Find $E \cap H$ and graph your solution on the number line.

18.   (i) Find the solution set G of $3x - 1 \leq 9 - 2x$, where $x \in \mathbb{R}$.

    (ii) Find the solution set H of $2 - 3x \leq 8 - x$, where $x \in \mathbb{R}$.

    (iii) Find $G \cap H$ and graph your solution on the number line.

19.   (i) Find the solution set M of $4 - x \leq 6$, where $x \in \mathbb{R}$.

    (ii) Find the solution set N of $3x - 1 \leq x + 9$, where $x \in \mathbb{R}$.

    (iii) If $M \cap N = a \leq x \leq b$, write down the value of a and the value of b.

20.   (i) Find the solution set P of $4x - 1 \leq 15$, where $x \in \mathbb{Z}$.

    (ii) Find the solution set Q of $\dfrac{x}{2} + \dfrac{x}{3} > \dfrac{5}{6}$, where $x \in \mathbb{Z}$.

    (iii) Find $P \cap Q$ and graph your solution on the number line.

21. Find the smallest integer value of n for which $6n > 37$.

22. Find the smallest natural number k such that $2x + 4(x + 3) + 7(2x + 4) < 20(x + k)$.

23. Show that there are no real numbers which simultaneously satisfy the two inequalities $2x - 1 \geq 9$ and $3x + 2 \leq 14$. Explain your answer.

24. Show that there is just one number which simultaneously satisfies the three inequalities and find this number:

$x - 1 \geq 2$ and $1 - 3x \leq 2(3 - 2x)$ and $\frac{1}{3}x \leq 1$.

25. The lengths of the sides of a triangle are x cm, $(x + 1)$ cm and $(5 - x)$ cm. Find the range of values of x for which this triangle can be constructed.

26. Find all the integer values of n for which $100 < 5^n < 10{,}000$.

27. The diagram shows a rectangle of length $(2x + 1)$ cm and width x cm. The perimeter of the rectangle is greater than 14 cm and less than 32 cm. The area is A cm^2. Find the range of values of **(i)** x **(ii)** A.

x cm

$(2x + 1)$ cm

28. The diagram shows a map of an island. A gold coin is buried at a place where the x and y coordinates are positive whole numbers. Use the clues to work out the coordinates where the gold coin is buried.

Clues:

- $x > 7$
- $y > 6$
- $x + y = 17$
- One of x and y is prime and the other is not

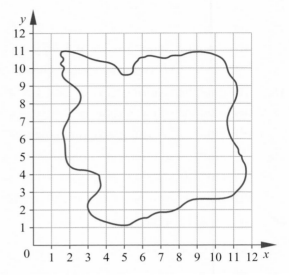

Single variable quadratic and rational inequalities

Quadratic inequalities are solved with the following steps.

1. Replace $\geq$, $\leq$, $>$ or $<$ with $=$ (make it an equation).
2. Solve the equation to find the roots.
   These roots are called the **critical values** of the inequality.
   The solution will be between the critical values or not between the critical values.
3. Test a number between the critical values in the **original** inequality (usually 0).
4. Two possibilities arise:
   - **(i)** If the inequality is true, then the solution lies **between** the critical values.
   - **(ii)** If the inequality is false, then the solution does **not** lie between the critical values.

Notes: We can also test a number **outside** of the critical values.

If the inequality uses $\geq$ or $\leq$, the critical values are **included**.

If the inequality uses $>$ or $<$, the critical values are **not included**.

Rational inequalities can be turned into quadratic inequalities. Therefore, it is very important to be able to solve quadratic inequalities.

EXAMPLE

Solve each of the following inequalities for $x \in \mathbb{R}$.

(i) $2x^2 - x - 6 \leq 0$

(ii) $\dfrac{x + 2}{x - 1} < 3, \quad x \neq 1$

Solution:

(i)
$$2x^2 - x - 6 \leq 0$$
$$2x^2 - x - 6 = 0 \qquad \text{(replace } \leq \text{ with } =\text{)}$$
$$(2x + 3)(x - 2) = 0$$
$$2x + 3 = 0 \quad \text{or} \quad x - 2 = 0$$
$$2x = -3 \quad \text{or} \quad x = 2$$
$$x = -\tfrac{3}{2} \quad \text{or} \quad x = 2 \qquad \text{(critical values of the inequality)}$$

Test 0 between the critical values in the original inequality.
$$2(0)^2 - (0) - 6 \leq 0$$
$$-6 \leq 0 \quad \text{True}$$

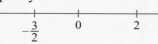

$\therefore$ The solution lies between the critical values $-\tfrac{3}{2}$ and 2.

$\therefore$ Solution is $-\tfrac{3}{2} \leq x \leq 2$.

(ii) $\dfrac{x + 2}{x - 1} < 3$

As $(x - 1)$ could be positive or negative, we multiply both sides by $(x - 1)^2$, which is positive. This reduces the problem to that of solving a quadratic inequality.

$$\frac{x + 2}{x - 1} < 3$$

$$\frac{(x - 1)^2(x + 2)}{(x - 1)} < 3(x - 1)^2 \qquad \text{(multiply both sides by } (x - 1)^2\text{)}$$

$$(x - 1)(x + 2) = 3(x - 2x + 1) \qquad \text{(simplify and replace } < \text{ with } =\text{)}$$

$$x^2 + x - 2 = 3x^2 - 6x + 3$$

$$-2x^2 + 7x - 5 = 0$$

$$2x^2 - 7x + 5 = 0$$

$$(2x - 5)(x - 1) = 0$$

$$2x - 5 = 0 \quad \text{or} \quad x - 1 = 0$$

$$2x = 5 \quad \text{or} \quad x = 1$$

$$x = \tfrac{5}{2} \quad \text{or} \quad x = 1 \qquad \text{(critical values of the inequality)}$$

Test 0, **not** between the critical values in the original inequality.

$$\frac{0 + 2}{0 - 2} < 3$$

$-2 < 3$ True

∴ The solution does **not** lie between the critical values.

∴ Solution is $x < 1$ or $x > \frac{5}{2}$.

Note: If 0 is one of the critical values, it cannot be used to test if the solution lies between the critical values or does not lie between the critical values. For example, $x^2 - 2x \le 0$.

Exercise 4.2

Solve the inequality for $x \in \mathbb{R}$ in questions 1–21.

1. $(x + 2)(x - 1) < 0$
2. $(x + 1)(x - 3) > 0$
3. $(x - 3)(x + 4) \le 0$
4. $(x + 2)(x - 2) \ge 0$
5. $(x + 5)(x - 5) \le 0$
6. $x(x - 3) < 0$
7. $x(x + 4) > 0$
8. $x^2 - x - 2 \le 0$
9. $x^2 - 2x - 8 \le 0$
10. $x^2 - x - 6 \ge 0$
11. $2x^2 - 11x + 5 < 0$
12. $x^2 - 3x \ge 10$
13. $x^2 - 3x \le 0$
14. $x^2 + 4x \ge 0$
15. $2x^2 \le 3x$
16. $x^2 - 9 \le 0$
17. $x^2 - 25 \ge 0$
18. $4x^2 - 9 \le 0$
19. $15 + 2x < x^2$
20. $12 - 5x - 2x^2 < 0$
21. $(2x - 3)^2 \ge 4$

22. (i) Solve the simultaneous equations $2x + y - 5 = 0$ and $x^2 - 4x - 3 - y = 0$.
    (ii) Hence or otherwise, solve the inequality $x^2 - 4x - 3 > 5 - 2x$.

23. Solve for $x \in \mathbb{Z}$: $x^2 - 3x < 8 - x$.

24. Let $f(x) = \dfrac{2x^3 - 13x^2 + 16x - 5}{2x - 1}$, where $x \ne \frac{1}{2}$.

    (i) Express $f(x)$ in the form $x^2 + ax + b$.
    (ii) Find the range of values of $x \in \mathbb{R}$ for which $f(x) \le 0$.

Solve the inequality for $x \in \mathbb{R}$ in questions 25–36.

25. $\dfrac{x + 1}{x - 1} > 3$
26. $\dfrac{x + 1}{x - 2} > 2$
27. $\dfrac{2x + 1}{x + 1} > 1$
28. $\dfrac{x - 5}{x - 1} > -3$
29. $\dfrac{2x - 1}{x - 4} > 1$
30. $\dfrac{4x - 1}{x + 2} < 1$
31. $\dfrac{2x - 1}{x} > 1$
32. $\dfrac{x + 3}{x - 5} \ge 0$
33. $\dfrac{2x}{x + 3} < 1$

34. $\dfrac{2x-3}{x-5} > \dfrac{3}{2}$

35. $\dfrac{2x+1}{x+2} < \dfrac{1}{2}$

36. $\dfrac{x-2}{x-1} > \dfrac{3}{2}$

37. $f(x) = \dfrac{4-3x}{1-x}$. Show that if $f(x) > 2$, then x cannot take any value between 1 and 2.

38. $f(x) = \dfrac{2x+1}{x^2+5}$. Find the values of $x \in \mathbb{R}$ for which $f(x) < \frac{1}{2}$.

39. **(i)** Let $f(x) = \dfrac{x^2+4x+3}{x^2+2x+1}$. If $(x+1) \neq 0$, express $f(x)$ in the form $\dfrac{x+a}{x+b}$, where $a, b \in \mathbb{N}$.

(ii) Find the range of values of $x \in \mathbb{R}$ for which $f(x) < 2$.

40. Let $f(x) = x^2 - 7x + 12$.

(i) Show that if $f(x+1) \neq 0$, then $\dfrac{f(x)}{f(x+1)}$ simplifies to $\dfrac{x-4}{x-2}$.

(ii) Find the range of values of x for which $\dfrac{f(x)}{f(x+1)} > 3$.

41. Let $f(x) = \dfrac{x^2+4}{x^2-4} - \dfrac{x}{x+2}$, $x \neq \pm 2$.

(i) If $f(x) = \dfrac{a}{x-a}$, $a \in \mathbb{N}$, find the value of a.

(ii) Find the range of values of x for which $f(x) < 1$.

42. Find the range of values of x which satisfy both of the inequalities
$$2(x+2) \geq x+5 \text{ and } x^2 - x - 6 \leq 0.$$

43. A is the set of values of x for which $x^2 - 5x + 6 \leq 0$.
B is the set of values of x for which $x^2 - 5x + 4 \geq 0$.
Are there any values of x that satisfy $A \cap B$? Justify your answer.

44. **(i)** If $x = \dfrac{y}{\sqrt{1+y^2}}$, express y in terms of x.

(ii) Hence, find the range of values of x for which $y \in \mathbb{R}$.

45. **(i)** A square has a length of x cm. A rectangle has a length of 5 cm and a width of x cm. Explain why $x > 0$.

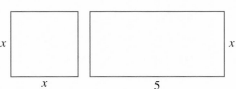

(ii) If the area of the square added to the area of the rectangle must be less than 36 cm², find the range of values of x.

46. A rectangle has length $(x+5)$ cm and width $(x+1)$ cm. Find the values of x for which the perimeter is less than or equal to 44 cm **and** the area is greater than or equal to 60 cm².

47. A rectangular tile has length x cm and width $(25-x)$ cm where $x \in \mathbb{N}$. Given that the area of the tile must be least 150 cm², find the set of possible values of x.

48. A gardener is given the following instructions about laying a rectangular lawn. The length, x m, must be 4 m longer than the width. The width must be greater than 3 m and the area must be less than 60 m². Find the range of possible values of x.

49. The diagrams show a rectangle and a right-angled triangle, where all lengths are in cm.

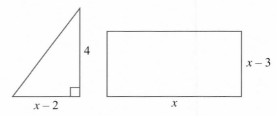

   (i) Explain why $x > 3$.

   (ii) Find the range of values of x for which the area of the rectangle is greater than the area of the triangle.

50. A ball is thrown by a boy from the top of a building. The ball leaves his hands 2 m above the building. The height, h m, reached by the ball above the ground after t seconds is given by $h = 9 + 8t - t^2$.

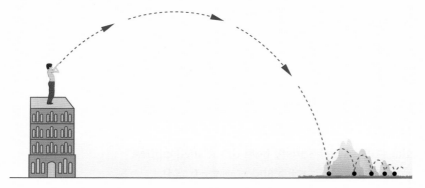

   (i) Find the height of the building.

   (ii) Find the time taken for the ball to hit the ground for the first time.

   (iii) Find the range of values of t for which the ball is more than 21 m above the ground.

51. A company manufactures envelopes in different sizes. All the envelopes have lengths and widths in the ratio 2:1, as shown. The smallest envelope that the company produces has an area of 144 cm² and the largest envelope has an area of 400 cm².

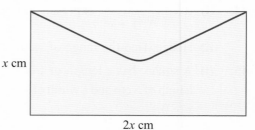

   (i) Find, in surd form, the smallest and largest values of x.

   (ii) The production team decides to stay in this range, but wants to produce envelopes of integer lengths. List all possible lengths which could be manufactured.

52. Four isosceles triangles of base $2x$ cm and height $(x - 2)$ cm are glued to the edges of a square of side $2x$ cm. The tips of the triangles are brought to a point to make a pyramid. If the total surface area of the pyramid, including the base, must be less than 160 cm², write this as an inequality and find the range of values of x.

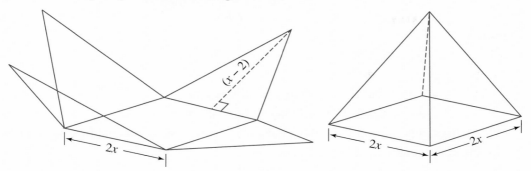

53. A person has 28 m of wire fencing, which he uses to make a rectangular plot with a wall on one side, as shown.

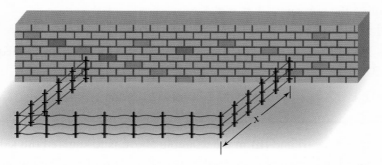

   (i) If the breadth is x m, as shown, show that the length is given by $(28 - 2x)$ m.

  (ii) Show that the area enclosed, A m², is given by $A = 28x - 2x^2$.

 (iii) Explain why $0 < x < 14$.

 (iv) Find the range of values of x for which   (a) $A \geq 90$ (b) $A < 90$.

Modulus inequalities

The modulus of a number is its positive value.
If $|x| = 2$, then x could be 2 or -2.

Modulus inequality		
If $\lvert x \rvert \leq a$, then $-a \leq x \leq a$	for $a \in \mathbb{R}$ and $a > 0$.
If $\lvert x \rvert \geq a$, then $x \leq -a$ or $x \geq a$	for $a \in \mathbb{R}$ and $a > 0$.

If $<$ or $>$ is used, then the critical values, $\pm a$, are not included.

EXAMPLE

Solve the inequality **(i)** $|2x - 1| \leq 9$ **(ii)** $|3x - 2| > 4$ for $x \in \mathbb{R}$.

Solution:

(i) $\qquad\qquad |2x - 1| \leq 9$

$\therefore -9 \leq 2x - 1 \leq 9$

$\qquad -8 \leq 2x \leq 10$ $\qquad$ (add 1 to all three parts)

$\qquad -4 \leq x \leq 5$ $\qquad$ (divide all three parts by 2)

Alternatively, we can write the inequality as two separate inequalities, solve these inequalities and combine the answers.

$$|2x - 1| \leq 9$$

$\therefore 2x - 1 > -9 \quad$ or $\quad 2x - 1 < 9$

$\qquad 2x > -8 \quad$ or $\qquad 2x < 10$

$\qquad x > -4 \quad$ or $\qquad x < 5$

Combining the answers: $-4 < x < 5$

(ii) $|3x - 2| > 4$

$\therefore 3x - 2 < -4 \quad$ or $\quad 3x - 2 > 4 \qquad$ (write as two separate linear inequalities)

$\qquad 3x < -2 \quad$ or $\qquad 3x > 6$

$\qquad x < -\dfrac{2}{3} \quad$ or $\qquad x > 2 \qquad$ (solve each linear inequality)

Note: An alternative method for **(i)** and **(ii)** in the example above is to square both sides and turn the inequality into a quadratic inequality and solve as before. However, it entails a lot more work.

Exercise 4.3

Solve the inequality for $x \in \mathbb{R}$ in questions 1–18.

1. $|x + 2| \leq 5$
2. $|x - 4| < 3$
3. $|x + 3| \leq 7$
4. $|x + 1| > 4$
5. $|x - 5| \geq 2$
6. $|x + 4| > 3$
7. $|x - 1| \leq 2$
8. $|x - 2| > 6$
9. $|x - 3| < 1$
10. $|2x - 1| \leq 3$
11. $|2x + 3| \geq 5$
12. $|3x - 2| < 1$
13. $|4x - 7| \geq 1$
14. $|5x + 2| < 3$
15. $|6x + 11| < 5$
16. $|x + \frac{1}{2}| \leq \frac{3}{4}$
17. $|x - \frac{1}{3}| < \frac{1}{2}$
18. $|x + \frac{1}{5}| \geq \frac{1}{3}$

19. On the number line, plot the values of x that satisfy the inequality $|x + 1| \leq 2$, where $x \in \mathbb{Z}$.

20. Solve $|x - 1| < 7$, where $x \in \mathbb{R}$, and graph your solution on the number line.

21. The solution to the inequality $|4x - 3| \leq 5$ is $-\dfrac{1}{n} \leq n \leq n$, where $n \in \mathbb{N}$. Find the value of n.

22. Solve: **(i)** $|x - 1| \leq 3$ **(ii)** $|4x - 4| \leq 12$. Comment on your answers.

23. The graphs of the functions $f: x \mapsto |x - 3|$ and $g: x \mapsto 2$ are shown in the diagram.

    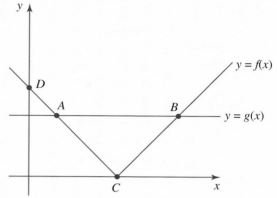

    (i) Find the coordinates of the points A, B, C and D.

    (ii) Hence or otherwise, solve the inequality $|x - 3| < 2$, where $x \in \mathbb{R}$.

24. On the same axes and scales, graph the functions $f(x) = |x + 1|$ and $g(x) = 4$.

    (i) Find the coordinates of A and B, the points where $f(x)$ intersects the x-and y-axis, respectively.

    (ii) Find the coordinates of the points when $f(x) = g(x)$.

    (iii) Hence or otherwise, solve the inequality **(a)** $f(x) \leq g(x)$ **(b)** $f(x) > g(x)$.

25. On the same axes and scales, graph the functions $f(x) = -|x - 2|$ and $g(x) = -1$.

    (i) Find the coordinates of the points where $f(x) = g(x)$.

    (ii) Hence or otherwise, solve the inequality **(a)** $f(x) > g(x)$ **(b)** $f(x) \leq g(x)$.

Abstract inequalities

An example of an **abstractly inequality** is $a^2 + b^2 \geq 2ab$.

Many of the abstract inequalities in this section are establised using the fact that:

> (any real number)$^2 \geq 0$ or $-$(any real number)$^2 \leq 0$

For example,
$a^2 \geq 0$, $(a - b)^2 \geq 0$, $-p^2 \leq 0$ and $-(x + y)^2 \leq 0$ are all true for a, b, p, x and $y \in \mathbb{R}$.

Abstract inequalities are usually solved with the following steps.

> 1. Write down the given inequality to be proved.
> 2. Using **reversible** steps for inequalities, arrive at an algebraic inequality that is true.
> 3. Therefore, the given inequality is true.

Note: We can only square both sides of an inequality when we are sure that both sides are positive (non-negative). For example, $-3 < 2$; squaring both sides gives $9 < 4$, which is not true.

EXAMPLE 1

Show that $x^2 + 6x + 10 \geq 0$ for all values of $x \in \mathbb{R}$.

Solution:
In this type of problem we will use the method of completing the square.

$$x^2 + 6x + 10 \geq 0$$
$$x^2 + 6x + 9 + 10 - 9 \geq 0 \qquad \text{(add and subtract } \left(\tfrac{6}{2}\right)^2 = 9 \text{ to the left-hand side)}$$
$$x^2 + 6x + 9 + 1 \geq 0$$
$$(x + 3)^2 + 1 \geq 0 \qquad \text{true} \quad ((x^2 + 6x + 9) = (x + 3)^2)$$
$$\therefore x^2 + 6x + 10 \geq 0$$

EXAMPLE 2

(i) Prove that $a^2 + b^2 \geq 2ab$ for all $a, b \in \mathbb{R}$.

(ii) Write down similar results for $b^2 + c^2$ and $c^2 + a^2$.

(iii) Hence, deduce that $a^2 + b^2 + c^2 \geq ab + bc + ca$.

Solution:

(i)
$$a^2 + b^2 \geq 2ab \qquad \text{(given inequality)}$$
$$a^2 - 2ab + b^2 \geq 0 \qquad \text{(subtract } 2ab \text{ from both sides)}$$
$$(a - b)^2 \geq 0 \qquad \text{true} \quad \text{(factorise the left-hand side)}$$
$$\therefore a^2 + b^2 \geq 2ab$$

(ii) Similarly, $b^2 + c^2 \geq 2bc$ and $c^2 + a^2 \geq 2ca$.

(iii) Using the results from **(i)** and **(ii)**:
$$a^2 + b^2 \geq 2ab$$
$$b^2 + c^2 \geq 2bc$$
$$\underline{c^2 + a^2 \geq 2ca}$$
$$2a^2 + 2b^2 + 2c^2 \geq 2ab + 2bc + 2ca \qquad \text{(add)}$$
$$\therefore a^2 + b^2 + c^2 \geq ab + bc + ca \qquad \text{(divide both sides by 2)}$$

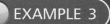

EXAMPLE 3

Show that $\dfrac{1}{a} + \dfrac{1}{b} \geq \dfrac{4}{a + b}$ where a and b are real numbers and $a, b > 0$.

Solution:

$$\frac{1}{a} + \frac{1}{b} \geq \frac{4}{(a + b)} \qquad \text{(given inequality, put brackets on } (a + b))$$

$$ab(a + b)\frac{1}{a} + ab(a + b)\frac{1}{b} \geq ab(a + b)\frac{4}{(a + b)} \qquad \text{(multiply each part by } ab(a + b), \text{ which is positive)}$$

$$b(a + b) + a(a + b) \geq 4ab \qquad \text{(simplify both sides)}$$

$$ab + b^2 + a^2 + ab \geq 4ab \qquad \text{(remove brackets)}$$

$$a^2 + 2ab + b^2 \geq 4ab \qquad \text{(simplify the left-hand side)}$$

$$a^2 - 2ab + b^2 \geq 0 \qquad \text{(subtract } 4ab \text{ from both sides)}$$

$$(a - b)^2 \geq 0 \quad \text{true} \qquad \text{(factorise the left-hand side)}$$

$$\therefore \frac{1}{a} + \frac{1}{b} \geq \frac{4}{a + b}$$

Exercise 4.4

In questions 1–14, prove the inequality where all the variables are real numbers.

1. $x^2 + 8x + 16 \geq 0$

2. $x^2 - 10x + 25 \geq 0$

3. $x^2 + 2x + 2 \geq 0$

4. $x^2 - 4x + 13 \geq 0$

5. $x^2 + 12x + 40 \geq 0$

6. $x^2 + 65 \geq 14x$

7. $a^2 + 2ab + b^2 \geq 0$

8. $(a + b)^2 \geq 4ab$

9. $x^2 + 2xy + 2y^2 \geq 0$

10. $a^2 \geq -2b(a + 5b)$

11. $p^2 + 10p + 25 + q^2 \geq 0$

12. $-x^2 - 4x - 4 \leq 0$

13. $(a + b)^2 - 2b(a - b) \geq 2(b^2 + ab)$

14. $\dfrac{a^2 + 4b^2}{4} \geq ab$

15. If $a, b \in \mathbb{R}$ and $a, b > 0$, show that:

    (i) $a + \dfrac{1}{a} \geq 2$

    (ii) $\dfrac{1}{a} + \dfrac{1}{b} \geq \dfrac{2}{a + b}$

    (iii) $a^4 + b^4 \geq 2a^2b^2$

16. If $x \in \mathbb{R}$ and $x \neq -1$, show that $\dfrac{x}{(x + 1)^2} \leq \dfrac{1}{4}$.

17. If $p, q \in \mathbb{R}$ and $p, q > 0$, show that:

    (i) $p^2 + \dfrac{1}{p^2} \geq 2$

    (ii) $\dfrac{p}{q} + \dfrac{q}{p} \geq 2$

    (iii) $(p + q)\left(\dfrac{1}{p} + \dfrac{1}{q}\right) \geq 4$

    (iv) $\left(p + \dfrac{1}{q}\right)\left(q + \dfrac{1}{p}\right) \leq \left(p + \dfrac{1}{p}\right)\left(q + \dfrac{1}{q}\right)$

    (v) $(p + 2q)\left(\dfrac{1}{p} + \dfrac{1}{2q}\right) \geq 4$

18. Prove that for all $x \in \mathbb{R}$, $\dfrac{x + 3}{2} > \sqrt{3x}$, where $x > 0$.

19. If $a, b \in \mathbb{R}$, $a, b > 0$ and $a \neq b$, show that:

   (i) $\dfrac{a+b}{2} > \sqrt{ab}$ (ii) $\sqrt{ab} > \dfrac{2ab}{a+b}$

20. Show that $(a^2 + b^2)(x^2 + y^2) \geq (ax + by)^2$ for all $a, b, x, y \in \mathbb{R}$.

21. $f(x) = 2x^2 + 20x + 56$. Express $f(x)$ in the form $2[(x + a)^2 + b]$.

22. $g(x) = 3x^2 + 12x + 15$. Show that $g(x) \geq 0$ for all values of $x \in \mathbb{R}$.

23. (i) Factorise: (a) $p^3 + q^3$ (b) $p^3 - q^3$ (c) $p^2q + pq^2$ (d) $p^2q - pq^2$

   (ii) If $p, q \in \mathbb{R}$, $p, q > 0$ and $p \neq q$, show that:

   (a) $p^3 + q^3 \geq p^2q + pq^2$ (b) $\dfrac{p^3 - q^3}{p^2q - pq^2} \geq 3$

24. (i) Prove that for all real numbers a and b, $a^2 - ab + b^2 \geq ab$.

   (ii) Let a and b be non-zero real numbers such that $a + b \geq 0$. Show that $\dfrac{a}{b^2} + \dfrac{b}{a^2} \geq \dfrac{1}{a} + \dfrac{1}{b}$.

25. (i) Express $a^4 - b^4$ as a product of three factors.

   (ii) Factorise $a^5 - a^4b - ab^4 + b^5$.

   (iii) Use your results from (i) and (ii) to show that $a^5 + b^5 > a^4b + ab^4$ where a and b are positive unequal real numbers.

26. (i) Prove that $x + \dfrac{9}{x+2} \geq 4$, where $x + 2 > 0$.

   (ii) Prove that $x + \dfrac{a^2}{x-2a} \geq 4a$, where $x - 2a > 0$.

   (iii) Prove that $x + \dfrac{9}{x+a} \geq 6 - a$, where $x + a > 0$.

27. If $a^2 + b^2 = 1 = c^2 + d^2$, where $a, b, c, d \in \mathbb{R}$, prove that $ab + cd \leq 1$.
   (Hint: Use the result $x^2 + y^2 \geq 2xy$.)

28. Show that if a and b are non-zero real numbers, then the value of $\dfrac{a}{b} + \dfrac{b}{a}$ can never lie between -2 and 2.

   (Hint: Consider the case where a and b have the same sign separately from the case where a and b have the opposite sign.)

29. (i) Show that $\dfrac{a+b}{2} \leq \sqrt{\dfrac{a^2+b^2}{2}}$, where a and b are real numbers.

   (ii) The lengths of the sides of a right-angled triangle are a, b and c, where c is the length of the hypotenuse. Using the result from part (i) or otherwise, show that $a + b \leq c\sqrt{2}$.

CHAPTER 5

INDICES

Indices

In the expression a^m, a is the base and m is the index or exponent. a^m is read as 'a to the power of m'.

	Rules of indices:			
1.	$a^p a^q = a^{p+q}$		**2.**	$\dfrac{a^p}{a^q} = a^{p-q}$
3.	$(a^p)^q = a^{pq}$		**4.**	$a^0 = 1$
5.	$a^{-p} = \dfrac{1}{a^p}$		**6.**	$(ab)^p = a^p b^p$
7.	$\left(\dfrac{a}{b}\right)^p = \dfrac{a^p}{b^p}$		**8.**	$a^{\frac{1}{q}} = \sqrt[q]{a}$
9.	$a^{\frac{p}{q}} = \sqrt[q]{a^p} = \left(\sqrt[q]{a}\right)^p$			

$8^{\frac{1}{3}}$ means 'what number multiplied by itself three times will equal 8?'

Thus, $8^{\frac{1}{3}} = 2$, as $2 \times 2 \times 2 = 8$.

Similarly, $25^{\frac{1}{2}} = 5$, as $5 \times 5 = 25$, and $81^{\frac{1}{4}} = 3$, as $3 \times 3 \times 3 \times 3 = 81$.

Note: $\sqrt{a} = a^{\frac{1}{2}}$, e.g. $\sqrt{16} = 16^{\frac{1}{2}} = 4$.

Also, $\sqrt{a}\,\sqrt{a} = a^{\frac{1}{2}} \times a^{\frac{1}{2}} = a^{\frac{1}{2}+\frac{1}{2}} = a^1 = a$.

Alternative notation: $a^{\frac{1}{n}} = \sqrt[n]{a}$,   example $8^{\frac{1}{3}} = \sqrt[3]{8}$

$\qquad\qquad\qquad\quad a^{\frac{m}{n}} = \sqrt[n]{a^m}$,   example $32^{\frac{2}{5}} = \sqrt[5]{32^2}$

When dealing with fractional indices, the calculations are simpler if the root is taken first and the result is raised to the power.

For example, $16^{\frac{3}{4}} = \left(16^{\frac{1}{4}}\right)^3 = (2)^3 = 8$.

         ↑   ↑

(root first)   (power next)

Using a calculator

A calculator can be used to evaluate an expression such as $32^{\frac{3}{5}}$.

▦ 32 $\boxed{y^x}$ $\boxed{(}$ 3 $\boxed{\div}$ 5 $\boxed{)}$ $\boxed{=}$

The calculator will give an answer of 8.

Note: Some calculators have buttons $\boxed{x^{\square}}$ or $\boxed{\wedge}$.

However, there are problems when dealing with negative indices or raising a fraction to a power, as the calculator can give the answer as a decimal.

For example:

$$8^{-\frac{2}{3}} = \frac{1}{8^{\frac{2}{3}}} = \frac{1}{\left(8^{\frac{1}{3}}\right)^2} = \frac{1}{(2)^2} = \frac{1}{4}$$

Using a calculator,

▦ 8 $\boxed{y^x}$ $\boxed{(}$ $\boxed{(-)}$ 2 $\boxed{\div}$ 3 $\boxed{)}$ $\boxed{=}$ can give an answer of 0·25.

Note: $\frac{1}{4} = 0·25$

Also, $\left(\dfrac{8}{27}\right)^{\frac{2}{3}} = \dfrac{8^{\frac{2}{3}}}{27^{\frac{2}{3}}} = \dfrac{\left(8^{\frac{1}{3}}\right)^2}{\left(27^{\frac{1}{3}}\right)^2} = \dfrac{(2)^2}{(3)^2} = \dfrac{4}{9}$

Using a calculator,

▦ $\boxed{(}$ 8 $\boxed{a\frac{b}{c}}$ 27 $\boxed{)}$ $\boxed{y^x}$ 2 $\boxed{a\frac{b}{c}}$ 3 $\boxed{=}$ can give an answer of 0·4̇ or 0·444444444....

Note: $\dfrac{4}{9} = 0·444444444.....$

Avoid using a calculator with negative indices or raising a fraction to a power.

EXAMPLE 1

Evaluate each of the following, expressing your answers as rational numbers.

(i) $32^{\frac{3}{5}}$ (ii) $8^{-\frac{2}{3}}$ (iii) $\left(2\frac{1}{4}\right)^{\frac{3}{2}}$ (iv) $4^{\frac{1}{2}}\left(27^{-\frac{1}{3}}\right)$ (v) $\left(\frac{16}{25}\right)^{-\frac{1}{2}}$ (vi) $\left(\frac{1}{16}\right)^{\frac{3}{4}}$

Solution:

(i) $32^{\frac{3}{5}} = \left(32^{\frac{1}{5}}\right)^3 = (2)^3 = 8$

(ii) $8^{-\frac{2}{3}} = \dfrac{1}{8^{\frac{2}{3}}} = \dfrac{1}{\left(8^{\frac{1}{3}}\right)^2} = \dfrac{1}{(2)^2} = \dfrac{1}{4}$

(iii) $\left(2\frac{1}{4}\right)^{\frac{3}{2}} = \left(\dfrac{9}{4}\right)^{\frac{3}{2}} = \dfrac{9^{\frac{3}{2}}}{4^{\frac{3}{2}}} = \dfrac{\left(9^{\frac{1}{2}}\right)^3}{\left(4^{\frac{1}{2}}\right)^3}$

$= \dfrac{(3)^3}{(2)^3} = \dfrac{27}{8}$

(iv) $4^{\frac{1}{2}}\left(27^{-\frac{1}{3}}\right) = \dfrac{4^{\frac{1}{2}}}{27^{\frac{1}{3}}} = \dfrac{2}{3}$

(vi) $\left(\dfrac{1}{16}\right)^{\frac{3}{4}} = \dfrac{1^{\frac{3}{4}}}{16^{\frac{3}{4}}} = \dfrac{1}{\left(16^{\frac{1}{4}}\right)^3} = \dfrac{1}{(2)^3} = \dfrac{1}{8}$

(v) $\left(\dfrac{16}{25}\right)^{-\frac{1}{2}} = \dfrac{16^{-\frac{1}{2}}}{25^{-\frac{1}{2}}} = \dfrac{25^{\frac{1}{2}}}{16^{\frac{1}{2}}} = \dfrac{5}{4}$

EXAMPLE 2

$$f(n) = \frac{3(2^{n+1}) - 4(2^{n-1})}{2^{n+1} - 2^n} = k \text{ for } n \in \mathbb{Z}.$$

(i) By choosing a suitable value for n, show that $k = 4$.

(ii) Prove that $k = 4$ for all values of n.

Solution:

(i) Select any suitable value for n, so let $n = 1$.

$$\frac{3(2^{1+1}) - 4(2^{1-1})}{2^{1+1} - 2^1}$$

$$= \frac{3(2^2) - 4(2^0)}{2^2 - 2^1}$$

$$= \frac{3(4) - 4(1)}{4 - 2}$$

$$= \frac{12 - 4}{2} = \frac{8}{2} = 4$$

(ii)
$$\frac{3(2^{n+1}) - 4(2^{n-1})}{2^{n+1} - 2^n}$$

$$= \frac{3(2^2 \times 2^{n-1}) - 4(2^{n-1})}{2^2 \times 2^{n-1} - 2^1 \times 2^{n-1}}$$

$$= \frac{3(2^2)(2^{n-1}) - 4(2^{n-1})}{2^2(2^{n-1}) - 2^1(2^{n-1})}$$

$$= \frac{3(2^2) - 4}{2^2 - 2}$$

$$= \frac{3(4) - 4}{4 - 2} = \frac{8}{2} = 4$$

Thus, $k = 4$.

The basic idea is to have the lowest power of 2, 2^{n-1}, present in every term, then divide each term by 2^{n-1}.

$$n + 1 = 2 + n - 1 = 2 + (n - 1)$$
$$\therefore 2^{n+1} = 2^{2+(n-1)} = 2^2 \times 2^{n-1}$$

$$n = 1 + n - 1 = 1 + (n - 1)$$
$$\therefore 2^n = 2^{1+(n-1)} = 2^1 \times 2^{n-1}$$

(divide each term by 2^{n-1})

Note: $3(2^{n+1}) = 3(2)^{n+1}$

Exercise 5.1

In questions 1–15, express your answer as a rational number in its simplest form.

1. $27^{\frac{2}{3}}$

2. $16^{\frac{5}{4}}$

3. $128^{\frac{4}{7}}$

4. $49^{-\frac{1}{2}}$

5. $32^{-\frac{2}{5}}$

6. $10{,}000^{\frac{3}{4}}$

7. $\left(12\frac{1}{4}\right)^{\frac{1}{2}}$

8. $\left(\frac{16}{81}\right)^{-\frac{3}{4}}$

9. $\left(27^{-\frac{1}{3}}\right)^2$

10. $\left(32^{-\frac{1}{5}}\right)^3$

11. $\left(\frac{4}{9}\right)^{-\frac{1}{2}}\left(\frac{1}{27}\right)^{\frac{1}{3}}$

12. $\frac{16^{-\frac{3}{4}}}{81^{-\frac{1}{2}}}$

13. $\frac{27^{-\frac{1}{3}}}{8^{-\frac{2}{3}}}$

14. $\frac{4^{-\frac{1}{2}}}{64^{\frac{2}{3}}}$

15. $\left(64^{\frac{5}{12}}\right)^2$

In questions 16–19, find the value of n.

16. $\dfrac{8^{-\frac{2}{3}}}{4^{-\frac{5}{2}}} = 2^n$

17. $\dfrac{27^{\frac{2}{3}} \times 81^{-\frac{1}{2}}}{9^{-1}} = 3^n$

18. $\dfrac{16^{\frac{1}{3}} \times 4^{\frac{1}{3}}}{8} = 2^n$

19. $\dfrac{8^0 \times 16^{-\frac{1}{2}}}{32^{-\frac{2}{3}}} = 2^n$

20. If $\sqrt{\dfrac{9^{\frac{1}{2}} - 2^{-1}}{32^{-\frac{3}{5}}}} = a\sqrt{b}$, where b is prime, find the value of a and the value of b.

Simplify each of the following in questions 21–24.

21. $\left(x^{\frac{1}{2}} + y^{\frac{1}{2}}\right)\left(x^{\frac{1}{2}} - y^{\frac{1}{2}}\right)$

22. $\dfrac{(x-1)^{\frac{1}{2}} + (x-1)^{-\frac{1}{2}}}{(x-1)^{-\frac{1}{2}}}$

23. $\dfrac{x^{\frac{3}{2}} - x^{-\frac{1}{2}}}{x^{\frac{1}{2}} - x^{-\frac{1}{2}}}$

24. $\dfrac{\left(x^{\frac{3}{2}} + x^{\frac{1}{2}}\right)\left(x^{\frac{1}{2}} - x^{-\frac{1}{2}}\right)}{\left(x^{\frac{3}{2}} - x^{\frac{1}{2}}\right)^2}$

25. $f(n) = 5(4^{3n+1}) - 20(8^{2n})$

    (i) Evaluate $f(1)$.   (ii) Show that $f(2) = f(1)$.

26. $f(n) = 7(3^{2n+1}) - 21(9^n)$

    (i) Evaluate $f(-4)$ and $f\left(\dfrac{3}{2}\right)$.

    (ii) Find $f(n+1)$.

    (iii) Show that $f(n+2) = f(n+1)$ for all values of n.

27. $f(n) = \dfrac{3(2^{n+2}) - 4(2^n)}{2^{n+2} - 2^{n+1}}$

    (i) Evaluate $f(-2)$ and $f(4)$.

    (ii) Find $f(n+1)$.

    (iii) Show that $f(n+2) = f(n+1)$.

28. $f(n) = \dfrac{3(2^n) - 4(2^{n-2})}{2^n - 2^{n-1}}$

    (i) Evaluate $f(0)$ and $f(-3)$.

    (ii) Find $f(n+1)$.

    (iii) Show that $f(n+3) = f(n+2)$.

29. $f(x) = 2^x$. If $f(x+3) - f(x+1) = kf(x)$, find the value of k.

30. $f(x) = 2^{x+2}$. If $f(x+2) - f(x+1) = kf(x)$, find the value of k.

Exponential equations

Exponent is another name for power or index.

An equation involving the variable in the power is called an **exponential equation**.

For example, $3^{2x+3} = 9$ is an exponential equation.

Exponential equations are solved with the following steps.

1. Write all the numbers as powers of the same number (usually a prime number).
2. Write both sides as one power of the same number, using the laws of indices.
3. Equate these powers and solve this equation.

EXAMPLE 1

Solve for x: (i) $9^{x^2+2} = 27^{x+3}$ (ii) $2^{3x-1} = \dfrac{\sqrt{2}}{8}$

Solution:

Write each side as a power of 3.

(i)
$$9^{x^2+2} = 27^{x+3}$$
$$(3^2)^{x^2+2} = (3^3)^{x+3}$$
$$3^{2(x^2+2)} = 3^{3(x+3)}$$
$$3^{2x^2+4} = 3^{3x+9}$$
$$\therefore \ 2x^2 + 4 = 3x + 9 \quad \text{(equate powers)}$$
$$2x^2 - 3x - 5 = 0$$
$$(2x - 5)(x + 1) = 0$$
$$2x - 5 = 0 \quad \text{or} \quad x + 1 = 0$$
$$x = \tfrac{5}{2} \quad \text{or} \qquad x = -1$$

Write each side as a power of 2.

(ii)
$$2^{3x-1} = \dfrac{\sqrt{2}}{8}$$
$$2^{3x-1} = \dfrac{2^{\frac{1}{2}}}{2^3}$$
$$2^{3x-1} = 2^{\frac{1}{2}-3}$$
$$2^{3x-1} = 2^{-\frac{5}{2}}$$
$$\therefore \ 3x - 1 = -\tfrac{5}{2} \quad \text{(equate powers)}$$
$$6x - 2 = -5$$
$$6x = -3$$
$$x = -\tfrac{1}{2}$$

Sometimes exponential equations lead to simultaneous equations

EXAMPLE 2

Solve for x and y: $2^{x+y} = 8$ and $9^x(3^{-y}) = 27$.

Solution:

Write each side as a power of 2.
$$2^{x+y} = 8$$
$$2^{x+y} = 2^3$$
$$\therefore \ x + y = 3 \quad ① \text{ (equate powers)}$$

Write each side as a power of 3.
$$9^x(3^{-y}) = 27$$
$$(3^2)^x(3^{-y}) = 3^3$$
$$3^{2x} \times 3^{-y} = 3^3$$
$$3^{2x-y} = 3^3$$
$$\therefore \ 2x - y = 3 \quad ② \text{ (equate powers)}$$

By solving the simultaneous equations ① and ② we get $x = 2$ and $y = 1$.

Exercise 5.2

Solve each of the following in questions 1–12.

1. $4^{x+1} = 128$

2. $3^{2x-5} = 27$

3. $5^{x^2} = 25^{3x-4}$

4. $4^{2x+3} = 8^{1-x}$

5. $5^{2-2x} = 125^{3-x}$

6. $8^{4+3x} = 32^{1+2x}$

7. $7^{2x-1} = \dfrac{49}{\sqrt{7}}$

8. $2^{2x-1} = \left(\dfrac{16}{\sqrt{8}}\right)^2$

9. $\sqrt{3}(3^x) = \left(\dfrac{243}{\sqrt{27}}\right)^2$

10. $8^{\frac{4}{3}} = \dfrac{2^{5x-3}}{\sqrt{2}}$

11. $8(2^{x^2}) = 16^x$

12. $\dfrac{(8^x)^x}{32^x} = 4$

13. Express **(i)** 27 as a power of 3 **(ii)** 32 as a power of 2.
    (iii) Hence, solve for x and y: $3^{2x+y} = 27$ and $2^{3x+y} = 32$.

Solve each of the following for x and y in questions 14–19.

14. $2^{5x-2y} = 8$
    $3^{x+y} = 9$

15. $2^x = 8^{y+1}$
    $3^{x-9} = 9^y$

16. $3^x \times 9^{-y} = 3$
    $2^x \times 4^{2y} = 2$

17. $\dfrac{2^{2x}}{2^y} = 32$
    $2^x \times 2^{3y} = \frac{1}{2}$

18. $5^{3x-y} = 1$
    $9^x \times 3^y = 243$

19. $\dfrac{3^x}{3^{-y}} = 9$
    $7^x \times 7^{2y} = 1$

20. Solve each of the following equations and state which ones have no solution, $x \in \mathbb{R}$.
    In each case, justify your answer.

    (i) $2^x = 4$ **(ii)** $3^x = 3$ **(iii)** $5^x = 1$ **(iv)** $2^x = \frac{1}{4}$

    (v) $3^x = \frac{1}{3}$ **(vi)** $2^x = -8$ **(vii)** $3^x = -\frac{1}{3}$ **(viii)** $5^x = \frac{1}{125}$

Solving by substitution

Often a substitution of the form $y = a^x$ is required to obtain an equation in y.

EXAMPLE

If $y = 2^x$, express **(i)** 2^{2x} and **(ii)** 2^{2x+1} in terms of y.
(iii) Hence, solve the equation $2^{2x+1} - 15(2^x) - 8 = 0$.

Solution:

(i) $2^{2x} = (2^x)^2 = y^2$ **(ii)** $2^{2x+1} = 2^{1+2x} = 2^1 \times 2^{2x} = 2y^2$

(iii) $2^{2x+1} - 15(2^x) - 8 = 0$

$\qquad 2y^2 - 15y - 8 = 0$

$\qquad (2y + 1)(y - 8) = 0$

$\qquad 2y + 1 = 0 \quad$ or $\quad y - 8 = 0$

$\qquad\quad y = -\frac{1}{2} \quad$ or $\qquad y = 8$

$y = 8$	$y = -\frac{1}{2}$
$2^x = 2^3$	$2^x = -2^{-1}$
$\therefore x = 3$	(no solution)

Thus, $x = 3$ is the solution.

Exercise 5.3

1. (i) If $y = 2^x$, express (a) 2^{2x} (b) 2^{x+1} in terms of y.
   (ii) Hence, solve the equation $2^{2x} - 5(2^{x+1}) + 16 = 0$.

2. (i) If $y = 2^x$, express (a) 2^{2x} (b) 2^{2x+1} in terms of y.
   (ii) Hence, solve the equation $2^{2x+1} - 15(2^x) = 8$

3. (i) If $y = 3^x$, express (a) 3^{2x} (b) 3^{2x+1} in terms of y.
   (ii) Hence, solve the equation $3^{2x+1} + 26(3^x) - 9 = 0$.

4. If $y = 3^x$, solve the equation $9^x - 3^x - 72 = 0$ for $x > 0$.

Use the substitution $y = a^x$ to solve each of the following equations in questions 5–13.

5. $2^{2x} - 5(2^x) + 4 = 0$ 6. $3^{2x} - 4(3^x) + 3 = 0$ 7. $2^{2x} - 6(2^x) + 8 = 0$

8. $2^{2x} - 12(2^x) + 32 = 0$ 9. $3^{2x+1} - 10(3^x) + 3 = 0$ 10. $3^{2x} - 4(3^{x+1}) + 27 = 0$

11. $2^{2x+1} - 3(2^x) + 1 = 0$ 12. $2^x - 6 + 2^{3-x} = 0$ 13. $3^{x+2} - 82 + 3^{2-x} = 0$

14. (i) If $2^x + 2^{x+1} + 2^{x+2} = k2^x$, find the value of k.
    (ii) Hence, solve the equation $2^x + 2^{x+1} + 2^{x+2} = 224$.

Recurrence equations

A recurrence equation is a formula which will generate any term in a sequence from previous terms. For example, $u_{n+1} = 2u_n + 4^n$ is a recurrence equation.

Note: The notation used here is called **sequence notation**.

EXAMPLE

If $u_n = 5^n - 140(2)^n$, show that $u_{n+2} - 7u_{n+1} + 10u_n = 0$ for all values of $n \in \mathbb{N}$.

Solution:

We express u_{n+1} and u_{n+2} in terms of 5^n and 2^n, the lowest powers of 5 and 2, and then substitute these into the given expression.

To find u_{n+1} replace n with $(n + 1)$. To find u_{n+2} replace n with $(n + 2)$.

$u_n = 5^n - 140(2^n)$

$u_{n+1} = 5^{n+1} - 140(2^{n+1}) = 5^n(5^1) - 140(2^n)2^1 = 5(5^n) - 2(140)(2^n) = 5(5^n) - 280(2^n)$

$u_{n+2} = 5^{n+2} - 140(2^{n+2}) = 5^n(5^2) - 140(2^n)2^2 = 5^n(25) - 140(2^n)4 = 25(5^n) - 560(2^n)$

$$\underset{u_{n+2}}{\downarrow} \quad - \quad \underset{7u_{n+1}}{\downarrow} \quad + \quad \underset{10u_n}{\downarrow}$$

$= (25 \times 5^n - 560 \times 2^n) - 7(5 \times 5^n - 280 \times 2^n) + 10(5^n - 140 \times 2^n)$

$= 25 \times 5^n - 560 \times 2^n - 35 \times 5^n + 1{,}960 \times 2^n + 10 \times 5^n - 1{,}400 \times 2^n$

$= 5^n(25 - 35 + 10) + 2^n(-560 + 1{,}960 - 1{,}400)$

$= 5^n(0) + 2^n(0)$

$= 0$

Thus, u_n satisfies the given equation.

Fibonacci sequence – a famous case of a recurrence equation

The Fibonacci sequence is named after Leonardo of Pisa, who was known as Fibonacci (an abbreviation of *filius Bonacci*, 'son of Bonaccio'). The Fibonacci sequence is a recurrence equation. Starting with the first two terms of $0, 1, \ldots$, it then follows that each term is equal to the sum of the two previous terms.

Thus, the sequence is $0, 1, 1, 2, 3, 5, 8, 13, 21, 34, 55, 89, \ldots$

The recurrence equation for the Fibonacci sequence is $u_n = u_{n-1} + u_{n-2}$.

Fibonacci numbers are used in computer algorithms, the analysis of financial markets, biological settings such as branching in trees, the arrangement of a pine cone, the fruit spouts of a pineapple, the flowering of an artichoke, the arrangement of leaves on a stem and an uncurling fern.

Exercise 5.4

1. (i) If for all positive integers, n, $u_n = 2^n + 3^n$, find in terms of n: (a) u_{n+1} (b) u_{n+2}.
   (ii) Hence, show that $u_{n+2} - 5u_{n+1} + 6u_n = 0$.

2. (i) If for all natural numbers, n, $u_n = 5(3^n) + 4^n$, find in terms of n: (a) u_{n+1} (b) u_{n+2}.
   (ii) Hence, show that $u_{n+2} - 7u_{n+1} + 12u_n = 0$.

3. (i) If for all $n \in \mathbb{N}$, $u_n = 2(3^n) - 5(2^n)$, find in terms of n: (a) u_{n+1} (b) u_{n+2}.
   (ii) Hence, verify that $u_{n+2} - 5u_{n+1} + 6u_n = 0$.

4. (i) If for all positive integers, n, $f(n) = 2(5)^n + 2(-1)^n$, find in terms of n: (a) $f(n + 1)$
   (b) $f(n + 2)$.
   (ii) Hence, show that $f(n + 2) = 4f(n + 1) + 5f(n)$.

5. If for all natural numbers, n, $f(n) = 3(4)^n + 2(-3)^n$, verify that $f(n + 2) = f(n + 1) + 12f(n)$.

6. (i) If for all positive integers, n, $u_n = (n - 20)2^n$, verify that $u_{n+2} - 4u_{n+1} + 4u_n = 0$.
   (ii) Find the values of n for which $u_{n+1} > 3u_n$.

7. (i) If for all natural numbers, n, $u_n = (n + 4)3^n$, show that $u_{n+2} - 6u_{n+1} + 9u_n = 0$.
   (ii) For what values of $n > 0$ is $u_{n+2} > 4(u_{n+1} - 6 \times 3^n)$?

8. If for all positive integers, n, $f(n) = n(n - 1)^2 + 3$, show that $f(n + 1) - f(n) = 3n^2 - n$.

9. If for all $n \in \mathbb{N}$, $u_n = (5n - 3)2^n$, verify that $u_{n+1} - 2u_n = 5(2^{n+1})$.

10. If for all positive integers, n, $f(n) = 2^{2n-1} + 2^{n-1}$, show that $f(n + 1) - 2f(n) - 2^{2n} = 0$.

11. If for all natural numbers, n, $u_n = a(-4)^n + b$, show that $u_{n+2} + 3u_{n+1} - 4u_n = 0$.

12. $f(n) = p(3^n) + q(4^n)$ for all $n \in \mathbb{N}$. Verify that $f(n + 2) - 7f(n + 1) + 12f(n) = 0$.

Logarithms

A **logarithm** ('log' for short) is an index (exponent).

Given any two positive numbers a and b, there exists a third number, c, such that $a = b^c$.

The number c is said to be the log of a to the base b. Thus:

$$a = b^c \iff \log_b a = c$$

Any statement in index form has an equivalent log form. For example:

$100 = 10^2$	(index form)
$\log_{10} 100 = 2$	(log form)

$8 = 2^3$	(index form)
$\log_2 8 = 3$	(log form)

It is very important to be able to change from **index form** to **log form** and vice versa.

Note: $\log_3 81 = 4$ is read 'the log of 81 to the base 3 is 4', i.e. $81 = 3^4$.

Laws of logarithms

As logs are indices, the laws of logs are directly related to the laws of indices.

	Laws of logs	Numerical example
1.	$\log_a(xy) = \log_a x + \log_a y$	$\log_2 32 = \log_2 (4 \times 8) = \log_2 4 + \log_2 8 = 2 + 3 = 5$
2.	$\log_a\left(\dfrac{x}{y}\right) = \log_a x - \log_a y$	$\log_3 27 = \log_3\left(\dfrac{81}{3}\right) = \log_3 81 - \log_3 3 = 4 - 1 = 3$
3.	$\log_a(x^q) = q \log_a x$	$\log_2 8 = \log_2 2^3 = 3 \log_2 2 = 3(1) = 3$
4.	$\log_a 1 = 0$	$1 = 5^0$, thus $\log_5 1 = 0$
5.	$\log_a\left(\dfrac{1}{x}\right) = -\log_a x$	$\log_2\left(\dfrac{1}{16}\right) = -\log_2 16 = -4$
6.	$\log_a a = 1$ $\log_a (a^x) = x$	$\log_4 4 = 1$ $\log_5(5^3) = 3$
7.	$a^{\log_a x} = x$	$6^{\log_6 4} = 4$
8.	$\log_b x = \dfrac{\log_a x}{\log_a b}$	$\log_4 64 = \dfrac{\log_2 64}{\log_2 4} = \dfrac{6}{2} = 3$

Note: Law 8 is usually referred to as the **change of base** law.

Natural logs

Logs to the base 10, i.e. $\log_{10} x$, are called **common logs**.

Logs to the base e, i.e. $\log_e x$, are called **natural logs**.

$\log_e x$ is written $\ln x$. The number $e = 2\cdot71828$ (correct to five decimal places) is an irrational number, just like π.

It is very important to remember that natural logs obey the same rules as logs to any other base.

EXAMPLE 1

Evaluate:

(i) $\log_{10} 2 + \log_{10} 500$ (ii) $\log_5 \frac{1}{5}$ (iii) $\log_8 16$

(iv) $\log_9 3$ (v) $\ln e^2$ (vi) $\ln\left(\frac{1}{e}\right)$

Solution:

(i) $\log_{10} 2 + \log_{10} 500$
$= \log_{10} (2 \times 500)$
$= \log_{10} 1,000$
$= 3$

(iv) $\log_9 3$
$= \dfrac{\log_3 3}{\log_3 9}$
$= \dfrac{1}{2}$

Alternatively, $\log_9 3$
$= \log_9 9^{\frac{1}{2}} = \frac{1}{2} \log_9 9$
$= \frac{1}{2}(1) = \frac{1}{2}$

(ii) $\log_5 \left(\frac{1}{5}\right)$
$= \log_5 1 - \log_5 5$
$= 0 - 1$
$= -1$

(v) $\ln e^2$
$= 2 \ln e$
$= 2(1)$
$= 2$

(iii) $\log_8 16$
$= \dfrac{\log_2 16}{\log_2 8}$
(16 and 8 can be written as powers of 2)
$= \frac{4}{3}$

(vi) $\ln\left(\frac{1}{e}\right)$
$= \ln 1 - \ln e$
$= 0 - 1$
$= -1$

$(\ln e = \log_e e = 1)$

EXAMPLE 2

(i) If $\log_x 125 = 3$, find the value of x.   (ii) Evaluate $2 \log_2 2 + \log_2 12 - \log_2 6$.

Solution:

(i) $\log_x 125 = 3$
$125 = x^3$
$5^3 = x^3$
$\therefore x = 5$

(ii) $2 \log_2 2 + \log_2 12 - \log_2 6$
$= \log_2 2^2 + \log_2 12 - \log_2 6$
$= \log_2 4 + \log_2 12 - \log_2 6$
$= \log_2 \dfrac{4 \times 12}{6} = \log_2 8 = 3$

Exercise 6.1

1. Write each of the following in the form $a = b^c$.
   - **(i)** $\log_2 16 = 4$
   - **(ii)** $\log_3 81 = 4$
   - **(iii)** $\log_{10} 1{,}000 = 4$
   - **(iv)** $\log_5 125 = 3$
   - **(v)** $\log_6 36 = 2$
   - **(vi)** $\log_4 2 = \frac{1}{2}$
   - **(vii)** $\log_{27} 3 = \frac{1}{3}$
   - **(viii)** $\log_4 8 = \frac{3}{2}$

2. Write each of the following in the form $\log_b a = c$.
   - **(i)** $100 = 10^2$
   - **(ii)** $8 = 2^3$
   - **(iii)** $27 = 3^3$
   - **(iv)** $49 = 7^2$
   - **(v)** $4 = 16^{\frac{1}{2}}$
   - **(vi)** $9 = 27^{\frac{2}{3}}$
   - **(vii)** $4 = 4$
   - **(viii)** $1 = 8^0$

3. Evaluate each of the following.
   - **(i)** $\log_2 8$
   - **(ii)** $\log_4 16$
   - **(iii)** $\log_3 81$
   - **(iv)** $\log_5 125$
   - **(v)** $\log_{10} 10{,}000$
   - **(vi)** $\log_2 32$
   - **(vii)** $\log_5 5$
   - **(viii)** $\log_4 1$
   - **(ix)** $\log_2 \frac{1}{2}$
   - **(x)** $\log_7 \frac{1}{49}$
   - **(xi)** $\log_4 32$
   - **(xii)** $\log_{16} 8$
   - **(xiii)** $\log_9 27$
   - **(xiv)** $\frac{1}{3}\log_2 8$
   - **(xv)** $\log_{27} \frac{1}{3}$
   - **(xvi)** $\log_2 2\sqrt{2}$

4. Evaluate each of the following.
   - **(i)** $\log_a a^2$
   - **(ii)** $\log_a a^3$
   - **(iii)** $(\log_6 4 + \log_6 9)^2$
   - **(iv)** $(\log_5 25 + \log_5 15 - \log_5 3)^4$
   - **(v)** $\log 3 + \log 16 - \log 4 - \log 12$

5. **(i)** $f(x) = 2\log_5 x$. Evaluate: **(a)** $f(5)$ **(b)** $f(25)$ **(c)** $f\left(\frac{1}{5}\right)$ **(d)** $f\left(\sqrt{5}\right)$.
   (ii) If $\log_4 x = 1 - p$ and $\log_4 y = 1 + p$, evaluate xy.

6. Evaluate $\log\dfrac{p}{q} + \log\dfrac{q}{r} + \log\dfrac{r}{p}$.

7. **(i)** Use the fact that $\log_b a = \dfrac{\log_c a}{\log_c b}$ to evaluate **(a)** $\log_{27} 81$ **(b)** $\log_{32} 8$.

   (ii) Evaluate $(\log_b a)(\log_c b)(\log_a c)$.

   (iii) Show that $\log_b a = \dfrac{1}{\log_a b}$.

   (iv) If $x > 0$ and $x \neq 1$, show that $\dfrac{1}{\log_2 x} + \dfrac{1}{\log_3 x} + \dfrac{1}{\log_5 x} = \dfrac{1}{\log_{30} x}$.

8. If $\log_r p = \log_r 2 + 3\log_r q$, express p in terms of q.

9. If $\log_a y = 2\log_a x - \log_a 5$, express y in terms of x.

10. If $3\log_2 y = 3 + \log_2(x + 4)$, show that $y^3 = 8(x + 4)$.

Logarithm equations

There are two methods for solving an equation involving logs.

Method 1

Get a single log on **both** sides in the equation, equate the expressions and solve, i.e. write the equation in the form $\log_b x = \log_b y, \Rightarrow x = y$ and solve.

Method 2

Get a single log in the equation and then change from log form to index form, i.e. write the equation in the form $\log_b a = c, \Rightarrow a = b^c$.

Note:

1. Make sure that all logs have the same base. If necessary, use the **change of base** law.
2. Logs are defined only for positive numbers. Therefore, reject any solutions that give rise to a log of a negative number in the **original** equation.

EXAMPLE 1

Solve for x: $\quad \log_2 x = 3 - \log_2(x - 2), \quad x \in \mathbb{R}$.

Solution:

Method 1

$$\log_2 x = 3 - \log_2(x - 2)$$
$$\log_2 x + \log_2(x - 2) = 3$$
$$\log_2 x(x - 2) = \log_2 8$$
$$\log_2(x^2 - 2x) = \log_2 8$$
$$x^2 - 2x = 8$$
$$x^2 - 2x - 8 = 0$$
$$(x - 4)(x + 2) = 0$$
$$x - 4 = 0 \quad \text{or} \quad x + 2 = 0$$
$$x = 4 \quad \text{or} \quad x = -2$$

Method 2

$$\log_2 x = 3 - \log_2(x - 2)$$
$$\log_2 x + \log_2(x - 2) = 3$$
$$\log_2 x(x - 2) = 3$$
$$\log_2(x^2 - 2x) = 3$$
$$x^2 - 2x = 2^3$$
$$x^2 - 2x = 8$$
$$x^2 - 2x - 8 = 0$$
$$(x - 4)(x + 2) = 0$$
$$x - 4 = 0 \quad \text{or} \quad x + 2 = 0$$
$$x = 4 \quad \text{or} \quad x = -2$$

Reject $x = -2$, as substitution into the **original** equation yields $\log_2(-2)$ or $\log_2(-4)$, which are not defined.

$\therefore x = 4$ is the solution (which can be checked in the original equation).

Sometimes a change of base is required

EXAMPLE 2

Solve for x: $\log_2 x + 4 \log_x 2 = 5$.

Solution:

First write the equation in terms of one base only.

$$\log_2 x + 4 \log_x 2 = 5$$

$$\log_2 x + 4 \left(\frac{1}{\log_2 x} \right) = 5$$

$$\log_2 x + \frac{4}{\log_2 x} = 5$$

Let $\log_2 x = y$ (using a substitution)

$$y + \frac{4}{y} = 5$$

$$y^2 + 4 = 5y$$

$$y^2 - 5y + 4 = 0$$

$$(y - 4)(y - 1) = 0$$

$$y = 4 \quad \text{or} \quad y = 1$$

$$\log_x 2$$
$$= \frac{\log_2 2}{\log_2 x}$$
$$= \frac{1}{\log_2 x}$$

Change both to the base of the constant 2.

$y = 4$	or	$y = 1$
$\log_2 x = 4$		$\log_2 x = 1$
$x = 2^4$		$x = 2^1$
$x = 16$		$x = 2$

Sometimes we have to solve simultaneous equations

EXAMPLE 3

Solve the simultaneous equations:

$2 \log x = \log(x + y)$ and $\log y = \log 2 + \log (x - 1)$, $x > 1, y > 0$.

Solution:

$$2 \log x = \log(x + y)$$
$$\log x^2 = \log(x + y)$$
$$x^2 = x + y \quad ①$$

From ② $y = 2(x - 1)$, put this into ①.

$$x^2 = y + x \quad ①$$
$$x^2 = 2(x - 1) + x$$
$$x^2 = 2x - 2 + x$$
$$x^2 - 3x + 2 = 0$$
$$(x - 2)(x - 1) = 0$$
$$x = 2 \quad \text{or} \quad x = 1$$

$$\log y = \log 2 + \log(x - 1)$$
$$\log y = \log 2(x - 1)$$
$$y = 2(x - 1) \quad ②$$

(replace y with $2(x - 1)$)

$x = 2:$ $y = 2(x - 1) = 2(2 - 1) = 2(1) = 2$
$x = 1:$ $y = 2(x - 1) = 2(1 - 1) = 2(0) = 0$
Thus, $x = 2$ and $y = 2$ or $x = 1$ and $y = 0$.
However, we are given $x > 1$ and $y > 0$.
$\therefore x = 2$ and $y = 2$ is the solution.

Sometimes we have to use a calculator

EXAMPLE 4

If $5^n = 3{,}000$, find the value of n, correct to four significant figures.

Solution:

$$5^n = 3{,}000$$
$$\log_{10} 5^n = \log_{10} 3{,}000 \qquad \text{(take the log of both sides)}$$
$$n \log_{10} 5 = \log_{10} 3{,}000 \qquad \text{(use law 3)}$$
$$n = \frac{\log_{10} 3{,}000}{\log_{10} 5} \qquad \text{(divide both sides by } \log_{10} 5\text{)}$$
$$n = 4 \cdot 974635869 \qquad (\boxed{} \ \boxed{\log} \ 3{,}000 \ \boxed{\div} \ \boxed{\log} \ 5 \ \boxed{=})$$
$$n = 4 \cdot 975 \qquad \text{(correct to four significant figures)}$$
$$(\text{check: } 5^{4 \cdot 975} = 3{,}001 \cdot 758655, \quad \boxed{} \ 5 \ \boxed{x^y} \ 4 \cdot 975 \ \boxed{=})$$

Note: Using natural logs to the base e would have given the same answer, i.e. $\dfrac{\ln 3{,}000}{\ln 5} = 4 \cdot 974635869$.

Exercise 6.2

In questions 1–14, solve for x, $x \in \mathbb{R}$.

1. $\log_2 3 + \log_2 x = \log_2 12$

2. $\log_3 x - \log_3 4 = \log_3 2$

3. $\log_{10} x^2 - \log_{10} 2 = \log_{10} 50$

4. $\log_5(x + 1) + \log_5(x - 1) = \log_5 8$

5. $\log_a(x - 6) + \log_a(x - 4) = \log_a x$

6. $\log_3(x^2 - 10) - \log_3 x = 2 \log_3 3$

7. $\log_2(x + 2) + \log_2(x - 2) = 5$

8. $\log_5(x - 2) = 1 - \log_5(x - 6)$

9. $\log_2(x + 2) - \log_2 x = 3$

10. $\log_{10}(x^2 + 24) - \log_{10} x = 1$

11. $2 \log_9 x = \frac{1}{2} + \log_9(5x + 18)$

12. $\log_7(x^2 + 4) - \log_7(x - 1) = \log_7(3x + 2)$

13. $\log_5 x = 1 + \log_5 \left(\dfrac{3}{2x - 1} \right)$

14. $2 \log_3(x + 2) - \log_3(x + 1) = \log_3(x + 5)$

In questions 15–20, solve for x and $y \in \mathbb{R}$.

15. $\log(5x - y) = \log 9$ and $\log(3x + 2y) = \log 8$

16. $\log_2(2x + y) = 3$ and $\log_2(3x - 4y) = 0$

17. $\log_3(3x - y) = \log_3(y + 1)$ and $\log_3 2 + \log_3(x + y) = 2$

18. $\log x^2 = \log y$ and $\log(2x + y) - \log 3 = 0$

19. $\log_2 2 + \log_2(x + 1) = \log_2 y$ and $\log_2 x + \log_2 y = 2$, $x > 0$, $y > 0$

20. $\log_2 x - \log_2 2 = \log_2(1 - y)$ and $\log_2 x + \log_2(x + 2y) = 3$

Questions 21–26 require changing the base. Solve each for $x \in \mathbb{R}$.

21. $\log_2 x = \log_4(x + 6)$

22. $\log_2(x - 1) = \log_4(4x - 7)$

23. $\log_3 x + 3 \log_x 3 = 4$

24. $\log_4 x + 2 \log_x 4 = 3$

25. $\log_5 x - 1 = 6 \log_x 5$

26. $4 \log_x 2 = \log_2 x + 3$

27. If $\log_4\left(\dfrac{x}{y}\right) = 5$, $x, y > 0$, find the value of $\log_2 x - \log_2 y$.

28. The point $a(p, k)$ lies on the curve with equation $y = \log_2 x$.
    The point $b(q, k)$ lies on the curve with equation $y = \log_4 x$.
    Find a relationship between p and q and hence evaluate p when $q = \frac{9}{16}$.

29. $\log_a 2 + 2 \log_a x = \log_a(5x - 2a) + 1$.
    Write a quadratic equation in terms of x and find, in terms of a, the values of x.

30. If $\log_4 xy = 2$, prove that $\log_2 x + \log_2 y = 4$.
    Solve the simultaneous equations $\log_4 xy = 2$ and $(\log_2 x)(\log_2 y) = 3$.
    (Hint: Let $\log_2 x = p$ and $\log_2 y = q$.)

31. If $\log_4 a = k$, express the following in terms of k.
    (i) $\log_4 a^2$ (ii) $\log_4 4a^2$ (iii) $\log_{16} a$ (iv) $\log_a 4$ (v) $\log_k \frac{1}{4}$

Questions 32–39 require a calculator. Solve each for n, correct to four significant figures.

32. $3^n = 2{,}500$ 33. $5^n = 680$ 34. $4^n = 20$ 35. $2^n = 31$

36. $4^{n+2} = 3{,}460$ 37. $3^{2n-1} = 4{,}800$ 38. $5^{n-1} = 2^n$ 39. $5^{2n-1} = 4^{n+1}$

Questions 40–45 involve using natural logarithms.

40. Evaluate each of the following.
    (i) $\ln e$ (ii) $\ln e^3$ (iii) $\ln\left(\dfrac{1}{e^2}\right)$ (iv) $\ln\sqrt{e}$

41. By taking the log of both sides, verify that if:
    (i) $e^x = a$, then $x = \ln a$ (ii) $e^{\ln x} = y$, then $x = y$

42. Solve each of the following.
    (i) $e^x = 2$ (ii) $e^x = 5$ (iii) $e^x = -4$ (iv) $e^x = \frac{1}{3}$
    (v) $e^x = -1$ (vi) $e^{2x} = 3$ (vii) $\ln x = 1$ (viii) $\ln x = 2$
    (ix) $\ln x = \frac{1}{2}$ (x) $\ln x = -1$ (xi) $\ln x = -3$ (xii) $\ln x = -\frac{1}{2}$

43. By writing $e^x = y$ or otherwise, solve each of the following equations.
    (i) $e^x - 5 + 6e^{-x} = 0$ (ii) $e^{2x} - 8e^x + 15 = 0$
    (iii) $e^{2x} - 3e^x - 4 = 0$ (iv) $3e^x - 7 + 2e^{-x} = 0$

44. (i) By letting $e^x = y$, write $e^{2x} + (k-2)e^x + (-3k-2) = 0$ as a quadratic equation in y, $k \in \mathbb{R}$.

   (ii) Find the values of k for which this equation has equal roots.

   (iii) Assuming these values of k, solve the equation $e^{2x} + (k-2)e^x + (-3k-2) = 0$.

45. Solve: (i) $(\ln x)^2 - 3 \ln x + 2 = 0$ (ii) $2(\ln x)^2 - 7 \ln x + 3 = 0$

Note: $(\log_x)^2$ can be written as $\log^2 x$.

Logarithms in the real world

Logarithms are used in many aspects of everyday life, such as calculating the interest on investments, depreciation on assets or population growth or decline.

 EXAMPLE

The amount A in an account after t years from an initial principal P invested at an annual rate r compounded continuously is given by $A = P(e^{rt})$, where r is expressed as a decimal. How many years, correct to the nearest year, will it take an initial investment of €1,000 to amount to €1,700 at the rate of 4·42% compounded continuously?

Solution:

$A = P(e^{rt})$

$1,700 = 1,000(e^{0·0442t})$ ($A = 1,700$, $P = 1,000$ and $N = 0·0442$)

$1·7 = e^{0·0442t}$ (divide both sides by 1,000)

$\log_e 1·7 = \log_e(e^{0·0442t})$ (take $\log_e$ of both sides)

$\log_e 1·7 = 0·0442t$ ($\log_e e^x = x \log_e e = x(1) = x$)

$0.0442t = \log_e 1·7$ (swap sides)

$t = \dfrac{\log_e 1·7}{0·0442}$ (divide both sides by 0·0442)

$t = 12·00516405$ (using a calculator)

$t = 12$ (correct to the nearest year)

∴ 12 years

Exercise 6.3

1. The amount A in an account after t years from an initial principal P invested at an annual rate r compounded continuously is given by $A = P(e^{rt})$, where r is expressed as a decimal. How many years will it take an initial investment of €500 to grow to €2,000 at the rate of 4% compounded continuously?

2. An initial deposit of €3,000 is made in a savings account for which the interest is compounded continuously. The amount, A, is found by $A = P(e^{rt})$. If the balance will double in seven years, what is the annual rate of interest for this account?

3. Jane has deposited €600 in an account that pays 5·64% interest, compounded continuously, so the amount, A, is found by $A = P(e^{rt})$. How long will it take for her money to double?

4. The amount A in an account after t years from an initial principal P invested at an annual rate r compounded continuously is given by $A = P(e^{rt})$, where r is expressed as a decimal. €20,000 is invested with compounded continuous interest at a rate of 8%. The bank returns €25,000 with compounded interest. How long was the money left in the bank, correct to one decimal place?

5. The number of bacteria present in a culture after t minutes is given as $B = 100e^{kt}$. If there are 5,287 bacteria present after 13 minutes, find k.

6. A population, P, is modelled as $P = 12{,}300(e^{0·073t})$, where t is in years. After how many years, correct to one decimal place, will the population reach 20,000 people, provided it keeps growing in the same fashion?

7. John purchased a car for €5,800. After t years its value is given by the exponential function $V = 5{,}800(0·8^t)$. John decides to replace the car when its value has declined to €500. After how long, to the nearest year, will the car be replaced?

8. The population, P, of a certain bacteria culture is given by a model $P = 100(e^{kt})$, where k is a constant to be determined and t is the number of days since the original population of 100 was established. Find the value of k if the population is expected to reach 200 in three days.

9. The population growth of a certain city with a current population of 27,345 is modelled by the equation $P = 27{,}345(e^{0·005t})$, where P is the population of the city after t years and 0·005 is the rate of growth.

   (i) What will the population of the city be 10 years from now?

   (ii) After how many years will the city's population reach 32,000?

10. The amount of radioactive tracer remaining after t days is given by $A = A_o(e^{-0·058t})$, where A_o is the starting amount at the beginning of the time period. How many days, to the nearest day, will it take for one half of the original amount to decay?

11. In a science experiment, a quantity, $Q(t)$, was observed at various points in time, t. Time is measured in seconds from the instant of the first observation. The table below gives the results.

t	0	1	2	3	4
$Q(t)$	2·920	2·642	2·391	2·163	1·957

Q follows a rule of the form $Q(t) = Ae^{-bt}$, where A and b are constants.

   (i) Use any two of the observations from the table to find the value of A and the value of b, correct to three decimal places.

   (ii) Use a different observation from the table to verify your values for A and b.

   (iii) Show that $Q(t)$ is a constant multiple of $Q(t-1)$, for $t \geq 1$.

   (iv) Find the value of the constant, k, for which $Q(t+k) = \frac{1}{2}Q(t)$, for all $t \geq 0$. Give your answer correct to two decimal places.

Revision

In all cases, (x_1, y_1) and (x_2, y_2) represent points. The slope of the line l_1 is m_1 and the slope of l_2 is m_2.

1. **Midpoint of a line segment**

$$\text{Midpoint} = \left(\frac{x_1 + x_2}{2}, \frac{y_1 + y_2}{2} \right)$$

2. **Distance between two points**

$$d = \sqrt{(x_2 - x_1)^2 + (y_2 - y_1)^2}$$

3. **Slope of a line, m, given two points**

$$m = \frac{y_2 - y_1}{x_2 - x_1}$$

Slope is $\dfrac{\text{Rise}}{\text{Run}} = \tan \theta$ where θ is the angle the line makes with the positive sense of the x-axis.

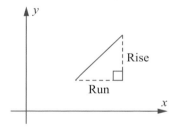
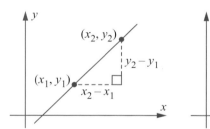
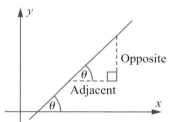

4. **Parallel lines have equal slopes**

If $l_1 \parallel l_2$, then $m_1 = m_2$.

Conversely, if two lines have equal slopes, then they are parallel.

5. **If two lines are perpendicular, then the product of their slopes is -1**

If $l_1 \perp l_2$, then $m_1 \times m_2 = -1$.

Conversely, if the slopes of two lines are multiplied and the result is -1, then the lines are perpendicular.

Note: If we know the slope of a line and we need to find the slope of a line perpendicular to it, simply do the following:

Turn the known slope upside down and change its sign.

For example, if a line has a slope of $-\frac{3}{5}$, then the slope of a line perpendicular to it has a slope of $\frac{5}{3}$ (turn upside down and change its sign), because $-\frac{3}{5} \times \frac{5}{3} = -1$.

6. **Equation of a line**

> To find the equation of a line, we need:
>
> 1. The slope of the line, m. 2. A point on the line, (x_1, y_1).
>
> Then use the formula: $y - y_1 = m(x - x_1)$.

In short, we need the **slope** and a **point** on the line.

Note: If the slope is a fraction, an alternative version might be useful:

$$(y - y_1) = m(x - x_1)$$

7. **Slope of a line when given its equation**
To find the slope of a line when given its equation, do the following.
Method 1:

> Get y on its own, and the number in front of x is the slope.

Note: The number in front of x is called the **coefficient** of x.
The number on its own is called the y **intercept**.
In short, write the line in the form $y = mx + c$.

$$y \quad = \quad mx \quad + \quad c$$
$$\downarrow \qquad\qquad \downarrow$$
$$y \quad = \quad (\text{slope})x \quad + \quad (\text{where the line cuts the } y\text{-axis})$$

Method 2:

> If the line is in the form $ax + by + c = 0$, then $-\dfrac{a}{b}$ is the slope.

In words: Slope $= -\dfrac{\text{Number in front of } x}{\text{Number in front of } y}$

Note: When using this method, make sure every term is on the left-hand side in the given equation of the line.

8. **Proving lines are parallel or perpendicular**

To prove whether or not two lines are parallel, do the following.

---

1. Find the slope of each line.
2. (a) If the slopes are the same, the lines are parallel.
   (b) If the slopes are different, the lines are **not** parallel.

To prove whether or not two lines are perpendicular, do the following.

---

1. Find the slope of each line.
2. Multiply both slopes.
3. (a) If the answer in step 2 is -1, the lines are perpendicular.
   (b) If the answer in step 2 is **not** -1, the lines are **not** perpendicular.

Note: $ax + by + k = 0$ is a line parallel to the line $ax + by + c = 0$.

$bx - ay + k = 0$ or $-bx + ay + k = 0$ is a line perpendicular to the line $ax + by + c = 0$.

9. **Verify that a point belongs to a line**

Substitute the coordinates of the point into the equation of the line. If the coordinates satisfy the equation, then the point is on the line. Otherwise, the point is not on the line.

10. **Point of intersection of two lines**

Use the method of solving simultaneous equations to find the point of intersection of two lines.

11. **Graphing lines**

To draw a line, only two points are needed. The easiest points to find are where lines cut the x- and y-axes. This is known as the **intercept method**.

Note:

On the x-axis, $y = 0$.   On the y-axis, $x = 0$.

To draw a line, do the following.

---

1. Let $y = 0$ and find x.
2. Let $x = 0$ and find y.
3. Plot these two points.
4. Draw the line through these points.

If the constant in the equation of a line is zero, e.g. $3x - 5y = 0$ or $4x = 3y$, then the line will pass through the origin, $(0, 0)$. In this case the intercept method will not work. To draw a line that contains the origin, $(0, 0)$, do the following.

> 1. Choose a suitable value for x and find the corresponding value for y (or vice versa).
> 2. Plot this point.
> 3. A line drawn through this point and the origin is the required line.

Note: A suitable value is to let x equal the number in front of y and then find the corresponding value for y (or vice versa).

12. **Lines parallel to the axes**

$x = 2$ is a line parallel to the y-axis through 2 on the x-axis.
$y = -1$ is a line parallel to the x-axis through -1 on the y-axis.

Note:

> $y = 0$ is the equation of the x-axis.
> $x = 0$ is the equation of the y-axis.

13. **Transformations of the plane**

(a) **Translation:** A translation moves a point in a straight line.
(b) **Central symmetry:** Central symmetry is a reflection in a point.
(c) **Axial symmetry:** Axial symmetry is a reflection in a line.
(d) **Axial symmetry in the axes or central symmetry in the origin.**

> The following three patterns emerge and it is worth memorising them:
> 1. Axial symmetry in the x-axis $\rightarrow$ change the sign of y.
> 2. Axial symmetry in the y-axis $\rightarrow$ change the sign of x.
> 3. Central symmetry in the origin, $(0, 0)$ $\rightarrow$ change the sign of both x and y.

Note: Under a translation or a central symmetry, a line is mapped onto a parallel line.

EXAMPLE

Find the equation of the line that contains the point of intersection of $2x + 3y - 12 = 0$ and $x - y - 1 = 0$ and is perpendicular to $3x - 5y - 2 = 0$.

Solution:

Method 1:

Simultaneous equations show the point of intersection to be $(3, 2)$.

Lines perpendicular to $3x - 5y - 2 = 0$ are of the form $5x + 3y + c = 0$.

$$5x + 3y + c = 0$$

Substitute $(3, 2)$: $5(3) + 3(2) + c = 0$

$$15 + 6 + c = 0$$

$$c = -21$$

$\therefore$ The equation of the line is $5x + 3y - 21 = 0$.

Method 2:

Simultaneous equations show the point of intersection to be $(3, 2)$.

The slope of $3x - 5y - 2 = 0$ is $\frac{3}{5}$.

$\therefore$ The slope of a line perpendicular to it $= -\frac{5}{3}$.

Point: $(3, 2)$ Slope: $-\frac{5}{3}$

$$(y - y_1) = m(x - x_1) \qquad \text{(alternative form as slope is a fraction)}$$

$$(y - 2) = -\frac{5}{3}(x - 3)$$

$$3(y - 2) = -5(x - 3)$$

$$3y - 6 = -5x + 15$$

$$5x + 3y - 21 = 0$$

Exercise 7.1

1. Show that the points $P(2, -3)$, $Q(3, 1)$ and $R(5, 9)$ are collinear.

2. Calculate the area of the triangle formed by the x-axis, the y-axis and the line $3x - y - 6 = 0$.

3. Which of the following represents the parallelogram $PQRS$?

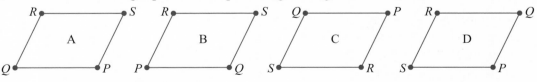

4. $A(2, -2)$ and $B(4, 4)$ are two points.

   (i) Find $|AB|$.

   (ii) Find the coordinates of M, the midpoint of $[AB]$.

   (iii) Find the slope and equation of the line AB.

   (iv) The point $(-2, r)$ is on the line AB. Find the value of r.

     (v) Find the equation of b, the perpendicular bisector of the line segment $[AB]$.

     (vi) b cuts the x-axis at the point $P(h, 0)$ and the y-axis at $Q(0, k)$.
        Find the value of h and the value of k.

5. The point $M(-2, -1)$ is the midpoint of $[PQ]$.
    If the coordinates of P are $(4, -5)$, find the coordinates of Q.

6.   **(i)** The line $l : 2x + 5y + c = 0$ contains the point $(4, -1)$. Find the value of c.

    (ii) Find the equation of the line parallel to l which contains $(-3, 2)$.

7.   **(i)** The line $l : 3x - 4y + 5 = 0$ is parallel to $3x + ky + 10 = 0$. Find the value of k.

    (ii) If $-6x + ty - 1 = 0$ is also parallel to l, find the value of t.

8. $l : 3x - 2y + 8 = 0$ and $k : 2x + 3y - 1 = 0$ are two lines. Prove that $l \perp k$.

9. $l : px + qy + r = 0$ and $n : qx - py + 5 = 0$ are two lines. Prove that $l \perp n$.

10. $l : ax + 3y = 0$ and $k : 3x - 5y - 4 = 0$ are two lines. If $l \perp k$, find the value of a.

11. $P(2, -3)$, $Q(3, 1)$ and $R(-1, k)$ are three points. If $PQ \perp QR$, find the value of k.

12. Find the equation of the line through the point $(2, -3)$ that makes an angle of:

    (i) $45°$

    (ii) $135°$ with the positive sense of the x-axis

13. $l : 2x - 5y - 9 = 0$ and $k : 3x - 2y - 8 = 0$ are two lines. l intersects k at the point Q.

    (i) Find the coordinates of Q.

    (ii) Find the equation of the line j such that $l \perp j$ and $Q \in j$.

    (iii) Show that the point $R(4, -6)$ is on j.

    (iv) Find the coordinates of the image of the point R under an axial symmetry in l.

14. The height of a tree in 2007 was 6·5 m. By 2010, its height was 8 m.

    (i) By finding the slope, find the rate of growth of the tree per year.

    (ii) If the tree continues to grow at this rate, what should its height be in 2020?

    (iii) Find the equation of the line which represents this growth and verify your answer
       from part **(ii)**.

15. The brakes on a car are tested on a hill as shown on the diagram.
It is considered unsafe to park a car on steeper hills.
A road follows the following path over a mountain:
$P_0(0, 0)$, $P_1(2, 5)$, $P_2(4, 7)$, $P_3(6, 8)$, $P_4(10, 11)$, $P_5(13, 7)$,
$P_6(16, 5)$, $P_7(20, 3)$ and $P_8(25, 0)$.

    (i) Show this on a coordinated graph.

    (ii) Calculate the slope of each section.

    (iii) Why are some of the slopes negative?

    (iv) Which sections are safe for parking?

16. $P(-1, -2)$, $Q(5, k)$, $R(8, 2)$ and $S(h, 1)$ are the four vertices of the parallelogram $PQRS$. Find the value of h and the value of k.

17. $P(-1, 5)$, $Q(-2, 1)$, $R(3, -2)$ and $S(a, b)$ are the four vertices of a parallelogram, with $PQ \parallel RS$. Find two pairs of coordinates of the point S.

18. $l : 3x + 2y - 5 = 0$, $k : 4x - y - 14 = 0$ and $j : 2x + 5y - 1 = 0$ are the equations of three lines. Find the equation of the line containing the point of intersection of l and k and perpendicular to j.

19. Show that the point $(2, -5)$ is on the line $l : 3x - 2y - 16 = 0$. Find the equation of the image of l under the following.

    (i) The translation $(2, -5) \rightarrow (4, -6)$.

    (ii) The central symmetry in the point $(-1, -1)$.

20. Find the image of the point $(-4, -5)$ under the axial symmetry in the line $3x + 2y - 4 = 0$.

21. Find the equations of the two lines which contain the point $(4, 2)$ and cut equal intercepts on the x- and y-axes.

22. $PQRS$ is a parallelogram in which the opposite vertices are $P(2, 1)$ and $R(4, 4)$. The slope of $PQ = \frac{1}{3}$ and the slope of $PS = -2$.

    (i) Find the equation of PQ.

    (ii) Find the equation of QR.

    (iii) Hence or otherwise, find the coordinates of Q and S.

23. The equation of the line l is $ax + by + c = 0$. l cuts the x-axis at P and the y-axis at Q. Give each answer in terms of a, b and c.

    (i) Find the coordinates of P and the coordinates of Q. (ii) Calculate $|PQ|$.

    (iii) Calculate the area of the triangle formed by the x-axis, the y-axis and the line $ax + by + c = 0$.

24. An undersea tunnel is to be built from Wicklow, Ireland to Morfa, Wales as shown in the diagram. The tunnel will be 45 m below sea level at P but will gradually rise 5 m to the point Q. S is 4·5 km from Wicklow and R is 4·8 km from Morfa. The distance from Wicklow to Morfa is 92·8 km.

(i) What is the slope of (a) *WP* (b) *PQ* (c) *QM*?

(ii) Taking *W* as the origin (0, 0) and using metres as units, find the equation of the tunnel from *P* to *Q*.

(iii) Calculate the length of the tunnel from *W* to *M*, correct to the nearest metre.

25. A new lifeboat station is being built. The boat will be held at the point *B* on the ramp so that the height |*BG*| is 21 m. The ramp angle, θ, is yet to be decided.

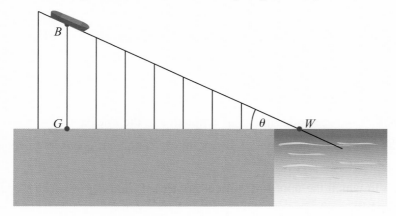

(i) What would the slope of the ramp be for θ = 25°, θ = 35° and θ = 45°?
   Where appropriate, round your result to one decimal place and give your answer as a simple fraction.

(ii) Take *G* as the origin (0, 0) and use metres as units. Using your answer from (i), find the equation of the ramp when θ = 25°, θ = 35° and θ = 45°.
   Write your answers in the form *y* = *mx* + *c*.

(iii) Find the coordinates of *W* when θ = 35°.

26. A plane leaves an airport in a direction 21·8° east of north. Take the airport as the origin and use kilometres as units.

   (i) Find the slope of the plane's path, giving your answer correct to one decimal place.

   (ii) Using your answer from (i), find the equation of the plane's path.

   (iii) If its destination, *D*, is 75 km east and 30 km north of this airport, will it need to change course during the flight?

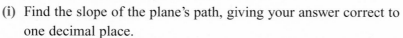

27. Find the equation of the line parallel to $ax + \dfrac{y}{a} = b$ containing the point $\left(\dfrac{b}{a},\ ab\right)$.

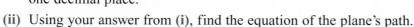

28. *A*(2*t*, 0) and *B*(0, −*t*) are two points. If |*AB*| = $\sqrt{20}$, find the two values of *t*.

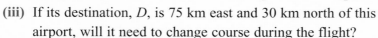

29. *P*(1, 6), *Q*(−3, −1) and *R*(2, *k*) are three points. If |*PQ*| = |*PR*|, find the two values of *k*.

30. *A*(0, 5), *B*(*x*, 10) and *C*(2*x*, *x*) are three points. If |*AB*| = |*BC*|, find the two values of *x*.

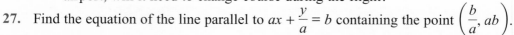

31. $A(5, 2)$, $B(2, -1)$, $C(x, 4)$ and $D(4, x)$ are four points and $|AB| = |CD|$. Show that $(x - 4)^2 = 9$ and solve for x.

32. $a : 3x - 2y - 5 = 0$ and $b : 2x + y - 8 = 0$ are two lines.

   (i) Find P, the point of intersection of a and b.

   (ii) Construct the equation of another line, c, by adding the equations a and b and show that $P \in c$.

   (iii) Investigate whether the line d, the difference of the equations a and b, also contains P.

   (iv) For what values of t does $a + tb = 0$ contain P?

Area of a triangle

The area of a triangle with vertices $(0, 0)$, (x_1, y_1) and (x_2, y_2) is given by the following formula:

$$\text{Area of triangle} = \tfrac{1}{2}|x_1 y_2 - x_2 y_1|$$

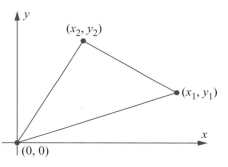

Notes:

1. The modulus symbol, $| \ |$, is included to make sure your answer is positive. Therefore, if the above formula gives a negative answer, simply ignore the negative sign, e.g. $\tfrac{1}{2}|-10| = \tfrac{1}{2}(10) = 5$.

2. If none of the vertices is at the origin, simply select one of the vertices and map (move) it to the point $(0, 0)$ by a translation. Then apply the same translation to the other two vertices to get (x_1, y_1) and (x_2, y_2).

3. To find the area of a quadrilateral (four-sided figure), divide it into two triangles. The diagonal of a parallelogram bisects its area.

EXAMPLE 1

Find the area of the triangle with vertices $(-2, 1)$, $(-4, 9)$ and $(3, -6)$.

Solution:

Map (move) the point $(-2, 1)$ to $(0, 0)$.
Rule: Add 2 to x, subtract 1 from y.

$(-2, 1) \qquad (-4, 9) \qquad (3, -6)$
$\downarrow \qquad\qquad \downarrow \qquad\quad \downarrow$
$(0, 0) \qquad (-2, 8) \qquad (5, -7)$
$\qquad\qquad (x_1, y_1) \qquad (x_2, y_2)$

$x_1 = -2, y_1 = 8 \qquad x_2 = 5, y_2 = -7$

$\text{Area of triangle} = \tfrac{1}{2}|x_1 y_2 - x_2 y_1|$
$= \tfrac{1}{2}|(-2)(-7) - (5)(8)|$
$= \tfrac{1}{2}|14 - 40|$
$= \tfrac{1}{2}|-26|$
$= \tfrac{1}{2}(26) = 13 \text{ sq. units}$

Sometimes we are given the area of a triangle and asked to find the unknown values of missing coordinates. We are given an equation in disguise and we solve this equation to find the unknown values of the missing coordinates.

Note: If we need to map one of the points to (0, 0), it is good practice to choose one of the **known** coordinates.

EXAMPLE 2

$A(3k, 5)$, $B(-2, 3)$ and $C(-k, 4)$ are vertices of the triangle ABC.
If the area of triangle ABC is 4 square units, find the values of k.

Solution:

Map the point $(-2, 3)$ onto $(0, 0)$.
Rule: Add 2 to x, subtract 3 from y.

$(3k, 5)$	$(-2, 3)$	$(-k, 4)$
↓	↓	↓
$(3k + 2, 2)$	$(0, 0)$	$(-k + 2, 1)$
(x_1, y_1)		(x_2, y_2)

Area of $\triangle ABC = \frac{1}{2}|x_1 y_2 - x_2 y_1|$
$= \frac{1}{2}|(3k + 2)(1) - (-k + 2)(2)|$
$= \frac{1}{2}|3k + 2 + 2k - 4|$
$= \frac{1}{2}|5k - 2|$

Given: Area of $\triangle ABC = 4$ (equation given in disguise)

$\frac{1}{2}|5k - 2| = 4$

$|5k - 2| = 8$ (multiply both sides by 2)

$5k - 2 = \pm 8$ (must include both positive and negative solutions)

$5k - 2 = 8$ or $5k - 2 = -8$

$5k = 10$ or $5k = -6$

$k = 2$ or $k = -\frac{6}{5}$

Exercise 7.2

In questions 1–6, find the area of each of the following triangles, whose vertices are as given.

1. (0, 0), (5, 2), (3, 4)
2. (0, 0), (10, 8), (3, 5)
3. (1, 5), (−5, −3), (4, 1)
4. (7, −1), (−5, 6), (3, −2)
5. (−4, 8), (4, −5), (3, −2)
6. (−1, −4), (2, −1), (−2, 3)

In questions 7–10, find the area of the parallelogram, whose vertices are as given.

7. (0, 0), (1, 3), (5, 5), (4, 2)
8. (−2, 4), (2, 4), (2, 7), (−2, 7)
9. (5, 1), (3, 1), (5, 4), (7, 4)
10. (−1, 3), (0, 2), (5, 4), (4, 5)

In questions 11–14, find the area of the quadrilateral, whose vertices are as given.

11. $(1, 1), (1, 2), (9, 3), (6, 1)$ 12. $(5, -6), (5, -4), (0, 1), (-2, -9)$

13. $(2, -4), (-1, -4), (-2, 2), (5, 5)$ 14. $(-2, 2), (-5, -6), (8, -4), (9, 0)$

15. $A(-1, -3), B(2, -1)$ and $C(5, 1)$ are the vertices of triangle ABC.
    By finding the area of triangle ABC, show that A, B and C are collinear.

16. $A(7, -4), B(4, 2)$ and $C(6, k)$ are the vertices of triangle ABC.
    If the area of triangle ABC is 9 square units, find the two values of k.

17. The area of the triangle with vertices $(0, 0), (5t, 3t)$ and $(t, 2t)$ is 14 square units.
    Find the two possible values of $t \in \mathbb{R}$.

18. The area of the triangle with vertices $P(-k, 1), Q(0, 3)$ and $R(2k, -1)$ is 8 square units.
    Find the two values of k.

19. $A(1, 3), B(-3, 1), C(5, -2), P(-1, 1), Q(9, 7)$ and $R(1, k)$ are six points.
    If $k > 0$ and the area of triangle ABC = the area of triangle PQR, find the value of k.

20. $P(h, k), Q(1, -2)$ and $R(8, -3)$ are the vertices of the triangle PQR.
    Calculate the coordinates of P if P is a point on the x-axis and area of triangle PQR is 8 square units.

Division of a line segment in a given ratio

The coordinates of the point $R(x, y)$ which divides the line segment $P(x_1, y_1)$ and $Q(x_2, y_2)$ internally in the ratio $a : b$ is given by:

Internal divisor
$R(x, y) = \left(\dfrac{bx_1 + ax_2}{b + a}, \dfrac{by_1 + ay_2}{b + a} \right)$

Note: you can avoid using the formula by using:
    (i) similar triangles
    (ii) translation

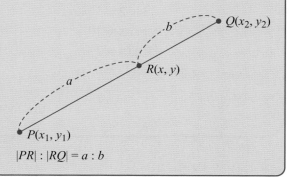

$|PR| : |RQ| = a : b$

Note: The syllabus states the internal case only. However, the unknown point could also be at the extreme, i.e. the unknown point could be P or Q above.

EXAMPLE

$A(-4, 3)$ and $B(6, -12)$ are two points. C is a point on $[AB]$ such that $|AC| : |CB| = 3 : 1$.
Find the coordinates of C.

Solution:

Method 1: Using the formula   **Method 2: Using similar triangles**

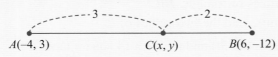   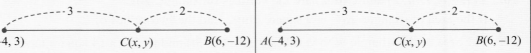

$$(x, y) = \left(\frac{bx_1 + ax_2}{b + a}, \frac{by_1 + ay_2}{b + a} \right)$$

	x coordinate	**y coordinate**

$$= \left(\frac{2(-4) + 3(6)}{2 + 3}, \frac{2(3) + 3(-12)}{2 + 3} \right)$$

$\dfrac{x - (-4)}{6 - x} = \dfrac{3}{2}$ $\quad$ $\dfrac{y - 3}{-12 - y} = \dfrac{3}{2}$

$$= \left(\frac{-8 + 18}{5}, \frac{6 - 36}{5} \right)$$

$2(x + 4) = 3(6 - x)$ $\quad$ $2(y - 3) = 3(-12 - y)$

$$= (2, -6)$$

$2x + 8 = 18 - 3x$ $\quad$ $2y - 6 = -36 - 3y$

$\therefore$ the coordinates of C are $(2, -6)$

$5x = 10$ $\qquad\qquad$ $5y = -30$

$x = 2$ $\qquad\qquad$ $y = -6$

$(2, -6)$

$\therefore$ the coordinates of C are $(2, -6)$

Method 3: Using a translation

Under the translation $A(-4, 3) \longrightarrow B(6, -12)$ we consider the translation of the x and y
coordinates separately.

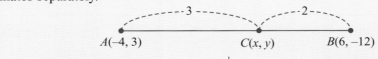

x coordinate	**y coordinate**

$-4 \longrightarrow 6$ $\qquad\qquad$ $3 \longrightarrow -12$

The x coordinate increases by 10 $\qquad$ The y coordinate decreases by 15

$3 + 2 = 5$ parts $\qquad\qquad$ $3 + 2 = 5$ parts

$\therefore 5$ parts $= 10$ $\qquad\qquad$ 5 parts $= -15$

1 part $= 2$ $\qquad\qquad$ 1 part $= -3$

3 parts $= 3(2) = 6$ $\qquad\qquad$ 3 parts $= 3(-3) = -9$

$\therefore -4 \longrightarrow -4 + 6 \longrightarrow 2$ $\qquad$ $\therefore 3 \longrightarrow 3 - 9 \longrightarrow -6$

$\therefore$ the coordinates of C are $(2, -6)$

Exercise 7.3

Copy and complete the following table by dividing the line segment [*AB*] internally in the given ratio.

	A	*B*	Ratio	Coordinates
1.	(3, 1)	(9, 4)	2 : 1	
2.	(−5, 3)	(10, −7)	3 : 2	
3.	(−4, 3)	(12, −5)	1 : 3	
4.	(1, −2)	(−20, 12)	4 : 3	
5.	(−3, −7)	(9, −19)	5 : 1	
6.	(−2, 5)	(14, −19)	5 : 3	

7. $A(-1, 3)$ and $B(6, -11)$ are two points. P is a point on [*AB*] such that $|AP| : |PB| = 3 : 4$. Find the coordinates of P.

8. $P(-2, 5)$ and $Q(1, 3)$ are two points.
   The point R is on [*PQ*], produced such that $|PQ| : |QR| = 1 : 2$. Find the coordinates of R.

9. The point $P(-1, 8)$ divides the line segment [*AB*] internally such that $|AP| : |PB| = 3 : 1$. If the coordinates of A are $(5, -1)$, find the coordinates of B.

10. $A(3, 2)$ and $B(18, 12)$ are two points.
    [*AB*] is produced to C such that $|AC| : |BC| = 7 : 2$. Find the coordinates of C.

11. A is a point on the *x*-axis and B is a point on the *y*-axis.
    P is $(9, -8)$ and P divides [*AB*] internally in the ratio $4 : 3$.
    Find the coordinates of A and B.

12. $A(2h, 3k)$ and $B(12h, -17k)$ are two points. C is a point on [*AB*] such that $|AC| : |CB| = 3 : 2$. Find, in terms of h and k, the coordinates of C.

Concurrencies of a triangle

1. **Centroid *G***

   A **median** of a triangle is a line segment from a vertex to the midpoint of the opposite side. The three medians of a triangle meet at a point called the centroid, *G*.
   G divides each median in the ratio 2 : 1.

   Coordinates of $G = \left(\dfrac{x_1 + x_2 + x_3}{3}, \dfrac{y_1 + y_2 + y_3}{3} \right)$.

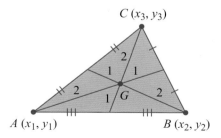

2. **Circumcentre *O***

   The circumcentre of a triangle is the point of intersection of the perpendicular bisectors of the sides.

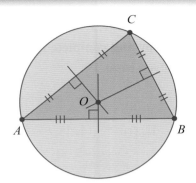

3. **Orthocentre *H***

   An altitude of a triangle is a perpendicular from a vertex to its opposite side. The orthocentre is the point of intersection of the altitudes.

   Note: The centroid, circumcentre and orthocentre in a triangle all lie on a straight line called *Euler's line.*

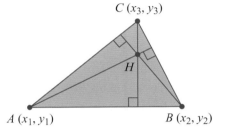

4. **Incentre *C***

   The incentre is the point of intersection of the bisectors of the angles in a triangle. Finding a bisector of an angle (and, hence, the incentre) is not on the coordinate geometry section of the syllabus.

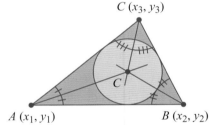

EXAMPLE

$A(-2, 7)$, $B(p, -4)$ and $C(4, q)$ are the coordinates of the vertices of the triangle ABC. If the coordinates of the centroid of triangle ABC are $(-1, 3)$, find the value of p and the value of q.

Solution:

The coordinates of the centroid, (x, y), are given by $\left(\dfrac{x_1 + x_2 + x_3}{3}, \dfrac{y_1 + y_2 + y_3}{3} \right)$.

Thus
$$\frac{x_1 + x_2 + x_3}{3} = x$$
$$\frac{-2 + p + 4}{3} = -1$$
$$\frac{p + 2}{3} = -1$$
$$p + 2 = -3$$
$$p = -5$$

and
$$\frac{y_1 + y_2 + y_3}{3} = y$$
$$\frac{7 - 4 + q}{3} = 3$$
$$\frac{q + 3}{3} = 3$$
$$q + 3 = 9$$
$$q = 6$$

Exercise 7.4

In questions 1–4, find the coordinates of the centroid of the following triangle, whose vertices are given.

1. $(0, -1), (2, -1), (7, 8)$ 2. $(5, -2), (1, 3), (6, 2)$

3. $(4, 3), (3, 5), (-4, -8)$ 4. $(3, -2), (-5, 6), (-4, -1)$

5. $A(2, -3), B(p, 0)$ and $C(-3, q)$ are the coordinates of the vertices of triangle ABC.
   If the coordinates of the centroid of triangle ABC are $(1, 2)$, find the value of p and the value of q.

6. $P(h, k), Q(7, 2)$ and $R(-3, 10)$ are the coordinates of the vertices of the triangle PQR.
   If the coordinates of the centroid of the triangle are $(-7, -13)$, find the value of h and the value of k.

In questions 7–10, find the coordinates of the circumcentre of the triangle, whose vertices are given.

7. $(5, -3), (3, -1), (-1, -5)$ 8. $(-3, -3), (5, 1), (11, -1)$

9. $(4, 6), (-4, -2), (10, 0)$ 10. $(-2, 2), (-4, -2), (5, -5)$

In questions 11–14, find the coordinates of the orthocentre of the triangle, whose vertices are given.

11. $(0, 3), (7, 4), (4, -5)$ 12. $(2, 2), (4, 1), (1, 5)$

13. $(-6, 3), (-2, 5), (1, 4)$ 14. $(3, 15), (10, -2), (-15, 3)$

15. **(i)** $A(-2, 2), B(2, -6)$, and $C(5, 3)$ are the coordinates of the vertices of triangle ABC.
    Find the coordinates of **(a)** the centroid **(b)** the circumcentre **(c)** the orthocentre.

    (ii) Find the equation of the line containing the circumcentre and the orthocentre and show that the centroid is also on this line.

16. In the isosceles triangle PQR, the length of its base, $|PQ|$, is $\frac{2}{3}$ of its height, $|RB|$.

    (i) Find the coordinates of B and the coordinates of R.

    (ii) Write down the equation of BR.

    (iii) Explain why the centroid, circumcentre and the orthocentre must lie on BR.

    (iv) Find the coordinates of

    (a) the centroid **(b)** the circumcentre **(c)** the orthocentre.

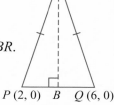

Perpendicular distance from a point to a line

The perpendicular distance, d, from the point (x_1, y_1)
to the line $ax + by + c = 0$ is given by:

$$d = \frac{|ax_1 + by_1 + c_1|}{\sqrt{a^2 + b^2}}$$

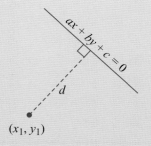

EXAMPLE 1

Find the perpendicular distance from the point $(-2, 4)$ to the line $3x + y - 8 = 0$.

Solution:
Point $(-2, 4)$.   Line $3x + y - 8 = 0$.
$x_1 = -2, y_1 = 4$ $a = 3, b = 1, c = -8$

$$\text{Distance} = \frac{|ax_1 + by_1 + c|}{\sqrt{a^2 + b^2}}$$

$$= \frac{|3(-2) + 1(4) - 8|}{\sqrt{3^2 + 1^2}}$$

$$= \frac{|-6 + 4 - 8|}{\sqrt{9 + 1}}$$

$$= \frac{|-10|}{\sqrt{10}} = \frac{10}{\sqrt{10}} = \sqrt{10}$$

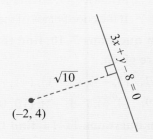

EXAMPLE 2

Find the slopes of the two lines through the point $(-3, 2)$ which are at a distance $2\sqrt{2}$ from the point $(-6, 1)$.

Solution:
We have a point $(-3, 2)$ and we need the slopes.

Equation: $(y - y_1) = m(x - x_1)$
$(y - 2) = m(x + 3)$
$y - 2 = mx + 3m$
$mx - y + (3m + 2) = 0$

Given: The distance from $(-6, 1)$ to this line is $2\sqrt{2}$.

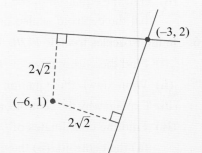

Thus,
$$\frac{|m(-6) - 1(1) + (3m + 2)|}{\sqrt{m^2 + (-1)^2}} = 2\sqrt{2} \qquad \text{(distance formula)}$$

$$\frac{|1 - 3m|}{\sqrt{m^2 + 1}} = 2\sqrt{2}$$

$$\frac{1 - 6m + 9m^2}{m^2 + 1} = 8 \qquad \text{(square both sides)}$$

$$1 - 6m + 9m^2 = 8m^2 + 8 \qquad \text{(multiply both sides by } m^2 + 1\text{)}$$

$$m^2 - 6m - 7 = 0$$

$$(m - 7)(m + 1) = 0$$

$$m = 7 \text{ or } m = -1$$

Distance between parallel lines

To find the distance between two parallel lines, do the following.

1. Find one point on one of the lines.
2. Find the distance from this point to the other line.

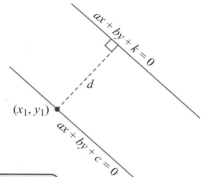

Points on the same side or opposite sides of a line

1. Substitute the coordinates of the points into the equation of the line.
2. Two possibilities arise:

   (a) Same signs, then same side of the line.
   (b) Opposite signs, then opposite sides of the line.

Note: The formula for the perpendicular distance from a point to a line, without the modulus bars, can also be used with the same results as above.

EXAMPLE

Investigate if the points $(101, 34)$ and $(58, 18)$ are on the same side of the line $5x - 13y - 60 = 0$.

Solution:

$(101, 34) : 5(101) - 13(34) - 60 = 505 - 442 - 60 = 3$

$(58, 18) : 5(58) - 13(18) - 60 = 290 - 234 - 60 = -4$

Opposite signs, therefore the points are on opposite sides of the line.

Exercise 7.5

In questions 1–6, find the perpendicular distance from the point P to the line l.

1. $P(1, 3)$; $l : 3x + 4y + 10 = 0$
2. $P(8, 3)$; $l : 5x - 12y + 9 = 0$
3. $P(-1, 3)$; $l : 15x - 8y + 5 = 0$
4. $P(3, 2)$; $l : 24x - 7y - 8 = 0$
5. $P(3, 2)$; $l : 2x - y + 1 = 0$
6. $P(4, 3)$; $l : x + y + 1 = 0$
7. Show that the point $(2, -1)$ is equidistant from the lines with equations $4x + 3y - 20 = 0$ and $12x - 5y + 10 = 0$.
8. Show that the point $(4, -\frac{1}{2})$ is on the line $3x + 4y - 10 = 0$ and hence find the distance between the parallel lines $3x + 4y - 10 = 0$ and $3x + 4y - 15 = 0$.

In questions 9–12, find the distance between each pair of parallel lines, *l* and *k*.

9. $l : 4x - 3y + 10 = 0$ and $k : 4x - 3y + 15 = 0$

10. $l : 5x + 12y - 5 = 0$ and $k : 5x + 12y + 10 = 0$

11. $l : 3x + 4y - 12 = 0$ and $k : 6x + 8y - 9 = 0$

12. $l : 2x + y + 5 = 0$ and $k : 2x + y = 0$

13. A plane is flying as shown in the diagram, where $\theta = \tan^{-1} \frac{4}{3}$.
    Place the plane at the origin and use kilometres as units.

    (i) Find the slope of *f*.
    (ii) Find the equation of *f*, the plane's path.
    (iii) Calculate how close the plane will pass by a tower, *T*, located
    30 km to the east and 45 km north of its current location.

14. A plane is flying toward a circular cloud of volcanic
    ash, as shown in the diagram. *C* is located 53 km east and 96 km
    north of the plane's current location and $\theta = \cos^{-1} \frac{5}{13}$.

    Place the plane at the origin and use kilometres as units.

    (i) Find the slope of *f*.
    (ii) Find the equation of the plane's path.
    (iii) Calculate the shortest distance between the plane and
    C, the centre of the ash cloud.
    (iv) If the radius of the ash cloud is 20 km, find the distance
    travelled within the ash cloud.

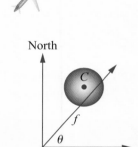

15. Show that the points (100, 72) and (59, 27) lie on opposite sides of the line $x + y - 120 = 0$.

16. Investigate whether the points $(-20, 10)$ and $(35, -40)$ are on the same side of the line
    $3x - 2y + 50 = 0$.

17. Investigate whether the points (30, 16) and $(-19, -11)$ are on the same side of the line
    $10x - 20y - 1 = 0$ as the origin (0, 0).

18. Find the values of *a* if the point (4, 1) is 2 units from the line $ax + 3y - 9 = 0$.

19. Find the values of *k* if the distance from the point $(3, -1)$ to the line $3x + 4y - k = 0$ is 6 units.

20. Find the equations of the two lines parallel to $3x - 4y + 1 = 0$ and 2 units from it.

21. A line, with slope *m*, contains the point $(-2, 1)$. Write its equation in the form $ax + by + c = 0$.
    Hence, find the equations of the two lines through the point $(-2, 1)$ and whose distance
    from the origin is 1 unit.

22. Find the equations of the two lines which contain the point (4, 1) and are a distance of $2\sqrt{2}$
    units from (1, 2).

23. Find the equations of the two lines which are perpendicular to the line $2x + 3y - 6 = 0$ and
    which are a distance of $\sqrt{13}$ units from (3, 2).

Angle between two lines

If two lines, l_1 and l_2, have slopes m_1, and m_2, respectively, and θ is the angle between them, then:

$$\tan \theta = \pm \frac{m_1 - m_2}{1 + m_1 m_2}$$

In practice, the best approach is to find the acute angle θ by using:

$$\tan \theta = \left| \frac{m_1 - m_2}{1 + m_1 m_2} \right|$$

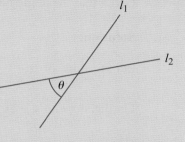

The obtuse angle is obtained by finding $180° - \theta$.

The formula has the variables θ, m_1 and m_2. In the question we are usually given two of these variables and we use the formula to find the third variable.

EXAMPLE 1

Find the measure of the obtuse angle between the lines $3x - 5y + 2 = 0$ and $x + 4y + 5 = 0$.

Solution:

Let θ be the acute angle between the lines.

Let the slope of $3x - 5y + 2 = 0$ be m_1. Thus, $m_1 = -\frac{3}{-5} = \frac{3}{5}$.

Let the slope of $x + 4y + 5 = 0$ be m_1. Thus, $m_2 = -\frac{1}{4}$.

$$\tan \theta = \left| \frac{m_1 - m_2}{1 + m_1 m_2} \right| = \left| \frac{\frac{3}{5} - \left(-\frac{1}{4}\right)}{1 + \left(\frac{3}{5}\right)\left(-\frac{1}{4}\right)} \right| = \left| \frac{\frac{3}{5} + \frac{1}{4}}{1 - \frac{3}{20}} \right| = \left| \frac{\frac{3}{5} + \frac{1}{4}}{1 - \frac{3}{20}} \times \frac{20}{20} \right| = \left| \frac{12 + 5}{20 - 3} \right|$$

$$= \left| \frac{17}{17} \right| = 1$$

$\therefore \theta = \tan^{-1} 1 = 45°$.

Thus, the obtuse angle $= 180° - 45° = 135°$.

EXAMPLE 2

$l : tx - y - 3 = 0$ and $k : x - 2y - 1 = 0$, $t \in \mathbb{R}$ are the equations of two lines.
Given that the angle between l and k is $45°$, find the two possible values of t.

Solution:

Let the slope of $tx - y - 3 = 0$ be m_1. Thus, $m_1 = -\dfrac{t}{-1} = t$.

Let the slope of $x - 2y - 1 = 0$ be m_2. Thus, $m_2 = -\dfrac{1}{-2} = \dfrac{1}{2}$.

$$\tan \theta = \left| \frac{m_1 - m_2}{1 + m_1 m_2} \right|$$

$$\tan 45° = \left| \frac{t - \frac{1}{2}}{1 + (t)\left(\frac{1}{2}\right)} \right|$$

$$1 = \left| \frac{t - \frac{1}{2}}{1 + \frac{1}{2}t} \right|$$

$$1 = \left| \frac{2t - 1}{2 + t} \right|$$

Taking the positive and negative separately:

$$\frac{2t - 1}{2 + t} = 1 \qquad \text{or} \qquad \frac{2t - 1}{2 + t} = -1$$

$2t - 1 = 2 + t$ or $2t - 1 = -2 - t$

$t = 3$ or $3t = -1$

$t = 3$ or $t = -\dfrac{1}{3}$

Exercise 7.6

In questions 1–4, find, to the nearest degree, the measures of the angles between the given lines.

1. $2x - y - 3 = 0$ and $x - 3y + 2 = 0$ 2. $5x - 2y - 1 = 0$ and $x - 2y + 4 = 0$

3. $x + y - 5 = 0$ and $2x + y + 3 = 0$ 4. $3x + 2y - 6 = 0$ and $4x - 3y + 8 = 0$

5. If θ is the acute angle between the lines $x + y - 3 = 0$ and $2x - y + 6 = 0$, find the value of $\tan \theta$.

6. Find the measure of the acute angle between the lines $2x - y + 3 = 0$ and $3x + y - 6 = 0$.

7. Find the measure of the obtuse angle between the lines $3x - y + 2 = 0$ and $x - 2y + 1 = 0$.

8. $P(2, 3)$, $Q(4, -3)$ and $R(6, 1)$ are three points. Find the acute angle between the lines PQ and PR.

9. Show that the line $6x - 2y + 5 = 0$ makes the same angle with each of the lines $2x - 4y - 1 = 0$ and $2x + y + 3 = 0$.

10.   (i) A line, with slope m, contains the point $(2, 3)$. Write its equation in the form $ax + by + c = 0$.

    (ii) Find the equations of the lines through the point $(2, 3)$ which make angles of $45°$ with $x - 2y - 1 = 0$.

11. Find the equations of the lines through the point (4, 3) which make an angle of 45° with $6x + y - 5 = 0$.

12. (i) Write down the measure of the acute angle between the lines $\sqrt{3}x + y + 5 = 0$ and $x - \sqrt{3}y - 2 = 0$.

   (ii) Find the measure of the acute angle between the lines $\sqrt{3}x + y + 5 = 0$ and $x + \sqrt{3}y - 2 = 0$.

   (iii) Find the measure of the acute angle between the lines $ax - by + c = 0$ and $(b - a)x + (a + b)y + d = 0$.

13. A line l, with slope m, contains the point (0, 1).
k is the line $2x - y + 3 = 0$ and θ is the acute angle between l and k.
If $\sin \theta = \frac{3}{5}$, find the two possible equations for l.

14. $P(2, 6)$ and $R(4, 0)$ are two vertices of a square $PQRS$, where $[PR]$ is a diagonal.

   (i) Find the slope of PR.

   (ii) Write down the acute angle between PQ and PR.

   (iii) Find the slope of PQ and PS.

   (iv) Find the coordinates of Q and S.

15. The line l has slop $= m$.
The line k has slope $= 3$.
The acute angle between the lines is given by $\theta = \tan^{-1}\left(\frac{1}{2}\right)$.
Find the values of m.

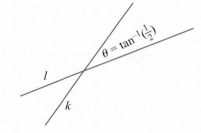

16. A long ladder is placed on level ground 10 m from the base of a vertical building. When the ladder has a slope of $\frac{4}{5}$ it can reach window W_1, while at a slope of $\frac{8}{5}$ it can reach window W_3.

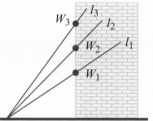

   (i) How high are W_1 and W_3 above the ground?

   (ii) Using the base of the ladder as the origin and metres as units, find the equations of l_1 and l_3.

   (iii) If the slope of l_2 is the average of the slopes of l_1 and l_3, will W_2 be the midpoint (average) of W_1 and W_3?

   (iv) Find the equation of l_2 and investigate whether it is the average of the equations of l_1 and l_3.

   (v) Find the angles of the three ladder positions and investigate whether the angle of l_2 is the average of the angles of l_1 and l_3.

COORDINATE GEOMETRY OF THE CIRCLE

Equation of a circle, centre (0, 0) and radius r

A circle is a set of points (a locus), each of which is equidistant from a fixed point called the **centre**.

The distance from the centre to any point on the circle is called the **radius**.

The diagram shows a circle with centre (0, 0), radius r and (x, y) is any point on the circle.

The distance between (0, 0) and (x, y) equals the radius, r.

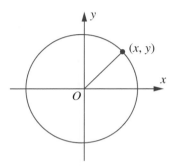

$$\therefore \sqrt{(x-0)^2 + (y-0)^2} = r \qquad \text{(distance formula)}$$
$$\sqrt{x^2 + y^2} = r$$
$$x^2 + y^2 = r^2 \qquad \text{(square both sides)}$$

Hence, $x^2 + y^2 = r^2$ is said to be the equation of the circle.

> Equation of a circle, centre (0, 0) and radius r, is
> $x^2 + y^2 = r^2$.

Two quantities are needed to find the equation of a circle:

> **1.** Centre   **2.** Radius
> If the centre is (0, 0), the equation of the circle will be of the form $x^2 + y^2 = r^2$.

EXAMPLE 1

Find the equation of the circle k, with centre (0, 0), which has a radius of $\sqrt{13}$.

Solution:
Centre is (0, 0), therefore k is of the form $x^2 + y^2 = r^2$.
Substitute $r = \sqrt{13}$ into this equation:
$$x^2 + y^2 = (\sqrt{13})^2$$
$$x^2 + y^2 = 13$$
Thus, the equation of the circle k is $x^2 + y^2 = 13$.

EXAMPLE 2

Find the equation of the circle c whose centre is $(0, 0)$ and which contains the point $(4, -1)$.

Solution:

Method 1:

Centre $(0, 0)$, therefore c is of the form $x^2 + y^2 = r^2$.

$$x^2 + y^2 = r^2$$
$$4^2 + (-1)^2 = r^2$$
$$16 + 1 = r^2 \Rightarrow r^2 = 17$$

Thus, the equation of the circle c is $x^2 + y^2 = 17$.

Method 2:

The radius is the distance from the centre $(0, 0)$ to $(4, -1)$.

Using the distance formula:

$$r = \sqrt{(4 - 0)^2 + (-1 - 0)^2} = \sqrt{16 + 1} = \sqrt{17}$$

Thus, the equation of the circle c is $x^2 + y^2 = 17$.

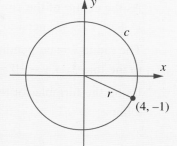

EXAMPLE 3

Find the radius of each of the following circles.　　(i) $x^2 + y^2 = 8$　　(ii) $4x^2 + 4y^2 = 25$

Solution:

Compare each to $x^2 + y^2 = r^2$.

(i) $x^2 + y^2 = 8$

$$x^2 + y^2 = r^2$$
$$r^2 = 8$$
$$r = \sqrt{8} \text{ or } 2\sqrt{2}$$

(ii) $4x^2 + 4y^2 = 25$

$$x^2 + y^2 = \frac{25}{4}$$
$$r^2 = \frac{25}{4}$$
$$r = \sqrt{\frac{25}{4}} = \frac{5}{2}$$

EXAMPLE 4

The diagram shows a tangent $3x + y - 10 = 0$ to the circle k.
Find the equation of k.

Solution:

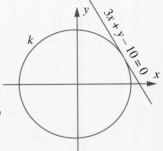

As the centre of the circle k is $(0, 0)$, its equation is of the form
$x^2 + y^2 = r^2$. We need to find the value of r.

The radius r = perpendicular distance from the centre $(0, 0)$
to the line $3x + y - 10 = 0$.

Using the formula for the perpendicular distance from a point to
a line:

$$d = \frac{|ax_1 + by_1 + c|}{\sqrt{a^2 + b^2}}$$

$$r = \frac{|3(0) + 1(0) - 10|}{\sqrt{3^2 + 1^2}} \qquad (a = 3, b = 1, c = -10, x = 0, y = 0)$$

$$= \frac{|-10|}{\sqrt{10}} = \frac{10}{\sqrt{10}} = \sqrt{10}$$

$$\therefore r^2 = (\sqrt{10})^2 = 10$$

Thus, the equation of the circle k is $x^2 + y^2 = 10$.

Exercise 8.1

In questions 1–14, find the equation of the circle of centre $(0, 0)$ and:

1. Radius 2
2. Radius 3
3. Radius 5
4. Radius $\sqrt{13}$
5. Radius $\sqrt{5}$
6. Radius $2\sqrt{3}$
7. Radius $\frac{1}{2}$
8. Radius $\frac{\sqrt{10}}{2}$
9. Containing the point $(3, 4)$
10. Containing the point $(-5, 12)$
11. Containing the point $(1, -5)$
12. Containing the point $(0, -3)$
13. Containing the point $(-1, 1)$
14. Containing the point $(2, -5)$

In questions 15–23, write down the radius length of the circle.

15. $x^2 + y^2 = 16$
16. $x^2 + y^2 = 100$
17. $x^2 + y^2 = 1$
18. $x^2 + y^2 = 13$
19. $x^2 + y^2 = 5$
20. $x^2 + y^2 = 29$
21. $4x^2 + 4y^2 = 9$
22. $9x^2 + 9y^2 = 25$
23. $16x^2 + 16y^2 = 1$

24. Find the equation of the circle which has the line segment joining $(3, -4)$ to $(-3, 4)$ as a diameter.

25. $A(6, 1)$ and $B(-6, -1)$ are two points. Find the equation of the circle with $[AB]$ as a diameter.

26. $(6, -3)$ is an extremity of a diameter of the circle $x^2 + y^2 = 45$. What are the coordinates of the other extremity of the same diameter?

27. What is the area of the circle $x^2 + y^2 = 40$? Leave your answer in terms of π.

In questions 28–33, find the equation of the circle, centre $(0, 0)$, and having the given line as a tangent.

28. $2x + y + 5 = 0$

29. $4x + y - 17 = 0$

30. $x + 3y + 10 = 0$

31. $5x - y - 26 = 0$

32. $x - y - 4 = 0$

33. $x + 2y - 10 = 0$

General equation of a circle, centre (h, k) and radius r

On the right is a circle with centre (h, k), radius r and (x, y) is any point on the circle.

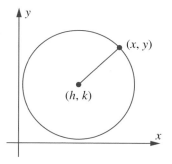

Distance between (h, k) and (x, y) equals the radius, r.

$$\therefore \sqrt{(x - h)^2 + (y - k)^2} = r \quad \text{(distance formula)}$$
$$(x - h)^2 + (y - k)^2 = r^2 \quad \text{(square both sides)}$$

Hence, $(x - h)^2 + (y - k)^2 = r^2$ is said to be the equation of the circle.

> The equation of a circle, centre (h, k) and radius r, is
> $(x - h)^2 + (y - k)^2 = r^2$.

Two quantities are needed to find the equation of a circle:

> 1. Centre, (h, k) 2. Radius, r
> Then use the formula $(x - h)^2 + (y - k)^2 = r^2$.

Note: If $(h, k) = (0, 0)$, the equation $(x - h)^2 + (y - k)^2 = r^2$ is reduced to $x^2 + y^2 = r^2$.

EXAMPLE 1

(i) Find the centre and radius of the circle $(x - 2)^2 + (y + 5)^2 = 9$.

(ii) Find the equation of the circle with a centre of $(1, -4)$ and a radius of $\sqrt{13}$.

Solution:

(i) $(x - 2)^2 + (y + 5)^2 = 9$

Compare exactly to:

$(x - h)^2 + (y - k)^2 = r^2$

$\downarrow \qquad \downarrow \qquad \downarrow$

$(x - 2)^2 + (y + 5)^2 = 9$

$\therefore h = 2, k = -5, r = 3$

Thus, centre $= (2, -5)$ and radius $= \sqrt{13}$.

(ii) Centre $(1, -4)$, radius $\sqrt{13}$

$h = 1, k = -4, r = \sqrt{13}$

Equation of the circle is:

$(x - h)^2 + (y - k)^2 = r^2$

$(x - 1)^2 + (y + 4)^2 = (\sqrt{13})^2$

$(x - 1)^2 + (y + 4)^2 = 13$

EXAMPLE 2

Find the equation of the circle that has the line segment from $A(-4, 1)$ to $B(2, 3)$ as a diameter.

Solution:

The **centre** and **radius** are needed.

The diagram on the right illustrates the situation.

Centre

The centre is the midpoint of $[AB]$.

$\text{Centre} = \left(\dfrac{-4 + 2}{2}, \dfrac{1 + 3}{2} \right) = \left(\dfrac{-2}{2}, \dfrac{4}{2} \right)$

$= (-1, 2) = (h, k)$

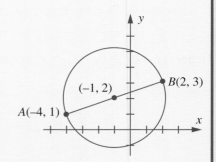

Radius

The radius is the distance from the centre $(-1, 2)$ to either $(-4, 1)$ or $(2, 3)$.

Distance from $(-1, 2)$ to $(2, 3)$:

$r = \sqrt{(2 + 1)^2 + (3 - 2)^2} = \sqrt{3^2 + 1^2} = \sqrt{9 + 1} = \sqrt{10}$

$h = -1, k = 2, r = \sqrt{10}$

Equation is $(x - h)^2 + (y - k)^2 = r^2$

$(x + 1)^2 + (y - 2)^2 = (\sqrt{10})^2$

$(x + 1)^2 + (y - 2)^2 = 10$

Exercise 8.2

In questions 1–10, find the equation of each circle with the given centre and radius.

1. Centre (2, 3) and radius 4
2. Centre (1, 4) and radius 5
3. Centre (2, −1) and radius 2
4. Centre (−5, 2) and radius 1
5. Centre (−4, −3) and radius $\sqrt{17}$
6. Centre (−3, 0) and radius $\sqrt{13}$
7. Centre (0, 2) and radius $\sqrt{5}$
8. Centre (−2, −6) and radius $\sqrt{29}$
9. Centre (−1, −1) and radius $\sqrt{10}$
10. Centre (−4, 2) and radius $\sqrt{12}$

In questions 11–16, find the equation of the circle with the following.

11. Centre (1, 2) and containing the point (2, 5)
12. Centre (2, −1) and containing the point (6, 4)
13. Centre (4, −3) and containing the point (0, 5)
14. Centre (−2, −5) and containing the point (3, 0)
15. Centre (1, −1) and containing the point (2, 4)
16. Centre (−4, −2) and containing the point (0, 0)

In questions 17–26, find the centre and radius of the circle.

17. $(x - 3)^2 + (y - 2)^2 = 16$
18. $(x + 4)^2 + (y + 5)^2 = 9$
19. $(x - 1)^2 + (y + 3)^2 = 25$
20. $(x - 3)^2 + (y - 5)^2 = 4$
21. $(x - 2)^2 + (y - 2)^2 = 49$
22. $(x - 8)^2 + (y - 7)^2 = 1$
23. $(x - 5)^2 + (y + 2)^2 = 20$
24. $(x - 1)^2 + (y + 5)^2 = 32$
25. $x^2 + (y - 2)^2 = 64$
26. $(x - 3)^2 + y^2 = 4$

27. $A(5, 2)$ and $B(1, 4)$ are two points. Find the equation of the circle with [AB] as a diameter.

28. The end points of a diameter of a circle are $P(2, 4)$ and $G(−4, 0)$. Find the equation of the circle.

29. $A(−1, 5)$, $B(5, 13)$ and $C(−2, 12)$ are the vertices of triangle ABC.

    (i) Show that the triangle is right-angled at C.
    (ii) Find the equation of the circle that passes through the points A, B and C.

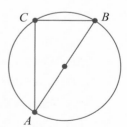

30. Find the equation of the circle with centre (1, 3) and having $3x + 4y + 10 = 0$ as a tangent.

31. Find the equation of the circle with centre (−6, 1) and having $x + y + 1 = 0$ as a tangent.

32. A manufacturer uses the following symbol for its products.

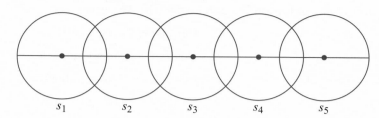

If the equation of s_1 is $x^2 + y^2 = 16$ and the equation of s_3 is $(x - 12)^2 + y^2 = 16$, find the equations of s_2, s_4 and s_5.

33. The circles $c_1 : x^2 + y^2 = 32$ and $c_2 : (x - 3)^2 + (y - 3)^2 = 1$ touch at the point $P(4, 4)$.

    (i) Write down the centre of c_1.

    (ii) Write down the centre of c_2.

    (iii) Find the equation of the line containing the two centre points.

    (iv) Show that the point of contact, P, is also on this line.

34. This pattern is being used on a tile. The equation of the middle circle is $x^2 + y^2 = 25$.

    (i) Write down the centre and radius length of the middle circle.

    (ii) Write down the coordinates of the point A.

    (iii) Write down the coordinates of the point B.

    (iv) Find the equations of the other circles.

35. A set of circles with a common point of contact $(0, 0)$ is shown. The radius of s_1 is 4 units and its centre is $A(4, 0)$.

$$|AB| = |BC| = |CD| = |DE|.$$

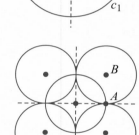

    (i) Find the equation of the circle s_1.

    (ii) Write down the coordinates of the point B.

    (iii) Write down the coordinates of the point C.

    (iv) What is the length of the diameter of the circle s_2?

    (v) What is the centre of s_2?

    (vi) Find the equation of s_2.

    (vii) Show that B is the centre of s_3.

  (viii) By finding the length of the diameter of s_4 or otherwise, find the equation of s_4.

General equation of a circle

The general equation of a circle is written as:

$$x^2 + y^2 + 2gx + 2fy + c = 0$$

When the equation of a circle is given in this form, we use the following method to find its centre and radius.

1. Make sure every term is on the left-hand side and the coefficients of x^2 and y^2 are equal to 1.
2. Centre $= (-g, -f) = (-\frac{1}{2}$ coefficient of x, $-\frac{1}{2}$ coefficient of y).
3. Radius $= \sqrt{g^2 + f^2 - c}$ (provided $g^2 + f^2 - c > 0$).

Notes: 1. The equation is of the second degree (highest power is 2).
2. The coefficients of x^2 and y^2 are equal.
3. There is no xy term.

EXAMPLE 1

Find the centre and radius of each of the following circles.

(i) $x^2 + y^2 - 4x + 2y - 11 = 0$ (ii) $x^2 + y^2 - 8y + 3 = 0$

Solution:

(i) $x^2 + y^2 - 4x + 2y - 11 = 0$
Centre $= (2, -1)$
Radius $= \sqrt{(2)^2 + (-1)^2 + 11}$
$= \sqrt{4 + 1 + 11} = \sqrt{16} = 4$

(ii) $x^2 + y^2 + 0x - 8y + 3 = 0$ (put in $0x$)
Centre $= (0, 4)$
Radius $= \sqrt{(0)^2 + (4)^2 - 3}$
$= \sqrt{0 + 16 - 3} = \sqrt{13}$

EXAMPLE 2

The equation of a circle with radius 5 is $x^2 + y^2 - 6x + 4ky + 20 = 0$, $k \in \mathbb{Z}$.

(i) Find the centre of the circle and the radius length in terms of k.
(ii) Find the values of k.

Solution:

(i) $x^2 + y^2 - 6x + 4ky + 20 = 0$
Centre $= (3, -2k)$
Radius $= \sqrt{(3)^2 + (-2k)^2 - 20}$
$= \sqrt{4k^2 - 11}$

(ii) Given: Radius $= 5$
$\therefore \sqrt{4k^2 - 11} = 5$
$4k^2 - 11 = 25$
$4k^2 = 36$
$k^2 = 9$
$k = \pm 3$

Points inside, on or outside a circle

Method 1:

To find whether a point is inside, on or outside a circle, calculate the distance from the centre, $(0, 0)$, to the point and compare this distance with the radius. Three cases arise.

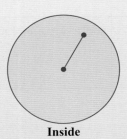

Inside

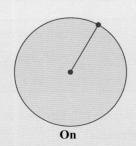

On

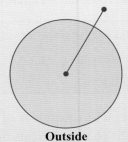

Outside

1. Distance from the centre to the point is **less** than the radius.

   ∴ Point is inside the circle.

2. Distance from the centre to the point is **equal** to the radius.

   ∴ Point is on the circle.

3. Distance from the centre to the point is **greater** than the radius.

   ∴ Point is outside the circle.

Method 2:

The equation of a circle can be of the form:

$$x^2 + y^2 = r^2$$
$$(x - h)^2 + (y - k)^2 = r^2$$
$$x^2 + y^2 + 2gx + 2fy + c = 0$$

If the coordinates of a point satisfy the equation of a circle, then the point is **on** the circle. Otherwise, the point is either **inside** or **outside** the circle. By substituting the coordinates into the equation of the circle, one of the following situations can arise.

1. LHS < RHS: the point is **inside** the circle.
2. LHS = RHS: the point is **on** the circle.
3. LHS > RHS: the point is **outside** the circle.

EXAMPLE

Determine whether the points $(-3, -2)$, $(5, -1)$ and $(-2, 1)$ are inside, on or outside the circle $x^2 + y^2 - 2x + 8y - 8 = 0$.

Solution:

Using Method 2:

$$x^2 + y^2 - 2x + 8y - 8 = 0$$

Substitute $(-3, -2)$: $(-3)^2 + (-2)^2 - 2(-3) + 8(-2) - 8 = 9 + 4 + 6 - 16 - 8 = -5 < 0$

∴ $(-3, -2)$ is inside the circle.

Substitute $(5, -1)$: $(5)^2 + (-1)^2 - 2(5) + 8(-1) - 8 = 25 + 1 - 10 - 8 - 8 = 0$

∴ $(5, -1)$ is on the circle.

Substitute $(-2, 1)$: $(-2)^2 + (1)^2 - 2(-2) + 8(1) - 8 = 4 + 1 + 4 + 8 - 8 = 9 > 0$

∴ $(-2, 1)$ is outside the circle.

Exercise 8.3

In questions 1–6, find the equation of the circle with the given centre and radius, writing your answer in the form $x^2 + y^2 + 2gx + 2fy + c = 0$.

1. Centre $(1, 2)$ and radius 3
2. Centre $(-2, 3)$ and radius 5
3. Centre $(-3, -5)$ and radius $\sqrt{17}$
4. Centre $(2, 0)$ and radius $\sqrt{10}$
5. Centre $(0, -3)$ and radius $2\sqrt{2}$
6. Centre $(\frac{1}{2}, -\frac{1}{2})$ and radius $\sqrt{5}$
7. A circle with centre $(-1, 3)$ passes through the point $(1, -1)$. Find the equation of the circle.
8. A circle with centre $(-3, -2)$ passes through the point $(1, 1)$. Find the equation of the circle.

In questions 9–20, find the centre and radius length of the circle.

9. $x^2 + y^2 - 6x - 8y - 11 = 0$
10. $x^2 + y^2 - 4x - 6y - 3 = 0$
11. $x^2 + y^2 - 2x + 4y - 4 = 0$
12. $x^2 + y^2 - 10x + 2y + 6 = 0$
13. $x^2 + y^2 + 8x - 6y = 0$
14. $x^2 + y^2 + 2x - 10y - 10 = 0$
15. $x^2 + y^2 + 6x - 7 = 0$
16. $x^2 + y^2 = 4y + 4$
17. $2x^2 + 2y^2 - 2x - 6y - 13 = 0$
18. $9x^2 + 9y^2 - 6x + 54y + 46 = 0$
19. $(x - 2)(x + 4) + (y - 1)(y - 5) = 3$
20. $(x - 3)(x + 3) + (y + 2)(y + 6) = 0$

In questions 21–26, determine whether the given point is inside, on or outside the given circle.

21. $(3, -2)$; $x^2 + y^2 = 13$
22. $(5, 3)$; $(x - 3)^2 + (y - 2)^2 = 20$
23. $(4, -1)$; $x^2 + y^2 + 6x - 4y - 3 = 0$
24. $(-1, 5)$; $x^2 + y^2 + 4x - 6y - 25 = 0$

25. $(4, 3);$ $x^2 + y^2 - 4x + 2y - 15 = 0$

26. $(-1, 4);$ $x^2 + y^2 + 10x - 6y + 21 = 0$

27. The circle c has the equation $x^2 + y^2 + 2x + 2y - 32 = 0$.
    The point $(-4, k)$ lies on c. Find the two real values of k.

28. The circle s has the equation $(x - 4)^2 + (y - 2)^2 = 13$.
    The point $(p, 0)$ lies on s. Find the two real values of p.

29. The equation of a circle with radius length 4 is $x^2 + y^2 - 6x + 2y + k = 0$, $k \in \mathbb{Z}$. Find the value of k.

30. The equation of a circle with radius length 6 is $x^2 + y^2 - 2kx + 4y - 7 = 0$, $k \in \mathbb{Z}$.

    (i) Find the centre of the circle and the radius length in terms of k.

    (ii) Find the values of k.

31. The equation of a circle with radius length 5 is $x^2 + y^2 + 2x - 4ty + 12 = 0$, $t \in \mathbb{Z}$. Find the values of t.

32. $A(k, 1)$ and $B(-7, -k)$ are end points of a diameter of circle c.
    If the centre of c is $(2, -5)$, find the value of k and the radius length of c.

33. $A(-2, 0)$ and $B(6, 2)$ are points of a circle of centre $C(2k, k)$.

    (i) Express the following in terms of k. (a) $|AC|^2$ (b) $|BC|^2$

    (ii) Find the value of k and the equation of the circle.

Intersection of a line and a circle

To find the points where a line and a circle meet, the **method of substitution** between their equations is used.

The method involves the following three steps.

1. Get x or y on its own from the equation of the line.
    (Look carefully and select the variable that will make the working easier.)
2. Substitute for this same variable into the equation of the circle and solve the resultant quadratic equation.
3. Substitute **separately** the value(s) obtained in step 2 into the linear equation in step 1 to find the corresponding value(s) of the other variable.

Note: If there is only **one point of intersection** between a line and a circle, then the line is a **tangent** to the circle.

EXAMPLE 1

The equation of a circle is $x^2 + y^2 + 4x - 2y - 5 = 0$.

The line $x - 2y - 1 = 0$ intersects the circle at the points P and Q.

Find the coordinates of P and the coordinates of Q.

Solution:

1. Get x or y on its own from the line:
$$x - 2y - 1 = 0$$
$$x = 2y + 1 \qquad \text{(x on its own)}$$

2. Substitute $(2y + 1)$ for x into the equation of the circle:

$$x^2 \quad + y^2 + 4x \quad - 2y - 5 = 0$$

$$(2y + 1)^2 + y^2 + 4(2y + 1) - 2y - 5 = 0 \qquad \text{(put in $(2y + 1)$ for x)}$$
$$4y^2 + 4y + 1 + y^2 + 8y + 4 - 2y - 5 = 0$$
$$5y^2 + 10y = 0$$
$$y^2 + 2y = 0 \qquad \text{(divide both sides by 5)}$$
$$y(y + 2) = 0$$
$$\therefore y = 0 \text{ or } y = -2$$

3. Substitute, separately, $y = 0$ and $y = -2$ into the equation of the line in step 1 to find the x coordinates:

$y = 0$	$y = -2$
$x = 2y + 1$	$x = 2y + 1$
$\quad = 2(0) + 1$	$\quad = 2(-2) + 1$
$x = 1$	$x = -3$

The point is $(1, 0)$. | The point is $(-3, -2)$.

Thus, the coordinates of the points of intersection are $P(-3, -2)$ and $Q(1, 0)$.

The diagram on the right illustrates the situation.

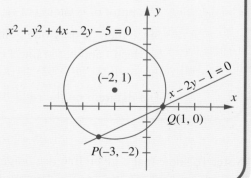

137

EXAMPLE 2

$l : 3x - y + 8 = 0$ is a line and $c : x^2 + y^2 - 4x - 8y + 10 = 0$ is a circle.
Verify that l is a tangent to c and find the point of contact.

Solution:

As we need the point of contact, we use an algebraic approach.

1. Get x or y on its own from the line:

$$3x - y + 8 = 0$$
$$- y = -3x - 8$$
$$y = 3x + 8 \qquad \text{(y on its own)}$$

2. Substitute $(3x + 8)$ for y into the equation of the circle:

$$x^2 + y^2 \quad -4x - 8y \qquad +10 = 0$$

$$x^2 + (3x + 8)^2 - 4x - 8(3x + 8) + 10 = 0 \qquad \text{(put in $(3x + 8)$ for y)}$$
$$x^2 + 9x^2 + 48x + 64 - 4x - 24x - 64 + 10 = 0$$
$$10x^2 + 20x + 10 = 0$$
$$x^2 + 2x + 1 = 0 \qquad \text{(divide both sides by 10)}$$
$$(x + 1)(x + 1) = 0$$
$$\therefore x = -1 \text{ (twice)}$$

3. Substitute $x = -1$ into the equation of the line in step 1 to find the y coordinate:

$$x = -1$$
$$y = 3x + 8$$
$$= 3(-1) + 8$$
$$= -3 + 8$$
$$y = 5$$

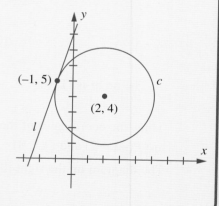

The point of contact is $(-1, 5)$.

Since there is only one point of contact, $(-1, 5)$, between l and c, the line l is a tangent to the circle c.

The diagram on the right illustrates the situation.

Note: To show that a given line is a tangent to a circle, it is sufficient to show that the perpendicular distance from the centre of the circle to the line is equal to the radius. However, to find the point of contact, an algebraic method (as shown above) is required.

Exercise 8.4

In questions 1–12, find the coordinates of the point(s) of intersection of the given line and circle. State whether or not the line is a tangent to the circle.

1. $x - 3y = 0$; $\qquad$ $x^2 + y^2 = 10$

2. $x + 2y - 5 = 0$; $\qquad$ $x^2 + y^2 = 10$

3. $x + 3y - 5 = 0$; $\qquad$ $x^2 + y^2 = 5$

4. $4x - y - 17 = 0$; $\qquad$ $x^2 + y^2 = 17$

5. $x - y - 1 = 0$; $\qquad$ $x^2 + y^2 - 2x - 2y + 1 = 0$

6. $x - 2y - 1 = 0$; $\qquad$ $x^2 + y^2 + 2x - 8y - 8 = 0$

7. $2x - y + 8 = 0$; $\qquad$ $x^2 + y^2 + 4x + 2y = 0$

8. $x - 3y + 5 = 0$; $\qquad$ $x^2 + y^2 - 6x - 2y - 15 = 0$

9. $x + 2y - 7 = 0$; $\qquad$ $x^2 + y^2 - 2x + 4y - 15 = 0$

10. $x - 4y - 6 = 0$; $\qquad$ $x^2 + y^2 + 6x - 4y - 4 = 0$

11. $5x - 3y - 17 = 0$; $\quad$ $x^2 + y^2 = 17$

12. $3x + 2y - 20 = 0$; $\quad$ $x^2 + y^2 - 6x + 2y - 3 = 0$

13. The line $x - 2y - 3 = 0$ intersects the circle $(x - 2)^2 + (y + 3)^2 = 25$ at P and Q. Calculate $|PQ|$.

14. The equation of a circle is $(x - 2)^2 + (y - 1)^2 = 10$.

    The line $x - 3y + 1 = 0$ intersects the circle at points A and B.

    (i) Find the coordinates of A and the coordinates of B.

    (ii) Investigate whether $[AB]$ is a diameter of the circle.

15. A plane is travelling along the line $x - y = -10$.
    Ahead lies a large cloud of ash from a volcanic eruption
    that can be represented by the circle $x^2 + y^2 = 52$.

    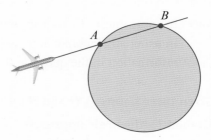

    Note: Each unit represents 1 kilometre.

    (i) What is the centre and radius of the cloud?

    (ii) Find the coordinates of the points A and B.

    (iii) If it is considered unsafe to travel more than 10 km through such an ash cloud, should the plane alter its course?

    (iv) Find the midpoint, C, of $[AB]$.

    (v) The point C is the nearest point on the plane's path to the centre of the cloud. If it is considered unsafe to travel further than 1 km inward from the edge of the cloud, should the plane alter its course?

16. As part of the opening ceremony of a sports event, an archer will fire a lit arrow at a balloon of gas, causing it to burst into flames.

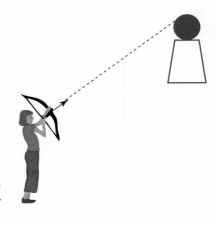

The arrow must **pass through** the balloon. If it misses, the effect will fail entirely, while if the arrow only nicks the balloon, it is unlikely that the gas will ignite despite bursting the balloon.

(i) If the balloon can be represented by the equation $x^2 + y^2 = 10$ and the path of the arrow by $x - y + 4 = 0$, how could you confirm mathematically that the arrow will burst the balloon?

(ii) Will the plan work? Show all your calculations.

Finding the equation of a circle

If the centre and radius are given, or can be found, then using the formula
$$(x - h)^2 + (y - k)^2 = r^2$$
is the preferred method for finding the equation of a circle.

However, for many questions it is difficult to find the centre and radius.
In these questions we have to use an algebraic approach or rely on our knowledge of the geometry of a circle to find the centre and radius.

Note: In some questions we can only use an algebraic approach.
In using an algebraic approach, we let the circle be $x^2 + y^2 + 2gx + 2fy + c = 0$ and use the information in the question to find g, f and c.

Given three points P, Q and R on the circle

Method 1: Algebraic approach

Let the equation of the circle be $x^2 + y^2 + 2gx + 2fy + c = 0$.

1. Substitute each point into this equation.

2. This gives three equations in three unknowns: g, f and c.

3. Solve these equations for g, f and c.

4. Put these values back into the equation.

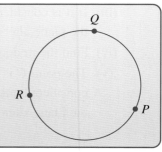

Method 2: Geometric approach

1. Find the equations of the perpendicular bisectors b_1 and b_2 of the chords $[PQ]$ and $[QR]$, respectively.
   (The perpendicular bisector of a chord passes through the centre.)

2. The centre of the circle is the point of intersection of b_1 and b_2 $(b_1 \cap b_2) = \{C\}$.
   (Solve the equations of b_1 and b_2 simultaneously.)

3. The radius is the distance from C to P, Q or R.

4. Use the formula $(x - h)^2 + (y - k)^2 = r^2$.

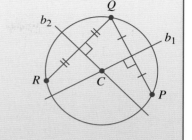

Note: There is only one circle that contains the points P, Q and R.

EXAMPLE

Points $P(-4, 2)$, $Q(-2, 6)$ and $R(4, 8)$ are on a circle s. Find the equation of s.

Solution:

Method 1: Algebraic approach

We are given three points on the circumference of the circle.

Let the equation of the circle be $x^2 + y^2 + 2gx + 2fy + c = 0$.

We need the value of g, f and c.

$(-4, 2)$ on the circle: $(-4)^2 + (2)^2 + 2g(-4) + 2f(2) + c = 0 \Rightarrow 8g - 4f - c = 20$ ①

$(-2, 6)$ on the circle: $(-2)^2 + (6)^2 + 2g(-2) + 2f(6) + c = 0 \Rightarrow 4g - 12f - c = 40$ ②

$(4, 8)$ on the circle: $(4)^2 + (8)^2 + 2g(4) + 2f(8) + c = 0 \Rightarrow 8g + 16f + c = -80$ ③

We now solve between the simultaneous equations ①, ② and ③.

Eliminate c from two different pairs of equations:

$8g - 4f - c = 20$	①		$4g - 12f - c = 40$	②
$8g + 16f + c = -80$	③		$8g + 16f + c = -80$	③
$16g + 12f = -60$	(add)		$12g + 4f = -40$	(add)
$4g + 3f = -15$	④		$3g + f = -10$	⑤

Now solve between ④ and ⑤ to find the values of g and f.

		Put $g = -3$ into ④ or ⑤.
$4g + 3f = -15$	④	$3g + f = -10$ ⑤
$-9g - 3f = 30$	⑤ × -3	$3(-3) + f = -10$
$-5g = 15$	(add)	$-9 + f = -10$
$5g = -15$		$f = -1$
$g = -3$		

Put $g = -3$ and $f = -1$ into ①, ② or ③ to find the value of c.

$$8g - 4f - c = 20 \quad ①$$
$$8(-3) - 4(-1) - c = 20$$
$$-24 + 4 - c = 20$$
$$-20 - c = 20$$
$$-c = 40$$
$$c = -40$$

Put in $g = -3$, $f = -1$ and $c = -10$ to find s.
The equation of the circle s is:
$$x^2 + y^2 + 2gx + 2fy + c = 0$$
$$x^2 + y^2 + 2(-3)x + 2(-1)y - 40 = 0$$
$$x^2 + y^2 - 6x - 2y - 40 = 0$$

Method 2: Geometric approach

The diagram on the right represents the situation.

We find the equation of b_1, the perpendicular bisector of $[PQ]$, and then the equation of b_2, the perpendicular bisector of $[QR]$.

The centre, C, is the point of intersection of b_1 and b_2.

The radius is $|PC|$, $|QC|$ or $|RC|$.

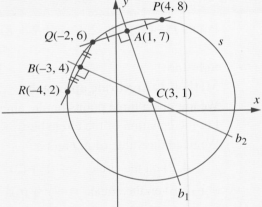

Slope of $PQ = \dfrac{8 - 6}{4 - (-2)} = \dfrac{2}{6} = \dfrac{1}{3}$

$\therefore$ Slope of $b_1 = -3$.

Midpoint of $[PQ] = \left(\dfrac{4 - 2}{2}, \dfrac{8 + 6}{2} \right)$

$$A = (1, 7)$$

Equation of b_1 [slope $= -3$, point $= (1, 7)$]
$$y - y_1 = m(x - x_1)$$
$$y - 7 = -3(x - 1)$$
$$y - 7 = -3x + 3$$
$$b_1 : 3x + y - 10 = 0$$

Slope of $QR = \dfrac{6 - 2}{-2 - (-4)} = \dfrac{4}{2} = 2$

$\therefore$ Slope of $b_2 = -\dfrac{1}{2}$.

Midpoint of $[QR] = \left(\dfrac{-2 - 4}{2}, \dfrac{6 + 2}{2} \right)$

$$B = (-3, 4)$$

Equation of b_2 [slope $= -\dfrac{1}{2}$, point $= (-3, 4)$]
$$y - y_1 = m(x - x_1)$$
$$y - 4 = -\tfrac{1}{2}(x + 3)$$
$$2y - 8 = -x - 3$$
$$b_2 : x + 2y - 10 = 0$$

Solving the simultaneous equations b_1 and b_2 gives the centre of the circle $C(3, 1)$.
The radius of s is $|PC|$ or $|QC|$ or $|RC|$.

$P(-4, 2)$, $C(3, 1)$

$|PC| = \sqrt{(x_2 - x_1)^2 + (y_2 - y_1)^2}$

$\quad = \sqrt{(3 + 4)^2 + (1 - 2)^2} = \sqrt{(7)^2 + (-1)^2} = \sqrt{49 + 1} = \sqrt{50}$

Thus, the centre of s is $(3, 1)$ and the radius length is $\sqrt{50}$.

Equation of s: $\quad (x - h)^2 + (y - k)^2 = r^2$

$\quad\quad\quad\quad\quad\quad (x - 3)^2 + (y - 1)^2 = (\sqrt{50})^2$

$\quad\quad\quad\quad\quad\quad (x - 3)^2 + (y - 1)^2 = 50$

or

$x^2 + y^2 - 6x - 2y - 40 = 0$

Exercise 8.5

In questions 1–6, find the equation of the circle that contains the given points.

1. $(2, 2)$, $(6, 4)$ and $(4, 8)$
2. $(-3, -4)$, $(-5, 2)$ and $(1, 8)$
3. $(0, 0)$, $(4, 0)$ and $(6, -2)$
4. $(10, -2)$, $(-2, 4)$ and $(2, -2)$
5. $(4, 1)$, $(-2, 1)$ and $(2, 3)$
6. $(-2, -1)$, $(0, -5)$ and $(1, -2)$

Given two points P and Q on the circle and the equation of a line, l, containing the centre $C(-g, -f)$

Method 1: Algebraic approach

Let the equation of the circle be $x^2 + y^2 + 2gx + 2fy + c = 0$.

1. Substitute each point into this equation.
2. Substitute $(-g, -f)$ into the equation of the given line, l.
3. This gives three equations in three unknowns: g, f and c.
4. Solve these equations for g, f and c.
5. Put these values back into the equation.

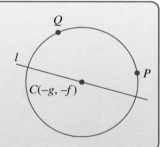

Method 2: Geometric approach

1. Find the equation of b, the perpendicular bisector of $[PQ]$.
2. Solve the simultaneous equations l and b to find the centre.
3. Find the radius, r, the distance from the centre C to P or Q.
4. Use the formula $(x - h)^2 + (y - k)^2 = r^2$.

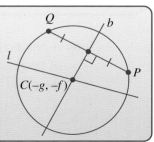

EXAMPLE

Find the equation of the circle that contains the points $(-4, 1)$ and $(0, 3)$ and whose centre lies on the line $x - 2y + 11 = 0$.

Solution:

Method 1: Algebraic approach

We are given two points on the circumference and the equation of a line containing the centre. Let the equation of the circle be $x^2 + y^2 + 2gx + 2fy + c = 0$.

$(-4, 1)$ on the circle: $(-4)^2 + (1)^2 + 2g(-4) + 2f(1) + c = 0$ $\Rightarrow$ $8g - 2f - c = 17$ ①

$(0, 3)$ on the circle: $(0)^2 + (3)^2 + 2g(0) + 2f(3) + c = 0$ $\Rightarrow$ $6f + c = -9$ ②

The centre $(-g, -f)$ is on the line $x - 2y + 11 = 0$.

Thus, $(-g) - 2(-f) + 11 = 0 \Rightarrow g - 2f = 11$ ③

Eliminate C from ① and ②:

$$8g - 2f - c = 17 \qquad ①$$
$$\underline{6f + c = -9 \qquad ②}$$
$$8g + 4f = 8 \qquad \text{(add)}$$
$$2g + f = 2 \qquad ④$$

Now solve between ③ and ④ to find the values of g and f:

$g - 2f = 11$	③	Put $g = 3$ into ③ or ④.
$\underline{4g + 2f = 4}$	④ × 2	$2g + f = 2$ ④
$5g = 15$	(add)	$2(3) + f = 2$
$g = 3$		$6 + f = 2$
		$f = -4$

Put $g = 3$ and $f = -4$ into ① or ② to find the value of c.

$6f + c = -9$	②	Put in $g = 3$, $f = -4$ and $c = 15$.
$6(-4) + c = -9$		The equation of the circle is:
$-24 + c = -9$		$x^2 + y^2 + 2gx + 2fy + c = 0$
$c = 15$		$x^2 + y^2 + 2(3)x + 2(-4)y + 15 = 0$
		$x^2 + y^2 + 6x - 8y + 15 = 0$

Note: Using method 2, the geometric approach, gives the same result.

Note: A line perpendicular to a tangent at the point of tangency passes through (contains) the centre of the circle.

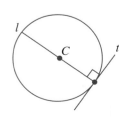

Given two points, *P* and *Q*, on the circle and the equation of the tangent at one of these points

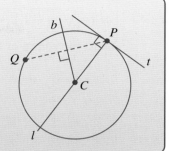

1. Find the equation of *l*, the line perpendicular to the tangent, *t*, passing through the given point of contact. This line will contain the centre, *C*.

2. Now we have two points on the circumference of the circle and the equation of a line that contains the centre of the circle.

3. Use the algebraic approach (as in the previous example) or use a geometric approach.

EXAMPLE

Find the equation of the circle that passes through the points $A(-3, -2)$ and $B(0, -1)$ and where the line $2x - y + 4 = 0$ is a tangent at the point $A(-3, -2)$.

Solution:

Method 2: Geometric approach

The diagram on the right represents the situation.

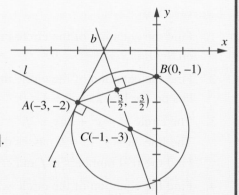

Find the equation of *l*, the line that is perpendicular to the tangent, *t*, at the point of contact $A(-3, -2)$. This line contains the centre, *C*.

Find the equation of *b*, the perpendicular bisector of [*AB*].

The centre, *C*, is the point of intersection of *b* and *l*.

The radius is $|AC|$ or $|BC|$.

The slope of the tangent $2x - y + 4 = 0$ is 2.	The slope of $AB = \dfrac{-1+2}{0+3} = \dfrac{1}{3}$.
$\therefore$ The slope of *l* is $-\frac{1}{2}$.	$\therefore$ The slope of *b* is -3.
Equation of *l* [slope $= -\frac{1}{2}$, point $= (-3, -2)$]:	Midpoint of [*AB*]
$y - y_1 = m(x - x_1)$	$= \left(\dfrac{-3+0}{2}, \dfrac{-2-1}{2}\right) = \left(-\dfrac{3}{2}, -\dfrac{3}{2}\right)$
$y + 2 = -\frac{1}{2}(x + 3)$	Equation of *b* $\left[$slope $= -3$, point $= \left(-\frac{3}{2}, -\frac{3}{2}\right)\right]$:
$2y + 4 = -x - 3$	$y - y_1 = m(x - x_1)$
$l : x + 2y + 7 = 0$	$y + \frac{3}{2} = -3\left(x + \frac{3}{2}\right)$
	$y + \frac{3}{2} = -3x - \frac{9}{2}$
	$b : 3x + y + 6 = 0$

Solving the simultaneous equations *l* and *b* gives the centre of the circle $C(-1, -3)$.

Radius:

The radius is $|AC|$ or $|BC|$.

$$|AC| = \sqrt{(x_2 - x_1)^2 + (y_2 - y_1)^2} = \sqrt{(-1 + 3)^2 + (-3 + 2)^2} = \sqrt{(2)^2 + (-1)^2} = \sqrt{4 + 1} = \sqrt{5}$$

Thus, the centre of the circle is $(-1, -3)$ and the radius is $\sqrt{5}$.

Equation of the circle: $(x - h)^2 + (y - k)^2 = r^2$

$$(x + 1)^2 + (y + 3)^2 = (\sqrt{5})^2$$

$$(x + 1)^2 + (y + 3)^2 = 5$$

or

$$x^2 + y^2 + 2x + 6y + 5 = 0$$

Note: After finding the equation of the line l, we could have let the equation of the circle be $x^2 + y^2 + 2gx + 2fy + c = 0$ and used an algebraic approach to find the values of g, f and c.

Exercise 8.6

1. Find the equation of the circle that contains the points $(3, 6)$ and $(5, 4)$ and whose centre lies on the line $x + y - 5 = 0$.

2. Find the equation of the circle that contains the points $(2, -6)$ and $(4, -2)$ and whose centre lies on the line $2x + y + 4 = 0$.

3. The circle $x^2 + y^2 + 2gx + 2fy + c = 0$ passes through the points $(4, 3)$ and $(6, -3)$.
   The line $3x - y - 7 = 0$ passes through the centre of the circle.
   Find the real numbers g, f and c.

4. Find the equation of the circle which passes through the points $(-1, 6)$ and $(-3, 0)$ and where the line $2x + y + 6 = 0$ is a tangent at the point $(-3, 0)$.

5. Find the equation of the circle which passes through the points $(-1, 3)$ and $(3, 5)$ and where the line $3x - y + 6 = 0$ is a tangent at the point $(-1, 3)$.

6. The circle $x^2 + y^2 + 2gx + 2fy + c = 0$ passes through the points $(4, 1)$ and $(6, -5)$.
   The line $2x - y - 17 = 0$ is a tangent to the circle at $(6, -5)$.
   Find the real numbers g, f and c.

Given the length of the radius

In some questions, we are given the radius. When this happens we let $\sqrt{g^2 + f^2 - c}$ be equal to the given radius. Then we square both sides. We then have to use the other information in the question to form two other equations in g, f and c and substitute these into the first equation to get a quadratic equation in one variable. In general, we end up with two circles that satisfy the given conditions.

EXAMPLE

A circle of radius length $\sqrt{20}$ contains the point $(-1, 3)$. Its centre lies on the line $x + y = 0$. Find the equation of the two circles that satisfy these conditions.

Solution:

Let the circle be $x^2 + y^2 + 2gx + 2fy + c = 0$.

Given:

$$\text{Radius} = \sqrt{20}$$
$$\sqrt{g^2 + f^2 - c} = \sqrt{20}$$
$$g^2 + f^2 - c = 20 \quad \text{①}$$

Contains the point $(-1, 3)$
$$(-1)^2 + (3)^2 + 2g(-1) + 2f(3) + c = 0$$
$$2g - 6f - c = 10 \quad \text{②}$$

The centre $(-g, -f)$ is on the line $x + y = 0$
$$\therefore -g - f = 0$$
$$g + f = 0 \quad \text{③}$$

We now have to solve between the simultaneous equations ①, ② and ③.

$$g + f = 0 \quad \text{③}$$
$$f = -g$$

Substitute this expression for f into ② to find c in terms of g only.

$$2g - 6f - c = 10 \quad \text{②}$$
$$2g - 6(-g) - c = 10 = 0$$
$$-c = -8g + 10$$
$$c = 8g - 10$$

We now have f and c in terms of g and we put these into ①.

$$g^2 + f^2 - c = 20 \quad \text{①}$$
$$g^2 + (-g)^2 - (8g - 10) = 20 \qquad \text{(put } f = -g \text{ and } c = 8g - 10)$$
$$g^2 + g^2 - 8g + 10 = 20$$
$$2g^2 - 8g - 10 = 0$$
$$g^2 - 4g - 5 = 0$$
$$(g + 1)(g - 5) = 0$$
$$g = -1 \quad \text{or} \quad g = 5$$

Case 1

$g = -1$
$f = -g = -(-1) = 1$
$c = 8g - 10 = 8(-1) - 10 = -8 - 10 = -18$
$$x^2 + y^2 + 2(-1)x + 2(1)y - 18 = 0$$
$$x^2 + y^2 - 2x + 2y - 18 = 0$$

Case 2

$g = 5$
$f = -g = -5$
$c = 8g - 10 = 8(5) - 10 = 40 - 10 = 30$
$$x^2 + y^2 + 2(5)x + 2(-5)y + 30 = 0$$
$$x^2 + y^2 + 10x - 10y + 30 = 0$$

These are the equations of the two circles that satisfy the given conditions.

Exercise 8.7

1. A circle of radius length 2 contains the point $(1, -1)$. Its centre lies on the line $x = 1$. Find the equations of the two circles that satisfy these conditions.

2. A circle of radius length $\sqrt{20}$ contains the point $(0, 2)$. Its centre lies on the line $x + y = 0$. Find the equations of the two circles that satisfy these conditions.

3. A circle of radius length $\sqrt{10}$ contains the point $(-5, 0)$. Its centre lies on the line $x + 2y = 0$. Find the equations of the two circles that satisfy these conditions.

4. A line $l : 2x - 3y = 0$ is a tangent to a circle c at the point $(0, 0)$. If the radius of c is $\sqrt{13}$, find two possible equations for c.

5. Two circles intersect at the points $P(1, 3)$ and $Q(3, -1)$.
   The line b joining the centres of the circles is the perpendicular bisector of $[PQ]$.
   (i) Find the coordinates of R, the midpoint of $[PQ]$, and the equation of the line b.
   (ii) If the distance from the centre of each circle to R is $\sqrt{20}$, find the radius length of each circle.
   (iii) Find the equation of each circle.

6. A circle of radius length $\sqrt{10}$ contains the points $(1, 2)$ and $(-1, 4)$. Find the equations of the two circles that satisfy these conditions.

Equation of a tangent 1

Equation of a tangent to a circle at a given point
A tangent is perpendicular to the radius that joins the centre of a circle to the point of tangency.

This fact is used to find the slope of the tangent.

In the diagram on the right, the radius, r, is perpendicular to the tangent, t, at the point of tangency, P.

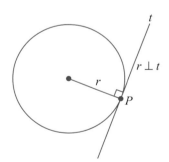

The equation of a tangent to a circle at a given point is found with the following steps.

1. Find the slope of the radius to the point of tangency.
2. Turn this slope upside down and change its sign. This gives the slope of the tangent.
3. Use the coordinates of the point of contact and the slope of the tangent at this point in the formula:
$$y - y_1 = m(x - x_1).$$
   This gives the equation of the tangent.

Notes: 1. A diagram is often very useful.
2. If the slope is a fraction, use the alternative formula: $(y - y_1) = m(x - x_1)$.

EXAMPLE

Find the equation of the tangent to the circle $x^2 + y^2 - 4x + 6y - 12 = 0$ at the point $(5, -7)$ on the circle.

Solution:

$x^2 + y^2 - 4x + 6y - 12 = 0$

The centre of the circle is $(2, -3)$.

$$\text{Slope of } r = \frac{-7 + 3}{5 - 2} = -\frac{4}{3}$$

$$\therefore \text{ Slope of } t = \tfrac{3}{4}.$$

Equation of t: $(y - y_1) = m(x - x_1)$ (alternative formula)

$$(y + 7) = \tfrac{3}{4}(x - 5)$$

$$4(y + 7) = 3(x - 5)$$

$$4y + 28 = 3x - 15$$

$$3x - y - 43 = 0$$

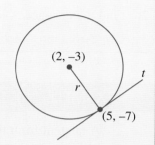

Proving that a line is a tangent to a circle

A line is a tangent to a circle if the perpendicular distance from the centre of the circle to the line is equal to the radius.

EXAMPLE

Prove that the line $2x - 3y - 27 = 0$ is a tangent to the circle $x^2 + y^2 - 8x + 4y + 7 = 0$.

Solution:

As we do not need the point of contact, we use the perpendicular distance method.

$$x^2 + y^2 - 8x + 4y + 7 = 0$$

Centre $= (4, -2)$

Radius $= \sqrt{(4)^2 + (-2)^2 - 7} = \sqrt{16 + 4 - 7} = \sqrt{13}$

Perpendicular distance from the centre $(4, -2)$ to the line $2x - 3y - 27 = 0$ is given by:

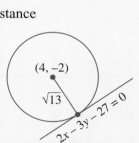

$$d = \frac{|ax_1 + by_1 + c|}{\sqrt{a^2 + b^2}} = \frac{|2(4) - 3(-2) - 27|}{\sqrt{(2)^2 + (-3)^2}} = \frac{|8 + 6 - 27|}{\sqrt{4 + 9}} = \frac{|-13|}{\sqrt{13}} = \frac{13}{\sqrt{13}} = \sqrt{13}$$

As the perpendicular distance from the centre of the circle to the line is equal to the radius, the line is a tangent to the circle.

Length of a tangent to a circle from a point outside the circle

The **length of a tangent** from a point outside a circle is the distance, d, from the point outside the circle to the point of tangency.

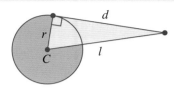

1. Find the centre, C, and radius length, r, of the circle.

2. Find the distance, l, between the centre and the point outside the circle.

3. Use Pythagoras' theorem to find d, i.e. $l^2 = r^2 + d^2$.

EXAMPLE

A tangent from the point $P(3, 0)$ touches the circle $x^2 + y^2 + 2x - 4y + 1 = 0$ at Q. Find $|PQ|$.

Solution:

$x^2 + y^2 + 2x - 4y + 1 = 0$

Centre $= C(-1, 2)$

Radius $= \sqrt{(-1)^2 + (2)^2 - 1} = \sqrt{1 + 4 - 1} = \sqrt{4} = 2$

Distance from the centre $C(-1, 2)$ to the point $P(3, 0)$:

$|PC| = \sqrt{(3 + 1)^2 + (0 - 2)^2} = \sqrt{4^2 + (-2)^2}$

$= \sqrt{16 + 4} = \sqrt{20}$

Using Pythagoras' theorem:

$$|PQ|^2 + |QC|^2 = |PC|^2$$
$$|PQ|^2 + 2^2 = (\sqrt{20})^2$$
$$|PQ|^2 + 4 = 20$$
$$|PQ|^2 = 16$$
$$|PQ| = 4$$

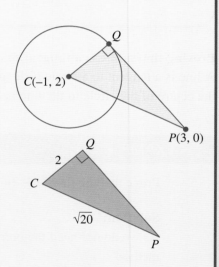

Exercise 8.8

In questions 1–10, find the equation of the tangent to the circle at the given point.

1. $x^2 + y^2 = 10$;   (3, 1)

2. $x^2 + y^2 = 29$;   (−2, 5)

3. $x^2 + y^2 = 50$;   (−7, −1)

4. $4x^2 + 4y^2 = 25$; $(2, -\frac{3}{2})$

5. $(x - 4)^2 + (y + 3)^2 = 10$;   (7, −4)

6. $x^2 + (y - 5)^2 = 29$;   (5, 3)

7. $x^2 + y^2 + 6x + 2y - 3 = 0$;   (−5, −4)

8. $x^2 + y^2 - 2x + 4y - 15 = 0$;   (3, 2)

9. $x^2 + y^2 - 4x - 6y - 12 = 0$; $(5, 7)$ 10. $x^2 + y^2 - 8x + 14 = 0$; $(3, -1)$

11.   Show that the tangents to the circle $x^2 + y^2 - 2x - 2y - 3 = 0$ at the points $(3, 2)$ and $(2, -1)$ are perpendicular to each other.

In questions 12–16, verify in each case that the line l is a tangent to the circle c.

12. $l : 3x + 4y - 25 = 0$; $c : x^2 + y^2 = 25$

13. $l : 4x + 3y - 14 = 0$; $c : x^2 + y^2 - 4x + 6y + 4 = 0$

14. $l : x - 4y + 31 = 0$; $c : x^2 + y^2 + 4x - 6y - 4 = 0$

15. $l : x - 6y - 9 = 0$; $c : x^2 + y^2 - 4x - 10y - 8 = 0$

16. $l : x - 2y + 10 = 0$; $c : x^2 + y^2 + 8x - 16y + 60 = 0$

In questions 17–22, find the distance from the point outside the circle to the point of tangency.

17. $(11, -2)$; $x^2 + y^2 = 25$ 18. $(0, -4)$; $x^2 + y^2 - 6x - 8y + 16 = 0$

19. $(3, 1)$; $x^2 + y^2 + 4x - 2y - 4 = 0$ 20. $(2, 5)$; $x^2 + y^2 - 2x + 4y - 20 = 0$

21. $(0, 0)$; $x^2 + y^2 - 8x - 6y + 20 = 0$ 22. $(5, 0)$; $x^2 + y^2 + 6x - 5 = 0$

23.   The length of the tangent from the point $(3, 2)$ to the circle $x^2 + y^2 - 8x - 8y + k = 0$ is 2. Find the value of k.

24.   A car is parked on a hill, as shown on the diagram. If the edge of one wheel can be represented by the equation
$$(x - 3)^2 + (y + 5)^2 = 20$$
and the point of contact with this wheel and the hill is $(5, -9)$, find the equation of the line which represents the hill.

Equation of a tangent 2

Tangents parallel or perpendicular to a given line

We make use of the fact that the perpendicular distance from the centre of a circle to the tangent is equal to the radius.

Note: $ax + by + k = 0$ is a line parallel to the line $ax + by + c = 0$.
       $bx - ay + k = 0$ is a line perpendicular to the line $ax + by + c = 0$.

EXAMPLE

Find the equations of the tangents to the circle $x^2 + y^2 - 6x - 2y - 15 = 0$ that are parallel to the line $3x + 4y + 20 = 0$.

Solution:

$x^2 + y^2 - 6x - 2y - 15 = 0$

Centre = $(3, 1)$

Radius = $\sqrt{(3)^2 + (1)^2 + 15} = \sqrt{9 + 1 + 15} = \sqrt{25} = 5$

Let the equations of the tangents parallel to $3x + 4y + 20 = 0$ both be represented by $3x + 4y + k = 0$.

As $3x + 4y + k = 0$ is a tangent to the circle, the perpendicular distance from the centre of the circle, $(3, 1)$, to this line is equal to the radius, 5.

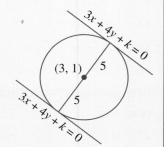

$$\therefore \frac{|3(3) + 4(1) + k|}{\sqrt{(3)^2 + (4)^2}} = 5$$

$$\frac{|9 + 4 + k|}{\sqrt{9 + 16}} = 5$$

$$\frac{|13 + k|}{5} = 5$$

$$|13 + k| = 25$$

$$\therefore 13 + k = 25 \text{ or } 13 + k = -25$$

$$k = 12 \text{ or } k = -38$$

Thus, the tangents are $3x + 4y + 12 = 0$ and $3x + 4y - 38 = 0$.

Equations of tangents from a point outside a circle

From a point outside a circle, two tangents can be drawn to touch the circle.

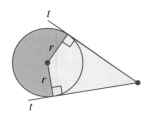

Method for finding the two equations of tangents from a point (x_1, y_1) outside a circle:

1. Find the centre and radius length of the circle (a rough diagram can help).

2. Let the equation be $y - y_1 = m(x - x_1)$ and write the equation in the form $ax + by + c = 0$.

3. Let the perpendicular distance from the centre of the circle to the tangent equal the radius.

4. Solve this equation to find two values of m.

5. Using these two values of m and the point (x_1, y_1), write down the equations of the two tangents.

EXAMPLE

Find the equations of the two tangents from the point $(5, -3)$ to the circle $x^2 + y^2 - 4x + 8y + 12 = 0$.

Solution:

$x^2 + y^2 - 4x + 8y + 12 = 0$

Centre $= (2, -4)$

Radius $= \sqrt{(2)^2 + (-4)^2 - 12} = \sqrt{4 + 16 - 12} = \sqrt{8}$

We have a point $(5, -3)$ and we need to find the slopes of the two tangents.

$$\text{Equation: } y - y_1 = m(x - x_1)$$
$$y + 3 = m(x - 5)$$
$$= mx - 5m$$
$$mx - y + (-5m - 3) = 0 \qquad \text{(in the form } ax + by + c = 0)$$

The perpendicular distance from the centre of the circle $(2, -4)$ to each tangent is equal to the radius, $\sqrt{8}$.

Thus,
$$\frac{|m(2) - 1(-4) + (-5m - 3)|}{\sqrt{m^2 + (-1)^2}} = \sqrt{8}$$

$$\frac{|2m + 4 - 5m - 3|}{\sqrt{m^2 + 1}} = \sqrt{8}$$

$$\frac{|-3m + 1|}{\sqrt{m^2 + 1}} = \sqrt{8}$$

$$\frac{9m^2 - 6m + 1}{m^2 + 1} = 8 \qquad \text{(square both sides)}$$

$$9m^2 - 6m + 1 = 8m^2 + 8 \qquad \text{(multiply both sides by } (m^2 + 1))$$

$$m^2 - 6m - 7 = 0$$

$$m = -1 \text{ or } m = 7$$

Equations of the two tangents:

Slope $= -1$; point $= (5, -3)$	Slope $= 7$; point $= (5, -3)$
$y + 3 = -1(x - 5)$	$y + 3 = 7(x - 5)$
$y + 3 = -x + 5$	$y + 3 = 7x - 35$
$x + y - 2 = 0$	$7x - y - 38 = 0$

Thus, the equations of the two tangents are $x + y - 2 = 0$ and $7x - y - 38 = 0$.

Exercise 8.9

1. The line $2x + y + k = 0$ is a tangent to the circle $x^2 + y^2 = 5$. Find the two values of k.

2. The line $3x + y + k = 0$ is a tangent to the circle $x^2 + y^2 - 4x + 8y + 10 = 0$. Find the two values of k.

3. Find the two values of k for which the line $2x + y + k = 0$ is a tangent to the circle $x^2 + y^2 - 4x - 6y + 8 = 0$.

4. Find the two values of t for which the line $2x + ty + 3 = 0$ is a tangent to the circle $x^2 + y^2 - 4x - 4y - 5 = 0$.

5. Find the two values of k for which the line $x + ky - 6 = 0$ is a tangent to the circle $x^2 + y^2 - 6x - 2y + 5 = 0$.

6. The line $3x + ky - k = 0$ is a tangent to the circle $x^2 + y^2 - 10x - 2y + 17 = 0$. Find the two values of k.

7. Find the equations of the tangents to the circle $x^2 + y^2 = 25$ that are parallel to the line $4x - 3y + 10 = 0$.

8. Find the equations of the tangents to the circle $x^2 + y^2 = 10$ that are parallel to the line $3x - y = 0$.

9. Find the equations of the tangents to the circle $x^2 + y^2 + 6x + 10y + 29 = 0$ that are parallel to the line $2x - y - 8 = 0$.

10. Find the equations of the tangents to the circle $x^2 + y^2 - 6x + 4y - 4 = 0$ that are parallel to the line $x + 4y - 3 = 0$.

11. Find the equations of the tangents to the circle $x^2 + y^2 + 6x - 2y - 15 = 0$ that are perpendicular to the line $4x + 3y + 5 = 0$.

12. The line $mx - y = 0$ is a tangent to the circle $x^2 + y^2 - 6x + 2y + 2 = 0$. Find the two values of m.

In questions 13–18, find the equations of the tangent from the given point to the given circle.

13. $(5, 0)$; $x^2 + y^2 = 5$

14. $(-10, -10)$; $x^2 + y^2 = 20$

15. $(0, 0)$; $x^2 + y^2 + 4x + 2y + 4 = 0$

16. $(3, -2)$; $x^2 + y^2 + 4x - 6y + 8 = 0$

17. $(0, 1)$; $x^2 + y^2 - 8x - 2y + 9 = 0$

18. $(1, 2)$; $x^2 + y^2 + 8x + 6y + 15 = 0$

19. The line $ax + by = 0$ is a tangent to the circle $x^2 + y^2 - 4x - 2y + 4 = 0$, where $a, b \in \mathbb{R}$ and $b \neq 0$.

    (i) Show that $\dfrac{a}{b} = -\dfrac{4}{3}$.

    (ii) Hence or otherwise, find the coordinates of the point of contact.

Circles with the axes as tangents

If a circle touches an axis (the x- or y-axis is a tangent to the circle), then one of the coordinates of the centre of the circle is equal to the radius.

1. **Circle touching the x-axis**

$$\text{Radius} = |-f|$$
$$\sqrt{g^2 + f^2 - c} = |-f|$$
$$g^2 + f^2 - c = f^2$$
$$g^2 - c = 0$$
$$g^2 = c$$

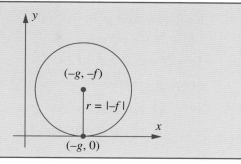

2. **Circle touching the y-axis**

$$\text{Radius} = |-g|$$
$$\sqrt{g^2 + f^2 - c} = |-g|$$
$$g^2 + f^2 - c = g^2$$
$$f^2 - c = 0$$
$$f^2 = c$$

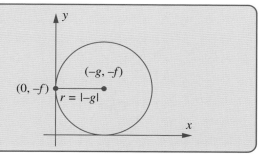

EXAMPLE

(i) The x-axis is a tangent to the circle $k : x^2 + y^2 + 2gx + 2fy + c = 0$.
Show that $g^2 = c$.

(ii) The points $(2, 1)$ and $(3, 2)$ are also on the circle k.
Find two possible equations for k.

Solution:

(i) $x^2 + y^2 + 2gx + 2fy + c = 0$
Centre $= (-g, -f)$, radius $= \sqrt{g^2 + f^2 - c}$
From the diagram:
$$\text{Radius} = |-f|$$
$$\sqrt{g^2 + f^2 - c} = |-f|$$
$$g^2 + f^2 - c = f^2$$
$$g^2 - c = 0$$
$$g^2 = c$$

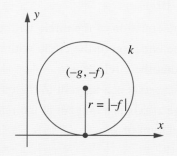

(ii) (2, 1) on the circle: $(2)^2 + (1)^2 + 2g(2) + 2f(1) + c = 0 \Rightarrow 4g + 2f + c + 5 = 0$

(3, 2) on the circle: $(3)^2 + (2)^2 + 2g(3) + 2f(2) + c = 0 \Rightarrow 6g + 4f + c + 13 = 0$

We now have three equations:

$g^2 = c$ ① $4g + 2f + c + 5 = 0$ ② $6g + 4f + c + 13 = 0$ ③

Replace c with g^2 in ② and ③:

$4g + 2f + c + 5 = 0$ ② $6g + 4f + c + 13 = 0$ ③

$4g + 2f + g^2 + 5 = 0$ ④ $6g + 4f + g^2 + 13 = 0$ ⑤

From ④, express f in terms of g and put this into ⑤.

$4g + 2f + g^2 + 5 = 0$ ④ $6g + 4f + g^2 + 13 = 0$ ⑤

$2f = -4g - g^2 - 5$ $6g + 4\left(\dfrac{-g^2 - 4g - 5}{2}\right) + g^2 + 13 = 0$

$f = \dfrac{-g^2 - 4g - 5}{2}$ $6g - 2g^2 - 8g - 10 + g^2 + 13 = 0$

$-g^2 - 2g + 3 = 0$

$g^2 + 2g - 3 = 0$

$(g + 3)(g - 1) = 0$

$g = -3$ or $g = 1$

Case 1

$g = -3$

$c = g^2 = (-3)^2 = 9$

$f = \dfrac{-g^2 - 4g - 5}{2}$

$= \dfrac{-9 + 12 - 5}{2} = \dfrac{-2}{2} = -1$

$x^2 + y^2 + 2(-3)x + 2(-1)y + 9 = 0$

$x^2 + y^2 - 6x - 2y + 9 = 0$

Case 2

$g = 1$

$c = g^2 = (1)^2 = 1$

$f = \dfrac{-g^2 - 4g - 5}{2}$

$= \dfrac{-1 - 4 - 5}{2} = \dfrac{-10}{2} = -5$

$x^2 + y^2 + 2(1)x + 2(-5)y + 1 = 0$

$x^2 + y^2 + 2x - 10y + 1 = 0$

Exercise 8.10

1. Find the equation of the circle with centre (2, 5) and which has the x-axis as a tangent.
2. Find the equation of the circle with centre (−3, 4) and which has the y-axis as a tangent.
3. Show that the circle $x^2 + y^2 - 4x - 4y + 4 = 0$ touches the x- and y-axes.
4. **(i)** The x-axis is a tangent to the circle $x^2 + y^2 + 2gx + 2fy + c = 0$. Show that $g^2 = c$.
   (ii) The x-axis is a tangent to a circle s at the point (5, 0). The point (1, 4) is on s. Find the equation of s.

5. **(i)** The y-axis is a tangent to the circle $x^2 + y^2 + 2gx + 2fy + c = 0$. Show that $f^2 = c$.

   (ii) The y-axis is a tangent to a circle k at the point $(0, 2)$. The point $(2, -2)$ is on k. Find the equation of k.

6. A circle has its centre in the first quadrant and touches the x- and y-axes. If the distance from the centre of the circle to the origin is $2\sqrt{2}$, find the equation of the circle.

7. The x-axis and the y-axis are tangents to the circle $x^2 + y^2 + 2gx + 2fy + c = 0$.

   Show that: **(i)** $g^2 = c$ **(ii)** $g^2 = f^2$

   (iii) The circle $s : x^2 + y^2 + 2gx + 2fy + c = 0$ has its centre in the first quadrant.

   The x- and y-axes are tangents to s. The point $(3, 6)$ is on s. Find two equations for s.

8. Show that the circle $x^2 + y^2 - 2rx - 2ry + r^2 = 0$ has radius r and has the x- and y-axes as tangents. Find the equations of the two circles that contain the point $(1, 2)$ and have the x- and y-axes as tangents.

Touching circles

Two circles are said to be **touching** if they have only one point of intersection. To investigate whether two circles touch, we compare the distance between their centres with the sum or difference of their radii.

Consider two circles of radius r_1 and r_2 (where $r_1 > r_2$) and let d be the distance between their centres.

1. Circles touch externally	**2. Circles touch internally**
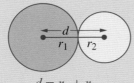	
$d = r_1 + r_2$	$d = r_1 - r_2$
Distance between their centres = sum of their radii.	Distance between their centres = difference of their radii.

EXAMPLE

$s : x^2 + y^2 - 16y + 32 = 0$ and $k : x^2 + y^2 - 18x + 2y + 32 = 0$ are two circles. Show that the circles touch externally and find their point of contact.

Solution:

Centre $= (0, 8) = C_1$

Radius $= \sqrt{0^2 + 8^2 - 32}$

$\qquad = \sqrt{64 - 32} = \sqrt{32} = 4\sqrt{2} = r_1$

Centre $= (9, -1) = C_2$

Radius $= \sqrt{9^2 + (-1)^2 - 32}$

$\qquad = \sqrt{81 + 1 - 32} = \sqrt{50} = 5\sqrt{2} = r_2$

Distance between centres

$$= \sqrt{(9-0)^2 + (-1-8)^2} = \sqrt{81 + 81} = \sqrt{162} = 9\sqrt{2}$$

Thus, the circles touch externally, as $4\sqrt{2} + 5\sqrt{2} = 9\sqrt{2}$.

$(r_1 + r_2 = |C_1C_2|)$

To determine the point of contact, divide the line segment joining the centres in the ratio 4 : 5.

Let the point of contact be (x, y).

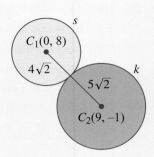

Method 1:

$$\frac{x-0}{9-x} = \frac{4}{5}$$

$$5x = 4(9-x)$$

$$5x = 36 - 4x$$

$$9x = 36$$

$$x = 4$$

$$\frac{y-8}{-1-y} = \frac{4}{5}$$

$$5(y-8) = 4(-1-y)$$

$$5y - 40 = -4 - 4y$$

$$9y = 36$$

$$y = 4$$

Thus, the point of contact is (4, 4).

Method 2: Using the formula

$$(x, y) = \left(\frac{bx_1 + ax_2}{b+a}, \frac{by_1 + ay_2}{b+a} \right)$$

$$= \left(\frac{5(0) + 4(9)}{5+4}, \frac{5(8) + 4(-1)}{5+4} \right)$$

$$= \left(\frac{36}{9}, \frac{36}{9} \right)$$

$$= (4, 4)$$

Thus, the point of contact is (4, 4).

Exercise 8.11

1. Prove that the circles $x^2 + y^2 + 2x + 2y - 7 = 0$ and $x^2 + y^2 - 6x - 4y + 9 = 0$ touch externally.

2. Prove that the circles $x^2 + y^2 + 6x + 16y + 9 = 0$ and $x^2 + y^2 - 4x - 8y - 5 = 0$ touch externally.

3. Prove that the circles $x^2 + y^2 + 12x - 6y - 76 = 0$ and $x^2 + y^2 - 4x + 6y + 12 = 0$ touch internally.

4. Prove that the circles $x^2 + y^2 = 80$ and $x^2 + y^2 - 12x - 6y + 40 = 0$ touch internally.

5. Prove that the circles $x^2 + y^2 - 2x - 4y - 20 = 0$ and $x^2 + y^2 - 18x - 16y + 120 = 0$ touch externally and find their point of contact.

6. Prove that the circles $x^2 + y^2 + 14x - 10y - 26 = 0$ and $x^2 + y^2 - 4x + 14y + 28 = 0$ touch externally and find their point of contact.

7. Prove that the circles $x^2 + y^2 - 6x + 4y + 11 = 0$ and $x^2 + y^2 + 4x - 6y - 19 = 0$ touch externally and find their point of contact.

8. Prove that the circles $x^2 + y^2 + 4x + 6y - 19 = 0$ and $x^2 + y^2 - 2x - 1 = 0$ touch internally and find their point of contact.

9. Prove that the circles $x^2 + y^2 + 8x - 8y + 24 = 0$ and $x^2 + y^2 + 2x - 2y = 0$ touch externally and find their point of contact.

10. The diagram shows the circle $c_1 : x^2 + y^2 = 16$ and the circle c_2 with centre (12, 5). If c_1 and c_2 touch externally, find the equation of c_2.

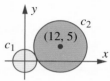

11. If the circles $x^2 + y^2 + 4x + 6y + k = 0$ and $x^2 + y^2 - 6x - 4y + 11 = 0$ touch externally, find the value of k.

12. $c_1 : x^2 + y^2 - 6x - 4y - 3 = 0$ and $c_2 : x^2 + y^2 - 18x - 4y + 81 = 0$ are two circles.
   - (i) Prove that c_1 and c_2 touch externally.
   - (ii) Find the point of contact of c_1 and c_2.
   - (iii) k is a third circle.
     Both c_1 and c_2 touch k internally.
     Find the equation of k.
     Note: All three centres lie on a straight line.

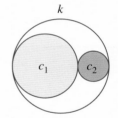

Chords of a circle

Circles intersecting the axes

To find where a circle intersects the axes, we use the following.

| The circle intersects the x-axis at $y = 0$. |
| The circle intersects the y-axis at $x = 0$. |

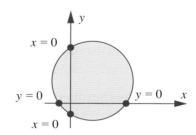

EXAMPLE

Find the coordinates of the points where the circle $x^2 + y^2 + 4x - 4y - 5 = 0$ intersects:

(i) The x-axis   (ii) The y-axis

Solution:

$$x^2 + y^2 + 4x - 4y - 5 = 0$$

(i) On the x-axis, $y = 0$
   (put in $y = 0$)
   $$x^2 + 4x - 5 = 0$$
   $$(x + 5)(x - 1) = 0$$
   $$x = -5 \text{ or } x = 1$$
   Coordinates on the x-axis:
   $$(-5, 0) \text{ and } (1, 0)$$

(ii) On the y-axis, $x = 0$
   (put in $x = 0$)
   $$y^2 - 4y - 5 = 0$$
   $$(y + 1)(y - 5) = 0$$
   $$y = -1 \text{ or } y = 5$$
   Coordinates on the y-axis:
   $$(0, -1) \text{ and } (0, 5)$$

Common chord or common tangent

If $s_1 = 0$ and $s_2 = 0$ are the equations of two circles in standard form, then $s_1 - s_2 = 0$ is the equation of the common chord or common tangent of the two circles.

Common chord	Common tangent
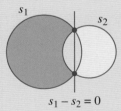	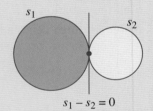
$s_1 - s_2 = 0$	$s_1 - s_2 = 0$
Two points of intersection	One point of intersection

Note: To find the equation of the common chord, or common tangent, of two circles, $s_1 = 0$ and $s_2 = 0$, the coefficients of x^2 and y^2 must be the same for both circles.

To find the coordinates of the points of intersection of two circles, do the following.

1. Find the equation of the common chord ($s_1 - s_2 = 0$).
2. Solve between the equation of the common chord and the equation of one of the circles.

EXAMPLE

The circles $x^2 + y^2 - 6x + 4y - 7 = 0$ and $x^2 + y^2 - 16x - 6y + 63 = 0$ intersect at the points P and Q. Find the equation of the line PQ.

Solution:

$$\text{The equation of the line } PQ \text{ is given by } s_1 - s_2 = 0.$$
$$x^2 + y^2 - 6x + 4y - 7 - (x^2 + y^2 - 16x - 6y + 63) = 0$$
$$x^2 + y^2 - 6x + 4y - 7 - x^2 - y^2 + 16x + 6y - 63 = 0$$
$$10x + 10y - 70 = 0$$
$$x + y - 7 = 0$$

Thus, the equation of the line PQ (common chord) is $x + y - 7 = 0$.

Note: To find the coordinates of P and Q, solve between the equations
$x + y - 7 = 0$ and either $x^2 + y^2 - 6x + 4y - 7 = 0$ or $x^2 + y^2 - 16x - 6y + 63 = 0$.

Radius perpendicular to a chord

A radius (or part of a radius) that is perpendicular to a chord bisects that chord. This also enables us to use Pythagoras' theorem:

$$d^2 + x^2 = r^2$$

Thus, knowing two of d, x and r, we can find the third.

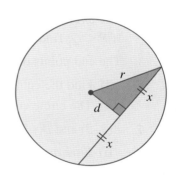

EXAMPLE

A circle c has centre $(2, 3)$ and makes a chord of $8\sqrt{2}$ units on the y-axis. Find the equation of c.

Solution:
A rough diagram is very useful.
We have the centre and require the radius.
The length of the perpendicular from the centre $(2, 3)$ to the y-axis is 2.
The length of the chord on the y-axis is $8\sqrt{2}$.

The perpendicular from the centre bisects the chord.
Thus, this length is $4\sqrt{2}$.
Using Pythagoras' theorem:
$r^2 = (4\sqrt{2})^2 + (2)^2 = 32 + 4 = 36$
$\therefore r = 6$

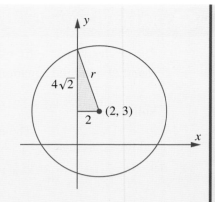

Equation: $\quad (x - h)^2 + (y - k)^2 = r^2$
$(x - 2)^2 + (y - 3)^2 = 6^2$
$(x - 2)^2 + (y - 3)^2 = 36$

or

$x^2 + y^2 - 4x - 6y - 23 = 0$

Exercise 8.12

1. The circle c has the equation $(x + 2)^2 + (y - 2)^2 = 13$. Find the coordinates of the points where c intersects the x- and y-axes.

2. The circle s has the equation $(x - 5)^2 + (y - 3)^2 = 18$. s intersects the x-axis at P and Q. If $P < Q$, find the coordinates of P and the coordinates of Q.

3. The end points of a diameter of a circle are $(2, 3)$ and $(-6, -1)$.
   (i) Find the equation of the circle.
   (ii) The circle cuts the y-axis at the points P and Q. Find $|PQ|$.

4. $A(3, 5)$ and $B(-1, -1)$ are the end points of a diameter of a circle k.
   (i) Find the centre and radius length of k.
   (ii) Find the equation of k.
   (iii) k intersects the x-axis at P and Q, $P < Q$. Find the coordinates of P and Q.

5. Find the coordinates of the points where the circle $x^2 + y^2 - 6x + 6y - 16 = 0$ intersects:
   (i) The x-axis   (ii) The y-axis

6. Find the length of the chord the y-axis makes with the circle $x^2 + y^2 - 8x - 10y + 16 = 0$.

7. Find the length of the chord the x-axis makes with the circle $x^2 + y^2 - 6x + 4y - 7 = 0$.

8. Find the equations of the tangents to the circle $x^2 + y^2 + 2x + 4y - 3 = 0$ at the points where the circle cuts the x-axis and show that these tangents are perpendicular to each other.

9. The circles $x^2 + y^2 + 4x - 10y + 20 = 0$ and $x^2 + y^2 - 4x - 2y + 12 = 0$ intersect at the points A and B. Find the equation of the line AB.

10. The circles $x^2 + y^2 - 6x + 4 = 0$ and $x^2 + y^2 - 2x + 12y + 12 = 0$ intersect at the points P and Q. Find the equation of the line PQ.

11. The circles $x^2 + y^2 - 10x - 10y + 40 = 0$ and $x^2 + y^2 - 16x + 2y + 40 = 0$ intersect at the points A and B. Find the equation of the line AB, the coordinates of the point A and the coordinates of the point B.

12. The circles $x^2 + y^2 + 14x - 12y + 65 = 0$ and $x^2 + y^2 + 4x - 2y - 5 = 0$ intersect at the points A and B. Find the coordinates of the point A and the coordinates of the point B.

13. The circles $x^2 + y^2 + 8x + 2y + 7 = 0$ and $x^2 + y^2 + 2x - 16y + 25 = 0$ intersect at the point P. Find the coordinates of the point P.

14. The line $2x + y - 10 = 0$ is a common tangent to the circles $x^2 + y^2 - 2x + 4y + h = 0$ and $x^2 + y^2 - 14x - 2y + k = 0$. Find the value of h and the value of k.

15. A circle c has centre $(5, 3)$ and makes a chord of 4 units on the y-axis. Find the equation of c.

16. A circle s has centre $(2, 0)$ and makes a chord of 6 units on the y-axis. Find the equation of s.

17. A circle of radius length 5 units has its centre in the first quadrant, touches the x-axis and intercepts a chord of length 6 units on the y-axis. Find the equation of this circle.

18. Find the equation of the circle with its centre in the first quadrant if it touches the y-axis at the point $(0, 2)$ and makes a chord of length $4\sqrt{3}$ units on the x-axis.

19. $l : 3x - 4y - 5 = 0$ is a line and $c : x^2 + y^2 - 4x + 12y + k = 0$ is a circle.

    The line l contains a chord of length 10 units of the circle c.

    (i) Find the radius length of c.

    (ii) Find the value of k.

20. **(i)** The equation of a circle c is $x^2 + y^2 + 4x - 2y + k = 0$. Write down its centre.
    (ii) The midpoint of a chord of length $4\sqrt{2}$ is $(1, 4)$. Find the distance from the centre of the circle to the chord.
    (iii) Calculate the radius length of c and the value of k.

21. Find the equation of the circle with centre $(4, 1)$ and which makes an intercept of length 4 units on the line $3x - 4y + 2 = 0$.

Right-angled triangles (revision)

In a right-angled triangle, special ratios exist between the angles and the lengths of the sides. We will look at three of these ratios.

Consider the right-angled triangle below with the acute angle θ

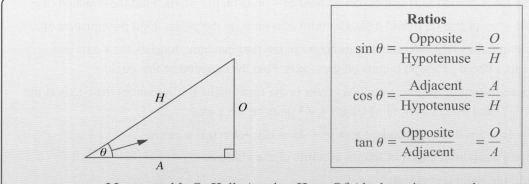

Ratios

$$\sin \theta = \frac{\text{Opposite}}{\text{Hypotenuse}} = \frac{O}{H}$$

$$\cos \theta = \frac{\text{Adjacent}}{\text{Hypotenuse}} = \frac{A}{H}$$

$$\tan \theta = \frac{\text{Opposite}}{\text{Adjacent}} = \frac{O}{A}$$

Memory aid: $\underline{O}$, $\underline{H}$ell, $\underline{A}$nother $\underline{H}$our $\underline{O}$f $\underline{A}$lgebra, $\underline{s}$in, $\underline{c}$os and $\underline{t}$an.
Each trigonometric ratio links two sides and an angle in a right-angled triangle.

Notes:

1. The side opposite the right angle is called the **hypotenuse, H**. The side opposite the angle θ is called the **opposite, O**. The other side near the angle θ is called the **adjacent, A**.

2. If the lengths of any two sides are known, the third side can be found using Pythagoras' theorem: $A^2 + O^2 = H^2$, where A, O and H are the lengths of the sides.

3. The three angles of a triangle add up to $180°$.

4. Sin, cos and tan are short for sine, cosine and tangent, respectively.

5. The arrow points to the side opposite the angle under consideration.

6. θ is a Greek letter, pronounced 'theta', often used to indicate an angle.

We can write trigonometric ratios for the two acute angles in a right-angled triangle. Make sure you know which angle you are using and which sides are the opposite and adjacent (the hypotenuse is always opposite the right angle). A good idea is to draw an arrow from the angle under consideration to indicate the opposite side to the angle. If we are given one trigonometric ratio, we can find the other two trigonometric ratios by representing the situation with a right-angled triangle and using Pythagoras' theorem to find the missing side.

The following summary of right-angled triangles is also in the booklet of formulae and tables.

Note: You should become familiar with the booklet of formulae and tables (approved for use in the state examinations).

Right-angled triangle

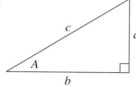

$$\sin A = \frac{a}{c} \qquad \cos A = \frac{b}{c} \qquad \tan A = \frac{a}{b}$$

Pythagoras' theorem $\qquad c^2 = a^2 + b^2$

Notes:

1. $\cos^2 \theta = (\cos \theta)^2$, $\sin^2 \theta = (\sin \theta)^2$ and $\tan^2 \theta = (\tan \theta)^2$.
2. If $\frac{5}{13}$ is keyed in as 5 ÷ 13, then brackets must be used: 🖩 2nd F sin (5 ÷ 13) =

Notation

The diagram shows the usual notation for a triangle in trigonometry.

- Vertices: A, B, C.
- Angles: A, B, C.
- Length of sides: a, b, c.

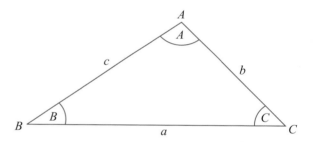

The lengths of the sides are denoted by a lower case letter and named after the angle they are opposite, i.e. a is opposite angle A, b is opposite angle B and c is opposite angle C.

Using the terminology, we also have the following:

$$A = |\angle BAC| \quad B = |\angle ABC| \quad C = |\angle ACB|$$
$$a = |BC| \qquad b = |AC| \qquad c = |AB|$$

Solving right-angled triangles

We can use a trigonometric ratio to calculate the length of a side in a right-angled triangle if we know the length of one side and one angle (other than the right angle). We can also find the size of an angle in a right-angled triangle if we know the lengths of two of its sides.

Practical applications

Many practical problems in navigation, surveying, engineering and geography involve solving a triangle. In this section we will restrict the problems to those that involve right-angled triangles. When solving practical problems using trigonometry in this section, represent each situation with a right-angled triangle.

Mark on your triangle the angles and lengths you know and label what you need to calculate, using the correct ratio to link the angle or length required with the known angle or length.

Angles of elevation, depression and compass directions

Angle of elevation
The **angle of elevation** of an object as seen by an observer is the angle between the horizontal line from the object to the observer's eye (upwards from the horizontal).

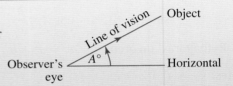

$A° =$ Angle of elevation of object

Angle of depression
If the object is below the level of the observer, the angle between the horizontal and the observer's line of vision is called the **angle of depression** (downwards from the horizontal).

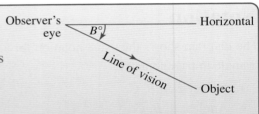

$B° =$ Angle of depression of object

Note: An angle of elevation has an equal angle of depression. The angle of elevation from A to B is equal to the angle of depression from B to A. The angles are alternate angles, as the horizontal lines are parallel.

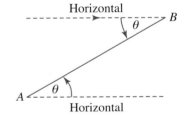

A note on clinometers

A clinometer is a device used to measure angles of elevation and/or angles of depression.

Q. Who might use a clinometer?

A. Motorway construction engineers, movie production engineers, forestry engineers and secondary school Maths students in Ireland!

There are many different types of clinometer. A very simple type looks like this:

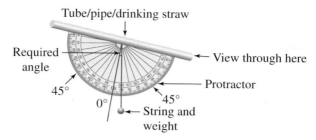

Tube/pipe/drinking straw

Required angle

View through here

45°

Protractor

0°   45°

String and weight

Compass directions

The direction of a point is stated as a number of degrees east or west of north and south.

- *A* is N 60° E
- *B* is N 40° W
- *C* is S 45° W (or SW)
- *D* is S 70° E

Note: N 60° E means start at north and turn 60° towards east.

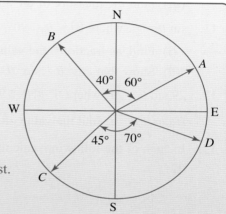

Mathematical modelling

When solving a problem, factors that have a negligible effect are often ignored. This has the advantage of simplifying the problem without sacrificing too much accuracy. This simplified problem is referred to as a **mathematical model** for the real situation.

Exercise 9.1 (Revision of Junior Certificate Higher Level)

In questions 1–8, find the measure of the angle θ, where $0° < \theta < 90°$, correct to the nearest degree.

1. $\sin \theta = \dfrac{2}{3}$

2. $\cos \theta = \dfrac{4}{7}$

3. $\tan \theta = \dfrac{1}{8}$

4. $\sin \theta = 0{\cdot}3$

5. $\tan \theta = 2$

6. $\cos \theta = \dfrac{3}{5}$

7. $\sin \theta = \dfrac{7}{10}$

8. $\tan \theta = \dfrac{1}{\sqrt{10}}$

9. $\cos \theta = \frac{4}{5}$, where $0° < \theta < 90°$.

   (i) Find, as fractions, the value of $\sin \theta$ and the value of $\tan \theta$.

   (ii) Show that: (a) $\cos^2 \theta + \sin^2 \theta = 1$ (b) $\cos \theta + \sin \theta > \tan \theta$

   (iii) Find the measure of the angle θ, correct to the nearest degree.

10. $\tan A = \frac{8}{15}$, where $0° < A < 90°$.

   (i) Find, as fractions, the value of $\sin A$ and the value of $\cos A$.

   (ii) Show that $\cos A + \sin A > \tan A$.

   (iii) Find the measure of the angle A, correct to the nearest degree.

11. $\sin \theta = \frac{7}{25}$, where $0° < \theta < 90°$.

   (i) Find, as fractions, the value of $\cos \theta$ and the value of $\tan \theta$.

   (ii) Show that $\cos^2 \theta + \sin^2 \theta = 1$.

12. $29 \sin \theta = 21$, where $0° < \theta < 90°$.

   If $\tan \theta = \dfrac{21}{k}$, find the value of k, where $k \in \mathbb{N}$.

13. In each of the following, calculate, to the nearest degree, the angles marked with a letter.

   (i)

   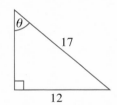

   (ii)

   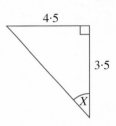

   (iii)

   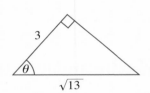

14. In each of the following, calculate the length of the sides marked with a letter correct to two decimal places.

   (i)

   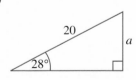

   (ii)

   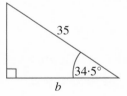

   (iii)

   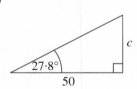

15. In triangle ABC, $|\angle ABC| = 90°$, $|AB| = 2$ and $|BC| = 1·5$.
   Find:

   (i) $|AC|$

   (ii) $|\angle BAC|$, correct to the nearest degree

   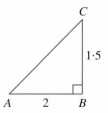

16. In the diagram, $XW \perp YZ, |XY| = 10, |\angle XYW| = 30°$
and $|WZ| = \frac{2}{5}|XY|$. Calculate:
    (i) $|XW|$ (ii) $|\angle WXZ|$, correct to the nearest degree

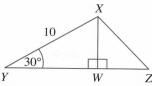

17. In the diagram, $|AB| = 16$ cm and $|\angle ABC| = 90°$. The point D
is on $[BC]$. $|BD| = 30$ cm and $|AD| = |DC|$. Find:
    (i) $|AD|$ (ii) $|BC|$
    (iii) $|\angle ACB|$, correct to the nearest degree

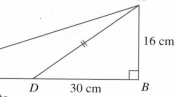

18. If $a^2 < b^2 + c^2$ in this triangle, which of the following statements
are true? Justify your answer.
    (i) $A = 90°$ (ii) $A > 90°$ (iii) $A < 90°$

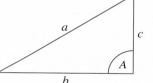

19. Assign values to a, b and c, the lengths of the sides, so that:
    (i) $A = 90°$ (ii) $A < 90°$ (iii) $A > 90°$

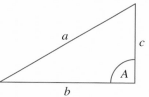

20. A vertical building on horizontal ground is 5 m tall. The building requires an outside
support beam to prevent it from collapsing. The maximum amount of space to erect a
support beam is 12 m to the left of the building.

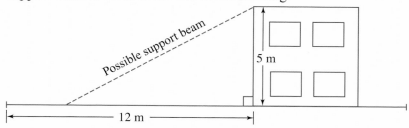

    (i) Using the diagram, calculate the maximum length the support beam can be.
    (ii) An engineer calculates that a support beam reaching up a height of 4 m on the building
    would be more effective. Find, correct to the nearest cm, the maximum length of this
    support beam.
    (iii) Further analysis indicates that the optimum (best) angle for the support beam is at 45° to the
    ground. Find, correct to the nearest cm, the length of this support beam if the point of
    support is at 4 m high, as in (ii).
    (iv) Give one reason why you think this mathematical model would be suitable or not in practice.

169

21. On the seafront at Bray, the beach slopes down at a constant angle of 9° to the horizontal. Ciara is 1·7 m tall. How far can she walk horizontally, correct to one decimal place, out to sea before the water just covers her head?

22. Lisa wishes to measure the height of a particular tree in her local park. She brings a tape, a homemade clinometer and her brother Bart.

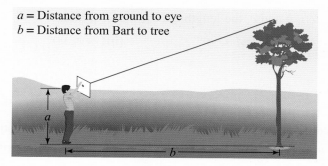

a = Distance from ground to eye
b = Distance from Bart to tree

With Bart operating the clinometer by looking through the straw/tube at the top of the tree, Lisa reads the angle of elevation, *E*.

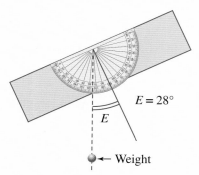

$E = 28°$

← Weight

Using the tape, she measures the distance from Bart to the tree, $b = 27·4$ m, and Bart's height to eye level, $a = 1·32$ m. How does she calculate the approximate height of the tree?

23. From a boat at sea, the angle of elevation to the top of a vertical cliff 200 m above sea level is 14°. After the boat has sailed directly towards the cliff, the angle of elevation of the cliff is found to be 28°. How far did the boat sail towards the cliff, correct to the nearest metre?

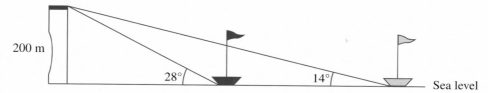

24. When a person stands on level ground at a point 100 m from the foot of a vertical cliff, the angle of elevation of the top of the cliff is 40°.

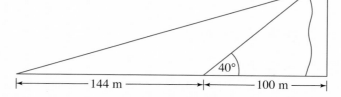

   (i) Calculate the height of the cliff, correct to the nearest metre.

   (ii) If the person moves to a different point on level ground, 244 m from the foot of the cliff, what will the measure of the angle of elevation be then? Give your answer correct to the nearest degree.

25. A rectangular plank of wood, *PQRS*, beams against a vertical wall, as shown. $|PQ| = 8$ m, $|PS| = 4$ m and $|\angle TPQ| = 25°$.

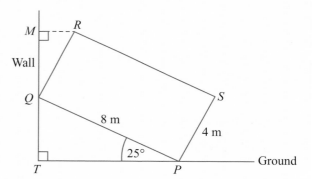

   (i) Are triangles *TPQ* and *MQR* similar? Justify your answer.

   (ii) Calculate the height of *R* above the ground, correct to the nearest metre.

26. Anne is swinging on a wooden garden swing. The seat, *S*, is held in position by two ropes, all of length 3 m. Her total angle of swing is 110° (55° each way).

   (i) What is the difference in height of the seat at the lowest and highest point in her swing? Give your answer to the nearest cm.

   (ii) In your solution, explain how you think the mathematical model below is arrived at.

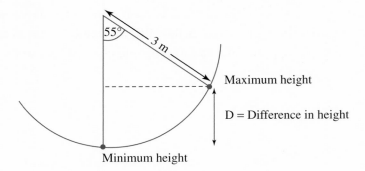

Maximum height

D = Difference in height

Minimum height

(iii) Do you think the mathematical model is accurate? Justify your answer.

Trigonometry 1

Radian measure

In more advanced trigonometry, and always in calculus, angles are measured in radians.

One radian is the measure of the angle at the centre of a circle subtended by an arc equal in length to the radius of the circle.

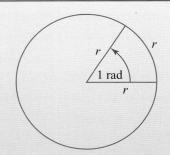

Note: Radians are often called **circular measure** and are denoted by rads.

The number of radians in one complete revolution is given by the following ratio:

$$\frac{\text{Circumference of a circle}}{\text{Length of its radius}} = \frac{2\pi r}{r} = 2\pi \text{ radians}$$

Relationship between radians and degrees

One complete revolution $= 2\pi$ radians $= 360°$, thus:

$$2\pi \text{ radians} = 360° \quad \text{or} \quad \pi \text{ radians} = 180°$$

Note: Very often the word radian is not used, thus we can write $\pi = 180°$, where π means π radian ($\pi \neq 180°$).

The more common angles used are given in the following table.

Degrees	0°	30°	45°	60°	90°	120°	150°	180°	270°	360°
Radians	0	$\dfrac{\pi}{6}$	$\dfrac{\pi}{4}$	$\dfrac{\pi}{3}$	$\dfrac{\pi}{2}$	$\dfrac{2\pi}{3}$	$\dfrac{5\pi}{6}$	π	$\dfrac{3\pi}{2}$	2π

These can be calculated from the equation π radians = 180°.

Note: 1 radian = $\dfrac{180°}{\pi} \approx 57 \cdot 3°$ (correct to one decimal place).

EXAMPLE 1

Convert: **(i)** 225° to radians   **(ii)** $\dfrac{5\pi}{3}$ radians to degrees

Solution:

(i) 180° = π radians

$$1° = \dfrac{\pi}{180} \text{ radians}$$

$$225° = 225 \times \dfrac{\pi}{180} \text{ radians}$$

$$225° = \dfrac{5\pi}{4} \text{ radians}$$

(ii) $\dfrac{5\pi}{3}$ radians

$$= \dfrac{5(180°)}{3}$$

(put in π = 180°)

$$= 300°$$

The diagram shows a sector of a circle of radius r, angle θ, arc length l and area A.

The length of the arc l and the area of the sector A may be found by multiplying the length of the circumference and the area of the circle by $\dfrac{\theta}{2\pi}$, respectively.

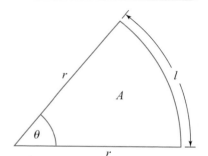

Note: $\dfrac{\theta}{2\pi}$ is the fraction of the circle required.

Length of arc, $l = \dfrac{\theta}{2\pi} \times 2\pi r = r\theta$.

Area of sector, $A = \dfrac{\theta}{2\pi} \times \pi r^2 = \tfrac{1}{2}r^2\theta$.

Arc length, $l = r\theta$.

Area of sector, $A = \tfrac{1}{2}r^2\theta$.

(θ in radians.)

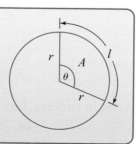

These formulae are on page 9 of the booklet of formulae and tables.

Each formula contains three variables. We are usually given two of these variables and asked to find the third one.

EXAMPLE 2

(i) The radius of a circle is 20 cm. Find the angle subtended at the centre by an arc of length 8π cm.

(ii) The area of a sector of a circle of radius r is 30 cm². If the angle subtended at the centre of the circle by this sector is $\frac{5}{3}$ radians, calculate r.

Solution:

(i) **Given:** $r = 20$, $l = 8\pi$. Find θ.
$$l = r\theta$$
$$8\pi = 20\theta$$
$$2\pi = 5\theta$$
$$\frac{2\pi}{5} = \theta$$

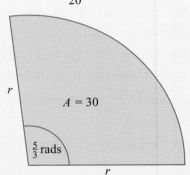

(ii) **Given:** $A = 30$, $\theta = \frac{5}{3}$ radians. Find r.
$$A = \tfrac{1}{2}r^2\theta$$
$$30 = \tfrac{1}{2}r^2 \times \tfrac{5}{3}$$
$$30 = \tfrac{5}{6}r^2$$
$$180 = 5r^2$$
$$36 = r^2$$
$$6 = r$$
$$\therefore r = 6 \text{ cm}$$

Exercise 9.2

In questions 1–10, express each of the number of radians in degrees.

1. π
2. $\dfrac{\pi}{6}$
3. $\dfrac{\pi}{4}$
4. $\dfrac{2\pi}{3}$
5. $\dfrac{3\pi}{5}$
6. $\dfrac{4\pi}{3}$
7. $\dfrac{5\pi}{4}$
8. $\dfrac{4\pi}{9}$
9. $\dfrac{5\pi}{18}$
10. $\dfrac{11\pi}{6}$

In questions 11–25, express each of the angles in radians, leaving π in your answers.

11. 30°
12. 45°
13. 60°
14. 90°
15. 120°
16. 150°
17. 210°
18. 240°
19. 135°
20. 450°
21. 390°
22. 72°
23. 288°
24. 105°
25. $22\frac{1}{2}°$

In questions 26–28, find the following:

(i) The length of the minor arc *PQ* (ii) The area of the corresponding minor sector *OPQ*

26.

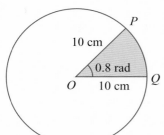

27.

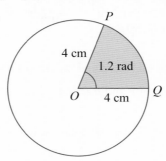

28.

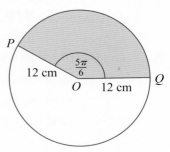

29. Find, in radians, the measure of the angle of a sector with:

   (i) Radius = 7 cm and arc length = 14 cm   (ii) Radius = 6 cm and arc length = 9 cm

   (iii) Radius = 4 cm and arc length = 4 cm   (iv) Radius = 10 cm and arc length = 24 cm

30. A sector has an angle of 1·5 radians and an arc length of 18 cm. Find the length of the radius.

31. A sector has an arc length of 3 cm and an angle of 0·6 radians. Find the length of the radius.

32. The area of a sector of a circle of radius 8 cm is 56 cm². Find, in radians, the angle of the sector.

33. Express 225° in radians. Hence or otherwise, find the area of a sector of a circle with a radius of 12 cm and an angle of 225° at the centre.

34. The circumference of a circle is 30π cm. The area of a sector of the circle is 75 cm². Find, in radians, the angle in this sector.

35. *P*, *Q* and *R* are points of a circle, centre *O*. The radius of the circle measures 3 cm. $|\angle QPR| = 60°$. Find the length of the minor arc *QR*.

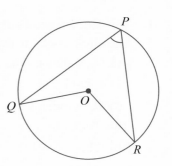

36. A slice of cheese 2 cm thick has a cross-section that is a sector of a circle, as shown. If the radius length is 5 cm and the arc length is 6 cm, find the volume of the cheese.

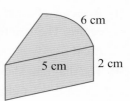

37. A windscreen wiper clears a flat region, *PQRS*, of a truck windscreen. *PQ* and *SR* are circular arcs centred at *O*. $|OR| = 20$ cm, $|RQ| = 60$ cm and $|\angle POQ| = 2 \cdot 2$ radians. Calculate the area of the region *PQRS*.

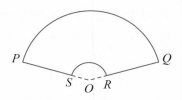

38. A sector *OAB* has an arc length of 12 cm and an area of 48 cm².

    (i) Write down two equations in *r* and *θ* (the radius and sector angle, as shown).

    (ii) Solve these equations to find the value of *r* and *θ*.

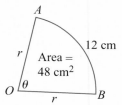

39. A piece of wire 40 cm in length is bent into the shape of a sector of area 100 cm². The length of the radius is *r* cm and the sector angle is *θ* radians.

    (i) Show that $\theta = \dfrac{40 - 2r}{r}$.   (ii) Find the value of (a) *r* (b) *θ*.

40. The diagram shows a sector of radius 3 cm and a square of side 3 cm. The area of the sector is one-third the area of the square. Find:

    (i) *θ*, in radians

    (ii) The ratio of the perimeter of the sector to the perimeter of the square

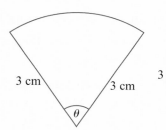

41. The diagram shows a circle of radius 15 cm and centre *O*. The circle contains two shaded sectors with arc lengths l_1 and l_2, as shown. The areas of the two shaded sectors are equal. Find:

    (i) *θ*, in radians

    (ii) The ratio $l_1 : l_2$

    (iii) The ratio of the perimeters of the two shaded sectors

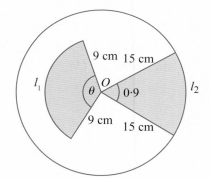

42. (i) A sector of a circle of radius *r* subtends an angle of 1 radian at its centre. The length of the arc is *l*. Write down an equation involving *r* and *l*.

    (ii) The diagram shows two concentric sectors with centre *O* and $|\angle COD| = 1$ radian. The radius of the smaller sector is *r* cm, i.e. $|OB| = r$ cm. The arc *CD* is 2 cm longer than the arc *AB*. The shaded region *ABDC* has an area of 10 cm². Calculate the value of *r*.

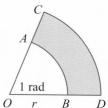

43. The diagram shows the cross-section of a cylindrical milk tank.
The diameter is 2 m and the length of the tank is 4 m. The
depth of the milk in the tank is 40 cm, as shown. Calculate, to
the nearest litre, the volume of milk in the tank.

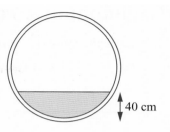

40 cm

44. The diagram shows a sector P of a circle of centre O
and radius 6 cm. AB and AC are tangents to the circle at
B and C, respectively, and $|\angle BOC| = 2\theta$, where θ is in
radians. The shaded area outside the circle is Q.

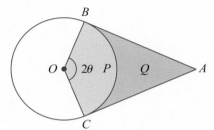

   (i) Write down the area of the sector P in terms of θ.
   (ii) Find the area of the triangle OAB in terms of $\tan\theta$.
   (iii) Deduce that the area of the region Q is
      $36(\tan\theta - \theta)$ cm^2.
   (iv) Given that the regions P and Q have equal areas, show that $\tan\theta - 2\theta = 0$.

45.   (i) Express $216°$ in radians.
   (ii) A piece of paper is cut in the shape of a
      sector of a circle of centre O, radius
      10 cm and angle $216°$, as shown. It is
      folded to form a cone of base radius r cm
      and height h cm in such a way that $[OP]$ and $[OQ]$ are joined.
      Find: **(a)** r **(b)** h.

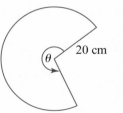
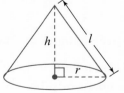

46. It may help with this question to make a paper model. A right-circular cone has base radius
r and slant height l. The curved surface is unrolled flat into the shape of a sector.

   (i) What is the radius of this sector?
   (ii) Express the angle of this sector, θ, in terms of π, r and l.
   (iii) Justify why the curved surface area of a right-circular cone is πrl.

47. The diagrams show a sector of a circle of radius
20 cm and angle θ which is formed into a cone
of slant height l cm. The vertical height, h cm,
of the cone and the radius, r cm, of the base of
the cone are equal.

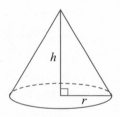

   (i) Write down the value of l.
   (ii) Show that **(a)** $r = 10\sqrt{2}$ **(b)** $\theta = \sqrt{2}\pi$.

Trigonometric ratios

The three trigonometric ratios for a right-angled triangle are defined as follows for all angles $0° < \theta < 90°$ (in degrees) or $0 < \theta < \dfrac{\pi}{2}$ (in radians).

$$\sin \theta = \frac{O}{H}$$

$$\cos \theta = \frac{A}{H}$$

$$\tan \theta = \frac{O}{A}$$

$$\frac{\sin \theta}{\cos \theta} = \frac{\dfrac{O}{H}}{\dfrac{A}{H}} = \frac{O}{A} = \tan \theta \qquad\qquad \boxed{\tan \theta = \frac{\sin \theta}{\cos \theta}}$$

$$\sin (90° - \theta) = \frac{A}{H} = \cos \theta \qquad\qquad \boxed{\sin (90° - \theta) = \cos \theta}$$

$$\cos (90° - \theta) = \frac{O}{H} = \sin \theta \qquad\qquad \boxed{\cos (90° - \theta) = \sin \theta}$$

Note: These ratios hold for all values of $\theta \in R$, not just for $0 < \theta < 90°$. We will look at this later on. The angle $(90° - \theta)$ is called the complementary angle to θ.

Note: Page 13 in the booklet of formulae and tables has three other ratios.

$$\sec A = \frac{1}{\cos A}, \quad \operatorname{cosec} A = \frac{1}{\sin A}, \quad \cot A = \frac{1}{\tan A} = \frac{\cos A}{\sin A}$$

These ratios are **not** on our course.

Special angles 45°, 60° and 30° or $\dfrac{\pi}{4}, \dfrac{\pi}{3}$ and $\dfrac{\pi}{6}$

There are three special angles whose sine, cosine and tangent ratios can be expressed as simple fractions or surds.

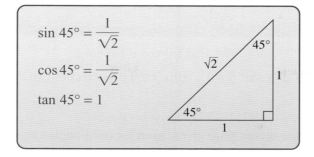

$$\sin 45° = \frac{1}{\sqrt{2}}$$

$$\cos 45° = \frac{1}{\sqrt{2}}$$

$$\tan 45° = 1$$

$$\sin 60° = \frac{\sqrt{3}}{2} \qquad \sin 30° = \frac{1}{2}$$

$$\cos 60° = \frac{1}{2} \qquad \cos 30° = \frac{\sqrt{3}}{2}$$

$$\tan 60° = \sqrt{3} \qquad \tan 30° = \frac{1}{\sqrt{3}}$$

These ratios can be used instead of a calculator.

See page 13 of the booklet of formulae and tables.

EXAMPLE 1

Evaluate the following.

(i) $\cos^2 45° + \sin 30°$ (ii) $2 \sin \dfrac{\pi}{6} \cos \dfrac{\pi}{6}$

Solution:

(i) $\cos^2 45° + \sin 30°$

    $= (\cos 45°)^2 + \sin 30°$

    $= \left(\dfrac{1}{\sqrt{2}}\right)^2 + \dfrac{1}{2}$

    $= \dfrac{1}{2} + \dfrac{1}{2}$

    $= 1$

(ii) $2 \sin \dfrac{\pi}{6} \cos \dfrac{\pi}{6}$

    $= 2\left(\dfrac{1}{2}\right)\left(\dfrac{\sqrt{3}}{2}\right)$

    $= \dfrac{\sqrt{3}}{2}$

EXAMPLE 2

(i) If $\sin \theta = \frac{1}{3}$ for $0° < \theta < 90°$, find (a) $\cos \theta$ (b) $\tan \theta$.

(ii) Verify that $\cos^2 \theta + \sin^2 \theta = 1$. (iii) Find θ, correct to two decimal places.

Solution:

(i) From the trigonometric ratio given, sketch a right-angled triangle to represent the situation and use Pythagoras' theorem to find the missing side.

Given: $\sin \theta = \frac{1}{3}$.

Opposite $= 1$, hypotenuse $= 3$, let the adjacent $= x$.

$x^2 + 1^2 = 3^2$ (Pythagoras' theorem)

$x^2 + 1 = 9$

$x^2 = 8$

$x = \sqrt{8}$

(a) $\cos \theta = \dfrac{A}{H} = \dfrac{\sqrt{8}}{3}$

(b) $\tan \theta = \dfrac{O}{A} = \dfrac{1}{\sqrt{8}}$

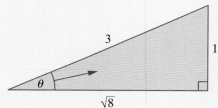

(ii) $\cos^2 \theta + \sin^2 \theta$

$= (\cos \theta)^2 + (\sin \theta)^2$

$= \left(\dfrac{\sqrt{8}}{3}\right)^2 + \left(\dfrac{1}{3}\right)^2$

$= \frac{8}{9} + \frac{1}{9}$

$= \frac{9}{9}$

$= 1$

(iii) $\sin \theta = \frac{1}{3}$

$\theta = \sin^{-1}\left(\frac{1}{3}\right)$ (exact value)

$\theta = 19.47122063$

$\theta = 19.47°$ (correct to two decimal places)

Exercise 9.3

Find the exact value of each of the following in questions 1–14 (write your answers as whole numbers, fractions or surds).

1. $\sin 30°$

2. $\tan 45°$

3. $\cos 30°$

4. $\tan 60°$

5. $\cos \dfrac{\pi}{3}$

6. $\sin \dfrac{\pi}{4}$

7. $4 \cos \dfrac{\pi}{6} \sin \dfrac{\pi}{3}$

8. $\tan \dfrac{\pi}{3} \tan \dfrac{\pi}{6}$

9. $\cos^2 45° + \sin^2 45°$

10. $\sin^2 30° + \tan^2 45°$

11. $\cos^2 \dfrac{\pi}{6} + \sin^2 \dfrac{\pi}{6}$

12. $1 - 2 \tan^2 60°$

13. $\sin \dfrac{\pi}{4} \cos \dfrac{\pi}{4} - \sin \dfrac{\pi}{6}$

14. $\tan^2 30° + \sin^2 60°$

15. $\tan A = \frac{2}{3}$, where $0° < A < 90°$.

    (i) Find, as surds, the value of $\sin A$ and the value of $\cos A$.

    (ii) Show that **(a)** $\cos A + \sin A > \tan A$ **(b)** $\cos^2 A + \sin^2 A = 1$.

    (iii) Find the measure of the angle A, correct to the nearest degree.

    (iv) Verify that $\cos (90° - A) = \sin A$.

16. $\sin A = \dfrac{2}{\sqrt{5}}$, where $0° < A < 90°$.

    (i) Find **(a)** $\cos A$ **(b)** $\tan A$.   **(ii)** Verify that $\cos^2 A + \sin^2 A = 1$.

    (iii) Find A, correct to two decimal places.   **(iv)** Verify that $\sin (90° - A) = \cos A$.

17. If $\tan A = \dfrac{m}{n}$, find $\sin A$, $\cos A$ and $\sin A \cos A$ in terms of m and n.

18. **(i)** Factorise **(a)** $a^2 + 2ab + b^2$ **(b)** $x^4 - 2x^2y^2 + y^4$.

    (ii) If $\sin \theta = \dfrac{2p}{p^2 + 1}$, find $\cos \theta$ and $\tan \theta$ in terms of p, where θ is acute.

19. Use a right-angled triangle to show that:

    (i) $\cos (90° - A) = \sin A$ **(ii)** $\sin (90° - A) = \tan (90° - A) \sin A$

Trigonometric ratios for any angle

The unit circle

The unit circle has its centre at the origin $(0, 0)$ and the length of the radius is 1.

Take any point $p(x, y)$ on the circle, making an angle of θ, from the centre.

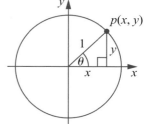

$\cos \theta = \dfrac{x}{1} = x$

$\sin \theta = \dfrac{y}{1} = y$

$\tan \theta = \dfrac{y}{x} = \dfrac{\sin \theta}{\cos \theta}$

This very important result indicates that the coordinates of any point on the unit circle can be represented by $p(\cos \theta, \sin \theta)$, where θ is any angle.

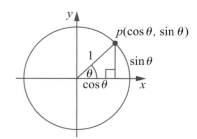

As the point p rotates, θ changes. These definitions of $\cos \theta$ and $\sin \theta$ in terms of the coordinates of a point rotating around the unit circle apply for **all** values of the angle $\theta°$.

Memory aid: (Christian name, Surname) = $(\cos \theta, \sin \theta) = (x, y)$.

Note: Using Pythagoras's theorem, $\cos^2 \theta + \sin^2 \theta = 1$ (where $\sin^2 \theta = (\sin \theta)^2$ and $\cos^2 \theta = (\cos \theta)^2$).

Values of sin, cos and tan for 0°, 90°, 180°, 270° and 360°

Both diagrams below represent the unit circle but using two different notations to describe any point p on the circle.

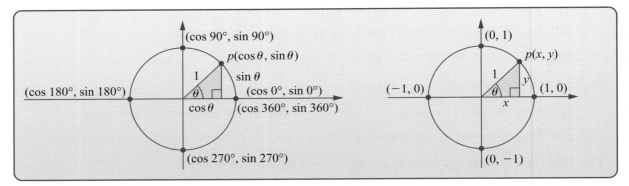

By comparing corresponding points on both unit circles, the values of sin, cos and tan for 0°, 90°, 180°, 270° and 360° can be read directly.

$(\cos 0°, \sin 0°) = (\cos 360°, \sin 360°) = (1, 0)$	$(\cos 90°, \sin 90°) = (0, 1)$
$\cos 0° = \cos 360° = 1$	$\cos 90° = 0$
$\sin 0° = \sin 360° = 0$	$\sin 90° = 1$
$\tan 0° = \tan 360° = \frac{0}{1} = 0$	$\tan 90° = \frac{1}{0}$ (undefined)
$(\cos 180°, \sin 180°) = (-1, 0)$	$(\cos 270°, \sin 270°) = (0, -1)$
$\cos 180° = -1$	$\cos 270° = 0$
$\sin 180° = 0$	$\sin 270° = -1$
$\tan 180° = \frac{0}{-1} = 0$	$\tan 270° = \frac{-1}{0}$ (undefined)

Note: Division by zero is undefined.

The x- and y-axes divide the plane into four quadrants. Consider the unit circle on the right:

$$\cos \theta = x \qquad \sin \theta = y$$

$$\tan \theta = \frac{\sin \theta}{\cos \theta} = \frac{y}{x}$$

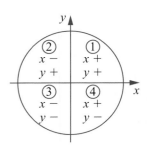

By examining the signs of x and y in the four quadrants, the signs of $\sin \theta$, $\cos \theta$ and $\tan \theta$ for any value of θ can be found.

Summary of signs

1st quadrant: sin, cos and tan are all positive.
2nd quadrant: sin is positive, cos and tan are negative.
3rd quadrant: tan is positive, sin and cos are negative.
4th quadrant: cos is positive, sin and tan are negative.

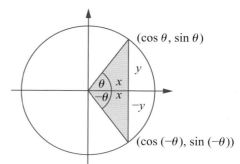

A very useful memory aid, *CAST*, in the diagram on the right, shows the ratios that are positive for the angles between 0° and 360°.

Negative angles

Consider the unit circle showing angles θ and $-\theta$.

$$\cos \theta = x \qquad \sin \theta = y \qquad \tan \theta = \frac{y}{x}$$

$$\cos(-\theta) = x \qquad \sin(-\theta) = -y \qquad \tan(-\theta) = -\frac{y}{x}$$

Thus:

$$\boxed{\cos(-\theta) = \cos \theta \qquad \sin(-\theta) = -\sin \theta \qquad \tan(-\theta) = -\tan \theta}$$

Reference angle

Each angle θ in the four quadrants has a **reference angle**, denoted by *R* in the diagram. The reference angle is the acute angle to the nearest horizontal. It can be calculated as follows:

Quadrant 1: $R = \theta$
Quadrant 2: $R = 180° - \theta$
Quadrant 3: $R = \theta - 180°$
Quadrant 4: $R = 360° - \theta$

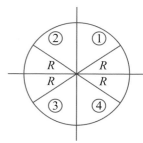

However, it is often easier to calculate the reference angle by drawing a rough diagram.

Note: The reference angle is also called the **related angle**.

To find the trigonometric ratio for any angle between 0° and 360°, do the following.

1. Draw a rough diagram of the angle.

2. Determine in which quadrant the angle lies and use $\begin{array}{|c|c|} \hline S & A \\ \hline T & C \\ \hline \end{array}$ to find its sign.

3. Find its **reference** angle (acute angle to nearest horizontal).

4. Use the trigonometric ratio of the reference angle with the sign in step 2.

EXAMPLE

Find cos 210°, leaving your answer in surd form.

Solution:
1. The diagram shows the angle 210°.
2. 210° is in the 3rd quadrant.
   cos is negative in the 3rd quadrant.
3. Reference angle is 30° (210° − 180°).
4. ∴ cos 210°
   $$= -\cos 30°$$
   $$= -\frac{\sqrt{3}}{2}$$

   (or use page 13 of the formulae and tables booklet)

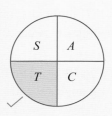

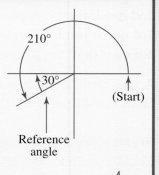

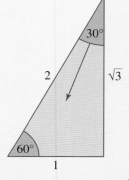

Exercise 9.4

In questions 1–8, write down the reference angle for the given angle.

1. 120°
2. 225°
3. 330°
4. 150°
5. −200°
6. −140°
7. $\frac{5\pi}{6}$
8. $\frac{4\pi}{3}$

In questions 9–27, write down the exact value of the given angle.

9. sin 150°
10. cos 315°
11. tan 120°
12. tan 210°
13. cos 120°
14. sin 135°
15. tan 330°
16. cos 150°
17. sin 120°
18. tan 240°
19. $\cos \frac{3\pi}{4}$
20. $\sin \frac{7\pi}{6}$
21. cos(−120°)
22. tan(−60°)
23. $\sin\left(-\frac{4\pi}{3}\right)$
24. $\cos\left(-\frac{5\pi}{6}\right)$
25. sin(−330°) cos(60°)
26. cos 120° tan 240°
27. $\tan \frac{4\pi}{3} \tan \frac{5\pi}{3}$

28. $\cos A = -\frac{1}{2}$. If $0° < A < 180°$, find the angle A.

29. $\sin A = \frac{1}{\sqrt{2}}$. If $90° < A < 180°$, find the angle A.

30. $\tan A = -1$. If $270° < A < 360°$, find the angle A.

General form

We can add or subtract any number of full rotations, $n(360°)$ or $2n\pi$ radians, where $n \in \mathbb{Z}$, to any angle without changing its sine, cosine or tangent. For example:

$$\sin 750° = \sin (750° - 360°) = \sin (390° - 360°) = \sin 30° = \tfrac{1}{2}$$

$$\cos (-210°) = \cos (-210° + 360°) = \cos (150°) = -\cos 30° = -\frac{\sqrt{3}}{2}$$

For $n \in \mathbb{Z}$:

$$\sin A = \sin (A + n(360°)) \qquad \text{or} \qquad \sin (A + 2n\pi)$$

$$\cos A = \cos (A + n(360°)) \qquad \text{or} \qquad \cos (A + 2n\pi)$$

$$\tan A = \tan (A + n(360°)) \qquad \text{or} \qquad \tan (A + 2n\pi)$$

This is known as **general angle form**.

Solving trigonometric equations

Between $0°$ and $360°$ there may be two angles with the same trigonometric ratios. For example, $\cos 120° = -\tfrac{1}{2}$ and $\cos 240° = -\tfrac{1}{2}$. Also, $\cos (120° + n(360°)) = \cos (240° + n(360°)) = -\tfrac{1}{2}$ for $n \in \mathbb{Z}$.

To solve a trigonometric equation, do the following.

1. Ignore the sign and calculate the reference angle.
2. From the sign of the given ratio, decide in which quadrants the angles lie.
3. Using a rough diagram, state the angles between $0°$ and $360°$.
4. If required, write down the general solution.

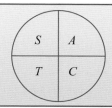

Maximum and minimum values for simple trigonometric equations

If $\sin \theta = k$, then	$-1 \leq k \leq 1$	min. value $= -1$, max. value $= 1$
If $\cos \theta = k$, then	$-1 \leq k \leq 1$	min. value $= -1$, max. value $= 1$
If $\tan \theta = k$, then	$k \in \mathbb{R}$	any value, $-\infty$ to ∞

Solving trigonometric equations 1

EXAMPLE 1

Solve the equation $\sin \theta = \dfrac{1}{\sqrt{2}}$ for $\theta \in \mathbb{R}$, where θ is in degrees.

Solution:

$\theta \in \mathbb{R}$ (this is asking for the general solution).

1. Find the reference angle.

$$\sin \theta = \frac{1}{\sqrt{2}}$$

$$\theta = \sin^{-1}\left(\frac{1}{\sqrt{2}}\right) = 45° \text{ (reference angle)}$$

2. sin is positive in the 1st and 2nd quadrants.

3. Rough diagram.

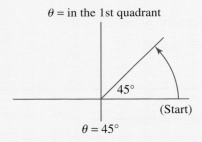

$\theta =$ in the 1st quadrant

$45°$

(Start)

$\theta = 45°$

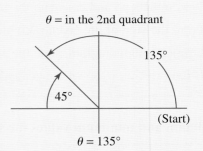

$\theta =$ in the 2nd quadrant

$135°$

$45°$

(Start)

$\theta = 135°$

Thus, if $\sin \theta = \dfrac{1}{\sqrt{2}}$, $\theta = 45°$ or $135°$.

4. General solution:

$$45° + n(360°) \qquad \text{or} \qquad 135° + n(360°) \text{ for } n \in \mathbb{Z}$$

This is known as the general solution to the equation $\sin \theta = \dfrac{1}{\sqrt{2}}$.

Note: It is essential to include $n \in \mathbb{Z}$.

EXAMPLE 2

Solve the equation $\cos 3\theta = \frac{1}{2}$ for **(i)** $\theta \in \mathbb{R}$ **(ii)** $0 \leq \theta \leq 2\pi$, where θ is in radians.

Solution:

(i) $\theta \in \mathbb{R}$ (this is asking for the general solution).

    1. Find the reference angle.

$$\cos 3\theta = \frac{1}{2}$$

$$3\theta = \cos^{-1}\left(\frac{1}{2}\right) = \frac{\pi}{3} \text{ (reference angle)}$$

    2. cos is positive in the 1st and 4th quadrants.

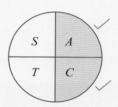

    3. Rough diagram

3θ in the 1st quadrant

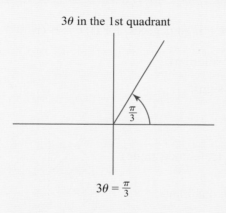

$3\theta = \frac{\pi}{3}$

3θ in the 4th quadrant

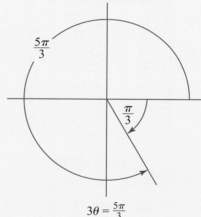

$3\theta = \frac{5\pi}{3}$

Thus, if $\cos 3\theta = \frac{1}{2}$, then $3\theta = \frac{\pi}{3}$ or $\frac{5\pi}{3}$.

    4. General angle form:

$$3\theta = \frac{\pi}{3} + 2n\pi \quad \text{or} \quad 3\theta = \frac{5\pi}{3} + 2n\pi$$

$$\theta = \frac{\pi}{9} + \frac{2n\pi}{3} \quad \text{or} \quad \theta = \frac{5\pi}{9} + \frac{2n\pi}{3}$$

$$\theta = \frac{\pi + 6n\pi}{9} \quad \text{or} \quad \theta = \frac{5\pi + 6n\pi}{9} \text{ for } n \in \mathbb{Z}$$

This is known as the general solution to the equation $\cos 3\theta = \frac{1}{2}$ for $n \in \mathbb{Z}$.

Note: It is essential to write the angle in general angle form **before** dividing by 3.

(ii) $0 \leq \theta \leq 2\pi$

What we do is let $n = 0, 1, 2, 3 \ldots$ until we go outside the domain $0 \leq \theta \leq 2\pi$.

$$\theta = \frac{\pi + 6n\pi}{9} \qquad\qquad \theta = \frac{5\pi + 6n\pi}{9}$$

$n = 0$: $\theta = \dfrac{\pi}{9}$ $\qquad\qquad$ $n = 0$: $\theta = \dfrac{5\pi}{9}$

$n = 1$: $\theta = \dfrac{\pi + 6\pi}{9} = \dfrac{7\pi}{9}$ $\qquad$ $n = 1$: $\theta = \dfrac{5\pi + 6\pi}{9} = \dfrac{11\pi}{9}$

$n = 2$: $\theta = \dfrac{\pi + 12\pi}{9} = \dfrac{13\pi}{9}$ $\qquad$ $n = 2$: $\theta = \dfrac{5\pi + 12\pi}{9} = \dfrac{17\pi}{9}$

Using $n = 3, 4, 5 \ldots$ brings us outside the domain $0 \leq \theta \leq 2\pi$.

Therefore, the solutions are $\dfrac{\pi}{9}, \dfrac{5\pi}{9}, \dfrac{7\pi}{9}, \dfrac{11\pi}{9}, \dfrac{13\pi}{9}$ and $\dfrac{17\pi}{9}$.

EXAMPLE 3

Solve the equation $\tan 2\theta = -\dfrac{1}{\sqrt{3}}$, where θ is in degrees, for **(i)** $\theta \in \mathbb{R}$ **(ii)** $0 \leq \theta \leq 360°$.

(i) $\theta \in \mathbb{R}$ (this is asking for the general solution).

   1. Find the reference angle (ignore sign).

$$\tan 2\theta = \frac{1}{\sqrt{3}}$$

$$2\theta = \tan^{-1}\left(\frac{1}{\sqrt{3}}\right) = 30° \text{ (reference angle)}$$

   2. tan is negative in the 2nd and 4th quadrants.

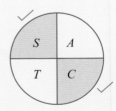

   3. Rough diagram

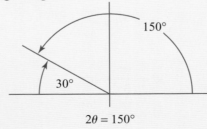

$$2\theta = 150°$$

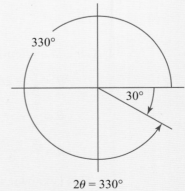

$$2\theta = 330°$$

4. General solution:

$$2\theta = 150° + n(360°) \qquad \text{or} \qquad 2\theta = 330° + n(360°)$$
$$\theta = 75° + n(180°) \qquad \text{or} \qquad \theta = 165° + n(180°), \, n \in \mathbb{Z}$$

This is known as the general solution to the equation $\tan 2\theta = -\dfrac{1}{\sqrt{3}}$.

Note: It is essential to write the angle in general form **before** dividing by 2.

(ii) $0° \le \theta \le 360°$

What we do is let $n = 0, 1, 2, 3 \ldots$ until we go outside the domain $0 \le \theta \le 360°$.

$$\theta = 75° + n(180°) \qquad\qquad\qquad \theta = 165° + n(180°)$$

$n = 0$: $\quad \theta = 75°$ $\qquad\qquad\qquad$ $n = 0$: $\quad \theta = 165°$

$n = 1$: $\quad \theta = 75° + 180° = 255°$ $\qquad$ $n = 1$: $\quad \theta = 165° + 180° = 345°$

Putting $n = 2, 3, 4 \ldots$ brings us outside the domain $0 \le \theta \le 360°$.

Therefore, the solutions are $75°, 165°, 255°$ and $345°$.

Note: As we will see later, the period of $\tan \theta$ is $180°$ or π radians. Thus, an alternative general solution to the equation $\tan 2\theta = -\frac{1}{\sqrt{3}}$, θ in degrees and $\theta \in \mathbb{R}$, is given by:

$$2\theta = 150° + n(180°)$$
$$\theta = 75° + n(90°), \, n \in \mathbb{Z}$$

This will generate all the same solutions as the solution in the example above.

Exercise 9.5

In questions 1–3, solve the equation, θ in degrees, for (i) $\theta \in \mathbb{R}$ (ii) $0° \le \theta \le 360°$.

1. $\sin \theta = \dfrac{1}{2}$ $\qquad\qquad$ 2. $\cos \theta = \dfrac{\sqrt{3}}{2}$ $\qquad\qquad$ 3. $\tan \theta = -1$

In questions 4–6, solve the equation, θ in radians, for (i) $\theta \in \mathbb{R}$ (ii) $0 \le \theta \le 2\pi$.

4. $\tan \theta = \sqrt{3}$ $\qquad\qquad$ 5. $\sin \theta = -\dfrac{1}{\sqrt{2}}$ $\qquad\qquad$ 6. $\cos \theta = -\dfrac{\sqrt{3}}{2}$

In questions 7–9, solve the equation, θ in degrees, for (i) $\theta \in \mathbb{R}$ (ii) $0° \le \theta \le 360°$.

7. $\cos 2\theta = \dfrac{1}{2}$ $\qquad\qquad$ 8. $\sin 3\theta = -\dfrac{\sqrt{3}}{2}$ $\qquad\qquad$ 9. $\tan 3\theta = \dfrac{1}{\sqrt{3}}$

In questions 10–12, solve the equation, θ in radians, for (i) $\theta \in \mathbb{R}$ (ii) $0 \le \theta \le 2\pi$.

10. $\sqrt{2} \sin 3\theta + 1 = 0$ $\qquad$ 11. $\tan 5\theta - 1 = 0$ $\qquad\qquad$ 12. $2 \cos 3\theta + 1 = 0$

In questions 13–15, solve the equation, θ in degrees, for (i) $\theta \in \mathbb{R}$ (ii) $0° \le \theta \le 360°$.

13. $\sin \theta = 0$ $\qquad\qquad\qquad$ 14. $\sin \theta = 1$ $\qquad\qquad\qquad$ 15. $\cos \theta = 0$

In questions 16–21, solve the equation, θ in radians, for (i) $\theta \in \mathbb{R}$ (ii) $0 \leq \theta \leq 2\pi$.

16. $\cos \theta = 1$

17. $\tan \theta = 0$

18. $\cos \theta = -1$

19. $\cos 2\theta = 0$

20. $\sin 3\theta = -1$

21. $\tan 4\theta = 0$

In questions 22–24, solve the equation, θ in degrees, for (i) $\theta \in \mathbb{R}$ (ii) $0° \leq \theta \leq 360°$ (answers correct to one decimal place).

22. $\sin \theta = 0.2$

23. $\cos 2\theta = 0.3$

24. $\tan 3\theta = 1.94$

25. If $0° < A < 180°$, is it possible to find a value for A such that $\sin A = -\dfrac{1}{2}$? Discuss.

26. If $270° < A < 360°$, is it possible to find a value for A such that $\tan A = \sqrt{3}$? Discuss.

Solving non-right-angled triangles

Area of a triangle

Area of triangle $ABC = \frac{1}{2}ab \sin C = \frac{1}{2}ac \sin B = \frac{1}{2}bc \sin A$.

Note: The first form, $A = \frac{1}{2}ab \sin C$, is given on page 9 in the booklet of formulae and tables.

To use this formula to find the area of a triangle, we need the length of two sides **and** the size of the angle between these sides.

Area of triangle $= \frac{1}{2}$(side)(side)(sine of angle **between** these sides)

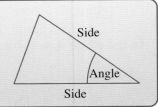

Note: Another method to find the area of triangle ABC:

Area $\triangle ABC = \sqrt{s(s - a)(s - b)(s - c)}$

where $s = \dfrac{a + b + c}{2}$

This formula is given on page 9 in the booklet of formulae and tables.

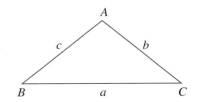

EXAMPLE 1

In triangle ABC, $|AB| = 3$ cm, $|BC| = 10$ cm and $|\angle ABC| = 62°$. Calculate the area of triangle ABC, correct to one decimal place.

Solution:
Let $B = |\angle ABC| = 62°$
$\quad a = |BC| = 10$
and $c = |AB| = 3$
Area $\triangle ABC = \frac{1}{2}ac \sin B$

$\qquad = \frac{1}{2}(10)(3) \sin 62°$

$\qquad = 13 \cdot 24421389$

$\qquad = 13 \cdot 2$ cm^2 $\qquad$ (correct to one decimal place)

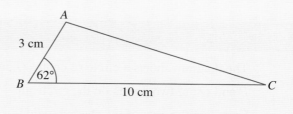

In some questions, we are given an equation in disguise.

EXAMPLE 2

In triangle PQR, $|PQ| = 14$ cm and $|PR| = 10$ cm. If the area of triangle PQR is 45 cm^2, find, correct to the nearest degree, two possible values for $|\angle QPR|$. Draw rough sketches of both triangles. Explain why there are two possible triangles.

Solution:
Let $|PR| = q$, $|PQ| = r$ and $|\angle QPR| = P$.
Equation given in disguise:
Area of triangle $PQR = 45$ m^2
$\therefore \qquad \frac{1}{2}qr \sin P = 45$
$\frac{1}{2}(10)(14) \sin P = 45$
$\qquad 70 \sin P = 45$
$\qquad \sin P = \frac{45}{70}$
$\qquad P = \sin^{-1}\left(\frac{45}{70}\right)$
$\qquad P = 40 \cdot 00520088°$
$\qquad P = 40°$
(correct to the nearest degree)
Second value for $P = 180° - 40° = 140°$.

Rough sketches

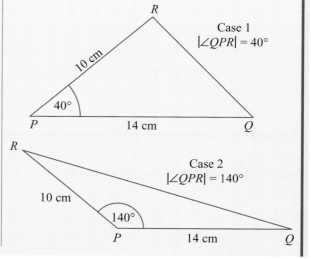

There are two possible triangles PQR that satisfy the above conditions because $\sin A = \sin(180° - A)$ for all values of A and sine is positive in the 1st and 2nd quadrants. In particular, $\sin 40° = \sin 140°$.

EXAMPLE 3

The diagram shows a circle of centre O and radius 6 cm. P and Q are two points on the circle and $|\angle POQ| = \dfrac{2\pi}{3}$. Calculate the area of the shaded region, leaving your answer in terms of π.

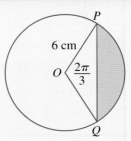

Solution:

Area of shaded region =

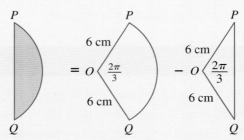

Area of shaded region = area of sector − area of triangle

$$= \tfrac{1}{2}r^2\theta \qquad\qquad - \tfrac{1}{2}ab\sin C$$

$$= \tfrac{1}{2}(6)(6)\left(\frac{2\pi}{3}\right) - \tfrac{1}{2}(6)(6)\sin\frac{2\pi}{3}$$

$$= 12\pi - 18\left(\frac{\sqrt{3}}{2}\right) \qquad \left(\sin\frac{2\pi}{3} = \frac{\sqrt{3}}{2}\right)$$

$$= 12\pi - 9\sqrt{3}$$

$$= 3(4\pi - 3\sqrt{3}) \text{ cm}^2$$

Note: The shaded region is called a **segment** of a circle.

Exercise 9.6

In questions 1–6, find, correct to two decimal places, the area of the triangle, where all lengths are in centimetres.

1.

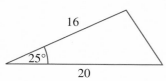

2.

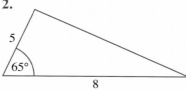

3.

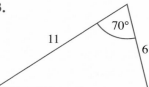

4.

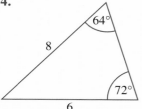

5.

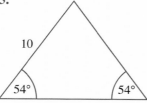

6.

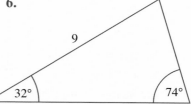

In questions 7–9, find, exactly, the area of the triangle, where all lengths are in centimetres.

7.

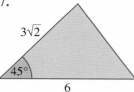

8.

9.

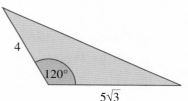

In questions 10 and 11, find, correct to two decimal places, the area of the parallelogram, where all lengths are in centimetres.

10.

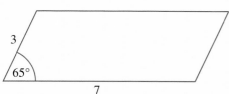

11.

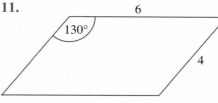

12. The diagram shows the quadrilateral $PQSR$.
$QP \perp PR$, $|PQ| = 2{\cdot}4$ cm, $|PR| = 1{\cdot}8$ cm, $|RS| = 2$ cm
and $|\angle QRS| = 70°$. Calculate:

    (i) $|QR|$

    (ii) The area of triangle PQR

    (iii) The area of $PQSR$, correct to two decimal places

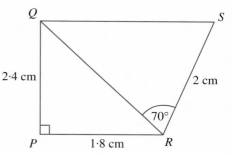

13. In the given triangle, $\cos A = \frac{4}{5}$. Without calculating A, find the area of the triangle exactly.

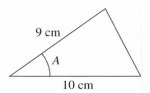

14. The area of triangle ABC is 28 cm². If $|AB| = 8$ cm and $|\angle ABC| = 30°$, find $|BC|$.

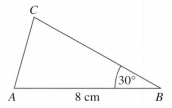

15. In triangle PQR, $|PQ| = 18$ cm and $|\angle QPR| = 40°$. If the area of triangle PQR is 92·56 cm², find $|PR|$, correct to the nearest centimetre.

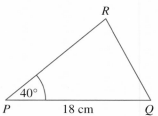

16. In triangle ABC, $|AB| = \sqrt{2}\,x$ cm, $|BC| = 5$ cm and $|\angle ABC| = 45°$. If the area of triangle $ABC = 17·5$ cm², find the value of x.

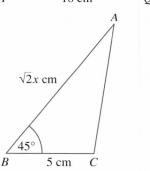

17. The area of the triangle shown on the right is 6 cm². Find the value of x.

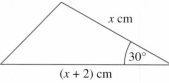

18. The area of the triangle shown is 12 square units. Find two different values of A and make a sketch of both triangles.

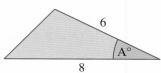

19. In triangle PQR, $|PQ| = 12$ cm and $|PR| = 8$ cm. If the area of triangle PQR is 43·5 cm², find, correct to the nearest degree, two possible values for $|\angle QPR|$. Draw rough sketches of both triangles. Explain why there are two possible triangles.

20. In $\triangle PQR$, $|QR| = 16$, $|PQ| = 10$ and $|\angle PQR| = |\angle PRQ|$.

    (i) Write down the value of $|PR|$. Justify your answer.

    (ii) Calculate the perpendicular distance from P to QR.

    (iii) Hence, write down the ratio $\sin Q$.

    (iv) Calculate the area of $\triangle PQR$ using:

        (a) $\frac{1}{2}bh$ **(b)** $\frac{1}{2}pq\sin R$

        (c) $\sqrt{s(s-p)(s-q)(s-r)}$, where $s = \dfrac{p+q+r}{2}$

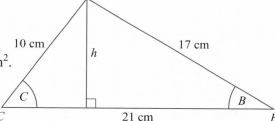

21. In $\triangle ABC$, $|BC| = 21$ cm, $|AB| = 17$ cm and $|AC| = 10$ cm.

    (i) Using the formula area $= \sqrt{s(s-a)(s-b)(s-c)}$, where $s = \dfrac{a+b+c}{2}$, show that the area of $\triangle ABC = 84$ cm^2.

    (ii) Hence or otherwise, calculate h, the distance from A to BC.

    (iii) Write down: **(a)** $\sin C$ **(b)** $\sin B$.

    (iv) Verify that $\frac{1}{2}ab\sin C = \frac{1}{2}ac\sin B = 84$ cm^2.

    (v) Calculate the perpendicular distance from B to AC.

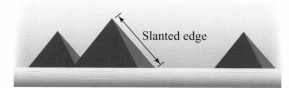

22. The great pyramid at Giza in Egypt has a square base and four triangular faces.

The base of the pyramid is of side 230 metres and the pyramid is 146 metres high.

The top of the pyramid is directly above the centre of the base.

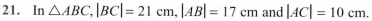

Slanted edge

    (i) Calculate the length of one of the slanted edges, correct to the nearest metre.

    (ii) Calculate, correct to two significant figures, the total area of the four triangular faces of the pyramid (assuming they are smooth, flat surfaces).

23.

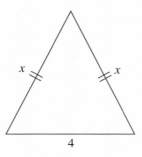

The area of the isosceles triangle is $2\sqrt{21}$. Find the value of x.

24.

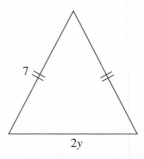

The area of the isosceles triangle is $6\sqrt{5}$. Find the value of y, where $y \in \mathbb{N}$.

25. **(i)** The area of an equilateral triangle is $121\sqrt{3}$ cm. Find the length of a side of the triangle.
(ii) If the lengths of the sides are doubled, is the area doubled? Justify your answer.

26. In the triangle PQR, $\cos |\angle QPR| = \dfrac{1}{x}$.

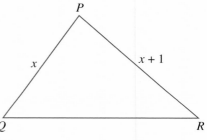

(i) Show that $\sin |\angle QPR| = \dfrac{\sqrt{x^2 - 1}}{x}$.

(ii) Hence, show that the area of the triangle can be written as $\frac{1}{2}(x + 1)^{\frac{3}{2}}(x - 1)^{\frac{1}{2}}$.

(iii) When $x = 17$, find the area of the triangle PQR. Write your answer in the form $a\sqrt{b}$, where b is prime.

27. ABC is a triangle with sides of lengths a, b and c, as shown. Its incircle has centre O and radius r.

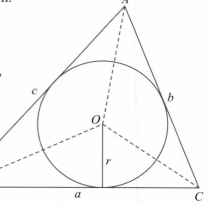

(i) Show that the area of $\triangle ABC$ is $\frac{1}{2}r(a + b + c)$.

(ii) The lengths of the sides of a triangle are $a = p^2 + q^2$, $b = p^2 - q^2$ and $c = 2pq$, where p and q are natural numbers and $p > q$. Show that this triangle is right-angled.

(iii) Show that the radius of the incircle of the triangle in part **(ii)** is a whole number.

28. **(i)** A department store is refitting the building it occupies into individual retail units. One such unit is bounded by a wall and a customer walkway. The customer walkway makes an angle of 68° with the wall. If the customer walkway frontage is 6·5 m, how far along the wall should the retail unit extend if the area is to be 40 m²? Give your answer correct to the nearest cm.

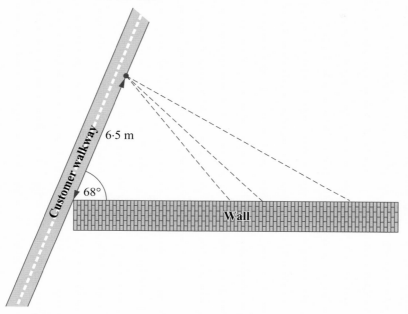

(ii) A retailer has an annual budget of €16,800 for rent. Given the department store charges a monthly rent of €28 per m² on the retail unit, find how far along the wall the retail unit should extend if it is made big enough to justify an annual rent of €16,800. Give your answer correct to the nearest cm.

29. The chord $[PQ]$ of a circle of radius 12 cm is subtended by an angle at the centre of $\dfrac{5\pi}{6}$, as shown in the diagram. Calculate the area of the shaded region, leaving your answer in terms of π.

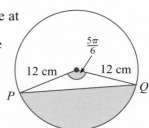

30. O is the centre of the circle of radius 6 cm. A and B are points on the circle and $|\angle AOB| = \dfrac{2\pi}{3}$. Find the area of the minor segment (shaded region). Write your answer in the form $a(b\pi - a\sqrt{a})$, where $a, b \in \mathbb{N}$.

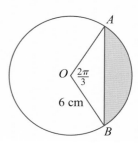

31. The diagram shows a circle of centre O and radius
    8 cm. A and B are points on the circle such that
    $|\angle AOB| = 135°$.

    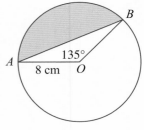

    (i) Express 135° in radians.

    (ii) Find the area of the shaded region. Write your answer
    in the form $a(b\pi - c\sqrt{c})$ where a, b and $c \in \mathbb{N}$.

32. The diagram shows a circle of centre O and radius r.
    P and Q are points on the circle and $|\angle POQ| = \theta$.
    The chord $[PQ]$ divides the circle into a minor segment
    (shaded region) and a major segment such that the ratio
    of the areas of the segments are $2 : 3$.

    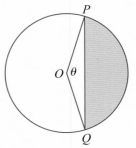

    (i) Show that the area of the minor segment is $\dfrac{1}{2}r^2\left(\theta - \sin\theta\right)$.

    (ii) Show that the area of the major segment is $r^2\left(\pi - \dfrac{\theta}{2} + \dfrac{\sin\theta}{2}\right)$.

    (iii) Show that $\sin\theta = \theta - \dfrac{4\pi}{5}$.

33. The diagram shows three beer mats, each of radius 6 cm,
    so that each touches the other two, as shown. Find the area
    between the mats. Write your answer in the form $a(b\sqrt{3} - \pi)$ cm^2.

34. A belt passes around two circular wheels,
    as shown. One wheel has a radius of 75 cm
    and the other has a radius of 15 cm.
    The centres, E and F, of the wheels
    are 120 cm apart.

    The belt consists of the common
    tangent $[AB]$, the minor arc BC, the
    common tangent $[CD]$ and the major
    arc DA.

    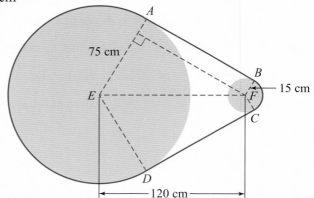

    (i) Find $|\angle AEF|$.

    (ii) Find $|AB|$ in surd form.

    (iii) Find the length, l, of the belt, giving your
    answer in the form $k\pi + l\sqrt{3}$ where $k, l \in \mathbb{N}$.

35. The diagram shows a circle of centre O and radius a. P, R, S and Q are points on the circumference such that $|\angle POQ| = \dfrac{3\pi}{4}$ and $|\angle ROS| = \dfrac{\pi}{4}$. Show that the area of the shaded region is $\frac{1}{4}\pi a^2$.

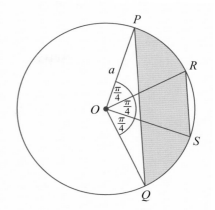

36. The diagram shows a circle of radius r and diameter $[PQ]$. The point R is the midpoint of the arc PQ. A circle with centre R passes through the points P and Q.

   (i) Express $|RP|$ in terms of r.

   (ii) Show that the area of the shaded region is r^2.

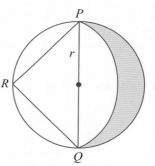

37. The diagram shows two concentric circles. A tangent to the inner circle cuts the outer circle at B and C, where $|BC| = 2x$.

   (i) Express the area of the shaded region in terms of x.

   (ii) In the case where the radius of the outer circle is $2x$, show that the portion of the shaded region that lies below BC has area $\left(\dfrac{2\pi}{3} - \sqrt{3}\right)x^2$.

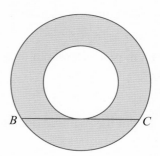

Sine rule

In any triangle ABC:

$$\frac{a}{\sin A} = \frac{b}{\sin B} = \frac{c}{\sin C}$$

or:

$$\frac{\sin A}{a} = \frac{\sin B}{b} = \frac{\sin C}{c}$$

(The first form is given on page 16 in the booklet of formulae and tables.)

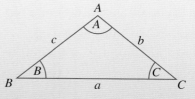

This is known as the **sine rule** and it applies to any triangle, including a right-angled triangle.

The sine rule can be used to:

1. Find an unknown side, *a*. Using the sine rule, we need two angles and one side.

    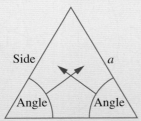

    If we know two angles, we can calculate the third angle, as the three angles add up to 180°.

2. Find an unknown angle, *A*°. Using the sine rule, we need two sides and the size of one angle opposite one of these sides.

    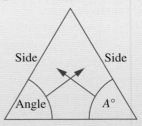

    The unknown angle, *A*°, must be opposite a known side.

Use the sine rule if you know:

1. Two angles and one side.
2. Two sides and an angle opposite one of these sides.

The sine rule connects each side with its opposite angle in a triangle.

Notes: 1. In practice we put only two fractions equal to each other. For example:

$$\frac{a}{\sin A} = \frac{b}{\sin B}$$

2. Put the required quantity, side or angle on the top of the first fraction.

To find *a*, use $\dfrac{a}{\sin A} = \dfrac{b}{\sin B}$.

To find *B*, use $\dfrac{\sin B}{b} = \dfrac{\sin A}{a}$.

Cosine rule

In any triangle ABC:

      side opposite   chosen
      chosen angle   angle
         ↓   ↓

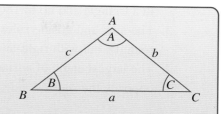

$$a^2 = b^2 + c^2 - 2bc \cos A$$
or $b^2 = a^2 + c^2 - 2ac \cos B$
or $c^2 = a^2 + b^2 - 2ab \cos C$

(The first form is given on page 16 in the booklet of formulae and tables.)

This is known as the **cosine rule** and it applies to any triangle, including a right-angled triangle.

The cosine rule can be used to:

1. Find the length of the third side, a, of a triangle when given the lengths of the other two sides and the angle contained between these sides.

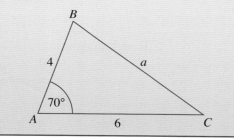

2. Find the measure of an angle, A, of a triangle when given the lengths of the three sides.

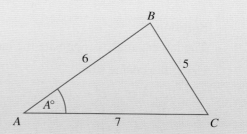

Note: In 1 and 2 above, the sine rule would not work.

If the unknown angle is between 90° and 180°, its cosine is negative.

For example, $\cos 120° = -\frac{1}{2}$.

Use the cosine rule if you know:

1. Two sides and the included angle.
2. The lengths of the three sides.

Notes:
1. As a general rule, if you cannot use the sine rule, then use the cosine rule.
2. If two angles are given, we can work out the third angle straight away, as the three angles in a triangle add up to 180°.
3. The sine and cosine rules and the area of a triangle formulae also apply to a right-angled triangle, but with right-angled triangles we usually use the basic trigonometric definitions.
4. The largest angle of a triangle is opposite the largest side and the smallest angle is opposite the shortest side. There can be only one obtuse angle in a triangle.

Tackling problems in trigonometry

1. If one is not given, draw a diagram and put in as much information as possible.
2. If two or more triangles are linked, redraw the triangles separately.
3. Watch for common sides that link the triangles (i.e. we can carry common values from one triangle to another triangle).
4. Use the sine or cosine rule as needed.

EXAMPLE 1

In triangle ABC, $|AB| = 3$ cm, $|AC| = 5$ cm and $|BC| = 7$ cm.
Calculate the measure of the largest angle of triangle ABC.

Solution:
The largest angle is opposite the largest side.

Using the cosine rule:
$$a^2 = b^2 + c^2 - 2bc \cos A$$
$$7^2 = 5^2 + 3^2 - 2(5)(3) \cos A$$
$$49 = 25 + 9 - 30 \cos A$$
$$30 \cos A = 25 + 9 - 49$$
$$30 \cos A = -15$$
$$\cos A = -\tfrac{1}{2}$$
$$A = \cos^{-1}\left(-\tfrac{1}{2}\right) = 120°$$

Rough diagram

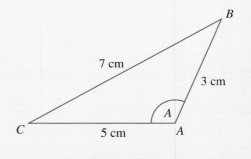

Ambiguous case

If $\sin A = \frac{\sqrt{3}}{2}$, then $A = 60°$ or $120°$: two possible solutions. Thus, we have to be very careful when using the sine rule to calculate an angle, as there may be two possible answers. Whenever we are given two sides and a non-included angle, there is a risk of having two triangles that satisfy the given conditions. However, it should not be assumed that there will always be two triangles satisfying the given conditions. For example, we might find that if we use the larger angle, the sum of the three angles in the triangle is greater than 180°. The ambiguous case arises only when the smaller of the two given sides is opposite the known angle.

EXAMPLE 2

In triangle ABC, $|BC| = 8$ cm, $|AC| = 9$ cm and $|\angle BAC| = 60°$. Find the possible values of $|\angle ABC|$ and $|\angle BCA|$, correct to the nearest degree. Sketch both triangles.

Solution:

Let $a = |BC|$, $b = |AC|$, $A = |\angle BAC|$, $B = |\angle ABC|$ and $C = |\angle BCA|$.

$\dfrac{\sin B}{b} = \dfrac{\sin A}{a}$ (B missing, put that first)

$\dfrac{\sin B}{9} = \dfrac{\sin 60°}{8}$

$\sin B = \dfrac{9 \sin 60°}{8}$

$B = \sin^{-1}\left(\dfrac{9 \sin 60°}{8}\right)$

$B = 77°$

(correct to the nearest degree)

or $B = 180° - 77° = 103°$

$A = 60°$, $B = 77°$, $C = 180° - 60° - 77° = 43°$

$A = 60°$, $B = 103°$, $C = 180° - 60° - 103° = 17°$

Two possible triangles

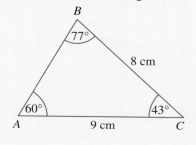

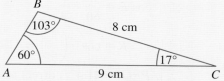

Note: In this example, the solution 103° is acceptable, because when this is added to the given angle, 60°, the total is not greater than 180°. If the sum of the two angles was greater than 180°, then only the smaller angle is acceptable.

There is no ambiguity when using the cosine rule. This is because cosine is positive in the 1st quadrant (giving an acute angle) but negative in the 2nd quadrant (giving an obtuse angle).

EXAMPLE 3

In the diagram, $|PQ| = 4$ cm, $|PR| = 5$ cm, $|QR| = 6$ cm and $|\angle PSR| = 22°$.
Find **(i)** $|\angle PRQ|$ **(ii)** $|PS|$.
Give both answers correct to one decimal place.

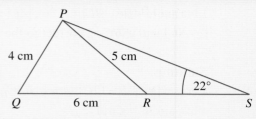

Solution:

(i) Consider triangle PQR separately. We are given the lengths of three sides. Thus, we use the cosine rule to find $|\angle PRQ|$.

Let $p = |QR|$, $q = |PR|$, $r = |PQ|$ and $|\angle R| = |\angle PRQ|$.

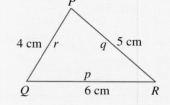

$$\cos R = \frac{p^2 + q^2 - r^2}{2pq} \quad \text{(cosine rule)}$$

$$\cos R = \frac{6^2 + 5^2 - 4^2}{2(6)(5)}$$

$$\cos R = \frac{45}{60} = \frac{3}{4}$$

$$R = \cos^{-1}\left(\frac{3}{4}\right) = 41 \cdot 40962211°$$

$\therefore |\angle PRQ| = 41 \cdot 4°$, correct to one decimal place.

(ii) Consider triangle PRS separately.
$|\angle PRS| = 180° - 41 \cdot 4° = 138 \cdot 6°$
We now use the sine rule to find $|PS|$.
Let $r = |PS|$, $s = |PR|$, $|\angle S| = |\angle PSR|$ and
$|\angle R| = |\angle PRS|$.

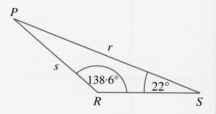

$$\frac{r}{\sin R} = \frac{s}{\sin S} \quad \text{(sine rule, } r \text{ missing so put that first)}$$

$$\frac{r}{\sin 138 \cdot 6°} = \frac{5}{\sin 22°} \quad \text{(put in known values)}$$

$$r = \frac{5 \sin 138 \cdot 6°}{\sin 22°} \quad \text{(multiply both sides by } \sin 138 \cdot 6°\text{)}$$

$$r = 8 \cdot 82671543$$

Thus, $|PS| = 8 \cdot 8$ cm (correct to one decimal place).

EXAMPLE 4

A vertical flagpole, [PS], of height h m, stands on horizontal ground. The angle of elevation of the top of the pole from a point Q on the ground is B. From a point R on the ground 10 m closer to the pole, the angle of elevation is A. Show that the height, h, of the pole is given by

$$h = \frac{10 \sin A \sin B}{\sin (A - B)}.$$

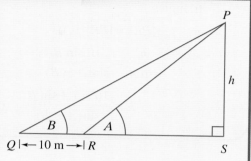

Solution:

First split the diagram into two separate triangles. The common side to both triangles is [PR]. We then find an expression for the common side separately and equate them.

Let $\angle C = \angle QPR$.

$$B + C = A \quad \text{(exterior angle)}$$
$$C = (A - B)$$

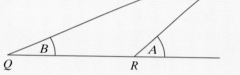

Consider the right-angled triangle PRS.

$$\sin A = \frac{h}{|PR|}$$
$$|PR| \sin A = h$$
$$|PR| = \frac{h}{\sin A}$$

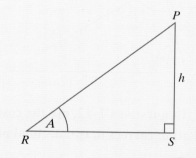

Consider the triangle PQR using the sine rule:

$$\frac{|PR|}{\sin B} = \frac{10}{\sin (A - B)}$$
$$|PR| = \frac{10 \sin B}{\sin (A - B)}$$

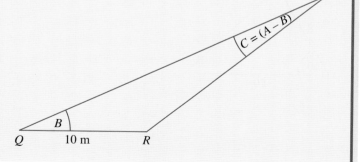

We now equate the two different expressions for $|PR|$, the common length on both triangles.

$$|PR| = |PR|$$

$$\frac{h}{\sin A} = \frac{10 \sin B}{\sin(A - B)}$$

$$h = \frac{10 \sin A \sin B}{\sin(A - B)} \qquad \text{(multiply both sides by } \sin A\text{)}$$

Exercise 9.7

In questions 1–6, find the value of a and the value of A, each correct to one decimal place.

1.

2.

3.

4.

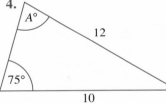

5.

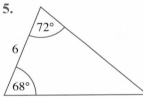

6.

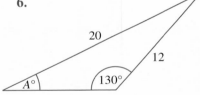

In questions 7–12, use the cosine rule to calculate:

(i) a, correct to two decimal places or (ii) A, correct to the nearest degree.

7.

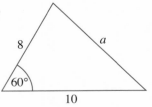

8.

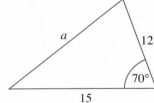

9.

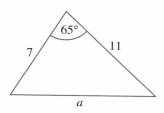

10.

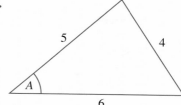

11.

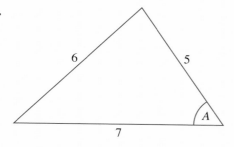

12.

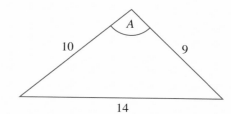

13. In the diagram, $PQ \perp SQ$, $|SR| = 60$ m, $|\angle PSR| = 42°$
and $|\angle PRQ| = 65°$. Calculate:

   (i) $|\angle SPR|$

  (ii) $|PR|$, correct to the nearest metre

 (iii) Hence or otherwise, calculate $|PQ|$ correct to the nearest metre

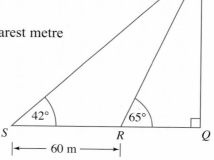

14. Use the sine rule to show that triangle ABC is an
impossible triangle.

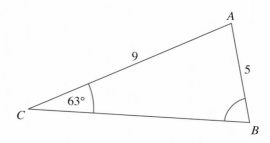

15. The lengths of the sides of a triangle are 21, 17 and 10.
The smallest angle in the triangle is A. Show that:

  (i) $\sin A = \frac{8}{17}$ **(ii)** $A = 28°$, correct to the nearest degree

16. Find, correct to one decimal place, the size of the smallest angle of the triangle which has sides of length 3, 5 and 7. Give your answer in degrees.

17. In the triangle ABC, $|AB| = 5$ cm, $|AC| = 8$ cm and $|\angle BAC| = \cos^{-1}(\frac{4}{5})$. Show that $|AB| = |BC|$.

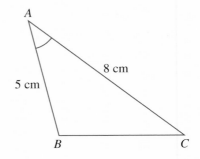

18. In triangle PQR, $|PQ| = 7$ cm, $|QR| = 5$ cm and $|\angle QPR| = 43°$. Find, correct to one decimal place, the value, or values, of $|\angle QRP|$.

19. In triangle ABC, $|BC| = 13$ cm, $|AC| = 11$ cm and $|\angle ABC| = 55°$. Find $|\angle BAC|$, correct to the nearest degree.

20. The area of triangle PQR is 21 cm². $|PQ| = 7$ cm and $|QR| = 6\sqrt{2}$ cm.
    (i) Find $|\angle PQR|$.
    (ii) Find $|PR|$, correct to one decimal place.

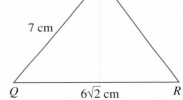

21. The area of an equilateral triangle is $4\sqrt{3}$ cm². Find the length of a side of the triangle.

22. In triangle XYZ, $|XY| = 8$ cm and $|YZ| = 6$ cm. The area of triangle XYZ is 12 cm².
    (i) Find the two possible values of $|\angle XYZ|$.
    (ii) Find the two possible values of $|XZ|$, correct to one decimal place.

23. The diagram shows triangle ABC. $|AB| = x$ cm, $|AC| = (x + 3)$ cm, $|BC| = (2x + 1)$ cm and $x > 1$. $|\angle BAC| = 60°$.
    (i) Use the cosine rule to show that x must satisfy the equation $3x^2 + x - 8 = 0$.
    (ii) Solve $3x^2 + x - 8 = 0$ to find the value of x, correct to one decimal place. Why is there only one value for x and not two values?

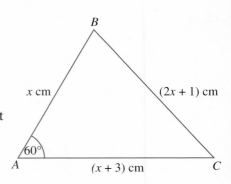

24. A rectangular block of cheese measures
16 cm × 16 cm × 8 cm.

One corner is cut away from the block in such
a way that three of the edges are cut through
their midpoints A, B and C.

Find the area of the triangular face ABC created
by the cut.

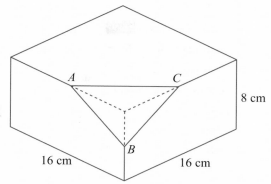

25. A triangle has sides of lengths a, b and c. The angle opposite the side of length a is A.
   (i) Prove that $a^2 = b^2 + c^2 - 2bc \cos A$.
   (ii) If a, b and c are consecutive whole numbers, show that $\cos A = \dfrac{a+5}{2a+4}$.

26. In triangle PQR, $|\angle QPR| = 120°$.
   (i) Show that
      $p^2 = q^2 + r^2 + qr$.
   (ii) Show that $p = 7$, $q = 5$ and
      $r = 3$ is one possible solution
      to the equation in part **(i)**.
   (iii) Attempt to find (guess) one
      other solution to the equation in
      part **(i)** for which p, q and r are
      integers and not multiples of 7, 5 and 3.

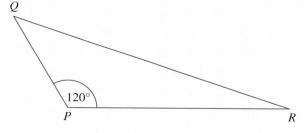

27. A snooker player cues the white (W) ball onto the cushion to rebound and hit the red (R)
ball, as shown in the diagram. The white ball travels 85 cm before being deflected 88° by
the cushion. It then travels 30 cm before hitting the red ball. The white ball then returns in a
straight line to its original position. Find the total distance travelled by the white ball,
correct to the nearest centimetre.

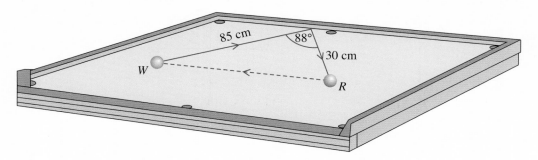

28. The goal posts on a soccer field are 8 m apart. A player kicks for a goal when he is 30 m from one post and 25 m from the other.

Find the angle opposite the goal line, measured from both goal posts to where the ball is positioned, correct to the nearest degree.

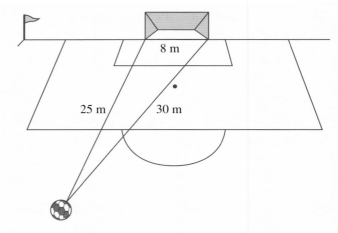

29. **(i)** A surveyor wishes to measure the height of a church. Measuring the angle of elevation, she finds that the angle increases from 30° to 40° after walking 25 m towards the church. What is the height of the church correct to the nearest metre?

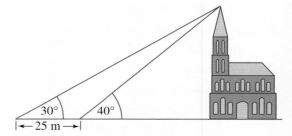

(ii) Name an instrument the surveyor could use to measure the angles of elevation.

(iii) Describe how that instrument is used to obtain one of the angles.

30. A ship, Q, is 37 km from a port, P. The direction of Q from P is N 45° E. A second ship, R, is 53 km from P. The direction of R from Q is S 75° E.

(i) Calculate $|\angle QRP|$, correct to one decimal place.

(ii) Calculate $|QR|$, correct to two decimal places.

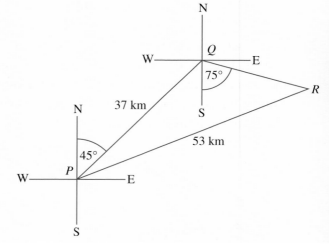

31. At 12:00 a ship, *S*, and a yacht, *Y*, set sail from a port, *P*. The ship sails on a bearing of N 43° E at a constant speed of 20 km/hr. The yacht sails on a bearing of W 5° S at a constant speed of 15 km/hr.

   (i) Calculate the distance, correct to the nearest metre, between the ships at 14:00.

   (ii) Calculate the time of day, to the nearest minute, when the ship and the yacht are exactly 100 km apart.

32. A piece of land, *ABCD*, is to be divided evenly between two brothers. They measure the diagonal *AC* and because the perimeter of △ *ADC* is the same as the perimeter of △ *ABC*, brother Jack is given △ *ADC* and brother Tom is given △ *ABC*.

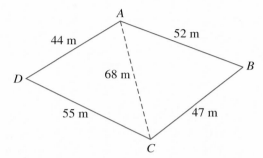

   (i) Which brother is in fact given the bigger piece of land?

   (ii) How much bigger is it, correct to one decimal place?

33. Windows are sometimes in the shape of a pointed arch, like the one shown in the picture.

A person is designing such an arched window. The outline is shown in the diagram next to the picture.

The centre for the arc *AB* is *C* and the centre for the arc *AC* is *B*. $|BD| = 2·4$ metres and $|DE| = 1·8$ metres.

   (i) Calculate $|\angle ABC|$. Justify your answer.

   (ii) Find the length of the arc *AB*. Give your answer in metres, correct to three decimal places.

   (iii) Find the length of the perimeter of the window. Give your answer in metres, correct to two decimal places.

   (iv) Find the height of the window. Give your answer in metres, correct to two decimal places.

   (v) Make an accurate scaled drawing of the outline of the window, using the scale 1:30, i.e. 1 cm on your diagram should represent 30 cm in reality.

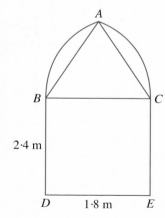

34. Roofs of buildings are often supported by frameworks of timber called *roof trusses*. A quantity surveyor needs to find the total length of timber needed in order to make the triangular truss shown below.

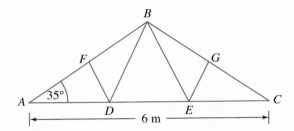

The length of [AC] is 6 m and the pitch of the roof is 35°, as shown.
$|AD| = |DE| = |EC|$ and $|AF| = |FB| = |BG| = |GC|$.
  (i) Calculate the length of [AB], in metres, correct to two decimal places.
  (ii) Calculate the total length of timber required to make the truss.

35. Two surveyors want to find the height of an electricity pylon. There is a fence around the pylon that they cannot cross for safety reasons. The ground is inclined at an angle. They have a clinometer (for measuring angles of elevation) and a 100-metre tape measure. They have already used the clinometer to determine that the ground is inclined at 10° to the horizontal.
  (i) Explain how they could find the height of the pylon. Your answer should be illustrated on the diagram. Show the points where you think they should take measurements, write down what measurements they should take and briefly outline how these can be used to find the height of the pylon.
  (ii) Write down possible values for the measurements taken and use them to show how to find the height of the pylon. (That is, find the height of the pylon using your measurements and showing your work.)

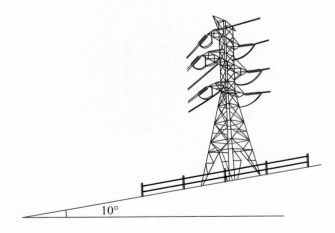

Three-dimensional problems

When tackling problems in three dimensions it is good practice to redraw each triangle separately and apply the sine and cosine rule to these triangles. Watch for common sides that link the triangles. We can carry common values from one triangle to another triangle.

EXAMPLE 1

ABCDE is a square-based pyramid of side 8 cm. The vertex, *E*, is 6 cm directly above *M*, the centre of the square *ABCD*. *N* is the midpoint of [*BC*].

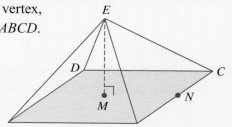

(i) Find $|MN|$.

(ii) Calculate, correct to one decimal place:
   (a) $|EN|$
   (b) The angle the face *BEC* makes with the base *ABCD*

Solution:

The situation can be represented with the right-angled triangle *EMN*.

(i) $|MN| = \frac{1}{2}|AB| = \frac{1}{2}(8 \text{ cm}) = 4 \text{ cm}$

(ii) (a) $|EN|^2 = |EM|^2 + |MN|^2$

$|EN|^2 = 6^2 + 4^2$

$|EN|^2 = 52$

$|EN| = \sqrt{52} = 7{\cdot}2 \text{ cm}$ (correct to one decimal place)

(b) $\tan \angle ENM = \frac{6}{4}$

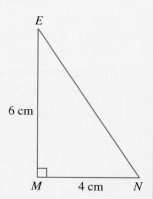

$\angle ENM = \tan^{-1}\left(\frac{6}{4}\right)$

$\therefore |\angle ENM| = 56{\cdot}3°$ (correct to one decimal place).

EXAMPLE 2

P, Q and R are three points on horizontal ground. $[SR]$ is a vertical pole of height h metres. The angle of elevation of S from P is $60°$ and the angle of elevation of S from Q is $30°$. $|PQ| = c$ metres. Given that $3c^2 = 13h^2$, find $|\angle PRQ|$.

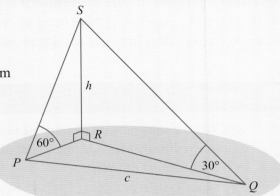

Solution:

$[PR]$ and $[QR]$ are common sides.
Thus, express $|PR|$ and $|QR|$ in terms of h.

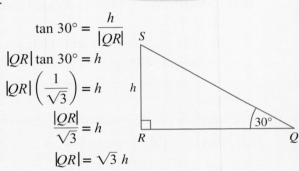

$$\tan 60° = \frac{h}{|PR|}$$

$$|PR| \tan 60° = h$$

$$|PR|(\sqrt{3}) = h$$

$$\sqrt{3}\,|PR| = h$$

$$|PR| = \frac{h}{\sqrt{3}}$$

$$\tan 30° = \frac{h}{|QR|}$$

$$|QR| \tan 30° = h$$

$$|QR|\left(\frac{1}{\sqrt{3}}\right) = h$$

$$\frac{|QR|}{\sqrt{3}} = h$$

$$|QR| = \sqrt{3}\,h$$

Using the cosine rule:

$$c^2 = |PR|^2 + |QR|^2 - 2\,|PR| \times |QR| \cos \theta$$

$$c^2 = \left(\frac{h}{\sqrt{3}}\right)^2 + (\sqrt{3}h)^2 - 2\left(\frac{h}{\sqrt{3}}\right)(\sqrt{3}h) \cos \theta$$

$$c^2 = \frac{h^2}{3} + 3h^2 - 2h^2 \cos \theta$$

Let $\angle PRQ = \theta$

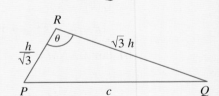

Given:

$$3c^2 = 13h^2$$

$$\therefore 3\left[\frac{h^2}{3} + 3h^2 - 2h^2 \cos \theta\right] = 13h^2$$

$$h^2 + 9h^2 - 6h^2 \cos \theta = 13h^2$$

$$1 + 9 - 6 \cos \theta = 13 \qquad \text{(divide each term by } h^2\text{)}$$

$$-6 \cos \theta = 3$$

$$6 \cos \theta = -3$$

$$\cos \theta = -\tfrac{1}{2}$$

$$\theta = \cos^{-1}(-\tfrac{1}{2})$$

$$\theta = 120°$$

$$\therefore |\angle PRQ| = 120°$$

Exercise 9.8

1. P, Q and R are three points on level ground. [QS]
    represents a vertical pole of height 8 m.
    $|\angle PQR| = 150°$, $|PS| = 10$ m and $|RS| = 17$ m. Find:
    (i) $|PQ|$ (ii) $|QR|$ (iii) Area of triangle PQR
    (iv) $|PR|$, correct to two decimal places

    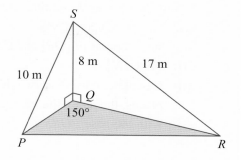

2. The diagram shows a cuboid with dimensions
    as shown. Calculate:
    (i) $|PR|$
    (ii) $|\angle RPY|$, correct to one decimal place

    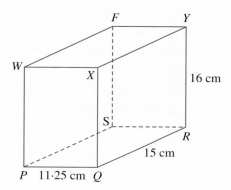

3. On the diagram, the rectangle PQUV
    represents an artificial ski slope. Rectangles
    PQRS and RSVU are at right angles to each
    other. Jack skis in a straight line from U to
    P at an average speed of 5 m per second.
    (i) How long, in seconds, does it take
         Jack to ski from U to P?
    (ii) A health and safety expert says that
         the maximum slope of an artificial ski
         slope must be 25°. Would this
         artificial ski slope be passed as safe
         by this expert? Justify your answer.

    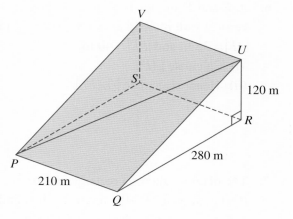

    (iii) Calculate, correct to one decimal place, the difference in the angle between skiing
          straight down the slope and skiing from U to P.

4. *PQRST* is a square-based pyramid of side
   12 cm. The vertex *T* is directly above *N*, the
   centre of the square *PQRS*.
   M is the midpoint of [*QR*] and |*TM*| = 10 cm.
   (i) Find |*TN*|.
   (ii) Calculate, correct to two decimal
   places, the angle the face *QRT* makes
   with the base *PQRS*.

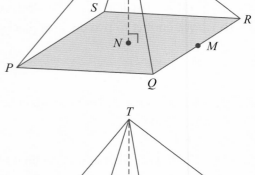

5. *PQRST* is a square-based pyramid of side
   6 cm. The vertex *T* is directly above *C*, the
   centre of the square *PQRS*. |*TC*| = 4 cm.
   Calculate:
   (i) |∠*TQR*|, to the nearest degree
   (ii) The total surface area of the pyramid

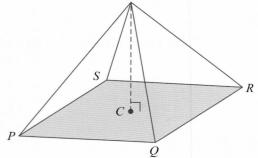

6. *A*, *F* and *E* are points on horizontal ground. *D* is a point on a
   vertical wall directly above *A*. |*AD*| = 72 m, |*DE*| = 97 m,
   |*AF*| = 35 m and |*FE*| = 40 m.
   (i) Calculate |*AE*|.
   (ii) Hence, calculate |∠*AFE*|.

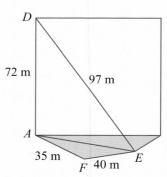

7. The diagram shows a rectangular box.
   Rectangle *ABCD* is the top of the box and
   rectangle *EFGH* is the base of the box.
   |*AB*| = 4 cm, |*BF*| = 3 cm and |*FG*| = 12 cm.
   (i) Find |*AF*|.
   (ii) Find |*AG*|.
   (iii) Find the measure of the acute angle
   between [*AG*] and [*DF*]. Give your
   answer correct to the nearest degree.

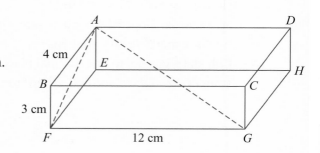

8. The diagram shows a river with parallel banks p m apart. A vertical tree, of height h m, is directly opposite the point A, as shown. A woman wants to find the height of the tree. From A the angle of elevation of the top of the tree is 45°. She then walks to a point B, which is 50 m downstream, as shown. The distance from B to the base of the tree is q m and the angle of elevation of the top of the tree from B is 30°.

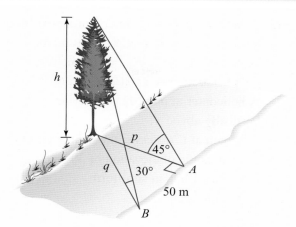

   (i) Express p and q in terms of h.
   (ii) Write a quadratic equation involving p and q.
   (iii) Calculate h and write your answer in the form $25\sqrt{k}$.

9. The diagram shows a tetrahedron $ABCD$, where $|AB| = 16$ m, $|DC| = 20$ m, $|\angle ACB| = 38°$ and $|\angle ADB| = 58°$. $[AB]$ is vertical and points B, C and D are on level ground. Find, correct to two decimal places:

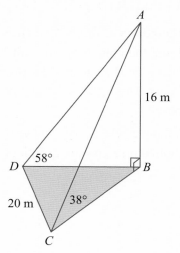

   (i) $|AC|$
   (ii) $|AD|$
   (iii) $|\angle DAC|$

10. A vertical radio mast $[PQ]$ stands on flat horizontal ground. It is supported by three cables that join the top of the mast, Q, to the points A, B and C on the ground. The foot of the mast, P, lies inside the triangle ABC. Each cable is 52 m long and the mast is 48 m high.

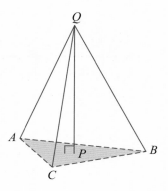

   (i) Find the (common) distance from P to each of the points A, B and C.
   (ii) Given that $|AC| = 38$ m and $|AB| = 34$ m, find $|BC|$, correct to one decimal place.

11. *A* and *B* are two helicopter landing pads on
    level ground. *C* is another point on the
    same level ground. $|BC| = 800$ metres,
    $|AC| = 900$ metres, and $|\angle BCA| = 60°$.
    A helicopter at point *D* is hovering
    vertically abvoe *A*.
    A person at *C* observes the helicopter to
    have an angle of elevation of 30°.
    (i)   Find $|AD|$, in surd form.
    (ii) Find $|BD|$.

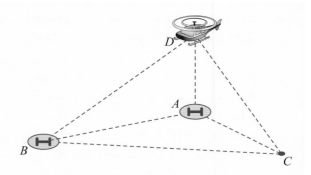

Graphing the trigonometrical functions

Functions of the form $a \sin n\theta$ and $a \cos n\theta$, $a, n \in \mathbb{N}$

From the unit circle, the value of sin *A* increases from 0 to 1 as the angle *A* increases from 0° to 90°.
However, the sine of 45° (the middle angle) is *not* 0·5 (the middle value), so the increase is not
linear. This tells us that the graph of the sine function is a curve and a range of values is required to
plot it.

Taking a selection of angles (0°, 30°, 60°, 90°, 115°, 140° and so on), the values of sine could be
plotted on a coordinated plane, as shown. This indicates the type of curvature.

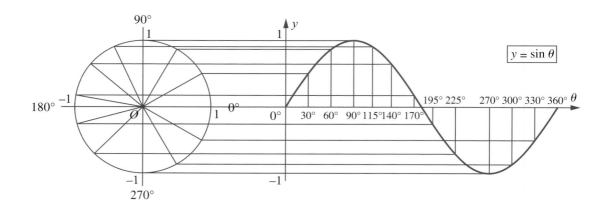

EXAMPLE

Graph the function $y = \sin x$, $0° \leq x \leq 360°$.

Solution:

To make sure the curvature is correct, use numerous values up to 180°. Using up to two decimals places of accuracy:

x	0°	30°	45°	60°	90°	120°	135°	150°	180°	225°	270°	315°	360°
$\sin x$	0	0·5	0·71	0·87	1	0·87	0·71	0·5	0	−0·71	−1	−0·71	0

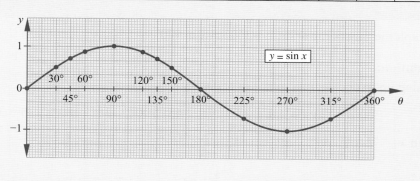

Analysing $y = \sin \theta$

The graph shows the function $y = \sin \theta$ for $0° \leq \theta \leq 360°$. It has been divided into four sections.

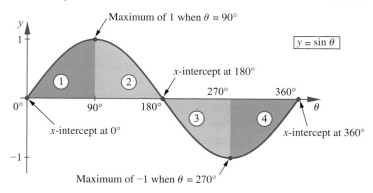

Although the diagram only shows part of the graph of $y = \sin \theta$, we can see that it is **continuous** (there are no breaks in the graph).

There are three x-intercepts (when $\theta = 0°$, 180° and 360°). The maximum value is 1 and the minimum value is −1.

Sin θ increases in section 1 and decreases in sections 2 and 3. It increases in section 4 and would continue to increase until $\theta = 450°$.

Periodic functions

The unit circle indicates that the values of sine and cosine repeat every 360°. If we were to extend the values in the domain of the previous example to be $0° \leq x \leq 720°$, we would see this clearly. Functions that repeat over regular intervals are called **periodic functions** and the minimum size of the interval is called its **period**.

The basic functions cos A and sin A are periodic with a period of 360°.

From both the unit circle and the previous graph, we can see that the values of sin x vary from −1 to 1. This **range** can be written as [−1, 1]. The range of cos x is also [−1, 1].

EXAMPLE 1

Graph the function $y = \sin x$, $-360° \leq x \leq 540°$.

Solution:
Using up to one decimal place of accuracy:

x	−360°	−270°	−180°	−90°	0°	45°	90°	135°	180°	270°	360°	450°	540°
sin x	0	1	0	−1	0	0·7	1	0·7	0	−1	0	1	0

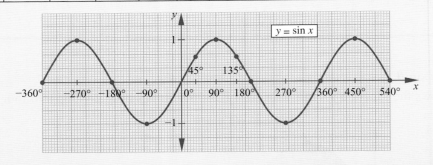

EXAMPLE 2

Graph the function $f(\theta) = 2\cos \theta$, $0 \leq \theta \leq 2\pi$. What is the period and the range of $2\cos \theta$?

Solution:
Using up to one decimal place of accuracy with the final values:

θ	0	$\frac{\pi}{4}$	$\frac{\pi}{2}$	$\frac{3\pi}{4}$	π	$\frac{3\pi}{2}$	2π
cos θ	1	0·71	0	−0·71	−1	0	1
2 cos θ	2	1·4	0	−1·4	−2	0	2

The period is 2π and the range is $[-2, 2]$.

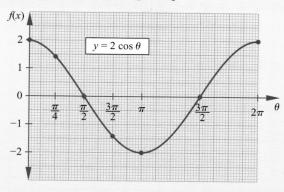

EXAMPLE 3

Graph the function $y = \cos 2x$, $0° \leq x \leq 360°$.

Using the same axes and scale, graph $y = -0.8$ in the same domain.

Hence, estimate the values of x for which $\cos 2x = -0.8$, $0° \leq x \leq 360°$.

Solution:

Using up to one decimal place of accuracy with the final values:

x	0°	30°	45°	60°	90°	135°	180°	270°	360°
$2x$	0°	60°	90°	120°	180°	270°	360°	540°	720°
$\cos 2x$	1	0·5	0	−0·5	−1	0	1	−1	1

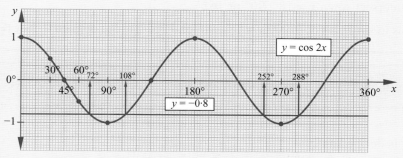

If $\cos 2x = -0.8$, then $x = 72°$, $108°$, $252°$ or $288°$.

EXAMPLE 4

Using the same axes and scale, graph the functions $y = \sin 2x$ and $y = \cos 3x$ in the domain $0° \leq x \leq 180°$.

Using your graph, estimate the values of x for which $\sin 2x = \cos 3x$.

Solution:

Using up to one decimal place of accuracy with the final values:

x	0°	30°	45°	60°	90°	120°	135°	150°	180°
2x	0°	60°	90°	120°	180°	240°	270°	300°	360°
sin 2x	0	0·9	1	0·9	0	−0·9	−1	−0·9	0

x	0°	30°	45°	60°	90°	120°	135°	150°	180°
3x	0°	90°	135°	180°	270°	360°	405°	450°	540°
cos 3x	1	0	−0·7	−1	0	1	0·7	0	−1

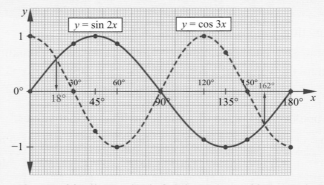

To solve $\sin 2x = \cos 3x$ graphically, we look for the points of intersection of the two graphs.

The two graphs intersect when $x = 18°$, $90°$ or $162°$.

Thus, the solutions to $\sin 2x = \cos 3x$ are $x = 18°$, $90°$ and $162°$, in the domain $0° \leq x \leq 180°$.

> If $f(x) = a \sin bx$, then $f(x)$ has a range $[−a, a]$ and a period of $\dfrac{360°}{b}$ or $\dfrac{2\pi}{b}$ radians.

The tangent function

The tangent of an angle θ is defined as

$$\tan \theta = \frac{\sin \theta}{\cos \theta}$$

except for those values of θ for which $\cos \theta = 0$. For example, $\tan 90°$ cannot be evaluated as

$$\tan 90° = \frac{\sin 90°}{\cos 90°} = \frac{1}{0},\qquad \text{which is } \textbf{undefined.}$$

This means that the graph will **not** be continuous. Testing values close to 90°, such as 89° and 91°, indicates that $y = \tan \theta$ has a significantly wider range than either $y = \sin \theta$ or $y = \cos \theta$.

The basic function tan x is periodic with a period of 180°.

The values of tan x vary from $-\infty$ to ∞. This **range** can be written as $[-\infty, \infty]$ or simply $\mathbb{R}$.

EXAMPLE

Graph the function $y = \tan x$, $-90° \leq x \leq 270°$. What is the period and range of $y = \tan x$? By drawing a suitable line, estimate the values of x for which $\tan x = 2$ in the given domain. Draw the line $x = 90°$. Does this line intersect the graph?

Solution:

Using up to one decimal place of accuracy with the final values:

x	−90°	0°	30°	45°	60°	75°	90°	105°	120°	135°	150°	180°	225	270
tan x	—	0	0·6	1	1·7	3·7	—	−3·7	−1·7	−1	−0·6	0	1	—

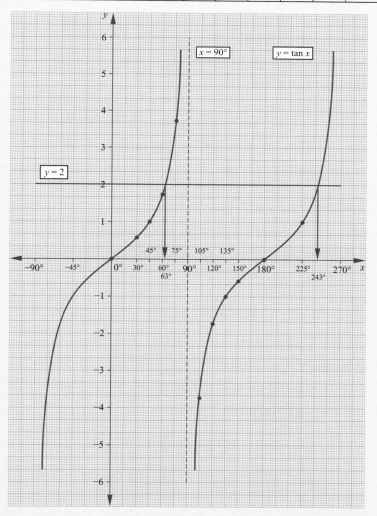

If $\tan x = 2$, then $x = 63°$ or $243°$.

The line $x = 90°$ never intersects the graph of $y = \tan x$, but it gets infinitesimally close.

Note: A line that gets infinitesimally close to a curve as both the line and the curve approach ∞ (or $-\infty$) is called an **asymptote**.

Exercise 9.9

1. (i) Graph the function $y = \cos x$, $0° \le x \le 360°$.
    (ii) Graph the line $y = 0{\cdot}7$.
    (iii) Using your graph, estimate the values of x for which $\cos x \le 0{\cdot}7$.

2. (i) Graph the function $y = 2 \sin x$, $0° \le x \le 360°$.
    (ii) Using your graph, estimate the values of x for which $2 \sin x = 1{\cdot}6$.

3. (i) Graph the function $y = \tan x$, $-180° \le x \le 180°$.
    (ii) Using your graph, estimate the values of x for which $-3 \le \tan x \le 3$.

4. Graph the function $y = \sin 3\theta$, $0° \le \theta \le 180°$.

5. Graph the function $y = 2 \cos 2x$, $0° \le x \le 180°$.

6. (i) Graph the function $y = \sin x$, $-\pi \le x \le \pi$.
    (ii) By drawing an appropriate line, find the values of x for which $2 \sin x = 1$.

7. Graph the function $y = 3 \sin 2\theta$, $-\pi \le \theta \le \pi$.

8. (i) Graph the functions $y = \sin \theta$ and $y = \cos \theta$, $0° \le \theta \le 360°$ on the same axes and using the same scale.
    (ii) 'The graphs of sine and cosine are $90°$ out of phase with each other.' Discuss.

9. (i) Graph the functions $y = \sin 2x$ and $y = 2 \cos x$, $0° \le x \le 360°$ on the same axes and using the same scale.
    (ii) Find the values of x for which $\sin 2x = 2 \cos x$.

10. (i) Name two properties that $y = \sin \theta$ and $y = \cos \theta$ have in common.
    (ii) Find three significant differences between $y = \tan \theta$ and either $y = \sin \theta$ or $y = \cos \theta$.

11. Using graphs, explain why:
    (i) $\cos(-x) = \cos x$
    (ii) $\sin(-x) = -\sin x$

12. (i) Draw the graph of $y = \sin \theta + \cos \theta$ for $0° \le \theta \le 360°$.
    (ii) What is the period and range of this function?

13. (i) Draw the graph of $y = \sin \theta + \sin 2\theta$ for $0° \le \theta \le 360°$.
    (ii) What is the period and range of this function?

Identifying the graph of a trigonometrical function

Although the graphs of $\sin \theta$ and $\cos \theta$ are very similar, they have different values when $\theta = 0$.

$$\sin 0° = 0 \qquad\qquad \cos 0° = 1$$

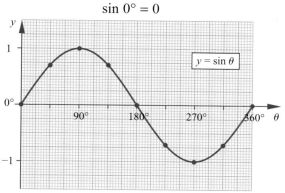

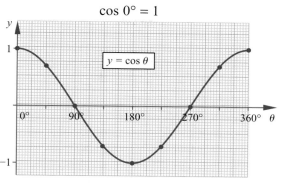

Period 360°, range $[-1, 1]$ Period 360°, range $[-1, 1]$

The range is affected when the function is of the form $y = a \sin \theta$ or $y = a \cos \theta$.

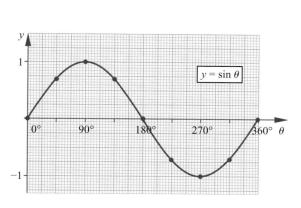

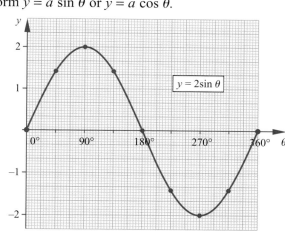

Period 360°, range $[-1, 1]$ Period 360°, range $[-2, 2]$

The period is affected when the function is of the form $y = \sin n\theta$ or $y = \cos n\theta$.

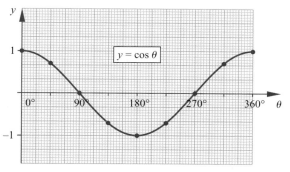

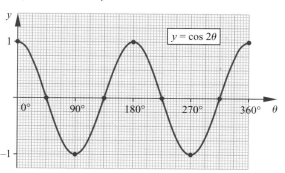

Period 360°, range $[-1, 1]$ Period 180°, range $[-1, 1]$

EXAMPLE

The diagram shows the functions $y = \sin x$, $y = \cos 2x$ and $y = 2 \cos x$. The graphs are labelled $f(x)$, $g(x)$ and $h(x)$. Identify which is which.

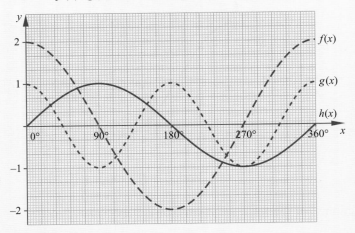

Solution:

The graph marked $f(x)$ does not pass through $(0, 0)$ so it must involve cosine. It seems to repeat after $360°$ so it is some multiple of $\cos x$. As its range is $[-2, 2]$, $f(x) = 2 \cos x$.

The graph marked $g(x)$ does not pass through $(0, 0)$ so it must involve cosine. It seems to repeat after $180°$ so it is possibly $\cos 2x$. As its range is $[-1, 1]$, $g(x) = \cos 2x$.

The graph marked $h(x)$ does pass through $(0, 0)$ so it must involve sine. It seems to repeat after $360°$ so it is possibly $\sin x$. As its range is $[-1, 1]$, $h(x) = \sin x$.

Exercise 9.10

In questions 1–6, identify the function of the graph and write down its period and range.

1.

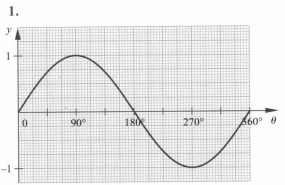

2.

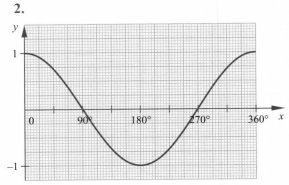

3.

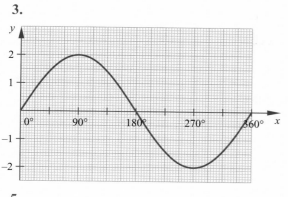

4.

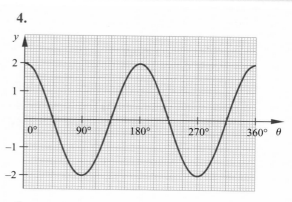

5.

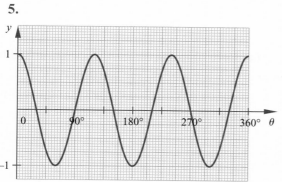

6.

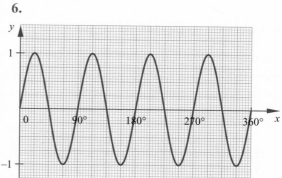

7. (i) Write down the period of the graph.
    (ii) Find the value of h and write down the range.
    (iii) For what value of θ is the function a minimum?
          Give your answer in general angle form.

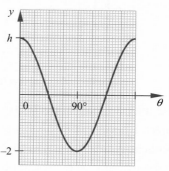

8. (i) Write down the period of the graph.
    (ii) Find the value of b and write down the range.
    (iii) For what value of θ is the function a minimum?
          Give your answer in general angle form.

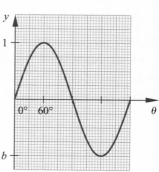

9. The graph of a function of the form $y = p \cos qx$ is shown.

   (i) Write down the value of p.

   (ii) Write down the value of q.

   (iii) Find the period and range of the function.

   (iv) For what value of x is the function a minimum? Give your answer in general angle form.

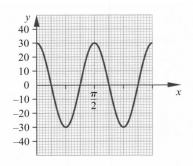

Practical applications

A number of scientific phenomena can be expressed in the form of a sine (or cosine) wave, including sounds, radio waves and electrical current. Although the graphs are similar, the words used to describe them are different. For example, a musical tone might be represented in the diagram below.

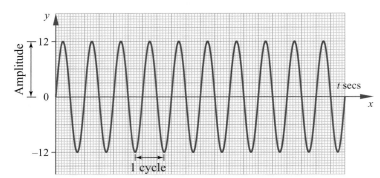

The diagram has 10 **cycles** (or periods) within one second and this is written as 10 Hz (10 hertz, where 1 hertz means *once a second*). The graph has a **frequency** or **pitch** of 10 Hz. The sounds we can hear typically vary from 20 Hz (a very low sound) to 20 kHz (20,000 hertz) (a very high sound), so the example above would be well below our hearing range. The **amplitude** of the wave is 12 and in this case is a measure of volume or sound level.

If the next diagram shows the sounds produced by a violin and a bass guitar, then we can deduce that the violin (red) is being played louder than the bass guitar (blue). In reality, a musical sound is a combination of changing waves, which is more complex to analyse, so the diagram has simplified the sounds to two musical tones.

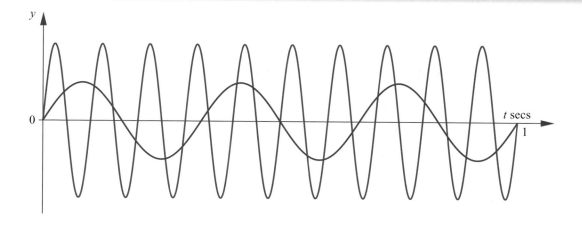

Exercise 9.11

1. The depth, in metres, of water in a harbour is given by the function $d = 4 \sin t°$, where t is in minutes and $0 \le t \le 1{,}440$.

   (i) Draw a sketch of d for the given time interval.

   (ii) Write down the range of d.

   (iii) Find the period of d in **(a)** minutes **(b)** hours.

   (iv) In practical terms, the depth of the water in the harbour cannot be negative but it could be zero. Adjust the scale on the vertical axis so that the lowest point represents a real depth of zero. What is the maximum depth of water in the harbour?

2. A model boat bobs up and down in a pond so that its height, h centimetres, above the bottom of the pond, at a time t seconds, is given by $h = a \cos bt° + c$.

   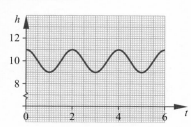

   (i) Redraw this graph, lowering it so that its equation becomes $h = a \cos bt$.

   (ii) Write down the period and range of this graph.

   (iii) Find the value of a and the value of b.

   (iv) For what values of t is the boat going down?

   (v) How high was the boat above the bottom of the pond after $4\frac{1}{2}$ seconds?

3. The graph shows the temperature measured at midday (in °Celsius) in Gorey over a period of 13 days starting with Day 0.

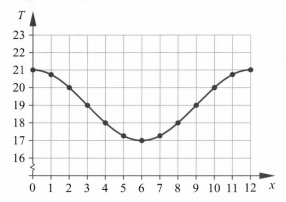

    (i) Write down the period and range of this graph.

    (ii) Which of the trigonometrical functions (sine, cosine or tangent) would best model the situation?

    (iii) Using the graph, find the number of days for which the midday temperature was less than 19·5°.

4. The graph shows the pollution levels (*P*) recorded hourly in a large city from early morning until the early evening on a certain day.

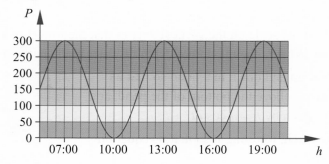

    (i) Write down the period and range of this graph.

    (ii) If the horizontal axis represents *h*, the time of day, write the domain in the form $a \le h \le b$, where *a* and *b* are times expressed in 24-hour format.

    (iii) If the levels of pollution can be described as *Good, Moderate, Unhealthy* and *Very Unhealthy,* write down the range of *Moderate* pollution.

    (iv) Give a likely cause of the peaks of the graph.

    (v) If the graph were continued, when would the next peak occur? Would this match the actual pollution at that time?

    (vi) If there are no peaks during the night, for how many hours is the pollution at the level of *Very Unhealthy*?

5. Caroline is suspended in a bouncer 25 cm above the floor,
   as shown. When she bounces up and down, the formula
   $b = 10 \sin 45t°$ models her bouncing height. b is measured in
   centimetres and t represents tenths of seconds.

   (i) When the baby is bouncing, what is the maximum and
        minimum heights she will be above the floor?
   (ii) Draw the graph for a duration of 2 seconds starting
        with $t = 0$.
   (iii) What is the period of this function?
   (iv) What vertical distance will the baby have travelled during
         these 2 seconds?
   (v) If Caroline giggles happily when she changes direction, how
        many times will she giggle during the 2 seconds?
   (vi) Some parents would prefer a bouncer which bounced less often. Find a formula which
         would maintain the range but produce one less giggle.
   (vii) Why would $b = (10 + m) \sin 45t°$ (where $m = 0, 1, 2 \ldots$ months from now) be a better
          model? At what point does this model suggest a safety issue?

6. The population of squirrels has been monitored each month for two years. The graph shows
   the results modelled using the equation $S = a \cos bt° + c$ where S represents thousands of
   squirrels and t represents months from the start of the recording of the data.

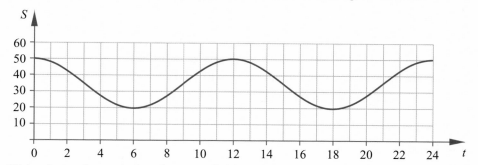

   (i) Write down the period and range of this graph.
   (ii) By lowering the graph so that it is centred about the t-axis, or otherwise, deduce the
         value of a and the value of b.
   (iii) On how many occasions was the population 42,000 squirrels?
   (iv) For how many months per year was the population less than 25,000?

7. Three tones have been recorded and their sound waves shown on a diagram.

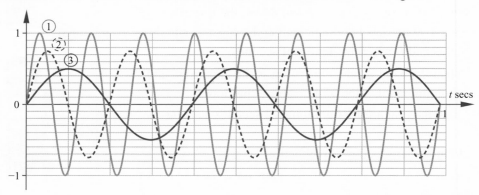

   (i) Estimate the period and range of each sound wave, giving the period in milliseconds.

   (ii) Find the amplitude and frequency of each wave.

8. The diagram shows a Ferris wheel with centre O and radius 24 m.
   Initially, seat A is at ground level. The next seat is B, where $|\angle AOB| = \frac{\pi}{6}$.

   (i) (a) How many seats are on this Ferris wheel?

   (b) Find the length of the arc AB.

   (c) Find the area of the sector AOB.

   (d) The wheel turns clockwise through an angle of $\frac{2\pi}{3}$ and stops. Find the height of seat A above the ground.

   (e) The wheel turns clockwise again. How many degrees will the wheel turn for seat A to be half the height above the ground as it was in part **(d)**? Give your answer correct to the nearest degree.

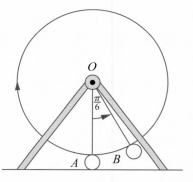

   (ii) The height, h m, of seat A above the ground after t seconds can be modelled by the function $h(t) = 24 - 24 \cos\left(\frac{\pi}{6}t\right)$.

   (a) Find the initial height of seat A.

   (b) Find the time at which seat A first reaches its highest point.

   (c) Find $h'(t)$.

   (d) Graph $h'(t)$ in the domain $0 \le t \le 12$.

   (e) Find the time at which the height is changing most rapidly.

Deriving the formulae

1. $\cos^2 A + \sin^2 A = 1$

Using the definition of sin A and cos A from the unit circle:

$(\cos A)^2 + (\sin A)^2 = 1^2$ (Pythagoras' theorem)

$\cos^2 A + \sin^2 A = 1$

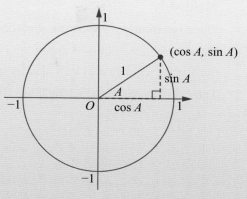

2. Sine formula: $\dfrac{a}{\sin A} = \dfrac{b}{\sin B} = \dfrac{c}{\sin C}$

Case 1: A is acute

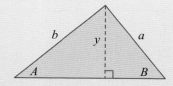

$\sin A = \dfrac{y}{b}$ $\sin B = \dfrac{y}{a}$

$b \sin A = y$ $a \sin B = y$

$$a \sin B = b \sin A$$

$$\frac{a \sin B}{\sin A \sin B} = \frac{b \sin A}{\sin A \sin B}$$

$$\frac{a}{\sin A} = \frac{b}{\sin B}$$

Case 2: A is obtuse

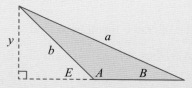

$E = 180° - A$

$\sin E = \sin(180° - A) = \sin A$

$\sin E = \dfrac{y}{b}$ $\sin B = \dfrac{y}{a}$

$\sin A = \dfrac{y}{b}$ $a \sin B = y$

$b \sin A = y$

$$a \sin B = b \sin A$$

$$\frac{a \sin B}{\sin A \sin B} = \frac{b \sin A}{\sin A \sin B}$$

$$\frac{a}{\sin A} = \frac{b}{\sin B}$$

(Now that *both* cases have been proven, we can continue.)

Similarly, we can show $\dfrac{a}{\sin A} = \dfrac{c}{\sin C}$.

Therefore, $\dfrac{a}{\sin A} = \dfrac{b}{\sin B} = \dfrac{c}{\sin C}$.

3. **Cosine formula:** $a^2 = b^2 + c^2 - 2bc \cos A$

Method 1:

Place the triangle with angle A placed at the origin and side c placed along the x-axis.

Draw a circle of radius b around the origin. As this circle is b times larger than the unit circle, the x and y coordinates will also be b times larger.

The coordinates of the triangle are $(0, 0)$, $(c, 0)$ and $(b \cos A, b \sin A)$.

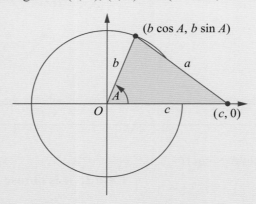

Use the distance formula to find an expression for the length a.

$$a = \sqrt{(b \cos A - c)^2 + (b \sin A - 0)^2} \qquad \text{(distance formula)}$$
$$a^2 = b^2 \cos^2 A - 2bc \cos A + c^2 + b^2 \sin^2 A \qquad \text{(square both sides; multiply out)}$$
$$= b^2(\cos^2 A + \sin^2 A) + c^2 - 2bc \cos A$$
$$= b^2(1) + c^2 - 2bc \cos A$$
$$a^2 = b^2 + c^2 - 2bc \cos A$$

Method 2:

Case 1: A is acute

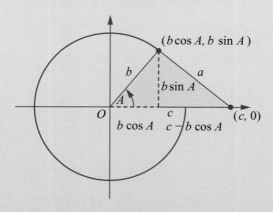

Case 2: A is obtuse

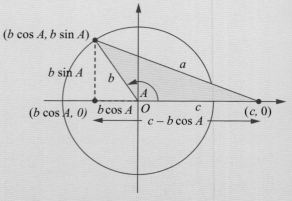

Place the triangle with angle A placed at the origin and side c placed along the x-axis.

Draw a circle of radius b around the origin. As this circle is b times larger than the unit circle, the x and y coordinates will also be b times larger.

The coordinates of the triangle are $(0, 0)$, $(c, 0)$ and $(b \cos A, b \sin A)$.

Drop a perpendicular from $(b \cos A, b \sin A)$ to create a right-angled triangle with hypotenuse a and apply Pythagoras' theorem.

$$a^2 = (b \sin A)^2 + (c - b \cos A)^2 \qquad \text{(Pythagoras' theorem)}$$
$$= b^2 \sin^2 A + c^2 - 2bc \cos A + b^2 \cos^2 A$$
$$= b^2(\sin^2 A + \cos^2 A) + c^2 - 2bc \cos A$$
$$= b^2(1) + c^2 - 2bc \cos A$$
$$a^2 = b^2 + c^2 - 2bc \cos A$$

Compound angles

4. $\cos(A - B) = \cos A \cos B + \sin A \sin B$

Let $P(\cos A, \sin A)$ and $Q(\cos B, \sin B)$ be two points on a unit circle.

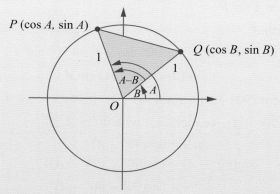

Using the distance formula:

$$|PQ|^2 = (\cos A - \cos B)^2 + (\sin A - \sin B)^2$$
$$= \cos^2 A - 2 \cos A \cos B + \cos^2 B + \sin^2 A - 2 \sin A \sin B + \sin^2 B$$
$$= (\cos^2 A + \sin^2 A) + (\cos^2 B + \sin^2 B) - 2(\cos A \cos B + \sin A \sin B)$$
$$= 2 - 2(\cos A \cos B + \sin A \sin B) \qquad ①$$

Using the cosine formula on $\triangle OPQ$:

$$|PQ|^2 = 1^2 + 1^2 - 2(1)(1) \cos(A - B)$$
$$= 2 - 2 \cos(A - B) \qquad ②$$

Equating ① and ②:

$$2 - 2 \cos(A - B) = 2 - 2(\cos A \cos B + \sin A \sin B)$$
$$\cos(A - B) = \cos A \cos B + \sin A \sin B$$

5. $\cos(A + B) = \cos A \cos B - \sin A \sin B$

$$\cos(A - B) = \cos A \cos B + \sin A \sin B$$

Replace B with $-B$:

$$\cos(A - (-B)) = \cos A \cos(-B) + \sin A \sin(-B)$$
$$\cos(A + B) = \cos A \cos B + \sin A(-\sin B)$$
$$\cos(A + B) = \cos A \cos B - \sin A \sin B$$

6. $\cos 2A = \cos^2 A - \sin^2 A$

$$\cos(A + B) = \cos A \cos B - \sin A \sin B$$

Replace B with A:

$$\cos(A + A) = \cos A \cos A - \sin A \sin A$$
$$\cos 2A = \cos^2 A - \sin^2 A$$

Complementary angles (A and $90° - A$)

$\cos(A - B) = \cos A \cos B + \sin A \sin B$

Replace A with $90°$ and B with A:

$$\cos(90° - A) = \cos 90° \cos A + \sin 90° \sin A$$
$$= (0) \cos A + (1) \sin A$$
$$\therefore \cos(90° - A) = \sin A$$

Using the result $\sin A = \cos(90° - A)$, we replace A with $90° - A$.

$$\sin A = \cos(90° - A)$$
$$\sin(90° - A) = \cos(90° - (90° - A))$$
$$= \cos(90° - 90° + A)$$
$$\therefore \sin(90° - A) = \cos A$$

7. $\sin(A + B) = \sin A \cos B + \cos A \sin B$

$$\cos(A - B) = \cos A \cos B + \sin A \sin B$$

Replace A with $(90° - A)$:

$$\cos(90° - A - B) = \cos(90° - A) \cos B + \sin(90° - A) \sin B$$
$$\cos(90° - (A + B)) = \sin A \cos B + \cos A \sin B$$
$$\sin(A + B) = \sin A \cos B + \cos A \sin B$$

8. $\sin(A - B) = \sin A \cos B - \cos A \sin B$

$$\sin(A + B) = \sin A \cos B + \cos A \sin B$$

Replace B with $-B$:

$$\sin(A + (-B)) = \sin A \cos(-B) + \cos A \sin(-B)$$
$$\sin(A - B) = \sin A \cos B + \cos A(-\sin B)$$
$$\sin(A - B) = \sin A \cos B - \cos A \sin B$$

9. $\tan(A + B) = \dfrac{\tan A + \tan B}{1 - \tan A \tan B}$

$$\tan(A + B) = \frac{\sin(A + B)}{\cos(A + B)}$$

$$= \frac{\sin A \cos B + \cos A \sin B}{\cos A \cos B - \sin A \sin B}$$

$$= \frac{\dfrac{\sin A \cos B}{\cos A \cos B} + \dfrac{\cos A \sin B}{\cos A \cos B}}{\dfrac{\cos A \cos B}{\cos A \cos B} - \dfrac{\sin A \sin B}{\cos A \cos B}}$$

$$= \frac{\tan A + \tan B}{1 - \tan A \tan B}$$

● EXAMPLE 1

Express **(i)** $\sin 15°$ and **(ii)** $\tan 105°$ in surd form.

Solution:

First express each angle as a combination of $30°$, $45°$ or $60°$.

Then use the compound angle formulae in the booklet of formulae and tables.

(i) $\sin 15°$

$= \sin(45° - 30°)$

$= \sin 45° \cos 30° - \cos 45° \sin 30°$

$= \left(\dfrac{1}{\sqrt{2}}\right)\left(\dfrac{\sqrt{3}}{2}\right) - \left(\dfrac{1}{\sqrt{2}}\right)\left(\dfrac{1}{2}\right)$

$= \dfrac{\sqrt{3}}{2\sqrt{2}} - \dfrac{1}{2\sqrt{2}}$

$= \dfrac{\sqrt{3} - 1}{2\sqrt{2}}$

(ii) $\tan 105°$

$= \tan(60° + 45°)$

$= \dfrac{\tan 60° + \tan 45°}{1 - \tan 60° \tan 45°}$

$= \dfrac{\sqrt{3} + 1}{1 - (\sqrt{3})(1)}$

$= \dfrac{\sqrt{3} + 1}{1 - \sqrt{3}}$

EXAMPLE 2

If $\tan(A + B) = 3$ and $\tan B = 2$, find the value of $\tan A$.

Solution:

$$\tan(A + B) = \frac{\tan A + \tan B}{1 - \tan A \tan B}$$

$$3 = \frac{\tan A + 2}{1 - (\tan A)(2)} \qquad \text{(given } \tan(A + B) = 3, \tan B = 2)$$

$$3 = \frac{\tan A + 2}{1 - 2 \tan A}$$

$$3 - 6 \tan A = \tan A + 2 \qquad \text{(multiply both sides by } (1 - 2 \tan A))$$

$$-7 \tan A = -1$$

$$7 \tan A = 1$$

$$\tan A = \frac{1}{7}$$

Alternatively:

$$\tan A = \tan[(A + B) - B] = \frac{\tan(A + B) - \tan B}{1 + \tan(A + B)(\tan B)} = \frac{3 - 2}{1 + (3)(2)} = \frac{1}{7}$$

EXAMPLE 3

If $\sin 2A = \frac{7}{25}$, $0 \leq A \leq \frac{\pi}{2}$, find $\tan A$, $\sin A$ and $\cos A$.

Solution:

$$\sin 2A = \frac{2 \tan A}{1 + \tan^2 A}$$

$$\frac{7}{25} = \frac{2 \tan A}{1 + \tan^2 A}$$

$$\frac{7}{25} = \frac{2t}{1 + t^2} \qquad \text{(let } t = \tan A)$$

$$7 + 7t^2 = 50t$$

$$7t^2 - 50t + 7 = 0$$

$$(7t - 1)(t - 7) = 0$$

$$7t - 1 = 0 \text{ or } t - 7 = 0$$

$$t = \tfrac{1}{7} \text{ or } t = 7$$

$$\tan A = \tfrac{1}{7} \text{ or } \tan A = 7$$

Case 1:

$$\tan A = 7$$

$$\sin A = \frac{7}{\sqrt{50}}$$

$$\cos A = \frac{1}{\sqrt{50}}$$

Case 2:

$$\tan A = \frac{1}{7}$$

$$\sin A = \frac{1}{\sqrt{50}}$$

$$\cos A = \frac{7}{\sqrt{50}}$$

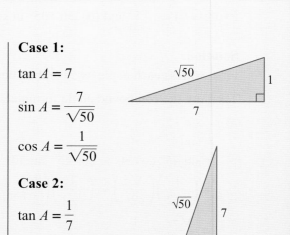

Exercise 9.12

1. A and B are acute angles such that $\sin A = \frac{12}{13}$ and $\cos B = \frac{4}{5}$.

   Without evaluating A or B, find the value of the following.

   (i) $\cos A$ **(ii)** $\tan A$ **(iii)** $\sin B$ **(iv)** $\tan B$

   (v) $\sin(A + B)$ **(vi)** $\cos(A + B)$ **(vii)** $\tan(A + B)$ **(viii)** $\sin 2A$

2. Given that $\tan \theta = \frac{1}{3}$, show that $\tan 2\theta = \frac{3}{4}$.

3. **(i)** $\tan \theta = \frac{20}{21}, 0 < \theta < \frac{\pi}{2}$. Without evaluating θ, find the value of the following.

   (a) $\sin 2\theta$ **(b)** $\cos 2\theta$ **(c)** $\tan 2\theta$

   (ii) If $\cos x = \frac{1}{\sqrt{5}}$, find the value of $\cos 2x$ without evaluating x.

In questions 4–9, express your answer in surd form.

4. $\cos 75°$ 5. $\sin 105°$ 6. $\tan 75°$

7. $\cos 15°$ 8. $\sin 165°$ 9. $\tan 15°$

10. A and B are acute angles such that $\tan A = 4$ and $\tan(A + B) = 5$. Find $\tan B$.

11. A and B are acute angles such that $\tan B = \frac{1}{4}$ and $\tan(A - B) = 2$. Find **(i)** $\tan A$ **(ii)** $\sin 2A$.

12. A and B are acute angles such that $\tan A = \frac{3}{5}$ and $\tan B = \frac{1}{4}$.
    Find $(A + B)$ without evaluating A or B.

Verify the statements in questions 13–18.

13. $\sin(90° - A) = \cos A$ 14. $\cos(90° + A) = -\sin A$

15. $\cos(180° - A) = -\cos A$ 16. $\sin(180° - A) = \sin A$

17. $\tan(45° + A) = \dfrac{1 + \tan A}{1 - \tan A}$ 18. $\sin\left(\dfrac{\pi}{2} + \alpha\right) - \sin\left(\dfrac{\pi}{2} - \alpha\right) = 0$

19. If $\cos 2A = \frac{1}{49}$, find the two values of $\cos A$ without evaluating A.

20. If $\cos 2A = \frac{12}{13}$, find the two possible values of $\tan A$ without evaluating A.

21. ABC is a triangle where $|\angle ABC| = 90°$, $|AC| = 3$, $|AB| = 2$ and $|\angle BAC| = \theta$.

   (i) Show that $\sin \theta = \dfrac{\sqrt{5}}{3}$.

   (ii) Show that $\sin 2\theta = \dfrac{4\sqrt{5}}{9}$.

   (iii) Find the exact value of $\cos 2\theta$.

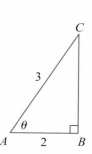

22. A triangle has sides of length 4, 5 and 6.
    The angles of the triangle are A, B and C as in the diagram.

    (i) Using the cosine rule, show that $\cos A + \cos C = \frac{7}{8}$.

    (ii) Show that $\cos(A + C) = -\frac{9}{16}$.

    (iii) Hence, explain why $(A + C)$ is obtuse.

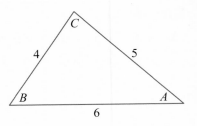

23. In the triangle XYZ, $|\angle XYZ| = 2\beta$, $|\angle XZY| = \beta$, $|XY| = 3$
    and $|XZ| = 5$.

    (i) Use this information to express $\sin 2\beta$ in the form $\dfrac{a}{b} \sin \beta$,
    where $a, b \in \mathbb{N}$.

    (ii) Hence, express $\tan \beta$ in the form $\dfrac{\sqrt{c}}{d}$, where $c, a \in \mathbb{N}$.

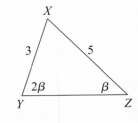

24. In the triangle PQR, $|\angle RSQ| = \theta$, $|\angle PRS| = \alpha$, $|RQ| = 1$,
    $|PS| = 1$ and $|SQ| = 1$.

    (i) Find $|SR|$ in terms of θ.

    (ii) Hence or otherwise, show that $\tan \theta = 3 \tan \alpha$.

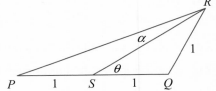

25. A, B, C and D are acute angles such that $\tan A = \frac{1}{3}$,
    $\tan B = \frac{1}{5}$, $\tan C = \frac{1}{7}$ and $\tan D = \frac{1}{8}$.

    (i) Evaluate (a) $\tan(A + B)$ (b) $\tan(C + D)$.

    (ii) Hence or otherwise, find the value of $\tan(A + B + C + D)$.

    (iii) Prove that $A + B + C + D = 45°$.

Sum and product formulae

Changing products into sums and differences

$$2 \cos A \cos B = \cos(A + B) + \cos(A - B)$$
$$2 \sin A \cos B = \sin(A + B) + \sin(A - B)$$
$$2 \sin A \sin B = \cos(A - B) - \cos(A + B)$$
$$2 \cos A \sin B = \sin(A + B) - \sin(A - B)$$

Changing sums and differences into products

$$\cos A + \cos B = 2 \cos \frac{A + B}{2} \cos \frac{A - B}{2}$$

$$\cos A - \cos B = -2 \sin \frac{A + B}{2} \sin \frac{A - B}{2}$$

$$\sin A + \sin B = 2 \sin \frac{A + B}{2} \cos \frac{A - B}{2}$$

$$\sin A - \sin B = 2 \cos \frac{A + B}{2} \sin \frac{A - B}{2}$$

These are given in the booklet of formulae and tables. The proofs of these eight formulae are not required.

EXAMPLE 1

(i) Express $\cos 3\theta \sin 5\theta$ as a sum or difference of two trigonometric functions.

(ii) Express $\sin 6\theta + \sin 4\theta$ as the product of two trigonometric functions.

Solution:

(i) Rearrange terms to have the larger angle first.

$\sin 5\theta \cos 3\theta$

$A = 5\theta \qquad B = 3\theta$

$\sin A \cos B = \frac{1}{2}[\sin(A + B) + \sin(A - B)]$

$\therefore \sin 5\theta \cos 3\theta$

$= \frac{1}{2}[\sin(5\theta + 3\theta) + \sin(5\theta - 3\theta)]$

$= \frac{1}{2}[\sin 8\theta + \sin 2\theta]$

(ii) $\sin 6\theta + \sin 4\theta$

$A = 6\theta \qquad B = 4\theta$

$\sin A + \sin B = 2 \sin \frac{A + B}{2} \cos \frac{A - B}{2}$

$\therefore \sin 6\theta + \sin 4\theta$

$= 2 \sin\left(\frac{6\theta + 4\theta}{2}\right) \cos\left(\frac{6\theta - 4\theta}{2}\right)$

$= 2 \sin 5\theta \cos \theta$

EXAMPLE 2

Find the exact value of $\sin 105° - \sin 15°$.

Solution:

$\sin 105° - \sin 15°$ $\qquad\qquad (A = 105°, B = 15°)$

$= 2 \cos \left(\dfrac{105° + 15°}{2} \right) \sin \left(\dfrac{105° - 15°}{2} \right)$ $\qquad \left(\sin A - \sin B = 2 \cos \dfrac{A + B}{2} \sin \dfrac{A - B}{2} \right)$

$= 2 \cos 60° \sin 45°$

$= 2 \times \dfrac{1}{2} \times \dfrac{1}{\sqrt{2}}$ $\qquad\qquad \left(\cos 60° = \dfrac{1}{2}, \sin 45° = \dfrac{1}{\sqrt{2}} \right)$

$= \dfrac{1}{\sqrt{2}}$

Exercise 9.13

In questions 1–9, write the expression as the product of two trigonometric functions.

1. $\sin 4\theta + \sin 2\theta$
2. $\cos 7\theta + \cos 5\theta$
3. $\cos 8\theta - \cos 2\theta$
4. $\sin 5\theta - \sin 3\theta$
5. $\cos 6\theta - \cos 2\theta$
6. $\cos \theta + \cos 7\theta$
7. $\sin \theta + \sin 3\theta$
8. $\cos \theta + \cos 5\theta$
9. $\sin 2\theta - \sin 8\theta$

In questions 10–18, write the expression as the sum or difference of two trigonometric functions.

10. $2 \sin 6\theta \cos 2\theta$
11. $2 \cos 3\theta \cos \theta$
12. $2 \cos 4\theta \cos \theta$
13. $2 \cos 6\theta \sin 3\theta$
14. $-2 \sin 4\theta \sin \theta$
15. $2 \cos 7\theta \sin 6\theta$
16. $\cos x \sin 5x$
17. $\sin 2A \sin A$
18. $\cos 3A \sin A$

Find the exact value of questions 19–24.

19. $\sin 75° - \sin 15°$
20. $\cos 105° - \cos 15°$
21. $\sin 255° - \sin 15°$
22. $2 \sin 75° \sin 105°$
23. $2 \cos 75° \cos 15°$
24. $\cos 37\frac{1}{2}° \sin 7\frac{1}{2}°$

25. Find the value of $k \in \mathbb{N}$ for which:

    (i) $\sin 75° - \sin 15° = \dfrac{1}{\sqrt{k}}$ (ii) $\cos 75° - \cos 15° = -\dfrac{1}{\sqrt{k}}$

26. A is an obtuse angle such that $\sin \left(A + \dfrac{\pi}{6} \right) + \sin \left(A - \dfrac{\pi}{6} \right) = \dfrac{4\sqrt{3}}{5}$.

    (i) Find $\sin A$ and $\tan A$.
    (ii) Given that $\tan (A + B) = \frac{1}{2}$, find $\tan B$ and express your answer in the form $\dfrac{p}{q}$ where $p, q \in \mathbb{Z}$ and $q \neq 0$.

Proving trigonometric identities

An identity is an equation that is true for all values of the variable.

Some identities we have met so far are:

$$\tan \theta = \frac{\sin \theta}{\cos \theta}$$

$$\cos^2 \theta + \sin^2 \theta = 1$$

$$\cos(-\theta) = \cos \theta \qquad \sin(-\theta) = -\sin \theta$$

$$\cos 2\theta = \cos^2 \theta - \sin^2 \theta$$

$$\sin 2\theta = 2 \sin \theta \cos \theta$$

$$\tan(-\theta) = -\tan \theta$$

Method for proving trigonometric identities

> The method is to take one side and convert it into the other side.
> It is usually easier to start with the side that is more complicated.

Note: Some identities are not true for all values of the given angle. For example, $\dfrac{1}{\cos 2\theta}$ is not defined for $\theta = 45°$ or $\dfrac{\pi}{4}$ radians.

EXAMPLE 1

Prove the following. **(i)** $1 + \tan^2 \theta = \dfrac{1}{\cos^2\theta}$ **(ii)** $2 \cos^2 \theta - \cos 2\theta = 1$

Solution:

(i) $\quad 1 + \tan^2 \theta$

$$= 1 + \frac{\sin^2 \theta}{\cos^2 \theta}$$

$$= \frac{\cos^2 \theta}{\cos^2 \theta} + \frac{\sin^2 \theta}{\cos^2 \theta}$$

$$= \frac{\cos^2 \theta + \sin^2 \theta}{\cos^2 \theta}$$

$$= \frac{1}{\cos^2 \theta}$$

(ii) $\quad 2 \cos^2 \theta - \cos 2\theta$

$$= 2 \cos^2 \theta - (\cos^2 \theta - \sin^2 \theta)$$

$$= 2 \cos^2 \theta - \cos^2 \theta + \sin^2 \theta$$

$$= \cos^2 \theta + \sin^2 \theta$$

$$= 1$$

EXAMPLE 2

Prove the following.

(i) $\dfrac{1}{1 - \sin A} + \dfrac{1}{1 + \sin A} = \dfrac{2}{\cos^2 A}$

(ii) $\dfrac{\cos \theta}{\sin \theta} + \dfrac{\sin \theta}{1 + \cos \theta} = \dfrac{1}{\sin \theta}$

Solution:

(i) $\dfrac{1}{1 - \sin A} + \dfrac{1}{1 + \sin A}$

$= \dfrac{1(1 + \sin A) + 1(1 - \sin A)}{(1 - \sin A)(1 + \sin A)}$

$= \dfrac{1 + \sin A + 1 - \sin A}{1 + \sin A - \sin A - \sin^2 A}$

$= \dfrac{2}{1 - \sin^2 A}$

$= \dfrac{2}{\cos^2 A}$

(ii) $\dfrac{\cos \theta}{\sin \theta} + \dfrac{\sin \theta}{1 + \cos \theta}$

$= \dfrac{\cos \theta(1 + \cos \theta) + \sin \theta(\sin \theta)}{\sin \theta(1 + \cos \theta)}$

$= \dfrac{\cos \theta + \cos^2 \theta + \sin^2 \theta}{\sin \theta(1 + \cos \theta)}$

$= \dfrac{1 + \cos \theta}{\sin \theta(1 + \cos \theta)}$

$= \dfrac{1}{\sin \theta}$

Exercise 9.14

Prove each of the identities in questions 1–17.

1. $\tan A \cos A = \sin A$

2. $(1 - \cos A)(1 + \cos A) = \sin^2 A$

3. $\tan^2 \theta(1 - \sin^2 \theta) = \sin^2 \theta$

4. $(\cos \theta + \sin \theta)^2 = 1 + \sin 2\theta$

5. $(\sin A + \cos A)^2 + (\sin A - \cos A)^2 = 2$

6. $2\cos^2 A - \cos 2A - 1 = 0$

7. $\dfrac{1}{1 + \cos A} + \dfrac{1}{1 - \cos A} = \dfrac{2}{\sin^2 A}$

8. $\dfrac{\cos A}{1 - \sin A} - \tan A = \dfrac{1}{\cos A}$

9. $\dfrac{\cos \theta}{1 + \sin \theta} + \dfrac{1 + \sin \theta}{\cos \theta} = \dfrac{2}{\cos \theta}$

10. $\dfrac{1 - \cos 2A}{1 + \cos 2A} = \tan^2 A$

11. $\sin 3\theta + \sin \theta = 4 \sin \theta \cos^2 \theta$

12. $\cos 3\theta + \cos \theta = 4 \cos^3 \theta - 2 \cos \theta$

13. $\cos(A + B)\cos B + \sin(A + B)\sin B = \cos A$

14. $2 \cos\left(\frac{\pi}{4} + \theta\right)\cos\left(\frac{\pi}{4} - \theta\right) = \cos 2\theta$

15. $(\sin A + \sin B)(\sin A - \sin B) = 1 - \cos^2 A - \sin^2 B$

16. $\sin(A + B)\sin(A - B) = \cos^2 B + \sin^2 A - 1$

17. $(\cos A + \cos B)^2 + (\sin A + \sin B)^2 = 2 + 2\cos(A - B)$

18.   **(i)** Prove that $\cos 2\theta = \cos^2 \theta - \sin^2 \theta$.

    (ii) Deduce that $\cos 2\theta = 2 \cos^2 \theta - 1$.

    (iii) Deduce that $\cos^2 \theta = \frac{1}{2}(1 + \cos 2\theta)$.

19.   **(i)** Show that $(\cos A + \sin A)^2 = 1 + \sin 2A$.

    (ii) Hence or otherwise, solve $(\cos A + \sin A)^2 = \frac{1}{2}$ for $A \in \mathbb{R}$.

20.   **(i)** Show that $\dfrac{2 \tan A}{1 + \tan^2 A} = \sin 2A$.

    (ii) Hence or otherwise, solve $\dfrac{2 \tan A}{1 + \tan^2 A} = \dfrac{1}{2}$ for $A \in \mathbb{R}$.

21.   **(i)** Show that $\dfrac{\sin 2\theta}{1 + \cos 2\theta} = \tan \theta$.

    (ii) Hence or otherwise, prove that $\tan 22\frac{1}{2}^{\circ} = \sqrt{2} - 1$.

22.   **(i)** Show that $\tan 2\theta = \dfrac{2 \tan \theta}{1 - \tan^2 \theta}$.

    (ii) By letting $\theta = 15°$, show that $\tan 15° = 2 - \sqrt{3}$.

23.   **(i)** Express $1 - (\cos x - \sin x)^2$ in the form $a \sin bx$, where $a, b \in \mathbb{Z}$.

    (ii) Hence, graph $y = 1 - (\cos x - \sin x)^2$ in the domain $0° \leq x \leq 360°$.

    (iii) Hence, solve $1 - (\cos x - \sin x)^2 = \frac{1}{2}$ for $x \in \mathbb{R}$.

24.   **(i)** Show that $\sqrt{\sin^2 \theta + 5 \cos^2 \theta - 1} = |2 \cos \theta|$ for all values of θ.

    (ii) Hence, graph $y = \sqrt{\sin^2 \theta + 5 \cos^2 \theta - 1}$ in the domain $0° \leq x \leq 180°$.

    (iii) What is the period and range of $y = \sqrt{\sin^2 \theta + 5 \cos^2 \theta - 1}$?

    (iv) Solve $\sqrt{\sin^2 \theta + 5 \cos^2 \theta - 1} = \sqrt{2}$ in the given domain.

Solving Trigonometric Equations 2

More complicated trigonometric equations can usually be reduced to one or more simple trigonometric equations by factorising or rearranging.

EXAMPLE 1

Solve the equation $\cos 2A + 3 \sin A - 2 = 0$ for **(i)** $0° \leq A \leq 360°$ **(ii)** $A \in \mathbb{R}$.

Solution:

$$\cos 2A + 3 \sin A - 2 = 0$$
$$\downarrow$$
$$(1 - 2 \sin^2 A) + 3 \sin A - 2 = 0 \qquad [\cos 2A = 1 - 2 \sin^2 A]$$

$-2 \sin^2 A + 3 \sin A - 1 = 0$

$2 \sin^2 A - 3 \sin A + 1 = 0$

$(2 \sin A - 1)(\sin A - 1) = 0$ [factorise]

$2 \sin A - 1 = 0$ or $\sin A - 1 = 0$

$\sin A = \frac{1}{2}$ or $\sin A = 1$

If $\sin A = 1$, $\theta = 90°$

If $\sin A = \frac{1}{2}$, $\theta = 30°$ or $150°$

The related angle is $30°$.

Sin is positive in the 1st and 2nd quadrants.

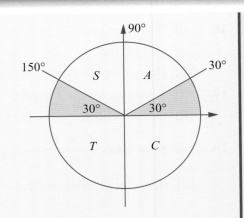

(i) For $0° \leq A \leq 360°$, $\theta = 30°$, $90°$ or $150°$.

(ii) For $A \in \mathbb{R}$ we need to find the general solution.

General Solution: $\text{Sin } A = \sin[A + n(360°)]$

$A = 30°;$ $A = 30° + n(360°),$ for $n \in \mathbb{Z}$.

$A = 90°;$ $A = 90° + n(360°),$ for $n \in \mathbb{Z}$.

$A = 150°;$ $A = 150° + n(360°),$ for $n \in \mathbb{Z}$.

Note: It is essential to include $n \in \mathbb{Z}$.

EXAMPLE 2

Solve the equation $\sqrt{2} \sin \theta \cos \theta + \cos \theta = 0$, for $0 \leq \theta \leq 2\pi$.

Solution:

Note: As we are given $0 \leq \theta \leq 2\pi$, the solutions must be given in radians.

$\sqrt{2} \sin \theta \cos \theta + \cos \theta = 0$

$\cos \theta (\sqrt{2} \sin \theta + 1) = 0$ [take out common factor $\cos \theta$]

$\cos \theta = 0$ or $\sqrt{2} \sin \theta + 1 = 0$

$\cos \theta = 0$ or $\sin \theta = -\dfrac{1}{\sqrt{2}}$

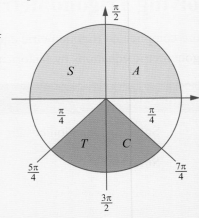

If $\cos \theta = 0$, $\theta = \dfrac{\pi}{2}$ or $\dfrac{3\pi}{2}$

If $\sin \theta = -\dfrac{1}{\sqrt{2}}$, $\theta = \dfrac{5\pi}{4}$ or $\dfrac{7\pi}{4}$

The related angle is $\dfrac{\pi}{4}$.

Sin is negative in the 3rd and 4th quadrants.

Thus, $\theta = \dfrac{\pi}{2}, \dfrac{5\pi}{4}, \dfrac{3\pi}{2}$ or $\dfrac{7\pi}{4}$.

Exercise 9.15

In questions 1–6, solve the equations for $0 \le \theta \le 360°$.

1. $\sin \theta (2 \sin \theta - 1) = 0$
2. $(2 \cos \theta - 1)(\cos \theta + 1) = 0$
3. $\tan \theta (\tan \theta - \sqrt{3}) = 0$
4. $\cos^2 \theta - \cos \theta = 0$
5. $\tan^2 \theta + \tan \theta = 0$
6. $2 \sin^2 \theta - \sin \theta - 1 = 0$

In questions 7–9, solve the equations for $0 \le x \le 2\pi$.

7. $2 \cos^2 x - \cos x = 0$
8. $\cos 2x = 1 - 2 \sin x$
9. $3 - 3 \cos x = 2 \sin^2 x$

10. Solve the equation $\sin 2\theta + \sin \theta = 0$ for **(i)** $0° \le \theta \le 360°$ **(ii)** $\theta \in \mathbb{R}$.

11. Solve the equation $\sqrt{2} \sin A \cos A - \sin A = 0$ for **(i)** $0 \le A \le 2\pi$ **(ii)** $A \in \mathbb{R}$.

12. Solve the equation $2 \sin \theta + 1 = \dfrac{1}{\sin \theta}$ for **(i)** $0 \le \theta \le 2\pi$ **(ii)** $\theta \in \mathbb{R}$.

13. Solve the equation $2 \sin \theta = \sqrt{3} \tan \theta$, where $0° \le \theta \le 360°$.

14. Solve the equations **(i)** $\tan^2 \theta - 3 = 0$, for $0 \le \theta = 2\pi$ **(ii)** $4 \cos^2 \theta = 3$.

15. Solve the equation $\sin^2 \theta + 3 \cos^2 \theta = 2$ for **(i)** $0 \le \theta \le 2\pi$ **(ii)** $\theta \in \mathbb{R}$.

16. **(i)** Express $\tan A$ in terms of $\sin A$ and $\cos A$.
    (ii) Solve for x, $\sin x = \cos x$, where $0 \le x \le 2\pi$.

17. **(i)** Explain why there is no solution to the equation $\sin \theta = 3$.
    (ii) Solve the equation $2 \sin^2 \theta + 5 \cos \theta - 4 = 0$ for **(i)** $0 \le \theta \le 2\pi$ **(ii)** $\theta \in \mathbb{R}$.

18. Find all the solutions of the equation $6 \cos^2 x + \sin x - 5 = 0$, where $0° \le x \le 360°$. Where necessary, give the solutions correct to the nearest degree.

19. $\theta = \dfrac{\pi}{6}$ is a solution to the equation $k \cos 2\theta - \sin^2 \theta - 1 = 0$, where $k \in \mathbb{Q}$.
    (i) Find the value of k. **(ii)** Hence, solve $k \cos 2\theta - \sin^2 \theta - 1 = 0$, for $0 \le \theta \le 2\pi$.

20. $x = 0°$ and $x = 60°$ are two solutions of the equation $a \sin^2 x + b \cos x - 3 = 0$, where $a, b \in \mathbb{N}$. Find the value of a and the value of b.
    Using these values of a and b, find all the solutions of the equation where $0° \le x \le 360°$.

21. **(i)** Prove $\tan 2\theta = \dfrac{2 \tan \theta}{1 - \tan^2 \theta}$.
    (ii) Find all seven solutions to the equation $\tan \theta + \tan 2\theta = 0$, where $0 \le A \le 2\pi$.

22. **(i)** Show that $\dfrac{\sin 5x + \sin x}{\cos 5x + \cos x} = \tan 3x$.
    (ii) Hence, solve $\dfrac{\sin 5x + \sin x}{\cos 5x + \cos x} = 1$, for **(i)** $x \in \mathbb{R}$ **(ii)** $0° \le x \le 360°$.

23. **(i)** Express $\sin 4x - \sin 2x$ as a product.
    (ii) Find all the solutions of the equation $\sin 4x - \sin 2x = 0$ in the domain $0° \le x \le 180°$.

24. Show that $\sin 5x - \sin x = 2 \cos 3x \sin 2x$.

Hence, solve the equation $\sin 5x - \sin 3x = \sqrt{3} \cos 3x$ for $0 \le x \le 360°$.

25. **(i)** Express $\tan 3x$ in terms of $\sin 3x$ and $\cos 3x$.

(ii) Show that $(\cos A + \cos B)^2 + (\sin A + \sin B)^2 = 2 + 2\cos(A - B)$.

(iii) Hence solve the equation $(\cos 4x + \cos x)^2 + (\sin 4x + \sin x)^2 = 2 + 2\sqrt{3} \sin 3x$ in the domain $0° \le x \le 360°$.

Identities involving the sine and cosine rules

We often have to prove identities involving the usual notation for a triangle using the sine and cosine rules. This usually involves rearranging the sine or cosine rule and substituting the rearranged expression to prove the required identity.

Cosine rule	**Sine rule**
$a^2 = b^2 + c^2 - 2bc \cos A$	$\dfrac{\sin A}{a} = \dfrac{\sin B}{b}$
then $\quad \cos A = \dfrac{b^2 + c^2 - a^2}{2bc}$	then $\quad \sin A = \dfrac{a \sin B}{b}$
Similarly for B and C.	or $\quad \sin B = \dfrac{b \sin A}{a}$

EXAMPLE

Using the usual notation for a triangle, prove that $c(b \cos A - a \cos B) = b^2 - a^2$.

Solution:

From the cosine rule,

$$\cos A = \frac{b^2 + c^2 - a^2}{2bc} \quad \text{and} \quad \cos B = \frac{a^2 + c^2 - b^2}{2ac}.$$

$$c(b \cos A - a \cos B)$$
$$= cb \cos A - ac \cos B$$
$$= cb \left(\frac{b^2 + c^2 - a^2}{2bc} \right) - ac \left(\frac{a^2 + c^2 - b^2}{2ac} \right) \quad \text{(this is the substitution)}$$
$$= \frac{b^2 + c^2 - a^2}{2} - \frac{a^2 + c^2 - b^2}{2}$$
$$= \frac{b^2 + c^2 - a^2 - (a^2 + c^2 - b^2)}{2} \quad \text{(same denominator)}$$
$$= \frac{b^2 + c^2 - a^2 - a^2 - c^2 + b^2}{2}$$
$$= \frac{2b^2 - 2a^2}{2}$$
$$= b^2 - a^2$$

Exercise 9.16

In questions 1–7, prove the identity using the usual notation for a triangle.

1. $b \sin C = c \sin B$

2. $bc \cos A + ac \cos B = c^2$

3. $c \cos B - b \cos C = \dfrac{c^2 - b^2}{a}$

4. $\dfrac{\cos A}{a} + \dfrac{\cos B}{b} + \dfrac{\cos C}{c} = \dfrac{a^2 + b^2 + c^2}{2abc}$

5. $a(\sin B - \sin C) + b(\sin C - \sin A) + c(\sin A - \sin B) = 0$

6. $\dfrac{\cos B}{b} - \dfrac{\cos C}{c} = \dfrac{c^2 - b^2}{abc}$

7. $a^2 + b^2 + c^2 = 2(bc \cos A + ac \cos B + ab \cos C)$

8.   (i) Show that $c = a \cos B + b \cos A$.

    (ii) Deduce $a + b + c = (b + c) \cos A + (a + c) \cos B + (a + b) \cos C$.

9.   (i) Show that $\cos (180° - \theta) = -\cos \theta$.

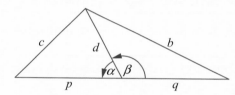

   (ii) Express $\cos \alpha$ and $\cos \beta$ in terms of the labelled lengths.

   (iii) Write α in terms of β.

   (iv) Hence or otherwise, show that $pb^2 + qc^2 = (p + q)(pq + d^2)$.

10. Show that the area of a triangle can be written as $\dfrac{a^2 \sin B \sin C}{2 \sin A}$.

Operations

The result of an operation is called an **outcome**.

For example, if we throw a die, one possible outcome is 5.

If we throw a regular six-sided die there are six possible outcomes: 1, 2, 3, 4, 5 or 6.

Fundamental principle of counting 1

> Suppose one operation has m possible outcomes and a second operation has n outcomes. The number of possible outcomes when performing the first operation **followed by** the second operation is $m \times n$.

Performing one operation **and** another operation means we **multiply** the number of possible outcomes.

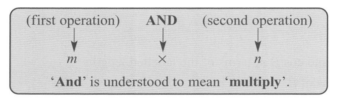

> (first operation)   **AND**   (second operation)
>
> m $\times$ n
>
> '**And**' is understood to mean '**multiply**'.

Note: We assume that the outcome of one operation does not affect the number of possible outcomes of the other operation.

The fundamental principle of counting 1 can be extended to three or more operations.

EXAMPLE

(i) If a regular six-sided die is thrown and a coin is tossed, how many different outcomes are possible?

(ii) Write out all the possible outcomes.

Solution: Die   Coin

(i) Represent each operation with an empty box: $\square \times \square$

     1. There are six possible outcomes for a die: 1, 2, 3, 4, 5 or 6.

     2. There are two possible outcomes for a coin: H or T.

     Hence, the number of different outcomes = $\boxed{6} \times \boxed{2} = 12$.

(ii)

T	•	•	•	•	•	•
H	•	•	•	•	•	•
	1	2	3	4	5	6

$(1, H), (2, H), (3, H), (4, H), (5, H), (6, H)$
$(1, T), (2, T), (3, T), (4, T), (5, T), (6, T)$

Permutations (arrangements)

> A **permutation** is an arrangement of a number of objects in a definite order.

Consider the three letters P, Q and R. If these letters are written down in a row, there are six different possible arrangements:

$$PQR \text{ or } PRQ \text{ or } QPR \text{ or } QRP \text{ or } RPQ \text{ or } RQP$$

The first letter can be written down in three ways, the second letter can then be written down in two ways and the third letter can be written down in only one way.

Thus, the three operations can be performed in $\boxed{3} \times \boxed{2} \times \boxed{1} = 6$ ways.

The boxes are an aid in helping to fill in the number of ways each choice can be made at each position.

In an arrangement, or permutation, the order of the objects chosen is important.

> If we have n **different** objects to arrange, then the total number of arrangements $= n!$
> $$n! = n(n-1)(n-2)(n-3)\cdots \times 3 \times 2 \times 1$$

For example, $6! = 6 \times 5 \times 4 \times 3 \times 2 \times 1 = 720$.

Using a calculator: $6\,\boxed{n!}\,\boxed{=}\,720$.

Suppose we have five different objects and we want to find the number of possible arrangements taking three objects at a time. We could use the fundamental principle of counting 1:

$$\begin{array}{ccccc} \text{1st} & \text{and} & \text{2nd} & \text{and} & \text{3rd} \\ \boxed{5} & \times & \boxed{4} & \times & \boxed{3} & = & 60 \end{array}$$

However, we can also do this type of calculation using factorials:

$$5 \times 4 \times 3 = \frac{5 \times 4 \times 3 \times 2 \times 1}{2 \times 1} = \frac{5!}{2!} = \frac{5!}{(5-3)!}$$

Similarly:

$$6 \times 5 = \frac{6 \times 5 \times 4 \times 3 \times 2 \times 1}{4 \times 3 \times 2 \times 1} = \frac{6!}{4!} = \frac{6!}{(6-2)!}$$

$$7 \times 6 \times 5 \times 4 = \frac{7 \times 6 \times 5 \times 4 \times 3 \times 2 \times 1}{3 \times 2 \times 1} = \frac{7!}{3!} = \frac{7!}{(7-4)!}$$

Notice that in each case the number of arrangements is given by:

$$\frac{\text{(Total number of objects)!}}{\text{(Total number of objects} - \text{number of objects to be arranged)!}}$$

> The number of arrangements of n different objects taking r at a time is:
>
> $$^{n}P_r = \frac{n!}{(n-r)!} = n(n-1)(n-2)\cdots(n-r+1)$$

Note: There is an 'nPr' button on most calculators.

Note: It can help to write down one possible outcome above each box.

	Die	Coin
One possible outcome:	5	T
Number of outcomes:	$\boxed{6}$ ×	$\boxed{2}$ = 12

This method is useful when trying to calculate the number of possible outcomes at a particular stage, especially when certain choices are restricted, such as in a question where the number must be even or where the word must begin with the letter K.

Fundamental principle of counting 2

> Suppose one operation has m possible outcomes and that a second operation has n outcomes. Then the number of possible outcomes of the first operation **or** the second operation is given by $m + n$.

Performing one operation **or** another operation means we **add** the number of possible outcomes.

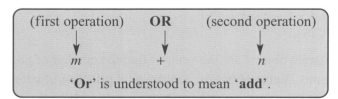

'**Or**' is understood to mean 'add'.

Note: We assume it is not possible for both operations to occur. In other words, there is no overlap of the two operations.

The fundamental principle of counting 2 can be extended to three or more operations, as long as none of the operations overlap.

EXAMPLE 1

A bag contains nine discs, numbered from 1 to 9. A disc is drawn from the bag.
If the number is even, then a coin is tossed. If the number is odd, then a six-sided die
is thrown.
How many outcomes are possible?

Solution:

Break the experiment into two different experiments and work out the number of
outcomes separately. Then add these results.

$$\left[\binom{\text{even}}{\text{number}} \text{ and } \binom{\text{toss a}}{\text{coin}}\right] \quad \text{or} \quad \left[\binom{\text{odd}}{\text{number}} \text{ and } \binom{\text{throw}}{\text{a die}}\right]$$

$$= \boxed{4} \quad \times \quad \boxed{2} \quad + \quad \boxed{5} \quad \times \quad \boxed{6}$$

$$= 8 + 30$$

$$= 38$$

EXAMPLE 2

How many arrangements can be made of the letters P, Q, R, S, T, taking two letters at a
time, if no letter can be repeated?

Solution:

Method 1: (using the fundamental principal of counting 1)

1st   and   2nd

$$\boxed{5} \quad \times \quad \boxed{4} = 20$$

Method 2: (using factorials)
We have five letters and want to arrange two.

$$^5P_2 = \frac{5!}{(5-2)!} = \frac{5!}{3!} = \frac{120}{6} = 20$$

Method 3: Use a calculator to evaluate $^5P_2$.

EXAMPLE 3

How many different arrangements can be made from the letters V, W, X, Y, Z, taking all the letters at a time, if V must be second and Z can never be last?

Solution:

Represent each choice with a box.

	1st	2nd	3rd	4th	5th
Possible outcome:	W	V	Z	Y	X
Number of ways:	3	1	2	1	3

$3 \times 1 \times 2 \times 1 \times 3 = 18$

(most restrictive, must be V)   (second most restrictive, cannot use V or Z)

Start with the choice that has the most restrictions and choose a possible letter each time.

In some questions we make use of the following fact:

$$\begin{pmatrix} \text{The number of arrangements in} \\ \text{which an outcome does } \textbf{not} \text{ occur} \end{pmatrix} = \begin{pmatrix} \text{Total number} \\ \text{of arrangements} \end{pmatrix} - \begin{pmatrix} \text{The number of arrangements} \\ \text{in which the outcome } \textbf{does} \text{ occur} \end{pmatrix}$$

EXAMPLE 4

A, B, C, D, E and F are six students. In how many ways can they be seated in a row if:

(i) There are no restrictions on the seating

(ii) A and B must sit beside each other

(iii) A and B must not sit beside each other

(iv) D, E and F must sit beside each other

(v) A and F must sit at the end of each row

Solution:

(i) **No restrictions**

Number of arrangements $= \boxed{6} \times \boxed{5} \times \boxed{4} \times \boxed{3} \times \boxed{2} \times \boxed{1} = 6! = 720$

(ii) **A and B must sit beside each other**

Consider A and B as one person.

$\boxed{A, B}, \boxed{C}, \boxed{D}, \boxed{E}, \boxed{F}$

The five people can be arranged in 5! ways.

But A and B can be arranged in 2! ways while seated together (i.e. AB or BA).

Thus, the number of arrangements $= 2! \times 5! = 2 \times 120 = 240$.

(iii) ***A* and *B* must not sit beside each other**

$$\begin{pmatrix} \text{Number of arrangements with} \\ A \text{ and } B \text{ not together} \end{pmatrix} = \begin{pmatrix} \text{Total number} \\ \text{of arrangements} \end{pmatrix} - \begin{pmatrix} \text{Number of arrangements} \\ \text{with } A \text{ and } B \text{ together} \end{pmatrix}$$

$$= 720 - 240 = 480$$

(iv) ***D, E* and *F* must sit beside each other**

Consider *D, E* and *F* as one person.

$\boxed{A}, \boxed{B}, \boxed{C}, \boxed{D, E, F}$

The four people can be arranged in 4! ways.

But *D, E* and *F* can be arranged in 3! ways while seated together.

Thus, the number of arrangements = 3! × 4! = 6 × 24 = 144.

(v) ***A* and *F* must sit at the end of each row**

Put *A* and *F* at the ends and *B, C, D* and *E* in between them.

$\boxed{A}, \boxed{B, C, D, E}, \boxed{F}$

B, C, D and *E* can be arranged in 4! ways while seated together.

A and *F* can exchange places.

Thus, the first and last can be arranged in 2! ways.

Thus, the number of arrangements = 2! × 4! = 2 × 24 = 48.

EXAMPLE 5

How many different four-digit numbers greater than 6,000 can be formed using the digits 1, 2, 4, 5, 6, 7 if **(i)** no digit can be repeated **(ii)** repetitions are allowed?

Solution:

Represent each choice with a box. The number must be greater than 6,000, so the first place can be filled in only two ways (with 6 or 7). Fill this in first, then fill the other places. Only use four boxes, as our choice is restricted to four digits at a time.

(i) No digit can be repeated

$\boxed{2} \times \boxed{5} \times \boxed{4} \times \boxed{3} = 120$

(ii) Repetitions are allowed

$\boxed{2} \times \boxed{6} \times \boxed{6} \times \boxed{6} = 432$

EXAMPLE 6

How many different five-digit numbers can be formed from the digits 1, 2, 3, 4 and 5 if:

  (i) There are no restrictions on digits and repetitions are allowed

  (ii) The number is odd and no repetitions are allowed

 (iii) The number is even and repetitions are allowed

 (iv) The number is greater than 50,000 and no repetitions are allowed

Solution:

Represent each choice with a box.

  (i) No restrictions and repetitions are allowed

$$\boxed{5} \times \boxed{5} \times \boxed{5} \times \boxed{5} \times \boxed{5} = 3{,}125$$

  (ii) Must be odd and no repetitions

Thus, the last place can be filled in only three ways (1, 3 or 5). Fill this in first, then fill in the other places.

$$\boxed{4} \times \boxed{3} \times \boxed{2} \times \boxed{1} \times \boxed{3} = 72$$

 (iii) Must be even and repetitions allowed

Thus, the last place can be filled in only two ways (2 or 4). Fill this in first, then fill in the other places.

$$\boxed{5} \times \boxed{5} \times \boxed{5} \times \boxed{5} \times \boxed{2} = 1{,}250$$

 (iv) Must be greater than 50,000 and no repetitions

Thus, the first place can be filled in only one way (with 5). Fill this in first, then fill in the other places.

$$\boxed{1} \times \boxed{4} \times \boxed{3} \times \boxed{2} \times \boxed{1} = 24$$

Exercise 10.1

1. A game consists of spinning an unbiased, five-sided spinner which can land on *A*, *B*, *C*, *D* or *E* and throwing an unbiased six-sided die. How many different outcomes of the game are possible?

2. A fifth year student must choose one subject from each of the following three groups.

Group 1: Music, Technical Graphics, Applied Mathematics or Classical Studies

Group 2: Physics, Chemistry or Biology

Group 3: Economics or Accounting

  (i) In how many ways can the student choose the three subjects?

 (ii) If Music must be included and Chemistry must be excluded, in how many ways can the student choose the three subjects?

3. **(i)** A number plate is to consist of three letters of the English alphabet and two digits. If no letter or digit can be repeated and 0 can never be used as the first digit, how many different plates can be manufactured?

> **BAT 45**
>
> (an example)

(ii) A number plate is to consist of three digits and two letters of the English alphabet. If no letter or digit can be repeated and 0 can never be used as the first digit, how many different plates can be manufactured?

> **402 QB**
>
> (an example)

(iii) The Ministry of Transport in a certain country decides to introduce a new type of number plate for motor vehicle registration. It is expected that there will be on average 86,000 new vehicle registrations in that country each year for the next five years. Which of **(i)** and/or **(ii)** above do you think would meet the needs of that Ministry of Transport? Justify your answer.

4. A personal identification number (PIN) for a credit card verification machine consists of four digits.

(i) Write down the smallest PIN number.

(ii) Write down the largest PIN number.

(iii) How many four-digit PIN numbers can be formed?

(iv) A bank issues 185,904 of its customers a credit card. Can the bank supply a different four-digit PIN number to each of those customers? Justify your answer.

5. **(i)** A permutation lock has four rings that can be rotated about an axle. There are 10 digits (0, 1, 2 . . . 8, 9) on each ring. If no digit can be repeated and 0 can never be first, find the maximum number of such locks that could be manufactured if no two locks have the same code and the lock will open only when a certain code of four digits is in line (see the diagram).

(ii) Aideen uses one of these permutation locks to secure her bicycle when she plays tennis. Her bicycle is locked unattended for 2 hours 10 minutes. Lee is a bicycle thief who can check such a lock permutation once every 12 seconds.

(a) How many such lock permutations can Lee check in the time Aideen's bicycle is left unattended?

(b) Hence, rate Lee's chances of opening the lock as poor, good or excellent. Justify your answer.

6. A student has five reference books, one each on Maths, Geography, Art, History and Economics. The books are to be placed in a row on a shelf.

(i) How many arrangements are possible?

(ii) How many arrangements have the Art book in the middle?

(iii) How many arrangements have the Art book on the left-hand end and the Maths book on the right-hand end?

7. **(i)** A person is asked to select a four-digit number from the digits 1, 2, 3, 4 and each digit can be used only once. How many different selections can be made?

(ii) A person is asked to select a five-digit number from the digits 1, 2, 3, 4, 5 and each digit can be used only once. How many different selections can be made?

(iii) From a group of 109 people, one person is chosen at random. Investigate which of **(i)** or **(ii)** above allocating a unique code to each person would be best suited to do this. Justify your answer.

8. A football club in a town with approximately 9,000 inhabitants decides to run a weekly fundraiser every Saturday evening, the Blotto. The Blotto draw consists of seven cards numbered 1 to 7 that are placed in a bag. The seven cards are drawn one by one without replacement and noted until all seven cards are drawn. This seven-digit number is the winning combination.

(i) How many different combinations are possible?

(ii) Each week the club sells about 2,200 tickets for this draw. Which of the following would it be better for the club to change the draw to?

(a) Six cards numbered 1 to 6 and draw all six cards for the winning selection

(b) Eight cards numbered 1 to 8 and draw all eight cards for the winning selection

(c) Stay with the existing method

Justify your answer.

9. Raffle tickets are each labelled with a digit from {1, 2, 3, 4, 5, 6, 7, 8, 9} followed by a letter from the English alphabet {A, B, C, D . . . X, Y, Z} (for example, 1A, 2A, 3A).

(i) How many different raffle tickets can be formed?

(ii) Would this amount of tickets be suitable for a raffle in your class? Justify your answer.

10. A password for a website consists of capital letters A, B, C . . . Z and/or digits 0, 1, 2 . . . 9. The password has four such characters and starts with a letter. For example, BA7A, C999 and DGKK are allowed, but 7DCA is not. Show that there are more than 1 million possible passwords.

11. Taking all the letters of the word *GALWAY*, in how many arrangements are the two As together?

12. **(i)** In how many ways can three girls and two boys be seated in a row of five seats?

(ii) In how many ways can this be done if the boys must sit together?

(iii) In how many ways can this be done if the boys must not sit together?

13. How many arrangements of the letters of the word *FORMULAS* are possible if:

(i) All letters are used in the arrangement

(ii) The three vowels must come together in the arrangement

(iii) The three vowels must not **all** come together in the arrangement

14. Six children are to be seated in a row on a bench.
    (i) How many arrangements are possible?
    (ii) How many arrangements are possible if the youngest child must sit at the left-hand end and the oldest child must sit at the right-hand end?
    (iii) If two of the children are twins, in how many ways can the children be arranged if:
        (a) The twins are together   (b) The twins are not together

15. Six discs of equal size are stacked one on top of the other. There are two identical red discs and one each of blue, yellow, green and white.

    In how many different ways can the six discs be stacked so that the two red discs are either at the top or at the bottom?

16. At the Olympic Games, eight lanes are marked on the running track. Each runner is allocated to a different lane. Find the number of ways in which the runners in a heat can be allocated to these lanes when there are:
    (i) Eight runners in the heat
    (ii) Five runners in the heat and any five lanes may be used

17. Five cars enter a car park. There are exactly five vacant spaces in the car park.
    (i) In how many different ways can the five cars park in the vacant spaces?
    (ii) Two of the cars leave the car park without parking. In how many different ways can the remaining three cars park in the five vacant spaces?

18. A bag contains five discs, numbered from 1 to 5 inclusive. A disc is drawn from the bag. If the number is even, then a six-sided die is thrown. If the number is odd, then a coin is tossed. How many outcomes are possible?

19. A bag contains seven discs, numbered from 1 to 7 inclusive. A disc is drawn at random from the bag and **not** replaced. If the number is even, a second disc is drawn from the bag. If the first number is odd, then a six-sided die is thrown. How many outcomes are possible?

20. How many different three-digit numbers can be formed using the digits 0, 1, 2, 3, 4 if 0 cannot be the first digit and:
    (i) No digit may be repeated   (ii) Repetitions are allowed

21. How many four-digit numbers can be formed from the digits 1, 2, 3, 5, 6, 8 if:
    (i) There are no restrictions and repetitions are allowed
    (ii) The number is odd and no repetitions are allowed
    (iii) The number is divisible by 5 and repetitions are allowed
    (iv) The number is greater than 5,000, divisible by 5 and no repetitions are allowed

22. How many numbers between 2,000 and 4,000 can be made with the digits 1, 2, 3, 4 if no digit may be repeated?

23. How many odd numbers between 2,000 and 3,000 can be formed from the digits 1, 2, 3, 4, 5, 6 if:

  (i) Repetitions are allowed   **(ii)** Repetitions are not allowed

24. **(i)** How many different numbers, each with three digits or fewer, can be formed from the digits 2, 3, 4, 5, 6? Each digit can be used only once in each number.

  (ii) How many of the above numbers are odd?

  (iii) How many odd numbers between 4,000 and 6,000 can be formed from the digits 3, 4, 5, 6, 7, 8 if no digit can be repeated?

25. **(i) (a)** How many numbers between 100 and 1,000 use only odd digits if repetitions are allowed?

  (b) How many numbers between 100 and 1,000 use only even digits if repetitions are allowed?

  (c) Hence or otherwise, calculate how many numbers between 100 and 1,000 consist of a mixture of even and odd digits if repetitions are allowed.

  (ii) A school with a total enrolment of 500 students wishes to allocate a unique three-digit code number between 100 and 1,000 to every student in the school. The headmaster wishes to identify three categories of student by a code:

  1. Senior girls   **2.** Senior boys   **3.** Junior students

  Note: In this school, transition year students are considered as senior students.
  Comment on each of the following and justify your opinion.

  (a) Would each student have a unique number?

  (b) What assumption, if any, would you make about the ratio of male to female students?

  (c) What assumption, if any, would you make about the ratio of senior to junior students?

  (d) Using part **(a)** or otherwise, suggest two ways to allocate a unique code to every student in this school.

Combinations (selections)

A **combination** is a selection of a number of objects in any order.

In making a selection of a number of objects from a given set, only the contents of the group selected are important, not the order in which the items are selected.

For example, *AB* and *BA* represent the same selection.
However, *AB* and *BA* represent different arrangements.

Note: What is called a combination lock should really be called a permutation lock, as the order of the digits is essential.

The $\binom{n}{r}$ notation

$\binom{n}{r}$ gives the number of ways of choosing r objects from n different objects.

Its value can be calculated in two ways:

1. $\binom{n}{r} = \dfrac{n!}{r!(n-r)!}$ (definition)

2. $\binom{n}{r} = \dfrac{n(n-1)(n-2)\ldots(n-r+1)}{r!}$ (in practice)

Both give the same result, but the second is easier to use in practical questions. For example:

1. $\binom{6}{2} = \dfrac{6!}{2!(6-2)!} = \dfrac{6!}{2!4!} = \dfrac{720}{2 \times 24} = 15$

2. $\binom{6}{2} = \dfrac{6 \times 5}{2 \times 1}$ $\longrightarrow$ start at 6, go down two terms
$\longrightarrow$ start at 2, go down two terms

$= 15$

Notes:

1. $\binom{n}{r}$ is pronounced '*n-c-r*' or '*n*-choose-*r*'.

2. $\binom{n}{r}$ is sometimes written as ^nC_r or $_nC_r$.

3. $\binom{n}{0} = 1$, i.e. there is only one way of choosing no objects out of n objects.

4. $\binom{n}{n} = 1$, i.e. there is only one way of choosing n objects out of n objects.

5. $\binom{n}{r} = \binom{n}{n-r}$; use this when r is greater than $\dfrac{n}{2}$.

Explanation for note 5:

Assume you have 13 soccer players and you can pick only 11 to play.

The number of ways of choosing 11 from 13 is given by $\binom{13}{11}$.

$$\binom{13}{11} = \dfrac{13 \times 12 \times 11 \times 10 \times 9 \times 8 \times 7 \times 6 \times 5 \times 4 \times 3}{11 \times 10 \times 9 \times 8 \times 7 \times 6 \times 5 \times 4 \times 3 \times 2 \times 1} = 78$$

However, every time you choose 11 to play, you choose two who cannot play.

Thus, $\binom{13}{11} = \binom{13}{2} = \dfrac{13 \times 12}{2 \times 1} = 78$ (same as before).

Notice that $11 + 2 = 13$.

Similarly: $\binom{20}{17} = \binom{20}{3}$ as $17 + 3 = 20$

and $\binom{100}{98} = \binom{100}{2}$ as $98 + 2 = 100$

If r is large, your calculator may not be able to do the calculation, so use $\binom{n}{r} = \binom{n}{n-r}$.

EXAMPLE 1

Ten people take part in a chess competition. How many games will be played if every person must play each of the others?

Solution:

We **have** 10 people to choose from, of whom we want to **choose** two (as two people play in each game). Thus, $n = 10$, $r = 2$.

$$\text{Number of games} = \binom{10}{2} = \frac{10 \times 9}{2 \times 1} = 45.$$

EXAMPLE 2

(i) In how many ways can a committee of four people be chosen from a panel of 10 people?

(ii) If a certain person must be on the committee, in how many ways can the committee be chosen?

(iii) If a certain person must not be on the committee, in how many ways can the committee be chosen?

Solution:

(i) We **have** a panel of 10 people to choose from and we need to **choose** a committee of four.

$$\therefore n = 10, \ r = 4$$

$$\binom{10}{4} = \frac{10 \times 9 \times 8 \times 7}{4 \times 3 \times 2 \times 1} = 210$$

Thus, from a panel of 10 people we can choose 210 different committees of four people.

(ii) One particular person **must** be on the committee.

Thus, we **have** a panel of nine people to choose from and we need to **choose** three (as one person is already chosen).

$$\therefore n = 9, r = 3$$

$$\binom{9}{3} = \frac{9 \times 8 \times 7}{3 \times 2 \times 1} = 84$$

Thus, from a panel of 10 people we can choose 84 different committees of four people if one particular person of the 10 must be on every committee.

(iii) One particular person **must not** be on the committee.

Thus, we **have** a panel of nine to choose from (as one person cannot be chosen) and we need to **choose** four.

$$\therefore n = 9, r = 4$$

$$\binom{9}{4} = \frac{9 \times 8 \times 7 \times 6}{4 \times 3 \times 2 \times 1} = 126$$

Thus, from a panel of 10 people we can choose 126 different committees of four people if one particular person of the 10 must not be on the committee.

Note: Answer **(i)** − answer **(ii)** = 210 − 84 = 126, answer **(iii)**.

EXAMPLE 3

(i) In how many ways can a group of five be selected from nine people?

(ii) How many groups can be selected if two particular people from the nine cannot be in the same group?

Solution:

(i) We have nine, from whom we want to choose five. Thus, $n = 9, r = 5$.

$$\binom{9}{5} = \frac{9 \times 8 \times 7 \times 6 \times 5}{5 \times 4 \times 3 \times 2 \times 1} = 126$$

(ii) In order to calculate how many groups of five can be selected if two particular people cannot be included, we first need to calculate the number of ways of selecting five people with these particular two people always included, i.e. we have seven, from whom we choose three (because two are already selected). Thus, $n = 7, r = 3$.

$$\binom{7}{5} = \frac{7 \times 6 \times 5}{3 \times 2 \times 1} = 35$$

$$\begin{pmatrix} \text{The number of ways of selecting} \\ \text{a group of five people from nine} \\ \text{when two particular people are} \\ \text{not to be in the same group} \end{pmatrix} = \begin{pmatrix} \text{Total number} \\ \text{of ways of} \\ \text{selecting a group} \\ \text{of five from nine} \end{pmatrix} - \begin{pmatrix} \text{The number of ways of} \\ \text{selecting a group of five} \\ \text{people from nine with} \\ \text{these two particular people} \end{pmatrix}$$

$$= 126 - 35$$
$$= 91$$

EXAMPLE 4

Four letters are selected from the word *SECTIONAL*.

(i) How many different selections are possible?

(ii) How many of these selections contain at least one vowel?

Solution:

(i) We have nine different letters to choose from and we need to select four.

$$\therefore n = 9, r = 4$$

$$\binom{9}{4} = \frac{9 \times 8 \times 7 \times 6}{4 \times 3 \times 2 \times 1} = 126$$

(ii) Split the word *SECTIONAL* into vowels and consonants.

The four vowels are *E, I, O, A* and the five consonants are *S, C, T, N, L*.

'At least one vowel' means one vowel, two vowels, three vowels or four vowels.

It is easier to calculate the number of selections containing no vowels (i.e. four consonants) and subtract this from the number of ways of selecting four letters without any restrictions.

Number of selections containing no vowels

$$= \text{number of selections containing four consonants} = \binom{5}{4} = \frac{5 \times 4 \times 3 \times 2}{4 \times 3 \times 2 \times 1} = 5$$

(There are five consonants and we want to select four, thus $n = 5$ and $r = 4$.)

In every other selection there must be at least one vowel. Thus, the number of selections containing at least one vowel

$$= \text{(total number of selections)} - \text{(number of selections containing no vowels)}$$

$$= 126 - 5$$

$$= 121$$

Exercise 10.2

Calculate each of the following in questions 1–9.

1. $\dbinom{5}{3}$ 　　　 2. $\dbinom{10}{2}$ 　　 3. $\dbinom{9}{5}$ 　　　　 4. $\dbinom{10}{1}$

5. $\dbinom{20}{18}$ 　　 6. $\dbinom{30}{27}$ 　　 7. $5\dbinom{4}{2} + 3\dbinom{7}{2}$ 　　 8. $10\dbinom{7}{2} - 6\dbinom{8}{5}$

9. $5\dbinom{8}{3} - 4\dbinom{8}{4}$ 　　　　 10. If $\dbinom{8}{5} = \dbinom{8}{k}$, $k \neq 5$, find the value of k.

11. If $\dbinom{13}{r + 5} = \dbinom{13}{3r - 4}$, $r + 5 \neq 3r - 4$, find the value of r.

12. In how many ways can a committee of four people be chosen from seven people?

13. In how many ways can a party of six children be chosen from a group of 10 children if:
    - (i) Any child may be selected
    - (ii) The oldest child must not be selected
    - (iii) The youngest child must be selected
    - (iv) The youngest and the oldest must both be selected

14. A fifth year student has to choose four subjects from the following list: Accounting, Biology, Chemistry, Physics, French, Applied Maths and Classical Studies.
    - (i) How many different choices are possible?
    - (ii) How many choices include French?
    - (iii) How many choices do not include French?
    - (iv) How many choices include Accounting and Biology?
    - (v) How many choices include Applied Maths and Chemistry but not Biology?

15. (i) In how many ways can a group of five be selected from 10 people?
    - (ii) How many groups can be selected if two particular people from the 10 cannot be in the same group?

16. Eight people, including Kieran and Anne, are available to form a committee. Five people must be chosen for the committee.
    - (i) In how many ways can the committee be formed if both Kieran and Anne must be chosen?
    - (ii) In how many ways can the committee be formed if neither Kieran nor Anne can be chosen?

17. (i) Find the number of different selections of four letters that can be made from the letters of the word *SPHERICAL*.
    - (ii) How many of these selections do not contain a vowel?
    - (iii) How many of these selections contain at least one vowel?

18. (i) Find the number of different selections of five letters that can be made from the letters of the word *CHEMISTRY*.
    - (ii) How many of these selections contain at least one vowel?

19. How many selections of two beads of different colours can be made from a bag containing 12 beads, five of which are red and the other beads are different colours?

20. Forty horses run in a race. All horses finish the race and no two horses finish the race at the same time.

    (i) A person is asked to predict, in any order, the first two horses to finish the race. How many different predictions can be made?

    (ii) A person is asked to predict, in any order, the first three horses to finish the race. How many different predictions can be made?

    (iii) Each year, a race with 40 horses, the Grand National, takes place in Liverpool. In the Grand National, do you think all predictions are equally likely? Justify your answer.

    (iv) Both types of predictions in part (i) and part (ii) are popular lotteries on the day of the race. Discuss which you think is best and explain your decision.

21. From a set of six different coins, in how many ways can four or more coins be selected?

22. Nine friends wish to travel in a car. Only two of them, John and Mary, have licences to drive. Only five people can fit in the car (i.e. the driver and four others). In how many ways can the group of five people be selected if:

    (i) Both John and Mary are included

    (ii) Either John or Mary is included, but not both

    (iii) Later, another one of the nine friends, Anne, gets a driving licence. The next time the journey is made, in how many ways can the group of five be chosen, given that at least one licensed driver must be included?

23.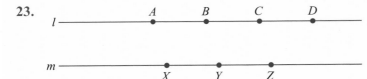

    l and m are distinct parallel lines.

    A, B, C and D are points on l such that $|AB|=|BC|=|CD|=1$ cm.

    X, Y and Z are points on m such that $|XY|=|YZ|=1$ cm.

    (i) How many different triangles can be constructed using three of the named points as vertices?

    (ii) How many different quadrilaterals can be constructed using four of the named points as vertices?

    (iii) How many different parallelograms can be constructed using four of the named points as vertices?

24. A team of six players is to be chosen from a group of 10 players. One of the six is then to be elected as captain and another as vice-captain. In how many ways can this be done?
    (Hint: Select and then arrange.)

Combinations from two different groups

Sometimes we have to deal with problems choosing objects from two different groups. This involves choosing a number of objects from one group **and** then choosing a number of objects from the other group.

Notes: There are two key words when applying the fundamental principle of counting:

1. 'And' is understood to mean 'multiply'. Thus, and = ×.

2. 'Or' is understood to mean 'add'. Thus, or = +.

EXAMPLE 1

How many different basketball teams, each consisting of three boys and two girls, can be formed from seven boys and five girls?

Solution:

$$\boxed{\text{And} = \times}$$

We have seven boys and five girls. These are the upper numbers in the combination bracket. A team must consist of five players.

We need to choose three boys and two girls. These are the lower numbers in the combination bracket.

Number of ways of choosing three boys from seven boys = $\binom{7}{3}$ = 35

Number of ways of choosing two girls from five girls = $\binom{5}{2}$ = 10

∴ The number of basketball teams consisting of three boys and two girls = 35 × 10 = 350.

EXAMPLE 2

There are five women and four men in a club. A team of four has to be chosen. How many different teams can be chosen if there must be exactly one woman or exactly two women on the team?

Solution:

$$\boxed{\text{And} = \times} \qquad \boxed{\text{Or} = +}$$

We have five women and four men and these are **always** the upper numbers in the combination bracket.

A team must consist of four people.

Thus, exactly one woman on the team means 'one woman **and** three men' and exactly two women on the team means 'two women **and** two men'.

We need to choose one woman **and** three men **or** two women **and** two men.

Let W stand for women and let M stand for men.

We have five women and four men – these are **always** the upper numbers.

$$1W \text{ and } 3M \qquad \text{or} \qquad 2W \text{ and } 2M \qquad \text{(lower numbers in each case)}$$

$$\binom{5}{1} \times \binom{4}{3} \qquad + \qquad \binom{5}{2} \times \binom{4}{2}$$

$$= 5 \quad \times \quad 4 \qquad + \qquad 10 \times 6$$

$$= 20 \ + \ 60$$

$$= 80$$

Thus, 80 teams can have either one woman or two women on the team.

EXAMPLE 3

How many bundles of five different books can be made from eight Maths books and six Physics books if the number of Maths books must always be greater than the number of Physics books?

Solution:

We have eight Maths books and six Physics books and these are **always** the upper numbers in the combination bracket.

A bundle must consist of five books. We need to have more Maths books than Physics books. Therefore, we need to choose:

(5 Maths and 0 Physics books) **or** (4 Maths and 1 Physics books) **or** (3 Maths and 2 Physics books).

Let M stand for a Maths book and P stand for a Physics book.

Possibilities:

$$5M \text{ and } 0P \quad \text{or} \quad 4M \text{ and } 1P \quad \text{or} \quad 3M \text{ and } 2P \quad \text{(lower numbers in each case)}$$

$$\binom{8}{5} \times \binom{6}{0} + \binom{8}{4} \times \binom{6}{1} + \binom{8}{3} \times \binom{6}{2}$$

$$= 56 \quad \times \quad 1 \ + \ 70 \ \times \ 6 \ + \ 56 \ \times \ 15$$

$$= 56 + 420 + 840$$

$$= 1{,}316$$

Exercise 10.3

1.   (i) In how many ways can a group of five people be selected from four women and four men?
     (ii) In how many of these groups are there exactly three women?

2.   (i) How many different groups of four can be selected from five boys and six girls?
     (ii) How many of these groups consist of two boys and two girls?

3. Students going on a school tour to Amsterdam must choose **three** activities from Van Gogh Museum, Anne Frank House, clog factory or canal cruise and choose **two** activities from disco, bowling, swimming or quiz.
     (i) How many different selections can be made?
     (ii) List all possible selections that include canal cruise and disco.

4. A committee of five is to be selected from six students and three teachers.
     (i) How many different committees of five are possible?
     (ii) How many of these possible committees have three students and two teachers?

5. In how many ways can a group of four people be selected from six men and four women if:
     (i) There are no restrictions
     (ii) There must be two women and two men
     (iii) There must be exactly three men or exactly two men

6. How many bundles of three different books can be selected from five Maths books and two Physics books if the selection contains:
     (i) Only Maths books
     (ii) Two Maths books and one Physics book
     (iii) One Maths book and two Physics books

7.   (i) In how many ways can a group of four people be selected from three men and four women?
     (ii) In how many of these groups are there more women than men?

8. In how many ways can a committee of six be selected from five men and four women if each committee consists of:
     (i) An equal number of men and women
     (ii) At least three men
     (iii) At least three women

9. A committee of six is to be formed from eight students and five teachers. How many different committees can be formed if there are to be more teachers than students?

10. A team of five players is to be chosen from six boys and five girls. If there must be more boys than girls, how many different teams can be formed?

11. A group consists of five men and seven women. A committee of four must be chosen from the group. How many committees can be chosen in which there are an odd number of men?

12. An examination consists of 10 questions: four in section A and the remainder in section B. A candidate must attempt five questions, at least two of which must be from each section. In how many different ways may the candidate select the five questions?

13. (i) Four Irish men, three French men and two German men are available for selection to a European committee of four. If each nation is to have at least one representative on the committee, in how many ways can the committee be selected?

(ii) What is wrong with the method shown below? Calculate the correct answer, showing all your work.

$\binom{4}{1}$ From four Irish men, select one.

$\binom{3}{1}$ From three French men, select one.

$\binom{2}{1}$ From two German men, select one.

$\binom{6}{1}$ From the remainder, select one.

Number of committees $= 4 \times 3 \times 2 \times 6 = 144$

Equations involving $\binom{n}{r}$

Sometimes we have to solve equations involving $\binom{n}{r}$.

In these questions, we make use of the following.

$$\binom{n}{1} = \frac{n}{1} = n \qquad \binom{n}{2} = \frac{n(n-1)}{(2)(1)} = \frac{n^2 - n}{2} \qquad \binom{n}{3} = \frac{n(n-1)(n-2)}{(3)(2)(1)} = \frac{n^3 - 3n^2 + 2n}{6}$$

EXAMPLE

Solve $\binom{n}{2} = 190$, where n is a natural number.

Solution:

The word 'solve' in the question means we are not allowed to guess the answer.

$$\binom{n}{2} = 190$$

$$\frac{n(n-1)}{2} = 190 \qquad \left(\binom{n}{2} = \frac{n(n-1)}{2 \times 1} = \frac{n(n-1)}{2} \right)$$

$$\frac{n^2 - n}{2} = 190 \qquad \text{(remove the brackets on top)}$$

$$n^2 - n = 380 \qquad \text{(multiply both sides by 2)}$$

$$n^2 - n - 380 = 0 \qquad \text{(quadratic equation)}$$

$$(n - 20)(n + 19) = 0$$

$$n - 20 = 0 \qquad \text{or} \qquad n + 19 = 0$$

$$n = 20 \qquad \text{or} \qquad n = -19$$

Reject $n = -19$, as -19 is not a natural number.

$\therefore n = 20$

Note: It is good practice to check your answer on a calculator. $\binom{20}{2} = 190$ (correct)

Exercise 10.4

Solve each of the following, where n is a natural number.

1. $\binom{n}{2} = 6$

2. $\binom{n}{2} = 10$

3. $\binom{n}{2} = 15$

4. $\binom{n}{2} = 28$

5. $\binom{n}{2} = 45$

6. $\binom{n}{2} = 2\binom{n}{1}$

7. $\binom{n}{2} = 12\binom{n}{1}$

8. $\binom{n+1}{2} = 21$

9. $\binom{n+1}{2} = \binom{n}{1} + 4\binom{7}{1}$

Probability

Probability involves the study of the laws of chance. It is a measure of the chance, or likelihood, of something happening.

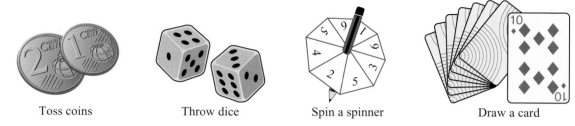

| Toss coins | Throw dice | Spin a spinner | Draw a card |

If you carry out an operation or experiment using coins, dice, spinners or cards, then each toss, throw, spin or draw is called a **trial**.

The possible things that can happen from a trial are called **outcomes**. The outcomes of interest are called an **event**. In other words, an event is the set of successful outcomes.

For example, if you throw a die and you are interested in the probability of throwing an even number, then the event is 2, 4, 6 – the successful outcomes.

If E is an event, then $P(E)$ stands for the probability that the event occurs. $P(E)$ is read as 'the probability of E'.

Definition

> The measure of the probability of an event, E, is given by:
>
> $$P(E) = \frac{\text{Number of successful outcomes}}{\text{Number of possible outcomes}}$$

The probability of an event is a number between 0 and 1, including 0 and 1.

$$0 \leq P(E) \leq 1$$

The value of $P(E)$ can be given as a fraction, decimal or percentage.

Note: $P(E) = 0$ means that an event is **impossible**.
   $P(E) = 1$ means that an event is **certain**.

The chance of an event happening can be shown on a **probability scale**:

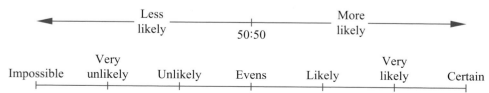

The probabilities of some events are shown on the probability scale below.

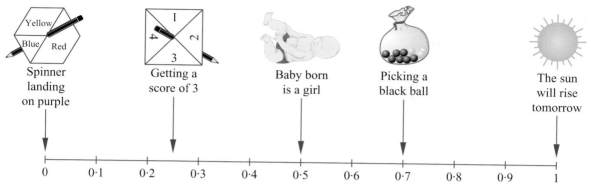

Probabilities should always be written as fractions, decimals or percentages.

Note: $\frac{1}{2} = 0\cdot5 = 50:50 = $ evens $= 50\%$.

The set of all possible outcomes is called the **sample space**. For example, the sample space for a six-sided die is 1, 2, 3, 4, 5 and 6.

Probability of an event not happening

If E is any event, then 'not E' is the event that E does not occur. Clearly, E and not E cannot occur at the same time. Either E or not E must occur. Thus, we have the following relationship between the probabilities of E and not E:

$$P(E) + P(\text{not } E) = 1$$
or
$$P(\text{not } E) = 1 - P(E)$$

Notes:

1. $P(\text{not } E)$ is often written as $P(E')$ or $P(\overline{E})$.

2. It is important **not** to count an outcome twice in an event when calculating probabilities.

3. In questions on probability, objects that are identical are treated as different objects.

4. The phrase '**drawn at random**' means each object is **equally likely** to be picked. '**Unbiased**' means '**fair**'. '**Biased**' means '**unfair**' in some way.

EXAMPLE 1

A bag contains eight red, three blue and 13 yellow discs. A disc is selected at random from the bag. What is the probability that the disc selected is:

(i) Red   (ii) Blue   (iii) Yellow   (iv) Not yellow

Solution:

There are $8 + 3 + 13 = 24$ discs in the bag.

(i) $P(\text{red disc}) = \dfrac{\text{Number of red discs}}{\text{Total number of discs}} = \dfrac{8}{24} = \dfrac{1}{3}$

(ii) $P(\text{blue disc}) = \dfrac{\text{Number of blue discs}}{\text{Total number of discs}} = \dfrac{3}{24} = \dfrac{1}{8}$

(iii) $P(\text{yellow disc}) = \dfrac{\text{Number of yellow discs}}{\text{Total number of discs}} = \dfrac{13}{24}$

(iv) We are certain that the disc selected is yellow or not yellow.

$\therefore P(\text{yellow disc}) + P(\text{not a yellow disc}) = 1$

$P(\text{not a yellow disc}) = 1 - P(\text{yellow disc})$

$= 1 - \dfrac{13}{24} = \dfrac{11}{24}$

Alternatively:

$P(\text{not a yellow disc}) = \dfrac{\text{Number of non-yellow discs}}{\text{Total number of discs}} = \dfrac{11}{24}$

(Number of non-yellow discs = number of red discs + number of blue discs = 8 + 3 = 11)

A pack of cards consists of 52 cards divided into four suits: clubs (black), diamonds (red), hearts (red) and spades (black). Each suit consists of 13 cards bearing the following values: 2, 3, 4, 5, 6, 7, 8, 9, 10, jack, queen, king and ace. The jack, queen and king are called picture cards. The total number of outcomes if one card is picked is 52.

EXAMPLE 2

A card is drawn at random from a normal pack of 52 playing cards.

What is the probability that the card will be:

(i) An ace   (ii) A spade   (iii) Black   (iv) Odd numbered

Solution:

(i) $P(\text{ace}) = \dfrac{\text{Number of aces}}{\text{Number of cards}} = \dfrac{4}{52} = \dfrac{1}{13}$

(ii) $P(\text{spade}) = \dfrac{\text{Number of spades}}{\text{Number of cards}} = \dfrac{13}{52} = \dfrac{1}{4}$

(iii) $P(\text{black card}) = \dfrac{\text{Number of black cards}}{\text{Number of cards}} = \dfrac{26}{52} = \dfrac{1}{2}$

(iv) Each suit has four odd numbers: 3, 5, 7 and 9. There are four suits.
Therefore, there are 16 cards with an odd number.

$P(\text{odd-numbered card}) = \dfrac{\text{Number of cards with an odd number}}{\text{Number of cards}} = \dfrac{16}{52} = \dfrac{4}{13}$

Note: If you count an ace as an odd number, then each suit has five odd numbers. (Ace = 1 could be considered ambiguous.) Therefore, there are $5 \times 4 = 20$ cards with odd numbers, so $P(\text{odd-numbered card}) = \frac{20}{52} = \frac{5}{13}$ would also be correct.

Conditional probability

With **conditional probability** we are given some prior knowledge or some extra condition about the outcome. This usually reduces the size of the sample space. Consider parts **(iv)** and **(v)** of the next example.

EXAMPLE 3

In a class, there are 21 boys and 15 girls. Three boys and five girls wear glasses. A pupil is picked at random from the class.

(i) What is the probability that the pupil is a boy?

(ii) What is the probability that the pupil wears glasses?

(iii) What is the probability that the pupil is a boy who wears glasses?

(iv) A girl is picked at random from the class. What is the probability that she wears glasses?

(v) A pupil wearing glasses is picked at random from the class. What is the probability that it is a boy?

Solution:

It is good practice to represent the information in a table (including the totals for each column and row).

There are $21 + 15 = 36$ pupils in the class.

	Boy	Girl	Total
Does not wear glasses	18	10	28
Wears glasses	3	5	8
Total	21	15	36

(i) $P(\text{boy}) = \dfrac{\text{Number of boys}}{\text{Number of pupils in the class}} = \dfrac{21}{36} = \dfrac{7}{12}$

(ii) $P(\text{pupil wears glasses}) = \dfrac{\text{Number of pupils who wear glasses}}{\text{Number of pupils in the class}} = \dfrac{8}{36} = \dfrac{2}{9}$

(iii) $P(\text{boy who wears glasses}) = \dfrac{\text{Number of boys who wear glasses}}{\text{Number of pupils in the class}} = \dfrac{3}{36} = \dfrac{1}{12}$

The next two questions require the use of conditional probability, where the size of the sample space has been reduced.

(iv) We are certain that the pupil picked is a girl. There are 15 girls in the class and five of these wear glasses.

$P(\text{when a girl is picked, she wears glasses})$

$= \dfrac{\text{Number of girls in the class who wear glasses}}{\text{Number of girls in the class}} = \dfrac{5}{15} = \dfrac{1}{3}$

(v) We are certain that the pupil picked wears glasses. There are eight pupils who wear glasses and three of these pupils are boys.

$$P(\text{when a pupil who wears glasses is picked, the pupil is a boy})$$
$$= \frac{\text{Number of boys in the class who wear glasses}}{\text{Number of pupils in the class who wear glasses}} = \frac{3}{8}$$

Note: We will meet more **conditional probability** later.

Combining two events

There are many situations where we have to consider two outcomes. In these situations, all the possible outcomes, the **sample space**, can be listed in a sample space diagram (often called a **two-way table**).

EXAMPLE 4

Two fair six-sided dice, one red and the other blue, are thrown. What is the probability of getting two equal scores or of the scores adding up to 10?

Solution:

Sample space diagram

There are 36 possible outcomes (6 × 6).

The dots indicate where the two scores are equal and/or they add up to 10.

There are eight dots.

$$\therefore P(\text{two equal scores or a total of } 10) = \frac{8}{36} = \frac{2}{9}.$$

Note: (5, 5) is **not** counted twice.

Exercise 10.5

1. A box contains 36 coloured balls. Twelve are red, 15 are blue, three are yellow and the rest are white. One ball is selected at random from the box. Calculate the probability of selecting a:

   (i) Red ball   (ii) Blue ball   (iii) Yellow ball   (iv) White ball

   (v) Given that the ball chosen is **not** red, calculate the probability that the selected ball is blue.

2. A card is drawn at random from a normal pack of 52 playing cards. What is the probability that the card will be:

   (i) The nine of spades   (ii) A red card   (iii) A club

   (iv) A king   (v) A picture card   (vi) A black picture card

   (vii) An even number   (viii) Not a queen   (ix) A joker

3. (i) A bag contains three red, three green and four blue discs. A disc is selected at random from the bag. What is the probability of selecting a blue disc?

   (ii) The selected disc is to be put back into the bag, plus a certain number of red discs. This causes the probability of selecting a red disc to equal $\frac{1}{2}$. Find the number of extra red discs that were placed in the bag.

4. (i) A fair spinner has eight sides, as shown. The sides are labelled A, B, B, C, C, C, C and F. The spinner is spun once. What is the probability that the spinner lands on:

   (a) A (b) B (c) C

   (ii) By replacing the letters A and F on the spinner, describe how to make the fair spinner behave like a fair coin.

5. A game consists of spinning an arrow on a square board.

   The board contains the letters A, B, C and D. The board is designed so that when the arrow stops spinning, it can only point at one letter.

   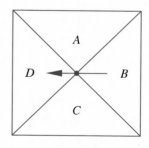

   The arrow is biased in favour of D so that the letter D is twice as likely as the letter A. The letters A, B and C are equally likely. Find the probability of:

   (i) The arrowing pointing to the letter A (ii) The arrowing pointing to the letter D

6. A card is chosen at random from a set of 25 cards numbered from 1 to 25. What is the probability that the card chosen is a multiple of 4, given that it is greater than 15?

7. A box contains 20 blue counters and 30 green counters. Each counter is numbered with an even or odd number. Five of the blue and 20 of the green counters are odd.

	Even	Odd	Total
Blue			20
Green			
Total			50

   (i) Complete the table opposite.

   (ii) One of the counters is chosen at random. What is the probability that the counter is:

   (a) Blue   **(b)** Green   **(c)** Blue and even   **(d)** Green and odd

   (iii) A green counter is chosen at random. What is the probability that it is odd?

   (iv) An odd-numbered counter is chosen at random. What is the probability that it is blue?

8. There are 80 members in a club: 32 males and 48 females. Four of the males and eight of the females wear glasses. A club member is selected at random.

   (i) What is the probability that the club member is a:

   (a) Male   **(b)** Female   **(c)** Person wearing glasses

   (d) Female not wearing glasses   **(e)** Male wearing glasses

   (ii) A male from the club is selected at random. What is the probability that he wears glasses?

   (iii) A member who wears glasses is selected at random.

   (a) What is the probability that it is a female?

   (b) All members who wear glasses resign from the club. What is the probability that a club member now selected at random is male?

9. The table shows the way that 150 first year students travel to school.

   (i) A first year student is chosen at random. What is the probability that the student:

   (a) Is a boy

   (b) Walks to school

   (c) Does not use the train

   (d) Is a girl who travels by bus

   (e) Is a boy who travels by train

	Walk	Bus	Car	Train	Bike
Boy	15	10	7	30	8
Girl	20	24	8	12	16

   (ii) A first year student who travels by bike is chosen at random. What is the probability that the student is a boy?

   (iii) A girl from first year is chosen at random. What is the probability that she:

   (a) Walks to school   **(b)** Does not travel by car

   (iv) If the number of girls in each category is doubled, find the total number of students now in first year. Hence, find the new probability that the student:

   (a) Is a boy   **(b)** Walks to school   **(c)** Does not use the train

10.

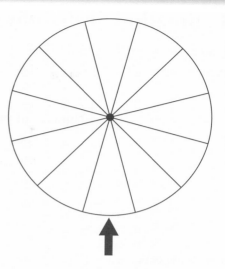

A TV game show has a wheel that spins freely around its centre point. The circle is divided into 12 equal sectors. Each sector of the circle is coloured green (G), blue (B) or red (R). The probability scale shows how likely it is for a colour to stop at the arrow. How many sectors are coloured:

(i) Green   **(ii)** Blue   **(iii)** Red

11. Write five numbers on each spinner such that each statement is true.

(i) It is certain that you will get a number that is greater than 3.

(ii) It is more likely that you will get an odd number than an even number.

(iii) It is impossible to get a number divisible by 3.

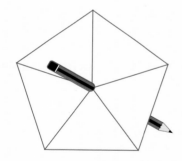
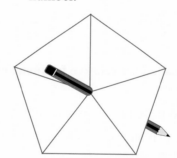
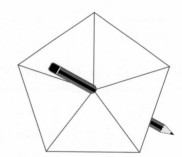

12. Copy and complete the spinner so that the probability of getting an even number is $\frac{1}{2}$ and the probability of getting a 2 is $\frac{1}{3}$.

Estimating probabilities from experiments

Elaina suspects that a six-sided die is biased. In an experiment, she throws the die 300 times. She records the results after 60, 120, 180, 240 and 300 throws. Her results are shown in the following table.

Number of throws	Score					
	1	2	3	4	5	6
60	8	11	13	11	7	10
120	19	23	25	19	15	19
180	31	32	35	27	25	30
240	40	44	44	36	36	40
300	50	53	52	45	51	49

Elaina **expects** each number to have an equal probability if the die is fair, i.e. $P(3) = \frac{1}{6} = 0.1667$ correct to four decimal places.

As the number of throws increases, the number of threes divided by the number of throws is $\frac{13}{60}$, $\frac{25}{120}$, $\frac{35}{180}$, $\frac{44}{240}$, $\frac{52}{300}$ = 0.2167, 0.2083, 0.1944, 0.1833, 0.1733.

When Elaina compares her expected probability of $\frac{1}{6} = 0.1667$, she could reasonably conclude the die is fair.

As the number of throws increases, the number of threes divided by the number of throws gets closer to $\frac{1}{6} = 0.1667$.

The values $\frac{13}{60}$, $\frac{25}{120}$, $\frac{35}{180}$, $\frac{44}{240}$, $\frac{52}{300}$ are called the **relative frequencies**. The more throws (trials) made, the more accurate the relative frequency.

The relative frequency gives an estimate that an event will happen.

Hence, to estimate the probability that an event will occur, we can use an experiment.

> The relative frequency of an event in an experiment is given by:
>
> $$P(E) = \text{Relative frequency of an event} = \frac{\text{Number of successful trials}}{\text{Number of trials}}$$

Relative frequency can be used to estimate how many times you would **expect** a particular outcome to happen in an experiment.

The expected number of outcomes is calculated as follows:

> Expected number of outcomes = (relative frequency) × (number of trials)
>
> or
>
> Expected number of outcomes = P(event) × (number of trials)

Note: To estimate the probability of some events, it is necessary to carry out a survey or look at historical data (past data).

EXAMPLE 1

Elaina throws her fair six-sided die a total of 1,200 times. Find the expected number of times the number 3 would appear.

Solution:

If the die is fair, then the probability of a score of 3 would be $\frac{1}{6}$.

Thus, the expected number of threes

$= P(\text{event}) \times \text{number of trials} = \frac{1}{6} \times 1,200 = 200$.

EXAMPLE 2

This spinner is biased.

The probability that the spinner will land on each of the numbers 1 to 5 is given in the probability distribution table below.

Number	1	2	3	4	5
Probability	0·25	0·2	0·25	0·15	B

(i) Write down the value of B.

(ii) If the spinner is spun 200 times, how many fives would you expect?

Solution:

(i) Since one of the numbers from 1 to 5 must appear, the sum of all the probabilities is 1.

$\therefore\ 0·25 + 0·2 + 0·25 + 0·15 + B = 1$

$0·85 + B = 1$

$B = 0·15$

(ii) Expected number of fives

$= P(5) \times (\text{number of trials})$

$= 0·15 \times 200 = 30$

Exercise 10.6

1. If a fair coin is tossed 250 times, how many tails would you expect to get?

2. Teddy thinks his coin is biased. He tosses it 100 times and gets 63 heads.

   (i) What is the experimental probability of getting a head with this coin?

   (ii) In 100 tosses, what is the expected value if the coin is fair?

   (iii) Is Teddy's coin biased? Justify your answer.

3. One ball is selected at random from the bag shown and then replaced. This procedure is repeated 280 times. How many times would you expect to select:

   (i) A blue ball
   (ii) A white ball

4. Joan wants to find out if a die is biased. She throws the die 600 times. The results are as follows.

Number of die	1	2	3	4	5	6
Frequency	56	84	110	130	105	115

   (i) For this die, calculate the experimental probability of obtaining a 4.
   (ii) For a fair die, write down the probability of scoring a 4.
   (iii) Do your answers suggest that Joan's die is fair? Justify your answer.

5. Hugh and Brendan play 35 games of chess. Hugh wins 20 of these games.

   (i) Find the probability that Hugh wins the next game.
   (ii) They play another series of 14 games. How many of these games would you expect Hugh to win?

6. The probability that a biased spinner will land on each of the numbers 1 to 5 is given in the probability distribution table.

Number	1	2	3	4	5
Probability	3 W	2 W	W	3 W	W

   (i) Calculate the value of W.
   (ii) Hence, find the probability that on one spin the result will be a number less than 3.
   (iii) If the spinner is spun 800 times, estimate the number of times it will show:

   (a) The number 4   (b) An odd number

7. (i) Molly, Nora and Margaret each rolled a different die 180 times. Only one of the dice was fair. Whose was it? Explain your answer.

   (ii) Whose die is the most biased? Explain your answer.

Number	Molly	Nora	Margaret
1	14	29	60
2	35	31	26
3	39	32	28
4	22	28	27
5	38	27	26
6	32	33	13

8. Red and green spinners were each spun 48 times. Each spinner has three sides indicating scores of 1, 2 and 3.

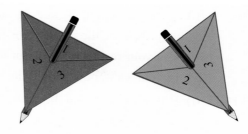

The bar chart shows the results.

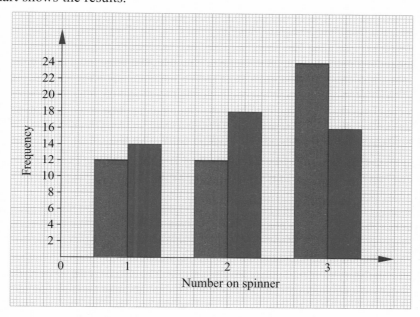

One spinner is biased and the other is unbiased. Which spinner do you think is biased? Justify your answer.

9. Four Las Vegas casino managers have an initial meeting to consider a new type of six-sided die. To use a die in their casinos, it must be perfectly fair. At the meeting they each throw the die a number of times and record the results.

Casino name	Number of throws	Results					
		1	2	3	4	5	6
Bellagio	60	12	8	11	9	7	13
Mirage	90	12	19	14	15	19	11
Luxor	30	4	6	5	5	7	3
Hard Rock	180	22	40	31	27	35	25

(i) Which casino's results are most likely to give the best estimate of the probability of getting each number? Justify your answer.

(ii) Construct a table by adding together all four results. Use your table to decide whether you think the die is biased or fair. Explain your answer.

(iii) Use your results to work out the probability of a score of 6. Comment on your answer.

(iv) In your view, how should the casino managers proceed?

10. (i) Bill has a six-sided die with sides numbered 1, 1, 1, 1, 2, 2. He throws the die eight times and gets a score of 1 twice. Bill thinks the die is not fair. Do you agree with Bill? Explain your answer.

(ii) Bill has another six-sided die with sides numbered 4, 5, 5, 6, 6, 6. He throws the die 450 times. The results are as follows.

Score	4	5	6
Frequency	69	147	234

(a) What do you think is the experimental (relative) frequency of throwing a 6?

(b) Do you think the die is fair? Justify your answer.

11. A biased five-sided spinner has sides labelled 1, 2, 3, 4 and 5. The probability that the spinner will land on each of the numbers 1 and 3 and 5 is given in the probability distribution table.

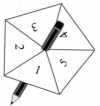

Number	1	2	3	4	5
Probability	0·3	x	0·15	x	0·35

(i) The probability that the spinner will land on 2 is equal to the probability that it will land on 4. Calculate the value of x.

(ii) Ronan spins the spinner 120 times. Estimate the number of times:

(a) It will land on 5

(b) It will land on 2

Show your work.

12. A TV game show plans to finish with the winner spinning a wheel. The wheel is fixed to a wall. It's divided equally into seven regions and the winning amounts are shown on the wheel in euro. The winner will receive the amount the arrow points to when the wheel stops.

The game show director suspects the wheel is not very fair, as some amounts seem to come up more often than others.

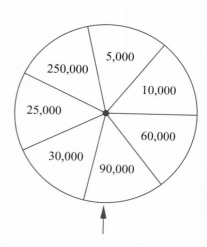

She spun the wheel 140 times and recorded the results. The results are shown in the table.

Amount won, in €1,000s	5	10	25	30	60	90	250
Number of times	7	19	17	8	29	42	18

(i) How many times would the director expect each number to occur if the wheel was fair?

(ii) Work out the experimental probability of spinning:

    (a) €5,000

    (b) €90,000

(iii) Do you think the director would conclude the wheel was fair? Justify your answer.

Combined events

If A and B are two different events of the same experiment, then the probability that the two events, A or B, can happen is given by:

$$P(A \text{ or } B) = P(A) + P(B) - P(A \text{ and } B)$$

(removes double counting)

It is often called the 'or' rule. It is important to remember that $P(A \text{ or } B)$ means A occurs, or B occurs, or both occur. By subtracting $P(A \text{ and } B)$, the possibility of double counting is removed.

Using set notation

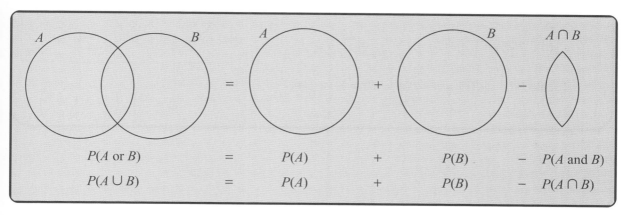

| $P(A \text{ or } B)$ | = | $P(A)$ | + | $P(B)$ | − | $P(A \text{ and } B)$ |
| $P(A \cup B)$ | = | $P(A)$ | + | $P(B)$ | − | $P(A \cap B)$ |

Mutually exclusive events

Events A and B are said to be mutually exclusive events if they cannot occur at the same time.

Consider the single event of drawing a card from a normal pack of 52 playing cards. Let A be the event that the card drawn is a king and B be the event that the card drawn is a queen. The single card drawn cannot be a king and a queen. The events A and B are said to be mutually exclusive events.

Consider the combined event of rolling two dice (or rolling one die twice) where a score is obtained by adding the numbers that turn up. Let X be the event of a score of 8 and Y be the event of a score of 11. A score cannot be 8 and 11. The events X and Y are said to be mutually exclusive.

If A and B are mutually exclusive events, then $P(A \cap B) = 0$. There is no overlap of A and B.

$$\boxed{\text{For mutually exclusive events, } P(A \cup B) = P(A) + P(B)}$$

Notes: (1) $P(\text{not } A) = P(A')$ and $P(A) + P(A') = 1$

(2) Two events, A and B, are said to be **exhaustive** if together they include every possible outcome in the sample space. In this case, $P(A \cup B) = 1$.

EXAMPLE 1

A and B are two events such that $P(A \cup B) = \frac{9}{10}$, $P(A) = \frac{7}{10}$ and $P(A \cap B) = \frac{3}{20}$.
Find: **(i)** $P(B)$ **(ii)** $P(B')$ **(iii)** $P[(A \cup B)']$

Solution:

(i) $P(A \cup B) = P(A) + P(B) - P(A \cap B)$

$$\frac{9}{10} = \frac{7}{10} + P(B) - \frac{3}{20}$$

$$P(B) = \frac{9}{10} - \frac{7}{10} + \frac{3}{20} = \frac{7}{20}$$

(ii) $P(B') = 1 - P(B) = 1 - \frac{7}{20} = \frac{13}{20}$

(iii) $P[(A \cup B)'] = 1 - P(A \cup B) = 1 - \frac{9}{10} = \frac{1}{10}$

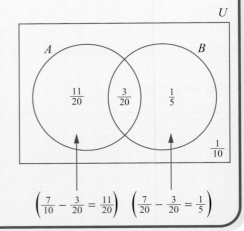

$$\left(\frac{7}{10} - \frac{3}{20} = \frac{11}{20}\right) \quad \left(\frac{7}{20} - \frac{3}{20} = \frac{1}{5}\right)$$

EXAMPLE 2

An unbiased 20-sided die, numbered 1 to 20, is thrown.

(i) What is the probability of obtaining a number divisible by 4 or by 5?

(ii) Are these events mutually exclusive?

Solution:

There are 20 possible outcomes.

(i) Numbers divisible by 4 are 4, 8, 12, 16 or 20. $\therefore P(\text{divisible by 4}) = \frac{5}{20}$

Numbers divisible by 5 are 5, 10, 15 or 20. $\therefore P(\text{divisible by 5}) = \frac{4}{20}$

Number divisible by 4 and 5 is 20. $\therefore P(\text{divisible by 4 and 5}) = \frac{1}{20}$

$P(\text{number divisible by 4 or 5})$

$= P(\text{number divisible by 4}) + P(\text{number divisible by 5}) - P(\text{number divisible by 4 and 5})$

(removes the double counting of the number 20)

$= \frac{5}{20} + \frac{4}{20} - \frac{1}{20}$

$= \frac{8}{20} = \frac{2}{5}$

The number 20 is common to both events, and if the probabilities were simply added, then the number 20 would have been counted twice.

(ii) $P(\text{number divisible by 4 and 5}) \neq 0$

$\therefore$ The events are **not** mutually exclusive.

EXAMPLE 3

A bag contains five red, three blue and two yellow discs. The red discs are numbered 1, 2, 3, 4 and 5; the blue discs are numbered 6, 7 and 8; and the yellow discs are numbered 9 and 10. A single disc is drawn at random from the bag. What is the probability that the disc is blue or even? Are these events mutually exclusive?

Solution:

There are 10 possible outcomes.

Let B represent that a blue disc is chosen and E represent that a disc with an even number is chosen.

$$P(B \text{ or } E) = P(B) + P(E) - P(B \text{ and } E)$$

$$= \frac{3}{10} + \frac{5}{10} - \frac{2}{10} \qquad \text{(removes double counting)}$$

$$= \frac{6}{10} = \frac{3}{5}$$

$$P(B \text{ and } E) = \frac{2}{10} \neq 0$$

∴ The events are **not** mutually exclusive.

Exercise 10.7

1. An unbiased six-sided die is thrown. Find the probability that the number obtained is:

   (i) Even   (ii) Prime   (iii) Even or prime

2. A number is chosen at random from the whole numbers 1 to 12 inclusive. What is the probability that it is:

   (i) Even   (ii) Divisible by 3   (iii) Even or divisible by 3   (iv) Not even or divisible by 3

3. A number is chosen at random from the whole numbers 1 to 30 inclusive. What is the probability that it is divisible by:

   (i) 3   (ii) 5   (iii) 3 or 5   (iv) Not 3 or 5

4. A letter is selected at random from the word *EXERCISES*. Find the probability that the letter is:

   (i) *I*   (ii) *S*   (iii) A vowel   (iv) A vowel or an *S*   (v) Not a vowel or an *S*

5. A bag contains three blue discs, five white discs and four red discs. A disc is chosen at random. Find the probability that the disc chosen is:

   (i) Red   (ii) Blue or white   (iii) Red or white   (iv) Not red or white

6. In a class of 20 students, four of the nine girls and three of the 11 boys play on the school hockey team. A student from the class is chosen at random. What is the probability that the student chosen is:

   (i) On the hockey team   (ii) A boy

   (iii) A boy or on the hockey team   (iv) A girl or not on the hockey team

7. A card is selected at random from a pack of 52. Find the probability that the card is:

   (i) A spade or a club   (ii) A queen or a red card

   (iii) A heart or a red 10   (iv) Not a heart or a red 10

8. Two unbiased six-sided dice, one red and the other blue, are thrown together. Calculate the probability that:

   (i) The numbers are the same or the sum of the numbers is 10

   (ii) The sum of the numbers is 8 or the difference between the two numbers is 2

9. A bag contains five red discs and three blue discs. The red discs are numbered 1, 2, 2, 3 and 3, while the blue discs are numbered 4, 5 and 5. A single disc is drawn at random from the bag. What is the probability that the disc is:

   (i) Red   (ii) Even   (iii) Red or even   (iv) Neither red nor even

10. A bag contains five purple markers, four green markers and three black markers. The purple markers are numbered 1, 2, 3, 4 and 5; the green markers are numbered 6, 7, 8 and 9; and the black markers are numbered 10, 11 and 12. A single marker is drawn from the bag. What is the probability that the marker is:

   (i) Odd   (ii) Black   (iii) Black or odd

   (iv) Purple or even   (v) Green or even   (vi) Not green or even

11. A fair six-sided die is thrown. A is the event of getting an even number and B is the event of getting a multiple of 3.

   (i) Are events A and B mutually exclusive? Justify your answer.

   (ii) Are events A and B exhaustive? Justify your answer.

12. (i) Two tetrahedral (four-sided) dice both have sides numbered 1, 2, 3 and 4. What is the probability that the sum of the scores is (a) even (b) prime?

   (ii) Are these two events in (i) mutually exclusive? Justify your answer.

13. Two fair six-sided dice are thrown, one red and the other blue, and the numbers that turn up are added together. A is the event that the sum of the scores is 10 and B is the event that the numbers are the same. Are A and B mutually exclusive events? Using a sample space diagram or otherwise, justify your answer.

14. Fifty passengers on a plane were surveyed as to how they spent their time on the flight. The activities were reading (R), listening to music (L) or watching the in-flight movie (M). Some of the results are shown in the Venn diagram.

   (i) How many passengers took part in none of these activities?

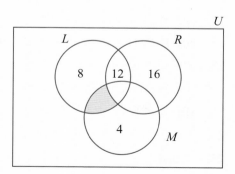

    (ii) A passenger is selected at random. What is the probability that the passenger selected is:

      (a) Reading   (b) Reading or watching the in-flight movie

      (c) Reading and listening to music

   (iii) Which of the following pairs of activities are mutually exclusive?

      (a) Reading and listening to music

      (b) Listening to music and watching the in-flight movie

15. An auctioneer has 60 houses for sale. Sixteen of these houses have a garden and a conservatory and six have a garden and an attic store. No house has all three features and 11 have none of these features. The probability of a house having only one of these features is 0·15. Illustrate the situation in a Venn diagram. Hence, find the probability that a house chosen at random has:

   (i) A conservatory and an attic store

  (ii) Which of the pairs of features, if any, in the Venn diagram are mutually exclusive features? Justify your answers.

16. (i) X and Y are two events such that $P(X) = \frac{4}{5}$, $P(Y) = \frac{1}{2}$ and $P(X \cap Y) = \frac{3}{10}$. Find $P(X \cup Y)$.

  (ii) What can you say about events X and Y?

17. A and B are two events such that $P(A \cup B) = \frac{4}{5}$, $P(A) = \frac{19}{30}$ and $P(B) = \frac{2}{5}$. Find $P(A \cap B)$.

18. A and B are two events such that $P(A \cup B) = 0·9$, $P(A) = 0·5$ and $P(A \cap B) = 0·3$.
Find: **(i)** $P(B)$ **(ii)** $P(B')$ **(iii)** $P[(A \cup B)']$

19. A and B are two mutually exclusive events, where $P(A) = \frac{3}{10}$ and $P(B) = \frac{2}{5}$.
Find: **(i)** $P(A \cap B)$ **(ii)** $P(A \cup B)$

20. A and B are two events, where $P(A) = 0·35$, $P(B) = 0·57$ and $P(A \cup B) = 0·92$. Are A and B:
(i) Mutually exclusive   (ii) Exhaustive? Justify your answers.

21. X and Y are mutually exclusive events.

   (i) Write down $P(X \cap Y)$.

  (ii) If $P(X) = \frac{3}{7}$ and $P(Y) = \frac{1}{5}$, find $P(X \cup Y)$.

22. A and B are exhaustive events.

   (i) Write down $P(A \cup B)$.

  (ii) If $P(A) = \frac{2}{3}$ and $P(B) = \frac{3}{4}$, find $P(A \cap B)$.

23. M and N are two mutually exclusive events.

   (i) Write down $P(M \cap N)$.

  (ii) If $P(M) = x$, $P(N) = 3x$ and $P(M \cup N) = 1 - x$, find the value of x.

24. A and B are two events such that $P(A) = P(B)$, $P(A \cap B) = 0·1$ and $P(A \cup B) = 0·7$. Find $P(A')$.

25. M and N are two events such that $P(M') = \frac{2}{3}$, $P(N) = \frac{1}{2}$ and $P(M \cap N) = \frac{1}{12}$. Find $P(M \cup N)$.

Conditional probability

Suppose that you are considering two related events, A and B, and we know that B has already occurred. This could influence the probability of A occurring. For example, if you randomly select a card from a pack of 52, then the probability that the card selected is a spade is $\frac{13}{52} = \frac{1}{4}$. However, if you were told that the card selected is black, then this increases the probability to $\frac{13}{26} = \frac{1}{2}$.

If A and B are two events, then the probability of A given that B has already occurred is written as $P(A\,|\,B)$.
This is known as **conditional probability**. This probability is illustrated in the following Venn diagram.

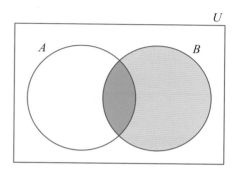

$$P(A\,|\,B) = \frac{P(A \cap B)}{P(B)} \qquad = \qquad \frac{A \cap B}{B}$$

In the Venn diagram, the sample space has been reduced to B, as B has already occured.

$$P(A\,|\,B) = \frac{P(A \cap B)}{P(B)}$$

$\therefore\ P(A\,|\,B) \times P(B) = P(A \cap B)$

(multiply both sides by $P(B)$)

Note: $P(A \cap B) = P(B \cap A)$

If A and B are mutually exclusive,
then $\quad P(A \cap B) = 0$
and $\qquad P(A\,|\,B) = 0$
(assuming $P(B) \neq 0$).

EXAMPLE 1

When a fair six-sided die was thrown, the score was an odd number. What is the probability that this score was a prime number?

Solution:

$$P(\text{prime} \mid \text{odd}) = \frac{P(\text{prime and odd})}{P(\text{odd})} = \frac{\frac{2}{6}}{\frac{3}{6}} = \frac{2}{3}$$

In this case, it is possible to deduce this easily since the sample space has been reduced to the odd numbers 1, 3 and 5 and two of these, 3 and 5, are prime.

EXAMPLE 2

A Maths teacher gave her class two tests: 24% of the class passed both tests and 40% of the class passed the first test. What percentage of those who passed the first test also passed the second test?

Solution:
We are being asked to find the percentage of students who passed the second test **given** that they passed the first test.

$$P(\text{second} \mid \text{first}) = \frac{P(\text{second and first})}{P(\text{first})} = \frac{0 \cdot 24}{0 \cdot 40} = 0 \cdot 6 = 60\%$$

EXAMPLE 3

A and B are two events such that $P(A \mid B) = 0 \cdot 4$, $P(A) = 0 \cdot 2$ and $P(B) = 0 \cdot 25$.
Find: **(i)** $P(A \cap B)$ **(ii)** $P(A \cup B)$

Solution:

(i) $P(A \mid B) = \dfrac{P(A \cap B)}{P(B)}$

$0 \cdot 4 = \dfrac{P(A \cap B)}{0 \cdot 25}$

$0 \cdot 4 \times 0 \cdot 25 = P(A \cap B)$

$0 \cdot 1 = P(A \cap B)$

(ii) $P(A \cup B) = P(A) + P(B) - P(A \cap B)$

$P(A \cup B) = 0 \cdot 2 + 0 \cdot 25 - 0 \cdot 1$

$P(A \cup B) = 0 \cdot 35$

Exercise 10.8

1. A card is picked at random from a pack of 30 cards numbered 1, 2, 3 . . . 29 and 30. Given that the card shows an odd number, find the probability that it is a multiple of 5. Answer this question **(i)** using a simple counting method with a sample space and **(ii)** using the formula for conditional probability.

2. At a school, 24% of all students play soccer and Gaelic football and 30% of all students play soccer. What is the probability that a student plays Gaelic football given that they play soccer?

3. In Ireland, 60% of all students get an allowance and 39% of all students get an allowance and do household chores. What is the probability that a student does household chores given that they get an allowance?

4. The probability of Sue obtaining a first-class honours degree at her university given that she does 21 hours of revision per week is 0·8. The probability that she obtains a first-class degree and does 21 hours of revision per week is 0·68. Find the probability that she does 21 hours of revision per week.

5. **(i)** A teacher gave his class two tests where every student passed at least one test. 72% of the class passed both tests and 80% of the class passed the second test. What percentage of those who passed the second test also passed the first test?

   (ii) What percentage of the class passed the first test but failed the second test?

6. A bag contains red and black discs. Two discs are drawn at random from the bag, one at a time, without replacement. The probability of drawing a red disc and then a black is 0·52. The probability of drawing a red disc on the first draw is 0·8. What is the probability of selecting a black disc on the second draw given that the first disc drawn was red?

7. **(i)** There are five days in the school week, Monday to Friday. A school day is chosen at random. What is the probability that it is Monday?

   (ii) In a school, the probability that it is Monday and that a student is absent is 0·03. What is the probability that a student is absent given that it is Monday?

8. **(i)** Two fair tetrahedral dice are thrown, one red and the other blue. The faces are marked 1, 2, 3 and 4 and the scores are added together. Represent this situation with a two-way table.

   (ii) From this table, show that the probability that the sum of the scores is 6 given that the probability that the red die lands on an even number is $\frac{1}{4}$.

   (iii) Find the probability that the sum of the scores is 6 and that the red die lands on an even number.

9. Two events, A and B, are such that $P(A \cap B) = 0·44$ and $P(B) = 0·8$. Find $P(A|B)$.

10. Two events, X and Y, are such that $P(X \cap Y) = 0·1$ and $P(X) = 0·45$. Find $P(Y|X)$.

11. Two events, X and Y, are such that $P(X|Y) = \frac{2}{5}$, $P(X) = \frac{1}{3}$ and $P(Y) = \frac{1}{4}$.
    Find: **(i)** $P(X \cap Y)$ **(ii)** $P(Y|X)$

12. A and B are two events such that $P(A|B) = 0.32$, $P(A) = 0.26$ and $P(B) = 0.5$.
    Find: **(i)** $P(A \cap B)$ **(ii)** $P(A \cup B)$ **(iii)** $P[(A \cup B)']$

13. Two events, A and B, are such that $P(A) = \frac{8}{15}$, $P(B) = \frac{1}{3}$ and $P(A|B) = \frac{1}{5}$.
    Find: **(i)** $P(A \cap B)$ **(ii)** $P(A \cup B)$ **(iii)** $P[(A \cup B)']$

14. For two events, A and B, it is given that $P(A) = \frac{5}{18}$, $P(B) = \frac{5}{9}$ and $P(A|B) = \frac{3}{14}$.
    Find: **(i)** $P(A \cap B)$ **(ii)** $P(B|A)$

15. Events A and B are such that $P(A) = \frac{3}{10}$, $P(B) = \frac{11}{20}$ and $P(A|B) = 0$.
    Find: **(i)** $P(A \cup B)$ **(ii)** $P[(A \cup B)']$

16. Two events, A and B, are such that $P(A) = \frac{4}{7}$, $P(A \cap B') = \frac{1}{3}$ and $P(A|B) = \frac{5}{14}$.
    Find: **(i)** $P(A \cap B)$ **(ii)** $P(B)$ **(iii)** $P(B|A)$

17. Given that $P(A \cap B) = P(B \cap A)$, prove that $P(A|B) \times P(B) = P(B|A) \times P(A)$.

18. Two events, Q and R, are such that $P(Q|R) = \frac{1}{5}$, $P(R|Q) = \frac{1}{4}$ and $P(Q \cap R) = x$.
    (i) Express the following in terms of x: **(a)** $P(Q)$ **(b)** $P(R)$.
    (ii) If $P(Q \cup R) = \frac{1}{2}$, find the value of x.

Independent events

Two events, A and B, are said to be independent if the occurrence, or non-occurrence, of one does not influence the probability of the other occurring, e.g. rolling a die and tossing a coin. The outcome on the die has no influence on the outcome of the coin (and vice versa). In other words, events A and B are independent if the probability of A given B is the same as the probability of A (and vice versa).

Events A and B are **independent** whenever:

$P(A|B) = P(A)$ or $P(B|A) = P(B)$

(the occurrence of B has no influence   (the occurrence of A has no influence

on the occurrence of A)   on the occurrence of B)

$P(A|B) = \dfrac{P(A \cap B)}{P(B)}$ (rule for conditional probability)

$P(A|B) \times P(B) = P(A \cap B)$ (multiply both sides by $P(B)$)

$P(A) \times P(B) = P(A \cap B)$ ($P(A|B) = P(A)$ if A and B are independent)

$P(A) \times P(B) = P(A \text{ and } B)$

This is known as the **multiplication** rule for independent events. It is also known as the '**and**' rule for independent events. Thus, there are three conditions for events A and B to be independent and **any** one of them can be used as a test for independence.

1. $P(A|B) = P(A)$	**2.** $P(B|A) = P(B)$	**3.** $P(A \cap B) = P(A) \times P(B)$

EXAMPLE 1

In a group of 30 students, 10 study Art, 12 study Geography and four study both Art and Geography. Are the events 'a student studies Art' and 'a student studies Geography' independent?

Solution:

Let A represent Art and G represent Geography.

$$P(A) = \frac{10}{30} = \frac{1}{3} \qquad\qquad P(G) = \frac{12}{30} = \frac{2}{5} \quad \text{and} \quad P(A \text{ and } G) = \frac{4}{30} = \frac{2}{15}$$

Method 1:

$P(A \text{ and } G) = P(A) \times P(G) = \frac{1}{3} \times \frac{2}{5} = \frac{2}{15}$

Thus, $P(A \text{ and } G) = P(A) \times P(G)$

$\therefore$ A and G are independent.

Method 2:

$$P(A|G) = \frac{P(A \text{ and } G)}{P(G)}$$

$$P(A|G) = \frac{\frac{2}{15}}{\frac{2}{5}}$$

$$P(A|G) = \frac{1}{3}$$

$$P(A|G) = P(A)$$

$\therefore$ A and G are independent.

Method 3:

$$P(G|A) = \frac{P(G \text{ and } A)}{P(A)}$$

$$P(G|A) = \frac{\frac{2}{15}}{\frac{1}{3}}$$

$$P(G|A) = \frac{2}{5}$$

$$P(G|A) = P(G)$$

$\therefore$ A and G are independent.

EXAMPLE 2

Events E_1 and E_2 are such that $P(E_1| E_2) = 0.4$, $P(E_2| E_1) = 0.25$ and $P(E_1 \cap E_2) = 0.12$.

(i) Calculate $P(E_2)$.   (ii) Are E_1 and E_2 independent? Give a reason for your answer.

Solution:

(i) $P(E_1| E_2) = \dfrac{P(E_1 \cap E_2)}{P(E_2)}$

$0.4 = \dfrac{0.12}{P(E_2)}$

$0.4\, P(E_2) = 0.12$

$P(E_2) = 0.3$

(ii) $P(E_2| E_1) = 0.25$

$P(E_2) = 0.3$

$P(E_2| E_1) \neq P(E_2)$

$\therefore$ E_1 and E_2 are **not** independent.

(In other words, the occurrence of E_1 **does** influence the occurrence of E_2.)

Note: Calculating $P(E_1)$ and showing $P(E_1 \cap E_2) \neq P(E_1) \times P(E_2)$ will also show that E_1 and E_2 are **not** independent.

It is important not to confuse mutually exclusive events and independent events. Mutually exclusive events are events that cannot happen together. For mutually exclusive events A and B, $P(A \text{ and } B) = 0$ (no double counting). Independent events are events that can happen at the same time or can happen one after the other. For independent events A and B, $P(A \text{ and } B) = P(A) \times P(B)$ or $P(A \mid B) = P(A)$ or $P(B \mid A) = P(B)$.

Note: Independent events cannot be mutually exclusive and mutually exclusive events cannot be independent.

Exercise 10.9

1. In a survey, 60 students were asked, 'Do you prefer to read a book or play sport?' The results of the survey are partially given in the table.

	Boys	Girls	Total
Read			
Sport	15	12	
Total	24		60

   (i) Complete the table.

   (ii) A student from the survey was selected at random. Find the probability that the student selected:

   (a) Prefers to read a book

   (b) Prefers to read a book, given that the student is a boy

   (c) Is a girl, given that they prefer to read a book

2. Two events, E_1 and E_2, are independent. $P(E_1) = \frac{1}{5}$ and $P(E_2) = \frac{1}{7}$. Find the following.

   (i) $P(E_1 \cap E_2)$ (ii) $P(E_1 \cup E_2)$

3. E_1 and E_2 are independent events such that $P(E_1) = 0.12$ and $P(E_2) = 0.25$.

   (i) Find (a) $P(E_1 \cap E_2)$ (b) $P(E_1 \cup E_2)$.

   (ii) Verify that (a) $P(E_1 \mid E_2) = P(E_1)$ (b) $P(E_2 \mid E_1) = P(E_2)$.

4. Events E and F are such that $P(F) = \frac{2}{5}$, $P(E \mid F) = \frac{1}{3}$ and $P(E \cup F) = \frac{4}{5}$.

   (i) Find (a) $P(E \cap F)$ (b) $P(E)$.

   (ii) Are E and F independent? Justify your answer.

5. Events E and F are such that $P(E) = \frac{9}{20}$, $P(F) = \frac{2}{5}$ and $P(E \cup F) = \frac{7}{10}$.

   (i) Find (a) $P(E \cap F)$ (b) $P(E \mid F)$ (c) $P(F \mid E)$.

   (ii) Are E and F independent? Give a reason for your answer.

6. Two fair six-sided dice, one blue and one white, are thrown.

   (i) Find the probability of the following.

   (a) Event E_1: The number on the white die will show a 5 or a 6

   (b) Event E_2: The sum of the numbers on the dice will be 7

   (c) Event E_3: The sum of the numbers on the dice will be 8

   (ii) Which of the pairs of events are mutually exclusive? Justify your answer.

   (iii) Are E_1 and E_2 independent? Justify your answer.

7. **(i)** $P(E|F)$ denotes the conditional probability of E given F. Write an equation to express the relationship between $P(F)$, $P(E|F)$ and $P(E \cap F)$.

   (ii) E and F are events such that $P(E|F) = \frac{1}{2}$, $P(F|E) = \frac{1}{3}$ and $P(E \cap F) = \frac{1}{7}$. Find $P(E \cup F)$.

   (iii) Are the events E and F in part **(ii)** independent? Give a reason for your answer.

8. A bag contains the following cardboard shapes: 10 red squares, 15 green squares, eight red triangles and 12 green triangles. One of the shapes is drawn at random from the bag. E is the event that a square is drawn. F is the event that a green shape is drawn.

   (i) Find $P(E \cap F)$.

   (ii) Find $P(E \cup F)$.

   (iii) State whether E and F are independent events. Give a reason for your answer.

   (iv) State whether E and F are mutually exclusive events. Give a reason for your answer.

9. **(i)** E and F are two events such that $P(E \text{ and } F) = P(E) \times P(F)$. What can you say about events E and F?

   (ii) If E is the event 'getting a head on a single toss of a coin', suggest a possible description for event F.

   (iii) A and B are two events such that $P(A \text{ or } B) = P(A) + P(B)$. What can you say about events A and B?

      (a) Write down the value of $P(A \text{ and } B)$.

      (b) If A is the event 'getting a 6 on a single roll of a die', suggest a possible description for event B.

10. E and F are independent events such that $P(E) = 0\cdot2$ and $P(E \cup F) = 0\cdot55$. Find $P(F)$.

11. A, B and C are three events such that A and C are mutually exclusive and events A and B are independent. Given that $P(A) = \frac{2}{5}$, $P(C) = \frac{1}{3}$ and $P(A \cup B) = \frac{4}{5}$, find:

   (i) $P(A \cup C)$

   (ii) $P(B)$

Multiplication rule ('and' rule)

> General multiplication rule: $P(A \text{ and } B) = P(A) \times P(B|A)$

This rule always works. However, if we take into account that A has already occurred when calculating $P(B)$, then we can use the following multiplication rule for successive events.

> The probability that two events, A and then B, both happen and in that order is given by:
> $$P(A \text{ and } B) = P(A) \times P(B)$$
> where $P(B)$ has been worked out assuming that A has already occurred.

Order must be taken into account. Also, be careful where the outcome at one stage affects the outcome at the next stage. This rule also applies to more than two events.

> When the question says **and**, then multiply.

Notes:
1. If we write out all the possible (mutually exclusive) outcomes, calculate their probabilities and then add these probabilities, the result is always 1.

2. Unless told otherwise, **always** assume non-replacement in an experiment. Consider the following type of question. 'A bag contains five white and four black discs. Three discs are removed at random from the bag. Calculate the probability that the three discs are white.' This can be interpreted as drawing one disc after another **without replacement**. In this case, a combinations approach **will** work. If the question tells us that the disc drawn is replaced (returned to the bag) before the next draw, then a combinations approach **will not** work. In both cases, a permutations approach or a tree diagram **will** work.

EXAMPLE 1

A fair coin is tossed and an unbiased die is thrown. Calculate the probability of obtaining a tail and a 3.

Solution:

Method 1: Using a sample space

Sample space diagram

Coin						
T			•			
H						
	1	2	3	4	5	6

Die

A successful outcome is indicated with a dot. The word '**and**' means we only count outcomes where both a tail and a 3 occur.

$$P(T \text{ and a } 3) = \tfrac{1}{12}$$

Method 2: Using rules of probability

$P(T) = \tfrac{1}{2}$ $\qquad P(3) = \tfrac{1}{6}$

$P(T \text{ and a } 3) = P(T) \times P(3)$

$$= \tfrac{1}{2} \times \tfrac{1}{6}$$

$$= \tfrac{1}{12}$$

Note: Tossing a coin and throwing a die are independent events.

EXAMPLE 2

A bag contains four red and six blue discs. Two discs are drawn at random, one after the other, from the bag. Find the probability of getting two red discs when:

(i) The first disc is not replaced

(ii) The first disc is replaced

(iii) Write all four outcomes. In each case (with and without replacement), show that the probabilities add up to 1.

Solution:

Let R_1 represent that a red disc is chosen first, B_2 represent that a blue disc is chosen second, and so on.

(i) Without replacement

$$P(R_1 \text{ and } R_2) = P(R_1) \times P(R_2)$$

$$= \frac{4}{10} \times \frac{3}{9}$$

$$= \frac{12}{90} = \frac{2}{15}$$

The probability of getting a red disc on the second draw depends on the outcome of the first draw. In other words, the second draw is influenced by the first draw.

These are not independent events.

(ii) With replacement

$$P(R_1 \text{ and } R_2) = P(R_1) \times P(R_2)$$

$$= \frac{4}{10} \times \frac{4}{10}$$

$$= \frac{16}{100} = \frac{4}{25}$$

The probability of getting a red disc on the second draw **does not** depend on the outcome of the first draw. In other words, the second draw is not influenced by the first draw.

These are independent events.

(iii) All four outcomes are: R_1 and R_2 or R_1 and B_2 or B_1 and R_2 or B_1 and B_2

Without replacement: $\quad \frac{4}{10} \times \frac{3}{9} \quad + \quad \frac{4}{10} \times \frac{6}{9} \quad + \quad \frac{6}{10} \times \frac{4}{9} \quad + \quad \frac{6}{10} \times \frac{5}{9}$

$$= \frac{12}{90} + \frac{24}{90} + \frac{24}{90} + \frac{30}{90} = \frac{90}{90} = 1$$

With replacement: $\quad \frac{4}{10} \times \frac{4}{10} \quad + \quad \frac{4}{10} \times \frac{6}{10} \quad + \quad \frac{6}{10} \times \frac{4}{10} \quad + \quad \frac{6}{10} \times \frac{6}{10}$

$$= \frac{16}{100} + \frac{24}{100} + \frac{24}{100} + \frac{36}{100} = \frac{100}{100} = 1$$

Note: 'And' means multiply and 'or' means add.

EXAMPLE 3

A bag contains three red and two yellow discs only. When a disc is drawn from the bag, it is returned before the next draw. What is the probability that two draws will yield both discs the same colour?

Solution:

Method 1: Using a sample space diagram

Let R represent that a red disc is chosen and let Y represent that a yellow disc is chosen.

Sample space diagram

Second selection						
Y				•	•
Y				•	•
R	•	•	•		
R	•	•	•		
R	•	•	•		
	R	R	R	Y	Y

First selection

There are 25 possible outcomes (five for the first draw and five for the second draw).
The dots indicate where the colours are the same (successful outcome), either two reds or two yellows.
There are 13 dots. P(both discs the same colour) $= \frac{13}{25}$.

Method 2: Picking one at a time with replacement

Let R_1 represent that a red disc is chosen first, Y_2 represent that a yellow disc is chosen second, and so on.

P(both discs the same colour)

$= P(R_1 \text{ and } R_2)$	or	$P(Y_1 \text{ and } Y_2)$	
$= P(R_1) \times P(R_2)$	+	$P(Y_1) \times P(Y_2)$	
$= \frac{3}{5} \times \frac{3}{5}$	+	$\frac{2}{5} \times \frac{2}{5}$	
$= \frac{9}{25} + \frac{4}{25}$			
$= \frac{13}{25}$			

> red and then a red
> or
> yellow and then a yellow

Method 3: Using arrangements

	red and red	or	yellow and yellow	
Number of desirable outcomes	$= 3 \times 3$	+	2×2	(discs are replaced)
	$= 9 + 4 = 13$			

Number of possible outcomes $= 5 \times 5 = 25$

$\therefore$ P(both discs the same colour) $= \frac{13}{25}$.

Note: A combinations approach will not work in this example, as the disc was returned before the next disc was picked.

Method 4: Using a probability tree diagram

Probability tree diagrams display all possible (mutually exclusive) outcomes.

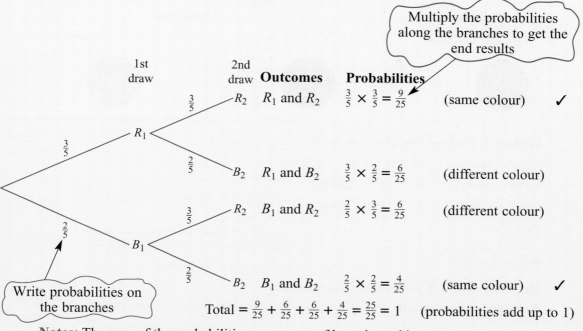

Multiply the probabilities along the branches to get the end results

1st draw	2nd draw	**Outcomes**	**Probabilities**		
	R_2	R_1 and R_2	$\frac{3}{5} \times \frac{3}{5} = \frac{9}{25}$	(same colour)	✓
R_1	B_2	R_1 and B_2	$\frac{3}{5} \times \frac{2}{5} = \frac{6}{25}$	(different colour)	
	R_2	B_1 and R_2	$\frac{2}{5} \times \frac{3}{5} = \frac{6}{25}$	(different colour)	
B_1	B_2	B_1 and B_2	$\frac{2}{5} \times \frac{2}{5} = \frac{4}{25}$	(same colour)	✓

Write probabilities on the branches

Total $= \frac{9}{25} + \frac{6}{25} + \frac{6}{25} + \frac{4}{25} = \frac{25}{25} = 1$ (probabilities add up to 1)

Notes: The sum of the probabilities on any set of branches adds up to 1.

If more than one set of results is required, simply add the end results together.

$P(\text{same colour}) = P(R_1 \text{ and } R_2) + P(B_1 \text{ and } B_2) = \frac{9}{25} + \frac{4}{25} = \frac{13}{25}.$

EXAMPLE 4

A box contains four blue spheres and two yellow spheres. Two spheres are drawn at random from the box. What is the probability that one sphere is blue and the other is yellow?

Solution:

Note: Two spheres drawn at random is equivalent to one at a time without replacement.

Let B_1 represent that a blue sphere is drawn first, Y_2 represent that a yellow is drawn second, and so on.

Diagram of the situation

There are two possible sample spaces for the second choice. It depends on whether a blue sphere is chosen first or a yellow sphere is chosen first.

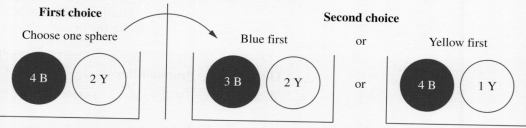

First choice
Choose one sphere

4 B   2 Y

Second choice
Blue first   or   Yellow first

3 B   2 Y   or   4 B   1 Y

Method 1: Picking one at a time without replacement

P(one sphere is blue and the other is yellow)

$= P(B_1 \text{ and } Y_2) \quad \text{or} \quad P(Y_1 \text{ and } B_2)$

$= P(B_1) \times P(Y_2) \quad + \quad P(Y_1) \times P(B_2)$

$= \frac{4}{6} \times \frac{2}{5} \quad\quad\quad + \quad\quad \frac{2}{6} \times \frac{4}{5}$

$= \frac{8}{30} + \frac{8}{30} = \frac{16}{30} = \frac{8}{15}$

blue first and then yellow second
or
yellow first and then blue second

Method 2: Using a probability tree diagram

Probability tree diagrams display all possible (mutually exclusive) outcomes.

Multiply the probabilities along the branches to get end results

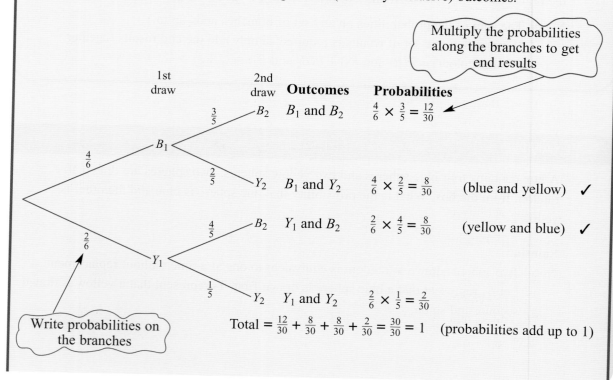

1st draw   2nd draw   **Outcomes**   **Probabilities**

$\frac{4}{6}$ B_1

$\frac{3}{5}$ — B_2 B_1 and B_2 $\frac{4}{6} \times \frac{3}{5} = \frac{12}{30}$

$\frac{2}{5}$ — Y_2 B_1 and Y_2 $\frac{4}{6} \times \frac{2}{5} = \frac{8}{30}$ (blue and yellow) ✔

$\frac{2}{6}$ Y_1

$\frac{4}{5}$ — B_2 Y_1 and B_2 $\frac{2}{6} \times \frac{4}{5} = \frac{8}{30}$ (yellow and blue) ✔

$\frac{1}{5}$ — Y_2 Y_1 and Y_2 $\frac{2}{6} \times \frac{1}{5} = \frac{2}{30}$

Write probabilities on the branches

Total $= \frac{12}{30} + \frac{8}{30} + \frac{8}{30} + \frac{2}{30} = \frac{30}{30} = 1$ (probabilities add up to 1)

Notes: The sum of the probabilities on any set of branches adds up to 1.

If more than one set of results is required, simply add the end results together.

P(one sphere is blue and the other is yellow) $= \frac{8}{30} + \frac{8}{30} = \frac{16}{30} = \frac{8}{15}$.

Method 3: Using combinations

As the first sphere is not replaced, combinations can be used.

There are six spheres and we want to choose two.

The total number of selections of two from six $= \binom{6}{2} = 15$.

The number of ways of selecting one blue and one yellow $= \binom{4}{1} \times \binom{2}{1} = 4 \times 2 = 8$.

$\therefore$ P(one sphere is blue and the other is yellow) $= \frac{8}{15}$.

Method 4: Using arrangements

$$\begin{array}{ccc} B \text{ and } Y & \text{or} & Y \text{ and } B \end{array}$$

Number of desirable outcomes $= 4 \times 2 \quad + \quad 2 \times 4$

$$= 8 + 8 = 16$$

Number of possible outcomes $= 6 \times 5 = 30$ \qquad (sphere not replaced)

$\therefore$ P(one sphere is blue and the other is yellow) $= \frac{16}{30} = \frac{8}{15}$.

EXAMPLE 5

(i) A bag contains four red discs and five blue discs. Three discs are selected at random. Find the probability that two are red and one is blue.

(ii) Given that there are two reds and one blue, calculate the probability that the first disc drawn was blue.

Solution:

(i) Let R_1 represent that a red disc is chosen first, B_2 represent that a blue disc is chosen second, and so on. Three discs selected at random is equivalent to selecting one disc after another **without** replacement.

Method 1: Picking one at a time without replacement

Two reds and one blue can occur in three ways:

$$\begin{array}{ccccccc} R_1 \text{ and } R_2 \text{ and } B_3 & \text{or} & R_1 \text{ and } B_2 \text{ and } R_3 & \text{or} & B_1 \text{ and } R_2 \text{ and } R_3 \end{array}$$

P(two red and blue)

$= P(R_1 \text{ and } R_2 \text{ and } B_3) \quad$ or $\quad P(R_1 \text{ and } B_2 \text{ and } R_3) \quad$ or $\quad P(B_1 \text{ and } R_2 \text{ and } R_3)$

$= \frac{4}{9} \times \frac{3}{8} \times \frac{5}{7} \qquad + \qquad \frac{4}{9} \times \frac{5}{8} \times \frac{3}{7} \qquad + \qquad \frac{5}{9} \times \frac{4}{8} \times \frac{3}{7}$

$= \frac{5}{42} \qquad\qquad\qquad + \qquad\qquad \frac{5}{42} \qquad\qquad\qquad + \qquad\qquad \frac{5}{42}$

$= \frac{15}{42} = \frac{5}{14}$

Method 2: Using combinations

There are nine discs and we want to choose three.

The total number of selections of three from nine = $\binom{9}{3}$ = 84.

The number of ways of selecting two red and one blue = $\binom{4}{2} \times \binom{5}{1}$ = 6 × 5 = 30.

∴ P(two red and one blue) = $\frac{30}{84}$ = $\frac{5}{14}$.

Method 3: Using arrangements

Number of desirable outcomes =	$R\ R\ B$	or	$R\ B\ R$	or	$B\ R\ R$	
	= 4 × 3 × 5	+	4 × 5 × 3	+	5 × 4 × 3	
	= 60	+	60	+	60	= 180

Number of possible outcomes = 9 × 8 × 7 = 504.

∴ P(two red and one blue) = $\frac{180}{504}$ = $\frac{5}{14}$.

Note: A probability tree diagram would also work.

(ii) P(blue first, given two reds and one blue)

$$= P(B_1 \mid RRB) = \frac{P(B_1 \text{ and } RRB)}{P(RRB)} = \frac{\frac{5}{42}}{\frac{5}{14}} = \frac{1}{3}$$

Alternatively, using the results from the previous section:

P(blue first, given two reds and one blue)

$$= \frac{P(B_1 R_2 R_3)}{P(R_1 R_2 B_3 + R_1 B_2 R_3 + B_1 R_2 R_3)} = \frac{\frac{5}{42}}{\frac{5}{14}} = \frac{1}{3}$$

EXAMPLE 6

A bag contains 16 marbles, six of which are white and the remainder are black. Three marbles are drawn at random, one at a time, without replacement. Find the probability that:

(i) All are black   **(ii)** At least one is white

Solution:

Note: The words 'one at time, without replacement' are not essential. However, non-replacement must always be assumed unless told otherwise.

Let B_1 represent that a black marble is chosen first, B_2 that a black marble is chosen second and B_3 that a black marble is chosen third.

There are 16 marbles: six white, 10 black.

(i) P(all are black) $= P(B_1) \times P(B_2) \times P(B_3)$

$$= \tfrac{10}{16} \times \tfrac{9}{15} \times \tfrac{8}{14}$$

$$= \tfrac{3}{14}$$

$P(B_1) = \tfrac{10}{16}$

$P(B_2) = \tfrac{9}{15}$ $\begin{pmatrix} 1 \text{ black removed,} \\ 9 \text{ black and 6 white left} \end{pmatrix}$

$P(B_3) = \tfrac{8}{14}$ $\begin{pmatrix} 2 \text{ blacks removed,} \\ 8 \text{ black and 6 white left} \end{pmatrix}$

(ii) In every other case there is **at least** one white.

P(at least one white) $= 1 - P$(none is white)

$$= 1 - P\text{(all are black)}$$

$$= 1 - \tfrac{3}{14} = \tfrac{11}{14}$$

Note: Using combinations, permutations or a probability tree diagram would also work.

EXAMPLE 7

Ten discs, each marked with a different whole number from 1 to 10, are placed in a box. Three of the discs are drawn at random from the box.

(i) What is the probability that the disc with the number 7 is drawn?

(ii) What is the probability that the three numbers on the discs drawn are odd?

(iii) What is the probability that the product of the three numbers on the discs drawn is even?

(iv) What is the probability that the smallest number on the discs drawn is 4?

Solution:

Ten discs, numbered from 1 to 10 inclusive.

Method 1: Picking one at a time without replacement

(i) P(disc with the number 7)

$= P(7, \text{not } 7, \text{not } 7) \quad \text{or} \quad P(\text{not } 7, 7, \text{not } 7) \quad \text{or} \quad P(\text{not } 7, \text{not } 7, 7)$

$= \tfrac{1}{10} \times \tfrac{9}{9} \times \tfrac{8}{8} \qquad + \qquad \tfrac{9}{10} \times \tfrac{1}{9} \times \tfrac{8}{8} \qquad + \qquad \tfrac{9}{10} \times \tfrac{8}{9} \times \tfrac{1}{8}$

$= \tfrac{1}{10} + \tfrac{1}{10} + \tfrac{1}{10} = \tfrac{3}{10}$

(ii) P(three numbers on the discs are odd)

$= P(\text{1st odd}) \times P(\text{2nd odd}) \times P(\text{3rd odd})$

$= \tfrac{5}{10} \times \tfrac{4}{9} \times \tfrac{3}{8} = \tfrac{60}{720} = \tfrac{1}{12}$

(iii) Product means the result of multiplying.

If at least one number is even, then the product of the three numbers will be even.

P(product of the three numbers on the discs is even)

$\quad = P$(at least one even number)

$\quad = 1 - P$(three numbers on the discs are odd)

$\quad = 1 - \frac{1}{12} = \frac{11}{12}$

Alternatively, let E_1 represent that an even number is picked first, O_2 represent that an odd number is picked second, and so on.

P(product of the three numbers on the discs is even)

$\quad = P(E_1, E_2, E_3) + P(E_1, E_2, O_3) + P(E_1, O_2, E_3) + P(O_1, E_2, E_3) + P(E_1, O_2, O_3)$
$\quad\quad + P(O_1, E_2, O_3) + P(O_1, O_2, E_3)$

$\quad = P(E_1, E_2, E_3) + 3P(E_1, E_2, O_3) + 3P(E_1, O_2, O_3)$

$\quad = \frac{5}{10} \times \frac{4}{9} \times \frac{3}{8} + 3 \times \frac{5}{10} \times \frac{4}{9} \times \frac{5}{8} + 3 \times \frac{5}{10} \times \frac{5}{9} \times \frac{4}{8}$

$\quad = \frac{60}{720} + \frac{300}{720} + \frac{300}{720} = \frac{660}{720} = \frac{11}{12}$

(iv) For the smallest number to be 4, we need to choose 4 and any two from 5, 6, 7, 8, 9, 10.

P(smallest number is 4)

$\quad = P(4, \text{not } 4, \text{not } 4) + P(\text{not } 4, 4, \text{not } 4) + P(\text{not } 4, \text{not } 4, 4)$

$\quad = \frac{1}{10} \times \frac{6}{9} \times \frac{5}{8} \quad\quad + \quad \frac{6}{10} \times \frac{1}{9} \times \frac{5}{8} \quad + \quad \frac{6}{10} \times \frac{5}{9} \times \frac{1}{8}$

$\quad = \frac{30}{720} + \frac{30}{720} + \frac{30}{720} = \frac{90}{720} = \frac{1}{8}$

Method 2: Using combinations

As the discs are **not** replaced, we can use combinations.

In each case, the number of possible outcomes $= \dbinom{10}{3} = 120$.

(i) One 7 and any two others

Number of favourable outcomes $= \dbinom{1}{1} \times \dbinom{9}{2} = 1 \times 36 = 36$

P(disc with the number 7) $= \frac{36}{120} = \frac{3}{10}$

(ii) Three numbers on the discs are odd

Number of favourable outcomes $= \dbinom{5}{3} = 10$

P(three numbers on the discs are odd) $= \frac{10}{120} = \frac{1}{12}$

(iii) Product of the three numbers on the discs is even

The product of the three numbers is either even or odd.

$$\therefore \quad \begin{pmatrix} \text{Number of possible} \\ \text{outcomes} \end{pmatrix} = \begin{pmatrix} \text{Number of outcomes} \\ \text{where the product is even} \end{pmatrix} + \begin{pmatrix} \text{Number of outcomes} \\ \text{where the product is odd} \end{pmatrix}$$

$$\begin{pmatrix} \text{Number of outcomes where} \\ \text{the product is even} \end{pmatrix} = \begin{pmatrix} \text{Number of possible} \\ \text{outcomes} \end{pmatrix} - \begin{pmatrix} \text{Number of outcomes where} \\ \text{the product is odd} \end{pmatrix}$$

$$= \binom{10}{3} - \binom{5}{3}$$

$$= 120 - 10 = 110$$

$P(\text{product of the three numbers on the disc is even}) = \frac{110}{120} = \frac{11}{12}$

(iv) The smallest number on the discs is 4

Choose 4 and any two from 5, 6, 7, 8, 9, 10.

Number of favourable outcomes $= \binom{1}{1} \times \binom{6}{2} = 1 \times 15 = 15$

$P(\text{smallest number is 4}) = \frac{15}{120} = \frac{1}{8}$

EXAMPLE 8

In a particular week (Monday to Sunday inclusive), three students, A, B and C, celebrate their birthdays. Assume that the birthdays are equally likely to fall on any day of the week and that the birthdays are independent of each other. What is the probability of the following?

(i) A has a birthday on Tuesday

(ii) B and C have their birthday on a Wednesday

(iii) B and C have their birthday on the same day

(iv) None of them has a birthday on Sunday

(v) At least two of them share the same birthday

Solution:

$P(\text{any person has a birthday on a particular day of the week}) = \frac{1}{7}$

$P(\text{any person does \textbf{not} have a birthday on a particular day of the week}) = \frac{6}{7}$

(i) $P(A \text{ has a birthday on Tuesday}) = \frac{1}{7}$

(ii) $P(B \text{ and } C \text{ have their birthday on Wednesday})$

$= P(B \text{ has a birthday on Wednesday}) \times P(C \text{ has a birthday on Wednesday})$

$= \frac{1}{7} \times \frac{1}{7} = \frac{1}{49}$

(iii) $P(B$ and C have their birthday on the same day)

Method 1:

$P(B$ and C have their birthday on the same day)

$$= P\left(\begin{array}{c}\text{both born on Monday or Tuesday or Wednesday or Thursday or Friday}\\ \text{or Saturday or Sunday}\end{array}\right)$$

$$= \tfrac{1}{7} \times \tfrac{1}{7} + \tfrac{1}{7} \times \tfrac{1}{7} + \tfrac{1}{7} \times \tfrac{1}{7} + \tfrac{1}{7} \times \tfrac{1}{7} + \tfrac{1}{7} \times \tfrac{1}{7} + \tfrac{1}{7} \times \tfrac{1}{7} + \tfrac{1}{7} \times \tfrac{1}{7}$$

$$= \tfrac{1}{49} + \tfrac{1}{49} + \tfrac{1}{49} + \tfrac{1}{49} + \tfrac{1}{49} + \tfrac{1}{49} + \tfrac{1}{49} = \tfrac{7}{49} = \tfrac{1}{7}$$

Method 2:

$P(B$ and C have their birthday on the same day)

$$= P(B \text{ has a birthday on some day of the week}) \times P(C \text{ has a birthday on the same day})$$

$$= \tfrac{7}{7} \times \tfrac{1}{7} = \tfrac{1}{7}$$

(iv) $P($none of them has a birthday on Sunday$)$

$$= P\left(\begin{array}{ccccc}A \text{ does not have a} & \text{and} & B \text{ does not have a} & \text{and} & C \text{ does not have a}\\ \text{birthday on Sunday} & & \text{birthday on Sunday} & & \text{birthday on Sunday}\end{array}\right)$$

$$= \tfrac{6}{7} \times \tfrac{6}{7} \times \tfrac{6}{7} = \tfrac{216}{343}$$

(v) $P($at least two of them share the same birthday$)$

$P(A \text{ has a birthday on some day of the week}) = \tfrac{7}{7} = 1$

$P(B \text{ has a birthday on a different day from } A) = \tfrac{6}{7}$

$P(C \text{ has a birthday on a different day from } A \text{ and } B) = \tfrac{5}{7}$

$\therefore P(\text{all three have birthdays on different days}) = 1 \times \tfrac{6}{7} \times \tfrac{5}{7} = \tfrac{30}{49}$

$\therefore P(\text{at least two of them share the same birthday})$

$= 1 - P(\text{all three have birthdays on different days})$

$= 1 - \tfrac{30}{49} = \tfrac{19}{49}$

EXAMPLE 9

A golf player finds that when the day is calm, the probability of him hitting his target is 0·8. When the day is not calm, the probability of him hitting his target is 0·55. According to the local weather forecasters, the probability that any particular day is calm is 0·6.

(i) A day is chosen at random. Using a tree diagram or otherwise, write out all the possible outcomes, calculate the probability of each outcome and show that the sum of the probabilities is 1. Hence, find the probability of him **(a)** hitting his target **(b)** not hitting his target.

(ii) Given that he does not hit his target, what is the probability that the day is calm?

Solution:

(i) Let C = calm day, C' = not a calm day, H = hits his target, H' = does not hit his target. Given: when the weather is calm, $P(H) = 0.8$. Therefore, when the weather is calm, $P(H') = 0.2$ (because $0.8 + 0.2 = 1$). Given: when the weather is not calm, $P(H) = 0.55$. Therefore, when the weather is not calm, $P(H') = 0.45$ (because $0.55 + 0.45 = 1$). Given: $P(C) = 0.6$. Therefore, $P(C') = 0.4$ (because $0.4 + 0.6 = 1$).

Method 1: Using a probability tree diagram

Tree diagrams display all possible (mutually exclusive) outcomes.

Write probabilities on the branches

Multiply the probabilities along the branches to get the end results

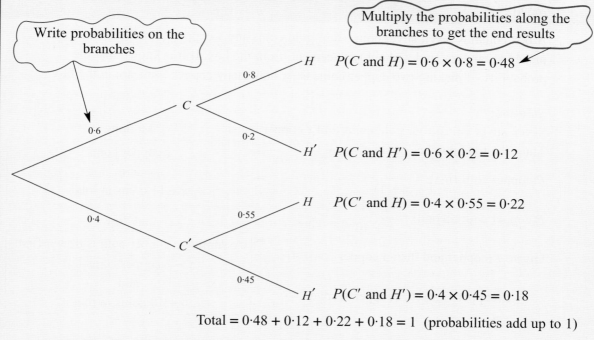

$$P(C \text{ and } H) = 0.6 \times 0.8 = 0.48$$

$$P(C \text{ and } H') = 0.6 \times 0.2 = 0.12$$

$$P(C' \text{ and } H) = 0.4 \times 0.55 = 0.22$$

$$P(C' \text{ and } H') = 0.4 \times 0.45 = 0.18$$

Total $= 0.48 + 0.12 + 0.22 + 0.18 = 1$ (probabilities add up to 1)

Note: The sum of the probabilities on **any set** of branches adds up to 1. If more than one set of results is required, simply add the end results together.

Method 2: Writing out all the outcomes

All four outcomes are:

C and H	or	C and H'	or	C' and H	or	C' and H'	
0.6×0.8	+	0.6×0.2	+	0.4×0.55	+	0.4×0.45	
$= 0.48$	+	0.12	+	0.22	+	0.18	$= 1$

(a)

$$P(H) = C \text{ and } H \quad \text{or} \quad C' \text{ and } H$$
$$= 0.48 \quad + \quad 0.22$$
$$= 0.7$$

(b)

$$P(H') = C \text{ and } H' \quad \text{or} \quad C' \text{ and } H'$$
$$= 0.12 \quad + \quad 0.18$$
$$= 0.3$$
$$(\text{or } P(H') = 1 - P(H) = 1 - 0.7 = 0.3)$$

(ii) P(day is calm, given that he does not hit his target)

$$= P(C|H') = \frac{P(C \text{ and } H')}{P(H')} = \frac{0\cdot12}{0\cdot3} = 0\cdot4$$

Note: You can use any letters you like. For example, not calm could be called 'windy' and use the letter W. Not hitting his target could be called 'missing target' and use the letter M.

EXAMPLE 10

A box contains seven silver coins, four gold coins and x copper coins. Two coins are picked at random, and without replacement, from the box. If it is known that the probability of picking two copper coins is $\frac{3}{14}$, how many copper coins are in the box?

Solution:

Seven silver coins, four gold coins and x copper coins.

Thus, the total number of coins $= x + 11$.

1st draw

x copper coins and $x + 11$ coins in total

$$P(\text{copper coin first}) = \frac{x}{x + 11}$$

$$P(\text{copper coin second}) = \frac{x - 1}{x + 10}$$

2nd draw

Assuming a copper coin is drawn first: $x - 1$ copper coins left and $x + 10$ coins in total

Given: $P(\text{copper and then a copper coin}) = \dfrac{3}{14}$

$$P(\text{copper first}) \times P(\text{copper second}) = \frac{3}{14}$$

$$\frac{x}{x + 11} \times \frac{x - 1}{x + 10} = \frac{3}{14}$$

$$\frac{x^2 - x}{x^2 + 21x + 110} = \frac{3}{14}$$

$14x^2 - 14x = 3x^2 + 63x + 330$ (multiply both sides by 14 and $x^2 + 21x + 110$)

$11x^2 - 77x - 330 = 0$

$x^2 - 7x - 30 = 0$

$(x - 10)(x + 3) = 0$

$x - 10 = 0$ or $x + 3 = 0$

$x = 10$ or $x = -3$

Thus, $x = 10$ (reject $x = -3$)

i.e. the number of copper coins is 10.

Exercise 10.10

1. One bag contains four red discs and six blue discs. Another bag contains five red discs and seven yellow discs. One disc is drawn from each bag. What is the probability that both discs are red?

2. **(i)** Every child born has an equal chance of being a boy or a girl. A mother has two children. Write out the sample space for the children born to this mother.

   (ii) What is the probability this mother has the following?

   (a) Two girls   **(b)** One girl and one boy

3. Three cards are drawn, one after the other, without replacement, from a pack of 52 playing cards. Find the probability that the first is a king, the second is an ace and the third is neither an ace nor a king.

4. Four students work separately on a mathematical problem. The probabilities that the four students have of solving the problem are as follows:

   $$\frac{3}{4}, \frac{1}{2}, \frac{4}{7}, \frac{2}{3}$$

   Show that the probability that the problem will be solved by at least one of the four students is $\frac{55}{56}$.

5. Two balls are taken at random at the same time from a box containing three black, three red and three yellow balls. Find the probability that:

   (i) Both balls are yellow

   (ii) Neither of the two balls is yellow

   (iii) At least one of the two balls is yellow

6. There are 24 students in a classroom. Each student plays only one sport. The table below gives their sport and gender.

	Football	Golf	Tennis
Female	6	5	4
Male	3	2	4

   (i) One student is selected at random.

       (a) Calculate the probability that the student is a male or is a football player.

       (b) Given that the student selected is female, calculate the probability that the student does not play golf.

   (ii) Two students are selected at random. Calculate the probability that neither student plays tennis.

7. To play a game, a player spins a wheel.

    The wheel is fixed to a wall. It spins freely around its centre point. Its rim is divided equally into 12 regions. Three of the regions are coloured red, four are coloured blue and five are coloured green.

    When the wheel stops, an arrow fixed to the wall points to one of the regions. All the regions are equally likely to stop at the arrow. The colour of this region is the outcome of the game.

    When the game is played twice, calculate the probability that:

    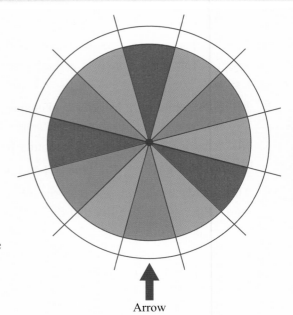
    Arrow

    (i) Both outcomes are green
    (ii) Both outcomes are the same colour
    (iii) The first outcome is red and the second is green
    (iv) One outcome is green and the other is blue

8. In a class of 56 students, each studies at least one of the following subjects: Biology, Chemistry, Physics. The Venn diagram shows the number of students studying the various combinations of subjects.

    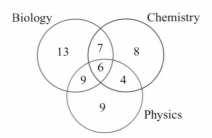

    (i) A student is picked at random from the whole class. Find the probability that the student does not study Biology.
    (ii) A student is picked at random from those who study at least two of the subjects. Find the probability that the student does not study Biology.
    (iii) Two students are picked at random from the whole class. Find the probability that they both study Physics.
    (iv) Two students are picked at random from those who study Chemistry. Find the probability that exactly one of them studies Biology.

9. The following data give the age and gender of 25 pupils in a class on a given day.

	Boys	Girls
Number of pupils aged 16 years	5	7
Number of pupils aged 17 years	7	6

(i) One of the pupils is picked at random. What is the probability that a boy aged 16 years or a girl aged 17 years is picked?

(ii) Each pupil in the class is given his/her examination results. Only three pupils scored full marks. Determine the probability that these three pupils are of the same age and the same gender.

10. (i) Two cards are drawn from a normal pack of 52 cards, where R = the probability of a red card and B = the probability of a black card. Complete the probability tree diagram.

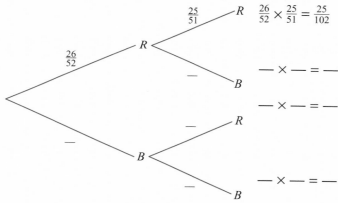

(ii) Hence, find the probability that both cards are black.

11. Three teachers, A, B and C, enter a 10 km race. The probability that each will complete the race are 0·8, 0·6 and 0·5, respectively. Assuming that their performances are independent, find the probability that:

(i) They all complete the race   (ii) At least two complete the race

12. A team of three students is to be chosen at random to take part in a chess competition. The team is to be chosen from seven maths students and three medical students. Find the probability that the team consists of:

(i) Only maths students   (ii) Only medical students

(iii) Two maths students and one medical student

13. The probability that a coffee machine will break down in its first year of operation is 0·05.

(i) What is the probability that the machine will not break down in its first year of operation?

(ii) A restaurant has just bought two of these machines, which are installed at the same time. Find the probability that at the end of the first year of operation just one machine has broken down. Assume that the performance of each machine is independent.

14. A student takes two tests, A and B. The tests are independent of each other. The probability of passing test A is $0\cdot6$ and the probability of passing test B is $0\cdot5$. Find the probability of passing:

    (i) Both tests   (ii) At least one of the two tests

15. A woman visits her local supermarket twice in one week. The probability that she uses a bank card is $0\cdot6$ and the probability that she uses cash is $0\cdot4$.

    (i) Find the probability that:

        (a) She uses cash on both visits   (b) She uses her bank card once and cash once

        (c) She uses cash

    (ii) Given that she uses cash, what is the probability that she uses her bank card on the first visit?

16. Bob catches a train to work every day from Monday to Friday. The probability that the train is late on Monday is $0\cdot45$. The probability that the train is late on any other day is $0\cdot3$.

    (i) A day is chosen at random. Find the probability of the following.

        (a) It is Monday and the train is late   (b) The train is late

    (ii) Given that the train is late, what is the probability that it is Monday?

17. For a lottery, 35 cards numbered 1 to 35 are placed in a drum. Five cards will be chosen at random from the drum as the winning combination.

    (i) How many different combinations are possible?

    (ii) How many of all the possible combinations will match exactly four numbers with the winning combination?

    (iii) How many of all the possible combinations will match exactly three numbers with the winning combination?

    (iv) Show that the probability of matching at least three numbers with the winning combination is approximately $0\cdot014$.

18. Two fair six-sided dice, A and B, are cast. What is the probability of getting:

    (i) A total of two or a total of six

    (ii) A total greater than nine or a total that is prime

    (iii) A total that is three times as great as other possible totals

19. There are two boxes on a table labelled A and B. Inside box A are four red spheres and two green spheres. Inside box B are five red cubes and three green cubes. Julie is invited to select one object at random. She may take an object from either box. Find the probability that the object she selects is:

    (i) A sphere

    (ii) Green

20. Karen is about to sit an examination at the end of an English course. The course has 20 prescribed texts. Six of these are novels, four are plays and 10 are poems. The examination consists of a question on one of the novels, a question on one of the plays and a question on one of the poems. Karen has studied four of the novels, three of the plays and seven of the poems. Find the probability of the following.

   (i) Karen has studied all three of the texts on the examination
   (ii) Karen has studied none of the texts on the examination
   (iii) Karen has studied at least two of the texts on the examination

21. Ten discs, each marked with a different whole number from 1 to 10, are placed in a box. Three of the discs are drawn at random (without replacement) from the box.

   (i) What is the probability that the disc with the number 5 is drawn?
   (ii) What is the probability that the three numbers on the discs drawn are even?
   (iii) What is the probability that the product of the three numbers on the discs drawn is odd?
   (iv) What is the probability that the largest number on the discs drawn is 5?

22. A fishing team has four members, Anthony, Bernard, Catherine and Denise. Of the fish caught, 50% are ray, 20% are salmon and the rest are trout, while 20% of the fish caught are made by Anthony, 45% by Bernard, 10% by Catherine and 25% by Denise. All catches are independent. A fish is selected at random.

   (i) Calculate the probability that the fish is:
       (a) A ray caught by Anthony   (b) A trout not caught by Anthony
   (ii) The probability of the selected fish being a ray caught by Catherine is 0·05. What is the probability that a catch made by Catherine is a ray?
   (iii) What is the probability that the fish selected is a ray caught by Bernard or Denise?
   (iv) Given that the fish selected is a ray, find the probability it is caught by Denise.

23. A factory has three machines, P, Q and R, producing large numbers of a certain item. Of the total production, 40% is produced on P, 50% on Q and 10% on R. The records show that 1% of items produced on P are defective, 2% of items produced on Q are defective and 6% of items produced on R are defective. The occurrence of a defective item is independent of each machine and all other items.

   (i) Using D for defective and D' for not defective, write out all possible outcomes and show that the sum of the probabilities add up to 1.

   One item is chosen at random from a certain day's output.
   (ii) Calculate the probability that the item chosen is defective.
   (iii) Given that the item chosen is defective, find the probability that it was produced on machine Q.

24. **(i)** The probability that a person has a disease is 0·02. What is the probability that they do not have the disease?

(ii) There is a test for the disease. However, the test has some errors. If you have the disease, there is a probability of 0·95 that the test is positive for the disease. If you do not have the disease, there is a probability of 0·01 that the test is positive for the disease. A person takes the test. Using a tree diagram or otherwise, calculate the probability that the person has:

    (a) The disease and a positive test result   **(b)** A positive result

(iii) Calculate the probability that the person has the disease, given that the person had a positive result. Give your answer correct to three decimal places.

(iv) Five thousand people have a positive result for the test. How many of these people would you expect to have the disease?

(v) Is this test worth carrying out? Justify your answer.

25. x and y are randomly selected integers with $1 \leq x \leq 10$ and $1 \leq y \leq 10$. p is the point with coordinates $(x, 0)$ and q is the point with coordinates $(0, y)$. Find the probability of the following.

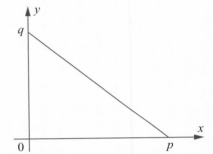

    (i) The slope of pq is equal to -1

    (ii) The slope of pq is greater than -1

    (iii) The length of $[pq]$ is less than or equal to 5

26. There are 30 days in June. Seven students have their birthdays in June. The birthdays are independent of each other and all dates are equally likely.

    (i) What is the probability that all seven students have the same birthday?

    (ii) What is the probability that all seven students have different birthdays?

    (iii) Show that the probability that at least two have the same birthday is greater than 0·5.

27. A classroom contains 15 desks, which are arranged in rows. The front row contains three desks. Fifteen students are seated at random in the classroom, eight of whom are boys and seven of whom are girls. Each desk seats only one student.

What is the probability of the following?

    (i) Three girls occupy the front row of desks

    (ii) There are more boys than girls seated in the front row

    (iii) There are two girls and one boy seated in the front row, with the two girls seated next to each other

28. A bag contains discs of three different colours. There are five red discs, one white disc and x black discs. Three discs are picked together at random.

    (i) Write down an expression in x for the probability that the three discs are all different colours.

    (ii) If the probability that the three discs are all different colours is equal to the probability that they are all black, find x.

29. w white discs and r red discs are placed in a box. Two of the discs are drawn at random from the box. The probability that both discs are red is p.

    (i) Find p in terms of w and r.

    (ii) When $w = 1$, find the value of r for which $p = \frac{1}{2}$.

    (iii) There are other values of w and r that also give $p = \frac{1}{2}$. The next smallest such value of w is even. By investigating the even numbers in turn, find this value of w and the corresponding value of r.

30. Eight cards are numbered 1 to 8. The cards numbered 1 and 2 are red, the cards numbered 3 and 4 are blue, the cards numbered 5 and 6 are yellow and the cards numbered 7 and 8 are black. Four cards are selected at random from the eight cards.

    Find the probability that the four cards selected are:

    (i) All different colours

    (ii) Two odd-numbered cards and two even-numbered cards

    (iii) All different colours, two odd-numbered and two even-numbered

Binomial distribution (Bernoulli trials)

An experiment that satisfies the following **four** conditions is called a **binomial distribution** or a **Bernoulli trial.**

1. A fixed number, n, of repeated trials.
2. Only two possible outcomes in each trial: success or failure.
3. The trials are independent.
4. The probability of a success in each trial is constant.

In this situation, we let:

$p = P(\text{success})$ and $q = P(\text{failure})$, where $(p + q) = 1$.

$$P(r \text{ successes}) = \binom{n}{r} p^r q^{n-r}$$

Method

1. Write down n, the number of trials.
2. Calculate p and q ($q = 1 - p$).
3. Let r = number of successes required.
4. Use the formula above.

Examples of Bernoulli trials are:

1. Tossing coins
2. Shots in a competition
3. A search for defective products

EXAMPLE 1

Five unbiased coins are tossed.

(i) Find the probability of getting three heads and two tails.

(ii) The five coins are tossed eight times. Find the probability of getting three heads and two tails exactly four times. Give your answer correct to three decimal places.

Solution:

$n = 5$ (no. of trials) $p = P(H) = \frac{1}{2}$ $q = P(T) = \frac{1}{2}$

(i) $P(\text{three heads, two tails}) = \binom{5}{3}(p)^3(q)^2 = \binom{5}{3}\left(\frac{1}{2}\right)^3\left(\frac{1}{2}\right)^2 = 10\left(\frac{1}{8}\right)\left(\frac{1}{4}\right) = \frac{10}{32} = \frac{5}{16}$

(ii) $n = 8$ (no. of trials)

$p = P(\text{three heads, two tails}) = \frac{5}{16}$ $\therefore q = 1 - p = 1 - \frac{5}{16} = \frac{11}{16}$

$P(\text{three heads, two tails, exactly four times})$

$= \binom{8}{4}(p)^4(q)^4 = \binom{8}{4}\left(\frac{5}{16}\right)^4\left(\frac{11}{16}\right)^4 = 0 \cdot 149$ (correct to three decimal places)

 **EXAMPLE 2**

In a large consignment of articles, 8% are defective. Show that the probability of a random sample of 10 articles containing at least two defectives is approximately 0·19.

Solution:

$n = 10$ (no. of articles)

$P(\text{success}) = P(\text{defective}) = 0\cdot08 = p$

$P(\text{failure}) = P(\text{non-defective}) = 0\cdot92 = q$

$$P(r \text{ successes}) = \binom{n}{r}p^r q^{n-r}$$

$P(\text{at least two defectives})$

$= 1 - P(\text{no defective}) - P(\text{one defective})$

$= 1 - \binom{10}{0}(0\cdot08)^0(0\cdot92)^{10} - \binom{10}{1}(0\cdot08)^1(0\cdot92)^9$

$= 1 - 0\cdot4344 - 0\cdot3777 = 0\cdot1879 \simeq 0\cdot19$ (correct to two decimal places)

EXAMPLE 3

During a match, John takes a number of penalty shots. The shots are independent of each other and his probability of scoring with each shot is $\frac{4}{5}$.

(i) Find the probability that John misses each of his first four penalty shots.

(ii) Find the probability that John scores exactly three of his first four penalty shots.

(iii) If John takes 10 penalty shots during the match, find the probability that he scores at least eight of them.

Solution:

(i) **Method 1**

$P(\text{misses first four penalty shots})$

$= P(m_1 \text{ and } m_2 \text{ and } m_3 \text{ and } m_4) = \frac{1}{5} \times \frac{1}{5} \times \frac{1}{5} \times \frac{1}{5} = \frac{1}{625}$

Method 2

$n = 4$ (no. of penalty shots) $P(\text{success}) = P(\text{miss}) = \frac{1}{5} = p$ $\therefore q = \frac{4}{5}$

$P(\text{misses first four penalty shots})$

$= \binom{4}{4}p^4q^0 = \binom{4}{4}\left(\frac{1}{5}\right)^4\left(\frac{4}{5}\right)^0 = (1)\left(\frac{1}{625}\right)(1) = \frac{1}{625}$

319

(ii) *P*(scores exactly three of his first four penalty shots)

$$= \binom{4}{1}p^3q^1 = \binom{4}{1}\left(\frac{4}{5}\right)^3\left(\frac{1}{5}\right)^1 = (4)\left(\frac{64}{125}\right)\left(\frac{1}{5}\right) = \frac{256}{625}$$

(iii) *n* = 10 (number of shots)

P(scores at least eight scores)

= *P*(scores 8)   +   *P*(scores 9)   +   *P*(scores 10)

$$= \binom{10}{8}p^8q^2 \quad + \quad \binom{10}{9}p^9q^1 \quad + \quad \binom{10}{10}p^{10}q^0$$

$$= \binom{10}{8}\left(\frac{4}{5}\right)^8\left(\frac{1}{5}\right)^2 \quad + \quad \binom{10}{9}\left(\frac{4}{5}\right)^9\left(\frac{1}{5}\right)^1 \quad + \quad \binom{10}{10}\left(\frac{4}{5}\right)^{10}\left(\frac{1}{5}\right)^0$$

$$= \frac{2,949,120}{9,765,625} \quad + \quad \frac{2,621,440}{9,765,625} \quad + \quad \frac{1,048,576}{9,765,625}$$

$$= \frac{6,619,136}{9,765,625}$$

Exercise 10.11

1. Calculate each of the following, correct to three decimal places.

   (i) $\binom{5}{2}(0\cdot2)^2(0\cdot8)^3$ (ii) $\binom{6}{3}(0\cdot7)^3(0\cdot3)^3$ (iii) $\binom{5}{4}\left(\frac{1}{3}\right)^4\left(\frac{2}{3}\right)^1$ (iv) $\binom{9}{1}\left(\frac{3}{4}\right)^1\left(\frac{1}{4}\right)^8$

2. Assuming independence, state which of the following is a binomial distribution.

   (i) A coin is tossed five times and we define a success as obtaining a head.
   (ii) A six-sided standard die is rolled four times and we define a success as obtaining a 3.
   (iii) Three cards are removed one at a time from a standard pack of 52 playing cards and we define a success as drawing an ace.
   (iv) A bag contains three red and two blue discs. Three discs are drawn at random from the bag, one at a time, and each time a disc is chosen it is returned to the bag before the next disc is drawn. A success is obtaining a red disc.

3. The following formula relates to the binomial distribution.

   $$P(X = r) = \binom{n}{r}p^rq^{n-r}$$

(i) State what each of the letters p, q, n and r represents in the formula above.

p is _____

q is _____

n is _____

r is _____

(ii) Describe the type of experiment that results in a random variable that has a binomial distribution.

4. A coin is tossed three times. What is the probability of obtaining the following?

   (i) Exactly one head   **(ii)** Exactly two heads

  (iii) Exactly three heads   **(iv)** At least one head

5. Twenty per cent of the items produced by a machine are defective. Four items are chosen at random. Find the probability that none of the chosen items is defective.

6. In a game of chess against a particular opponent, the probability that Boris wins is 85%. He plays five games against this opponent, where no draws are allowed. What is the probability, correct to three decimal places, that Boris will:

   (i) Only win the second and fourth games

  (ii) Win exactly two games

7. Whenever Anne's mobile phone rings, the probability that she answers the call is $\frac{3}{4}$. A friend phones Anne six times.

   (i) What is the probability that she misses all the calls?

  (ii) What is the probability that she misses the first two calls and answers the others?

 (iii) What is the probability that she answers exactly one of the calls?

  (iv) What is the probability that she answers at least two of the calls?

8. A multiple choice test has seven questions. Each question has three choices. Tony takes the test and guesses the answer on each question. Find, correct to three decimal places, the probability that Tony gets:

   (i) All seven correct   **(ii)** Exactly four questions correct

 (iii) At least two questions correct

9. David plays a game by spinning a fair five-sided spinner, as shown. He wins with a score of 2, otherwise he loses. The spinner is spun nine times. Find the probability that David:

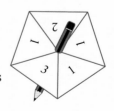

   (i) Loses each time **(ii)** Wins exactly once **(iii)** Wins at least two times

10. In a certain type of archery competition, Laura hits the target with an average of two out of every three shots. The shots are independent of each other. During one such competition, she has 10 shots at the target. Find, correct to three decimal places, the probability that Laura hits the target:

(i) Exactly three times   (ii) Fewer than nine times

11. A factory manufactures light bulbs. Over a long period of time is was found that 5% of the bulbs were defective. Alan is inspecting, one at a time, a large quantity of light bulbs. Find, correct to three decimal places, the probability that the first bulb he finds that is defective is the:

(i) 10th bulb   (ii) 20th bulb   (iii) 30th bulb

12. The probability of obtaining heads on a biased coin is 0.2. The coin is tossed five times. Find the probability of obtaining:

(i) Exactly two heads   (ii) At least two heads

13. Doreen can hit the target with an average of three out of every four pistol shots. During a competition she has eight shots at the target. Assuming the shots are independent of each other, find the probability that she hits the target:

(i) Exactly seven times

(ii) Seven times or more

Give each answer correct to three decimal places.

14. A family has six children. The probability of having a boy or a girl is equal and independent of each other. Find the probability that in this family there are:

(i) No boys   (ii) No girls   (iii) At least one boy and one girl

15. A fair coin is tossed five times. By applying the binomial distribution, find the probability of obtaining no head, one head, two heads, three heads, four heads and five heads. Hence, on a suitable diagram, draw a graph of the distribution.

16. In a large consignment of articles, 5% are defective. Show that the probability of a random sample of 12 articles containing at least two defective articles is approximately 0.12.

17. Four unbiased coins are tossed.

(i) Find the probability of obtaining two heads and two tails.

(ii) The four coins are tossed five times. Find the probability of getting two heads and two tails exactly three times.

18. Kenny is a very good dart player. Over a long period of time it was found that he hits a bull's eye with 90% accuracy. What is the probability that Kenny hits his fourth bull's eye on his sixth shot?

19. Anne and Brendan play a game in which they take turns throwing a die. The first person to throw a 6 wins. Anne has the first throw.

(i) Find the probability that Anne wins on her second throw.

(ii) Find the probability that Anne wins on her first, second or third throw.

(iii) By finding the sum to infinity of a geometric series, or otherwise, find the probability that Anne wins the game.

Normal distribution and probability

One reason the normal distribution is so important is that the measurement of many natural phenomena are normally distributed (or nearly so), such as heights, weights, IQ scores and examination results. We have already met the empirical rule and the normal curve. It can be shown that approximately:

---

1. 68% of the total area under the curve lies between $\mu - \sigma$ and $\mu + \sigma$.

2. 95% of the total area under the curve lies between $\mu - 2\sigma$ and $\mu + 2\sigma$.

3. 97·7% of the total area under the curve lies between $\mu - 3\sigma$ and $\mu + 3\sigma$.

The most frequently used normal distribution is the standard normal distribution. We usually reserve the letter z for this distribution. In particular, we learned how to change a scale from x-units to z-units.

We defined the standard unit as $z = \dfrac{x - \mu}{\sigma}$

where x = the given variable, μ = the given mean and σ = the given standard deviation.

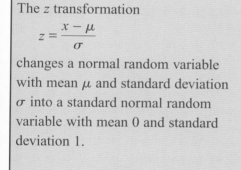

The z transformation

$$z = \frac{x - \mu}{\sigma}$$

changes a normal random variable with mean μ and standard deviation σ into a standard normal random variable with mean 0 and standard deviation 1.

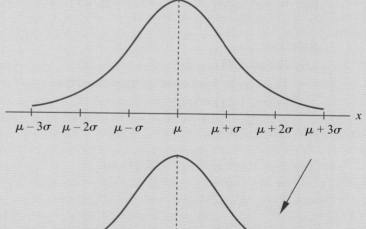

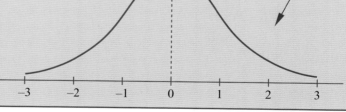

Note: The area under the curve of **any** normal distribution is **always** equal to 1.

Finding areas under normal curves (revision)

The mathematical tables give us the area to the left of a specified value of z. This table can be used to obtain a required area. The three graphs below summarise how to use the tables on pages 36 and 37.

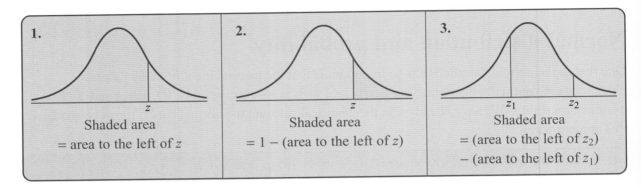

| 1. Shaded area = area to the left of z | 2. Shaded area = 1 − (area to the left of z) | 3. Shaded area = (area to the left of z_2) − (area to the left of z_1) |

Note: Alternative to graph 3: Find the area to the left of z_1 and the area to the right of z_2 and subtract both from 1.

EXAMPLE 1

If z is a random variable with standard normal distribution, use the mathematical tables to find:

(i) $P(z \leq 1.75)$ (ii) $P(z \geq 0.93)$

(iii) $P(z \leq -1.23)$ (iv) $P(-1.2 \leq z \leq 0.72)$

Solution:

(i) $P(z \leq 1.75)$

This can be read directly from the tables

$P(z \leq 1.75) = 0.9599$

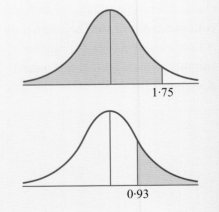

1·75

(ii) $P(z \geq 0.93)$ Right tail

$P(z \geq 0.93)$

$= 1 - P(z \leq 0.93)$

$= 1 - 0.8238$

$= 0.1762$

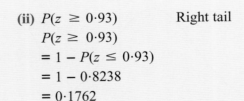

0·93

(iii) $P(z \leq -1.23)$ Left tail

$P(z \leq -1.23)$

$= 1 - P(z \leq 1.23)$

$= 1 - 0.8907$

$= 0.1093$

(iv) $P(-1.2 \leq z \leq 0.72)$

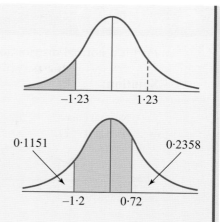

Calculations:

$P(z \geq 0.72) = 1 - 0.7642 = 0.2358$

$P(z \leq -1.2) = 1 - 0.8849 = 0.1151$

$P(-1.2 \leq z \leq 0.72)$

$= 1 - 0.2358 - 0.1151 = 0.6491$

Sometimes we are given the area (or probability) and asked to find the value of z.

EXAMPLE 2

If $P(z \leq k) = 0.7324$, find k.

Solution:

The area to the left of 0 is 0.5.

As $P(z \leq k) = 0.7324$, k must be positive.

By reading the mathematical tables backwards, 0.7324

gives $k = 0.62$.

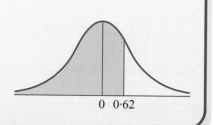

Transforming (converting) x-values to z-values is often referred to as **standardising**.

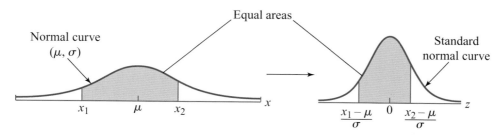

EXAMPLE 3

$P(x)$ is a normal distribution with $\mu = 5$ and $\sigma = 2$. Calculate $P(3 \leq x \leq 8)$.

Solution:

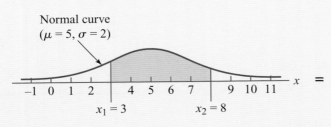

Normal curve
$(\mu = 5, \sigma = 2)$

$x_1 = 3$ $x_2 = 8$

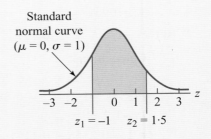

Standard
normal curve
$(\mu = 0, \sigma = 1)$

$z_1 = -1$ $z_2 = 1 \cdot 5$

$$\left(\begin{array}{c}\text{The area under the curve between}\\ x_1 = 3 \quad \text{and} \quad x_2 = 8\end{array}\right) = \left(\begin{array}{c}\text{The area under the curve between}\\ z_1 = -1 \quad \text{and} \quad z_2 = 1 \cdot 5\end{array}\right)$$

$z_1 = \dfrac{x_1 - \mu}{\sigma} = \dfrac{3 - 5}{2} = -1$

$z_2 = \dfrac{x_2 - \mu}{\sigma} = \dfrac{8 - 5}{2} = 1 \cdot 5$

Using the tables:

$P(3 \leq x \leq 8)$
$= P(-1 \leq z \leq 1 \cdot 5)$
$= 1 - 0 \cdot 0668 - 0 \cdot 1587$
$= 0 \cdot 7745$

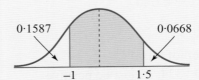

0·1587   0·0668

-1 $1 \cdot 5$

EXAMPLE 4

The heights of students in a certain class are normally distributed with a mean of 165 cm and a standard deviation of 10 cm. If a student is chosen at random, find the probability that the student's height is less than 170 cm.

Solution:
Given: $\mu = 165$, $\sigma = 10$, $x = 170$. Find $P(x < 170)$.

$z = \dfrac{x - \mu}{\sigma}$

$z = \dfrac{170 - 165}{10} = \dfrac{5}{10} = 0 \cdot 5$

From the tables, $P(z < 0 \cdot 5) = 0 \cdot 6915$.

$\therefore P(\text{student's height is less than 170 cm}) = 0 \cdot 6915$.

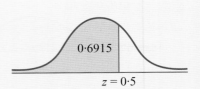

0·6915

$z = 0 \cdot 5$

EXAMPLE 5

The lifetime of a particular type of electric bulb is normally distributed with a mean of 1,500 hours and a standard deviation of 120 hours. If 140 bulbs are purchased, how many can be expected to have a lifetime between 1,400 hours and 1,730 hours inclusive?

(i)   Give your answer correct to the nearest whole number.

(ii) Give your answer under quality control conditions in a factory.

(iii) Justify the difference between answer (i) and answer (ii).

Solution:

(i) Given: $\mu = 1,500$, $\sigma = 120$, $x_1 = 1,400$ and $x_2 = 1,730$. Find $P(1,400 < x < 1,730)$.

We first convert the x-values into z-values using $z = \dfrac{x - \mu}{\sigma}$.

$$z_1 = \frac{x_1 - \mu}{\sigma}$$

$$= \frac{1,400 - 1,500}{120} = \frac{-100}{120} = -0.83$$

$$z_2 = \frac{x_2 - \mu}{\sigma}$$

$$= \frac{1,730 - 1,500}{120} = \frac{230}{120} = 1.92$$

Area under the curve between
$z_1 = -0.83$ and $z_2 = 1.92$
$= 1 - 0.0274 - 0.2033$
$= 0.7693$

0.2033   0.0274

−0.83 0   1.92

$\therefore P(1,400 < x < 1,730) = P(-0.83 < z < 1.92) = 0.7693$.

Expected number of bulbs $= np = 140(0.7693) = 107.702$.

Thus, the number of bulbs out of 140 that we would expect to have a lifetime between 1,400 hours and 1,730 hours is 108.

(ii) The number of bulbs under quality control conditions is 107.

(iii) The difference between the answers can be accounted for by noting that 107.702 bulbs makes no sense in the real world, i.e. .702 of a bulb does not count for quality control purposes. Hence, quality control expects that 107 bulbs out of 140 will work.

EXAMPLE 6

Three sisters, Essie, Bessie and Tessie, are identical triplets. They have just received the results of their trial Higher Level Maths examination. They are each in a different school in a normal class of typical non-streamed Higher Level Maths students. In addition, each school set a different examination and had a different marking examiner. In each class, the results were normally distributed. Their raw results were as follows: Essie got 84%, Bessie got 72% and Tessie got 58%. In Essie's class, the mean was 80% with a standard deviation of 10%, in Bessie's class the mean was 74% with a standard deviation of 4% and in Tessie's class the mean was 50% with a standard deviation of 5%.

(i) Which student did best? Justify your answer.

(ii) How do you think the reporting of the results could be improved?

Solution:

(i) First represent the information in a table.

Student	Result	μ	σ
Essie	84	80	10
Bessie	72	74	4
Tessie	58	50	5

Without the class means and standard deviations, it seems obvious that Essie did best with 84% and Tessie did worst with 58%. However, the raw percentage scores give no indication of the level of difficulty of the examination for each class or the consistency of the marking examiners for each class. In addition, we require the mean, μ, and the standard deviation, σ, for each class.

To decide who did best in the trial exam, we calculate the z-score for each student and then compare the result.

$$z = \frac{x - \mu}{\sigma}$$

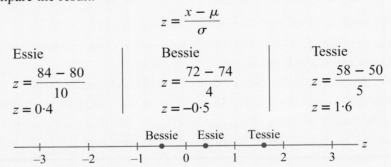

Essie
$$z = \frac{84 - 80}{10}$$
$$z = 0\cdot4$$

Bessie
$$z = \frac{72 - 74}{4}$$
$$z = -0\cdot5$$

Tessie
$$z = \frac{58 - 50}{5}$$
$$z = 1\cdot6$$

Based on the z-scores, Tessie did best. She is $1\cdot6$ standard deviations above the mean. However, we are assuming that each marking examiner was consistent in their marking, that is, marking **all** scripts too easy, too hard, etc. If a marking examiner was not consistent in their marking, then the z-scores above are unreliable. In the question we are told that each class is a normal class of typical non-streamed Higher Level students. If the classes were of different abilities, then the z-scores of the better class would be reduced and the z-scores of the weaker class would be increased.

(ii) **How do you think the reporting of the results could be improved?**

It would be better if the three schools gave the same trial exam and at the same time to avoid copying, as in the real Leaving Certificate examination. It would also be better if there was only one consistent marking examiner. This would avoid the problems of different marking examiners and the problem caused by classes of different abilities. In this case, the raw scores would be just as good as the z-scores. Alternatively, the three Maths teachers could meet and agree a consistent marking scheme, as they do in the real Leaving Certificate.

Note: Many students and parents are not familiar with z-scores. Imagine coming home to tell your parents that you got a z-score of 2·15 in your Christmas Maths examination. It could be difficult to explain that this means you are more than two standard deviations above the mean for your class and that you are in the top 2% based on this examination.

Exercise 10.12

1. Using the tables on pages 36 and 37 of the booklet of formulae and tables, find the area of the shaded region under each of the following standard normal curves.

(i)
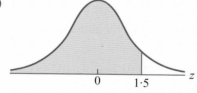

(ii)
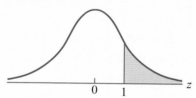

(iii)
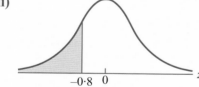

(iv)
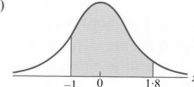

If z is a random variable with a standard normal distribution, calculate questions 2–13.

2. $P(z \leq 1\cdot2)$
3. $P(z \leq 0\cdot8)$
4. $P(z \leq 2\cdot3)$
5. $P(z \geq 1\cdot9)$
6. $P(z \geq 1\cdot25)$
7. $P(z \geq 0\cdot68)$
8. $P(z \leq -1)$
9. $P(z \leq -1\cdot6)$
10. $P(z \leq -2\cdot12)$
11. $P(0\cdot5 \leq z \leq 1\cdot5)$
12. $P(-1 \leq z \leq 1)$
13. $P(-1\cdot3 \leq z \leq 1\cdot8)$

Find the value of z_1 in questions 14–16.

14. $P(z \leq z_1) = 0\cdot8849$
15. $P(z \leq z_1) = 0\cdot9664$
16. $P(z \leq z_1) = 0\cdot33$

x is a random variable with a normal distribution with given mean μ and standard deviation σ. Find the required probability in questions 17–20.

17. If $\mu = 50$, $\sigma = 10$, find: (i) $P(x \leq 60)$ (ii) $P(x \geq 75)$
18. If $\mu = 80$, $\sigma = 12$, find: (i) $P(x \leq 98)$ (ii) $P(x \geq 104)$

19. If $\mu = 150$, $\sigma = 20$, find: **(i)** $P(130 \le x \le 160)$ **(ii)** $P(170 \le x \le 190)$

20. If $\mu = 180$, $\sigma = 8$, find: **(i)** $P(168 \le x \le 184 \cdot 5)$ **(ii)** $P(178 \le x \le 186)$

21. A normal distribution of scores has a standard deviation of 8. Find the z-scores corresponding to a score that is:

    (i) 8 above the mean   **(ii)** 16 below the mean

    (iii) 12 above the mean   **(iv)** 20 below the mean

22. A random variable, x, is normally distributed with a mean of 100 and a standard deviation of 8. Find the value of x that is:

    (i) $1 \cdot 5$ standard deviations **above** the mean

    (ii) $1 \cdot 2$ standard deviations **below** the mean

23. The amounts due on monthly mobile phone bills are normally distributed with a mean of €53 and a standard deviation of €15. If a bill is chosen at random, find the probability that the amount due is between €47 and €74.

24. The lifetime of a particular type of electric bulb is normally distributed with a mean of 1,500 hours and a standard deviation of 120 hours. If 300 bulbs are purchased, how many can be expected to have a lifetime between 1,410 hours and 1,680 hours inclusive? Give your answer correct to the nearest whole number.

25. **(i)** A machine fills jars with marmalade so that the weight of marmalade in each jar is normally distributed with a mean of 500 g and a standard deviation of 8 g. A jar is selected at random. Find the probability that its weight is:

    (a) Less than 488 g   **(b)** Between 490 g and 510 g

    (ii) If 400 jars are purchased, how many would be expected to have a weight between 490 g and 510 g, correct to the nearest whole number?

26. The marks awarded in an examination are normally distributed with a mean of 60 and a standard deviation of 10. A university calls candidates for interview if their mark is above the upper quartile, Q_3.

    (i) A student is chosen at random. Find the probability that the student's mark is above Q_3.

    (ii) Find, correct to the nearest integer, the mark associated with Q_3.

27. **(i)** A normal distribution of raw scores has a mean of 60. The z-score for a raw score of 65 is -1. Why is this z-score incorrect?

    (ii) A normal distribution of raw scores has a mean of 72. The z-score for a raw score of 66 is $2 \cdot 3$. Why is this z-score incorrect?

28. In a normal distribution, a raw score of 70 corresponds to a z-score of 1 and a raw score of 75 corresponds to a z-score of 2. Find **(i)** the standard deviation and **(ii)** the mean of this distribution.

29. In a normal distribution, a raw score of 56 corresponds to a z-score of -1 and a raw score of 66 corresponds to a z-score of 1·5. Find **(i)** the standard deviation and **(ii)** the mean of this distribution.

30. On her French class exam, a student's mark was 72%. If the mean mark for this exam was 65%, would she prefer a standard deviation of 9% or 18%? Justify your answer.

31. Eggs have masses that are normally distributed with a mean of 60 g and a standard deviation of 15 g. Eggs of mass less than 45 g are classified as small. The remainder are classified into two further divisions, called standard and large.

   (i) If an egg is selected at random from the batch, find the probability that it is small.

   (ii) It is required that the number of standard-sized eggs and the number of large eggs should be the same. Estimate the mass at which the division should be made.

32. A particular drug gives relief from pain. The period of pain relief reported by people who are treated with the drug is normally distributed with a mean of 50 hours and a standard deviation of 16 hours.

   (i) A patient who uses the drug is selected at random. Find the probability that this patient has pain relief for 10 hours or more.

   (ii) A second patient who uses the drug is selected at random. Find the probability that:

      (a) Both patients have pain relief for 10 hours or more

      (b) Neither patient has pain relief for 10 hours or more

   (iii) Hence or otherwise, find the probability that only one of them has pain relief for 10 hours or more.

33. In a large school, the heights of all third year students were recorded. The heights of the girls are normally distributed with a mean of 160 cm and a standard deviation of 10 cm. The heights of the boys are normally distributed with a mean of 164 cm and a standard deviation of 12 cm.

   (i) Find the probability that a girl chosen at random is taller than 168 cm.

   (ii) Nine per cent of the girls are shorter than x cm. Find the value of x.

   (iii) Ninety per cent of the boys have heights between p cm and q cm, where p and q are symmetrical about 164 cm. Find the value of p and q, where $p < q$.

34. The weights of chickens in a butcher shop are normally distributed with a mean of 2·8 kg and a standard deviation of 0·2 kg.

   (i) A chicken is chosen at random. Find the probability that it weighs:

      (a) Less than 2·68 kg

      (b) More than 3·16 kg

      (c) Between 2·68 kg and 3·16 kg

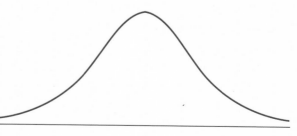

(ii) Copy the diagram three times. Shade the areas that represent the probabilities in part (i).

(iii) A customer buys two chickens. Find, correct to four decimal places, the probability that both chickens weigh between 2·68 kg and 3·16 kg.

35. A factory manufactures aluminium rods. One of its machines can be set to produce rods of a specified length. The lengths of these rods are normally distributed with a mean equal to the specified length and a standard deviation equal to 0·2 mm. The machine has been set to produce rods of length 40 mm.

(i) What is the probability that a randomly selected rod will be less than 39·7 mm in length?

(ii) Three rods are selected at random. What is the probability that all of them are less than 39·7 mm in length, correct to five decimal places?

Probability distributions

Random variable

A **random variable** is a number determined by the outcome of an experiment. For example, if four coins are tossed, then the number of heads which occur must belong to the set $\{0, 1, 2, 3, 4\}$. If $x = $ the number of heads which occur, then x is a random variable.

A random variable is discrete if we can list its possible values (as above). A random variable is continuous if it can take any value within a certain range, e.g. the height of a person. In this section we will deal with discrete random variables. For each value of x there is an associated probability that x will have that particular value, i.e. $P(x = 0)$, $P(x = 1)$, $P(x = 2)$, $P(x = 3)$, $P(x = 4)$. All the possible values of x together with associated probabilities are called a **probability distribution**.

x	0	1	2	3	4
$P(x)$	$P(0)$	$P(1)$	$P(2)$	$P(3)$	$P(4)$

Expected value and standard deviation of a discrete random variable x

The mean value, μ, of the random variable x is called the **expected value** of x and is written as $E(x)$. The standard deviation is denoted by $\sigma(x)$.

$$\text{Mean } = \mu = E(x) = \Sigma x P(x)$$

$$\text{Standard deviation} = \sigma(x) = \sqrt{\Sigma(x - \mu)^2 P(x)}$$

EXAMPLE 1

Three coins are tossed. Let x represent the number of heads that occur.

(i) Show the probability distribution for x.　　(ii) Calculate $E(x)$.

Solution:

(i) x = number of heads　　　$\therefore x \in \{0, 1, 2, 3\}$

0 heads:　TTT
1 head:　　HTT, THT, TTH
2 heads:　HHT, HTH, THH
3 heads:　HHH
8 possible outcomes

0 heads:　$P(x = 0) = \frac{1}{8}$　　2 heads:　$P(x = 2) = \frac{3}{8}$

1 head:　$P(x = 1) = \frac{3}{8}$　　3 heads:　$P(x = 3) = \frac{1}{8}$

Probability distributions can be represented in tabular and graphical form.

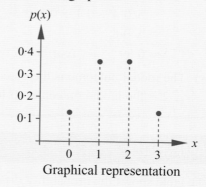

x	0	1	2	3
$P(x)$	$\frac{1}{8}$	$\frac{3}{8}$	$\frac{3}{8}$	$\frac{1}{8}$

Tabular representation

Graphical representation

(ii) $E(x) = \Sigma x\,P(x) = 0\left(\frac{1}{8}\right) + 1\left(\frac{3}{8}\right) + 2\left(\frac{3}{8}\right) + 3\left(\frac{1}{8}\right) = \frac{3}{2}$ heads

Note: The expected value is **not** one of the outcomes (value of x).

EXAMPLE 2

A child throws a ball at a group of three skittles. The probability that the ball will knock 0, 1, 2 or 3 of the skittles is given in the following probability distribution table.

x	0	1	2	3
$P(x)$	0·1	0·1	0·5	k

(i) Find the value of k.

(ii) Find the mean of the distribution.

(iii) Find the standard deviation of the distribution, correct to two decimal places.

(iv) Write down the modal outcome.

Solution:

(i)
$$\Sigma P(x) = 1$$
$$\therefore 0{\cdot}1 + 0{\cdot}1 + 0{\cdot}5 + k = 1$$
$$0{\cdot}7 + k = 1$$
$$k = 0{\cdot}3$$

(ii) Mean
$$= \mu$$
$$= \Sigma x\, P(x)$$
$$= 0(0{\cdot}1) + 1(0{\cdot}1) + 2(0{\cdot}5) + 3(0{\cdot}3)$$
$$= 0 + 0{\cdot}1 + 1 + 0{\cdot}9$$
$$= 2$$

(iii) Standard deviation
$$= \sigma = \sqrt{\Sigma (x - \mu)^2\, P(x)}$$
$$= \sqrt{(0 - 2)^2(0{\cdot}1) + (1 - 2)^2(0{\cdot}1) + (2 - 2)^2(0{\cdot}5) + (3 - 2)^2(0{\cdot}3)}$$
$$= \sqrt{4(0{\cdot}1) + 1(0{\cdot}1) + 0(0{\cdot}5) + 1(0{\cdot}3)}$$
$$= \sqrt{0{\cdot}4 + 0{\cdot}1 + 0 + 0{\cdot}3}$$
$$= \sqrt{0{\cdot}8}$$
$$= 0{\cdot}89 \qquad \text{(correct to two decimal places)}$$

(iv) The modal outcome is the outcome with the highest probability.
$$\therefore 2 \text{ is the modal outcome. (It has the highest probability of } 0{\cdot}5.)$$

EXAMPLE 3

The table shows the probability distribution for the random variable x.

x	1	2	3	4	5
$P(x)$	0·1	0·2	a	b	0·2

Given $E(x) = 3{\cdot}1$, calculate the value of a and the value of b.

Solution:

$$\Sigma P(x) = 1$$
$$\therefore 0{\cdot}1 + 0{\cdot}2 + a + b + 0{\cdot}2 = 1$$
$$a + b + 0{\cdot}5 = 1$$
$$a + b = 0{\cdot}5$$
$$2a + 2b = 1 \quad \text{①}$$

Given: $E(x) = 3{\cdot}1$
$$\therefore \Sigma x P(x) = 3{\cdot}1$$
$$\therefore 1(0{\cdot}1) + 2(0{\cdot}2) + 3(a) + 4(b) + 5(0{\cdot}2) = 3{\cdot}1$$
$$0{\cdot}1 + 0{\cdot}4 + 3a + 4b + 1 = 3{\cdot}1$$
$$3a + 4b + 1{\cdot}5 = 3{\cdot}1$$
$$3a + 4b = 1{\cdot}6$$
$$15a + 20b = 8 \quad \text{②}$$

Solving ① and ② gives $a = 0{\cdot}4$ and $b = 0{\cdot}1$.

Applications of expected value

The expected value can be used in areas such as decision-making, insurance premiums and in gambling to see if a game is fair. In gambling, a game is said to be fair if the stake (amount bet) and the expected value are equal. In a casino, the gambling games are arranged so that the casino always wins. In other words, in a casino the expected gain for a customer is always negative. However, an individual customer could walk in off the street, make one bet, win and then leave. However, over the long term the casino always wins. All forms of gambling where the expected gain is negative indicate a long-term profit for the casino.

To calculate the expected value, we need the **payout** and its **associated probability** for each outcome. Then we multiply each payout by its probability and add the results.

In short, expected value = Σ (payout)(probability).

Note: The term 'expected value' can be misleading. It is not to be confused with 'the most probable value'. The expected value is generally **not** a typical value that the random variable can take. Expected value is similar to the long-run average of many independent repetitions of the same experiment.

EXAMPLE 4

A game consists of rolling a fair six-sided die. If the outcome is 1 you win €2, if the outcome is 2 you win €4, if the outcome is 3 you win €6, and so on. It costs €8 to roll the die once. Would you play this game to win money? Justify your answer.

Solution:

The payout for each roll of the die, €2, €4, €6, €8, €10 and €12, is a random variable because its value is based on the outcome of a random event. It helps to put the information in a table.

$P(1) = P(2) = P(3) = P(4) = P(5) = P(6) = \frac{1}{6}$ (equally likely).

Outcome	1	2	3	4	5	6
Payout	2	4	6	8	10	12
Probability	$\frac{1}{6}$	$\frac{1}{6}$	$\frac{1}{6}$	$\frac{1}{6}$	$\frac{1}{6}$	$\frac{1}{6}$

Expected payout = Σ (payout)(probability)

$$= 2\left(\tfrac{1}{6}\right) + 4\left(\tfrac{1}{6}\right) + 6\left(\tfrac{1}{6}\right) + 8\left(\tfrac{1}{6}\right) + 10\left(\tfrac{1}{6}\right) + 12\left(\tfrac{1}{6}\right)$$

$$= \tfrac{1}{6}(2 + 4 + 6 + 8 + 10 + 12) = \tfrac{1}{6}(42) = €7$$

However, you have to pay €8 (the stake) to play the game.

Thus, your expected gain = €7 − €8 = −€1.

This means that in the long run you would expect to lose €1 each time you played this game. In other words, the expected value is negative (as in all casinos).

Thus, I would **not** play this game to win money.

EXAMPLE 5

In a certain country, each year one out of every 1,000 people die and two out of every 1,000 people are permanently disabled. An insurance company offers the following death or permanent disability policy that pays €100,000 when you die or €50,000 if you are permanently disabled. It charges €600 a year for this benefit. Is the company likely to make a profit selling this policy?

Solution:

To answer this question, imagine the company sells this policy to 1,000 individuals chosen at random from the population. The amount the company pays out on an individual policy, €100,000 (if you die), €50,000 (if you are permanently disabled) or €0 (if neither happens), is a random variable because its value is based on the outcome of a random event.

It helps to put the information in a table.

Outcome	Death	Disability	Neither
Payout	100,000	50,000	0
Probability	$\frac{1}{1,000}$	$\frac{2}{1,000}$	$\frac{997}{1,000}$

Expected payout = Σ(payout)(probability)

$$= 100,000\left(\tfrac{1}{1,000}\right) + 50,000\left(\tfrac{2}{1,000}\right) + 0\left(\tfrac{997}{1,000}\right) = €200$$

Thus, the total expected payout per policy is €200.

Since the company is charging €600 per policy, the company can expect to make €600 − €200 = €400 profit per policy per year (not bad).

Note: We can't predict what will happen during any given year, but we can work out what we expect to happen.

Exercise 10.13

In each of the following probability distributions for questions 1–3, find the value of p and $E(x)$.

1.

x	1	2	3
$P(x)$	p	0·5	0·2

2.

x	1	2	3	4
$P(x)$	0·1	0·3	p	0·2

3.

x	0	2	4	6	8
$P(x)$	0·1	p	0·3	p	0·2

In each of the following probability distributions for questions 4 and 5, find the value of p, $E(x)$ and $\sigma(x)$, correct to one decimal place.

4.

x	2	4	6	8
$P(x)$	0·1	0·3	0·1	p

5.

x	3	4	5	6	7
$P(x)$	0·1	p	0·4	p	0·1

6. The following table shows the probability distribution of a discrete random variable, x.

x	0	1	2	3
$P(x)$	0·3	$10\,k^2$	$4\,k$	0·2

    (i) Find the value of k. (ii) Write down the modal value.

    (iii) Calculate (a) $E(x)$ (b) $\sigma(x)$, correct to two decimal places.

7. The table shows the probability distribution for the random variable x, where $E(x) = 1·5$. Find the value of a and the value of b.

x	0	1	2	3
$P(x)$	a	0·4	0·1	b

8. The table shows the probability distribution for the random variable x, where $E(x) = 2·6$. Find the value of a and the value of b.

x	1	2	3	4
$P(x)$	0·1	a	0·5	b

9. A bag contains four red and six black discs. Two discs are removed at random from the bag. Let x denote the number of red discs in the outcome.

    (i) Show the probability distribution for x.

    (ii) Show that $\Sigma P(x) = 1$.

    (iii) Calculate $E(x)$.

    (iv) If this experiment was carried out 1,000 times, how many red discs would you expect to get?

10. In a game, two fair six-sided dice are thrown and an outcome is the sum of the two scores. One die has scores 1, 2, 3, 4, 5 and 6. The other has scores with the Fibonacci numbers 1, 2, 3, 5, 8 and 13.

    (i) What is the probability of an outcome of equal scores on both dice or a total of 6?

    (ii) Find the expected outcome for the game.

11. The warranty on your washing machine is about to expire and you are debating whether to extend the warranty for one more year at a cost of €49. The consumer association information shows that 12% of washing machines like yours require an annual repair that costs €196 on average. Would you extend the warranty? Justify your answer.

12. **(i)** On a multiple-choice test, a student is given five possible answers for each question. The student receives 4 marks for a correct answer and −1 mark for a wrong answer. If the student has no idea of the correct or incorrect answer for a particular question and has a guess at the answer, what is the student's expected gain or loss for that question?

　　(ii) Suppose that on another question the student is sure that two of the answers are wrong. If the student makes a guess at one of the three remaining answers, what is the student's expected gain or loss for that question?

13. A charity got a licence to run a raffle. There is one grand prize of €20,000 and 20 additional prizes of €500. Tickets cost €10. When you read the small print, you discover that 10,000 tickets will be sold. Shiela bought one ticket and all the tickets were sold.

　　(i) Calculate the probability that Shiela wins **(a)** the grand prize **(b)** a €500 prize **(c)** no prize.

　　(ii) Represent the situation with a probability distribution.

　　(iii) Calculate the expected value.

　　(iv) Is this a good bet? Justify your answer.

14. A newsagent sells phone cards valued at €5, €10, €20 and €30. The value, in euro, of a phone card sold may be regarded as a random variable, *x*, with the following probability distribution.

x	5	10	20	30
P(x)	0·4	0·3	*k*	0·1

　　(i) Calculate **(a)** *k* **(b)** *E(x)* **(c)** $\sigma(x)$.

　　(ii) What is the probability that the next phone card sold is €10 or €20?

　　(iii) What is the modal card sold in this newsagent?

15. A girl asks her father for some extra money. Instead of giving her the money, he offers to flip a coin. If the coin lands on a head he will give her €20. If it lands on a tail she receives nothing. Her mother hears the conversation and makes an alternative offer. She will roll a die. If the outcome is 1 she gets €3, if the outcome is 2 she gets €6, if the outcome is 3 she gets €9, and so on. If her father and mother will not both give her money, which offer should she take? Justify your answer.

16. **(i)** A game consists of spinning an unbiased five-sided spinner that can land on *A*, *B*, *C*, *D* and *E* and rolling a standard fair six-sided die. List all possible outcomes.

　　(ii) A director of a TV show decides to use this game as part of a weekly show with the following conditions for contestants:

　　　• Spinner lands on *A*, guaranteed to win €4,000. Other letters win nothing.
　　　• Die lands on 6, guaranteed to win €5,000. Other numbers win nothing.
　　　• Spinner lands on *A* **and** die lands on 6 wins a total of €18,000.

　　Find the probability that a contestant wins:

　　　(a) €18,000　　　**(b)** €5,000　　　**(c)** €4,000　　　**(d)** Nothing

(iii) The show's accountant estimates that the expected payout per contestant will be approximately €1,933. Explain how the accountant arrived at this figure.

17. On a school fundraising evening, it was proposed to organise a game of 'spin and win' to make some money. The proposal was to charge €5 to spin the wheel. The wheel has six equal sectors, as shown, and all sectors are equally likely to stop at the arrow. However, the school's Maths teacher, who loves statistics, said that this is a fair game and will win no money at all for the school.

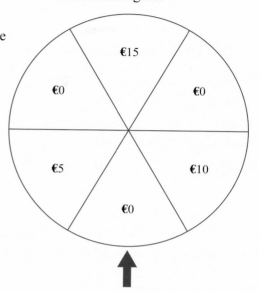

    (i) Is the Maths teacher correct? Justify your answer.

   (ii) How would you redesign the wheel so that the school would make an expected €1 for each spin?

18. The table below gives motor insurance information for fully licensed 17- to 20-year-old drivers in Ireland in 2007. All drivers who had their own insurance policy are included.

	Number of drivers	Number of claims	Average cost per claim
Male	9,634	977	€6,108
Female	6,743	581	€6,051

Questions **(i)** to **(v)** below refer to drivers in the table above only.

  (i) What is the probability that a randomly selected male driver made a claim during the year? Give your answer correct to three decimal places.

  (ii) What is the probability that a randomly selected female driver made a claim during the year? Give your answer correct to three decimal places.

 (iii) What is the expected value of the cost of claims on a male driver's policy?

 (iv) What is the expected value of the cost of claims on a female driver's policy?

  (v) The male drivers were paying an average of €1,688 for insurance in 2007 and the female drivers were paying an average of €1,024. Calculate the average surplus for each group and comment on your answer. (Note: The *surplus* is the amount paid for the policy minus the expected cost of claims.)

 (vi) A 40-year-old female driver with a full licence has a probability of 0·07 of making a claim during the year. The average cost of such claims is €3,900. How much should a company charge such drivers for insurance in order to show a surplus of €175 per policy?

Limits of functions

The phrase 'x approaches zero', written $x \to 0$, means that x can be made as close to 0 as we please without actually reaching 0.

Similarly, the phrase 'x approaches 4', written $x \to 4$, means that x can be made as close to 4 as we please without actually reaching 4.

We need the ability to be **very close to** a value when investigating expressions such as

$$\frac{4 - x^2}{x - 2}.$$

If we try to evaluate this when $x = 2$ using a calculator, we will get an error. However, we **can** evaluate the expression when x is close to 2, for example $x = 1\cdot9$ or $x = 2\cdot1$.

Definition of a limit

$$\lim_{x \to a} f(x) = L$$

means that $f(x)$ approaches the number L as x approaches a.

Note: lim is the abbreviation for limit.

When we have an expression to evaluate as $x \to a$, we will first try using $x = a$. If this fails, then we need a more subtle approach.

EXAMPLE 1

Evaluate: **(i)** $\lim_{x \to 3} \dfrac{x + 5}{x - 1}$ **(ii)** $\lim_{x \to 1} \dfrac{3x - 4}{x + 1}$

Solution:

(i) $\lim_{x \to 3} \dfrac{x + 5}{x - 1}$

$= \dfrac{3 + 5}{3 - 1}$ (put in 3 for x)

$= \dfrac{8}{2} = 4$

(ii) $\lim_{x \to 1} \dfrac{3x - 4}{x + 1}$

$= \dfrac{3(1) - 4}{1 + 1}$ (put in 1 for x)

$= \dfrac{-1}{2} = -\dfrac{1}{2}$

However, it often happens that when we try to evaluate a function for a particular value we end up with one of the following:

$$\frac{0}{0} \quad \text{or} \quad \frac{\infty}{\infty}.$$

These are called **indeterminate forms** because we cannot determine the limit directly. In other words, the expressions $\frac{0}{0}$ and $\frac{\infty}{\infty}$ are undefined.

When this happens, do the following.

> **1.** Factorise the top and bottom.
> **2.** Divide the top and bottom by the common factor(s).
> **3.** Try to evaluate the limit again.

EXAMPLE 2

Evaluate: **(i)** $\lim\limits_{x\to5}\dfrac{x^2-25}{x-5}$ **(ii)** $\lim\limits_{x\to2}\dfrac{x^3-8}{x^2-4}$

Solution:

(i) Try $\dfrac{x^2-25}{x-5}\Big|_{x=5}=\dfrac{0}{0}$. (indeterminate)

Thus, factorise the top and bottom, simplify and try again.

$$\lim_{x\to5}\frac{x^2-25}{x-5}$$
$$=\lim_{x\to5}\frac{(x-5)(x+5)}{x-5}$$
$$=\lim_{x\to5}(x+5)$$
$$=5+5=10$$

(ii) Try $\dfrac{x^3-8}{x^2-4}\Big|_{x=2}=\dfrac{0}{0}$. (indeterminate)

Thus, factorise the top and bottom, simplify and try again.

$$\lim_{x\to2}\frac{x^3-8}{x^2-4}$$
$$=\lim_{x\to2}\frac{(x-2)(x^2+2x+4)}{(x-2)(x+2)}$$
$$=\lim_{x\to2}\frac{x^2+2x+4}{x+2}$$
$$=\frac{2^2+2(2)+4}{2+2}=\frac{12}{4}=3$$

Limits at infinity

The phrase 'x **tends to infinity**', written $x\to\infty$, means that x can be made as large as we please.

Let's us consider the value of the expression $\dfrac{1}{x}$ as $x\to\infty$.

x	$\dfrac{1}{x}$
10	0·1
100	0·01
1,000	0·001
1,000,000	0·000001
1,000,000,000	0·000000001

The table indicates that as

$$x \to \infty, \qquad \frac{1}{x} \to 0.$$

This is written:

$$\lim_{x \to \infty} \frac{1}{x} = 0$$

This limit can be extended:

$$\lim_{x \to \infty} \frac{c}{x^n} = 0, \text{ for } n > 0, c \text{ is a constant.}$$

Notes: 1. Infinity is **not** a number.

2. The $\to$ symbol cannot be read as 'approaches' as it not possible to get as close as we please to infinity.

3. It is possible to consider functions of x as $x \to -\infty$.

To evaluate the limit, $\displaystyle\lim_{x \to \infty} \frac{f(x)}{g(x)}$ **do the following.**

Divide the top and bottom by the dominant term and use the limit above.

The dominant term is the largest term as $x \to \infty$.
In this section the dominant term is the highest power of x.

EXAMPLE 3

Evaluate: **(i)** $\displaystyle\lim_{x \to \infty} \frac{3x^2 - 2}{5x^2 + x}$ **(ii)** $\displaystyle\lim_{x \to \infty} \frac{5}{2 + x}$

Solution:

(i) $\displaystyle\lim_{x \to \infty} \frac{3x^2 - 2}{5x^2 + x}$

$= \displaystyle\lim_{x \to \infty} \frac{3 - \frac{2}{x^2}}{5 + \frac{1}{x}}$ $\begin{pmatrix} \text{divide top and} \\ \text{bottom by } x^2, \text{the} \\ \text{dominant term} \end{pmatrix}$

$= \dfrac{3 - 0}{5 + 0}$

$= \dfrac{3}{5}$

(ii) $\displaystyle\lim_{x \to \infty} \frac{5}{2 + x}$

$= \displaystyle\lim_{x \to \infty} \frac{\frac{5}{x}}{\frac{2}{x} + 1}$ $\begin{pmatrix} \text{divide top and} \\ \text{bottom by } x, \text{the} \\ \text{dominant term} \end{pmatrix}$

$= \dfrac{0}{0 + 1}$

$= \dfrac{0}{1} = 0$

Exponential functions

Consider the three functions $f(x) = 2\left(\frac{1}{2}\right)^x$, $g(x) = \left(-\frac{1}{4}\right)^x$ and $h(x) = 3(2)^x$ as $x \to \infty$.

x	$f(x) = 2\left(\frac{1}{2}\right)^x$	$g(x) = \left(-\frac{1}{4}\right)^x$	$h(x) = 3(2)^x$
5	0·0625	−0·0009765625	96
10	0·001953125	0·00000095367	3,072
15	0·00006103515	−0·00000000093	98,304
20	0·000001907	≈ 0	3,145,728
25	0·0000000596	≈ 0	100,663,296

As we can see, some exponential functions tend toward zero while others increase rapidly. Functions of x which have a limit **must** approach a finite number as $x \to \infty$. Those which do not, have **no limit**.

A function of the form $f(x) = ab^x$ may have a limit as $x \to \infty$.

Value of b	$\lim\limits_{x\to\infty} ab^x$	Example
$b \le -1$	No limit	$f(x) = 4(-2)^x$
$-1 < b < 1$	0	$f(x) = 2\left(\frac{2}{3}\right)^x$
$b = 1$	a	$f(x) = 7(1)^x$
$b > 1$	No limit	$f(x) = 5\left(\frac{3}{2}\right)^x$

The most important of these results is: $\lim\limits_{x\to\infty} ab^x = 0$, for $-1 < b < 1$

Exercise 11.1

In questions 1–36, evaluate the limit.

1. $\lim\limits_{x\to 0}(5x + 3)$

2. $\lim\limits_{x\to 3}(2x^2 - 10)$

3. $\lim\limits_{x\to 2}\dfrac{x^2 + 5x + 6}{x + 2}$

4. $\lim\limits_{x\to 3}\dfrac{x^2 - 9}{x + 3}$

5. $\lim\limits_{x\to 2}\dfrac{x^2 + x - 6}{x - 2}$

6. $\lim\limits_{x\to 1}\dfrac{x - 1}{x^2 + x - 2}$

7. $\lim\limits_{x\to 2}\dfrac{x^2 - 4}{x - 2}$

8. $\lim\limits_{x\to 1}\dfrac{x^2 - 1}{x - 1}$

9. $\lim\limits_{x\to 6}\dfrac{x^2 - 36}{x - 6}$

10. $\lim\limits_{x\to 4}\dfrac{x - 4}{x^2 - 16}$

11. $\lim\limits_{x\to 2}\dfrac{x^3 - 8}{x - 2}$

12. $\lim\limits_{x\to 3}\dfrac{x - 3}{x^3 - 27}$

13. $\lim\limits_{x \to 2} \dfrac{x^2 - 2x}{x - 2}$

14. $\lim\limits_{x \to 4} \dfrac{x^3 - 64}{x^2 - 16}$

15. $\lim\limits_{x \to 0} \dfrac{3x^2 + x}{x}$

16. $\lim\limits_{x \to -2} \dfrac{x^2 - 4}{x + 2}$

17. $\lim\limits_{x \to 4} \dfrac{x^2 + x - 20}{x - 4}$

18. $\lim\limits_{x \to -1} \dfrac{2x^2 + 7x + 5}{x + 1}$

19. $\lim\limits_{x \to 3} \dfrac{27 - x^3}{3 - x}$

20. $\lim\limits_{x \to 2} \dfrac{8 - x^3}{4 - x^2}$

21. $\lim\limits_{x \to -1} \dfrac{x + 1}{x^2 - 1}$

22. $\lim\limits_{x \to \frac{1}{2}} \dfrac{4x^2 - 1}{2x - 1}$

23. $\lim\limits_{x \to \infty} \dfrac{2x - 1}{x + 1}$

24. $\lim\limits_{x \to \infty} \dfrac{4x + 3}{3x + 5}$

25. $\lim\limits_{x \to \infty} \dfrac{1 + 2x}{3x - 4}$

26. $\lim\limits_{x \to \infty} \dfrac{4x^2 - 3x}{5x^2 - 2}$

27. $\lim\limits_{x \to \infty} \dfrac{3x^2 - 2x + 1}{2x^2 + 5x - 7}$

28. $\lim\limits_{x \to \infty} \dfrac{x^2 + 1}{1 + 2x^3}$

29. $\lim\limits_{x \to \infty} 3\left(\dfrac{1}{2}\right)^x$

30. $\lim\limits_{x \to \infty} 2\left(\dfrac{1}{3}\right)^x$

31. $\lim\limits_{x \to \infty} 7(2)^x$

32. $\lim\limits_{x \to \infty} \left(\dfrac{3}{4}\right)^x$

33. $\lim\limits_{x \to \infty} 4\left(\dfrac{3}{2}\right)^x$

34. $\lim\limits_{x \to \infty} 2\left(-\dfrac{2}{5}\right)^x$

35. $\lim\limits_{x \to \infty} 5(0{\cdot}4)^x$

36. $\lim\limits_{x \to \infty} 3(\pi)^x$

37. $f(x) = 8\left(\dfrac{1}{2}\right)^x$

    (i) Sketch the graph of $y = f(x)$ for $0 \le x \le 5$.   **(ii)** Describe the behaviour of the curve as $x \to \infty$.   **(iii)** Evaluate $\lim\limits_{x \to \infty} 8\left(\dfrac{1}{2}\right)^x$.

38. $f(x) = (-2)^x$

    (i) Plot points on $y = f(x)$ for $0 \le x \le 4$, $x \in \mathbb{Z}$ and join them with line segments.

    (ii) Describe the behaviour of the curve as $x \to \infty$ and hence explain why $\lim\limits_{x \to \infty} (-2)^x$ does not exist.

Limits of trigonometric functions

Let's consider the value of the expression $\dfrac{\sin \theta}{\theta}$ as θ approaches 0 (θ in radians).

θ (in radians)	$\sin \theta$	$\dfrac{\sin \theta}{\theta}$
1	0·8414709848	0·8414709848
0·5	0·4794255386	0·9588510772
0·1	0·0998334166	0·9983341665
0·01	0·0099998333	0·9999833334
0·001	0·0009999998	0·9999998333

As θ approaches 0, the expression $\dfrac{\sin \theta}{\theta}$ approaches 1.

This is written:

$$\lim_{\theta \to 0} \frac{\sin \theta}{\theta} = 1, \ \theta \text{ in radians}$$

It follows that:

$$\lim_{\theta \to 0} \frac{\theta}{\sin \theta} = 1, \ \theta \text{ in radians}$$

The result can be extended to multiple angles:

$$\lim_{\theta \to 0} \frac{\sin k\theta}{k\theta} = 1, \theta \quad \text{and} \quad \lim_{\theta \to 0} \frac{k\theta}{\sin k\theta} = 1, k \in \mathbb{R}$$

Similarly, where θ is in radians:

$$\lim_{\theta \to 0} \frac{\tan k\theta}{k\theta} = 1, \theta \quad \text{and} \quad \lim_{\theta \to 0} \frac{k\theta}{\tan k\theta} = 1, k \in \mathbb{R}$$

Note: Since $\cos 0 = 1$, it follows that $\lim\limits_{\theta \to 0} \cos \theta = 1$.

EXAMPLE 1

Evaluate: **(i)** $\lim\limits_{\theta \to 0} \dfrac{\sin 4\theta + \sin 2\theta}{\theta}$ **(ii)** $\lim\limits_{\theta \to 0} \dfrac{\tan 4\theta}{5\theta}$

Solution:

(i)

$$\frac{\sin 4\theta + \sin 2\theta}{\theta}$$

$$= \frac{\sin 4\theta}{\theta} + \frac{\sin 2\theta}{\theta}$$

$$= 4\left(\frac{\sin 4\theta}{4\theta}\right) + 2\left(\frac{\sin 2\theta}{2\theta}\right)$$

$$\therefore \lim_{\theta \to 0} \frac{\sin 4\theta + \sin 2\theta}{\theta}$$

$$= 4\left(\lim_{\theta \to 0}\left(\frac{\sin 4\theta}{4\theta}\right)\right) + 2\left(\lim_{\theta \to 0}\left(\frac{\sin 2\theta}{2\theta}\right)\right)$$

$$= 4(1) + 2(1)$$

$$= 6$$

(ii)

$$\frac{\tan 4\theta}{5\theta} = \frac{\tan 4\theta}{\theta} \times \frac{1}{5}$$

$$= \frac{\tan 4\theta}{4\theta} \times \frac{4}{5}$$

$$\therefore \lim_{\theta \to 0} \frac{\tan 4\theta}{5\theta} = \frac{4}{5}\left(\lim_{\theta \to 0} \frac{\tan 4\theta}{4\theta}\right)$$

$$= \frac{4}{5}(1)$$

$$= \frac{4}{5}$$

Sometimes we have to change sums and differences of trigonometric functions to products (using page 15 of the booklet of formulae and tables).

EXAMPLE 2

Evaluate $\lim\limits_{x \to 0} \dfrac{\cos 5x - \cos 3x}{\cos 4x - \cos 2x}$.

Solution:

From page 15 of the booklet of formulae and tables:

$$\cos A - \cos B = -2\sin \frac{A+B}{2} \sin \frac{A-B}{2}$$

$$\frac{\cos 5x - \cos 3x}{\cos 4x - \cos 2x} = \frac{-2\sin\left(\dfrac{5x+3x}{2}\right)\sin\left(\dfrac{5x-3x}{2}\right)}{-2\sin\left(\dfrac{4x+2x}{2}\right)\sin\left(\dfrac{4x-2x}{2}\right)}$$

$$= \frac{-2\sin 4x \sin x}{-2\sin 3x \sin x}$$

$$= \frac{\sin 4x}{\sin 3x}$$

$\lim\limits_{x \to 0} \dfrac{\sin 4x}{\sin 3x}$

$$= \lim\limits_{x \to 0}\left(\frac{\sin 4x}{1} \times \frac{1}{\sin 3x}\right)$$

$$= \lim\limits_{x \to 0}\left(\frac{\sin 4x}{4x} \times \frac{3x}{\sin 3x} \times \frac{4}{3}\right)$$

$$= 1 \times 1 \times \frac{4}{3}$$

$$= \frac{4}{3}$$

Exercise 11.2

In questions 1–21, evaluate the limit.

1. $\lim\limits_{x \to 0} \dfrac{\sin 3x}{x}$

2. $\lim\limits_{x \to 0} \dfrac{\sin 5x}{x}$

3. $\lim\limits_{x \to 0} \dfrac{x}{\sin 2x}$

4. $\lim\limits_{x \to 0} \dfrac{x}{\sin 4x}$

5. $\lim\limits_{x \to 0} \dfrac{\sin 3x}{4x}$

6. $\lim\limits_{x \to 0} \dfrac{\sin 3x}{\sin 2x}$

7. $\lim\limits_{x \to 0} \dfrac{\tan 8x}{x}$

8. $\lim\limits_{x \to 0} \dfrac{\tan 6x}{2x}$

9. $\lim\limits_{x \to 0} \dfrac{\sin^2 x}{2x^2}$

10. $\lim\limits_{x \to 0} \dfrac{\sin^2 x}{3x^2}$

11. $\lim\limits_{x \to 0} \dfrac{\sin x \tan x}{x^2}$

12. $\lim\limits_{x \to 0} \dfrac{\tan^2 2x}{3x^2}$

13. $\lim\limits_{x \to 0} \dfrac{\sin 4x + \sin 2x}{x}$

14. $\lim\limits_{x \to 0} \dfrac{\sin 8x - \sin 2x}{x}$

15. $\lim\limits_{x \to 0} \dfrac{\cos 4x - \cos 2x}{\cos 5x - \cos 3x}$

16. $\lim\limits_{x \to 0} \dfrac{x \sin x}{\sin 3x + \sin x}$

17. $\lim\limits_{x \to 0} \dfrac{\sin 3x \tan 2x}{x^2}$

18. $\lim\limits_{x \to 0} \dfrac{4x}{\sin 4x + \sin 2x}$

19. $\lim\limits_{x \to 0} \dfrac{\sin x^2}{x \tan x}$

20. $\lim\limits_{x \to 0} \dfrac{x \sin 2x}{2 - 2\cos^2 x}$

21. $\lim\limits_{x \to 0} \dfrac{x \sin x}{1 - \cos x}$

22. (i) Prove that $\cos 2x = 1 - 2\sin^2 x$.

    (ii) Hence, show that $\lim\limits_{x \to 0} \dfrac{2x^2}{1 - \cos x} = 4$.

FUNCTIONS

Terminology and notation

In the real world there are many relationships in which one thing depends on another. For example, a golf score depends on the number of hours of practice. In mathematics, we use functions to express these ideas. A function is a rule that changes input into output. For example, a computer can change a bar code into a price. This can be written as an ordered pair (bar code, price). A relation is any set of ordered pairs. A function is defined as a set of ordered pairs (a relation) in which no two ordered pairs have the same first element.

> A function must give exactly one **unique** output for each input.

In other words, if the same input is put into a function then the same unique output must come out. Consider if two people are standing in a queue to pay for the same product, with the same bar code. If the **same** bar code produced a **different** price, then the machine is not acting as a function.

Functions are often represented by the letters f, g, h or k. We can think of a function, f, as a number machine which changes an input, x, into an output, $f(x)$.

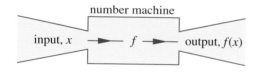

$f(x)$, which denotes the output, is read as 'f of x'.

For example, let's represent the function 'double input and then add 5' by the letter f.
This can be written as:

$$f : x \rightarrow 2x + 5 \quad \text{or} \quad f(x) = 2x + 5 \quad \text{or} \quad y = 2x + 5$$
$$(\text{input, output}) = (x, f(x)) = (x, 2x + 5) = (x, y)$$

Note: A **function** is also called a **mapping** or simply a **map**.

The set of input numbers is called the **domain**. The set of output numbers is called the **range**.

The set of **all possible outputs** is called the **codomain**.
In general, the range is a subset of the codomain. However, sometimes the range and the codomain are the same.

Consider the function f shown:
$f = \{(1, a), (2, b), (3, d), (4, d)\}$
from set X to set Y.

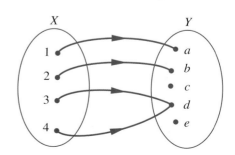

Domain: The set of elements from which the arrows leave: $\{1, 2, 3, 4\}$.

Range: The set of elements where the arrows arrive: $\{a, b, d\}$.

Codomain: The **possible** set of elements into which the arrows go: $\{a, b, c, d, e\}$.

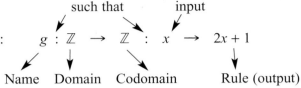

Consider the function:

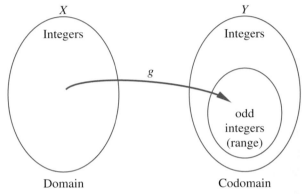

The function g maps the set of **integers**, the domain, onto the set of **odd integers**, the range. The set of odd integers is a subset of the integers.

Consider the graph on the right.

The domain of $f(x)$ is the set of x values used by the graph.

Domain: $-3 \leq x \leq 10$.

The range of $f(x)$ is the set of y values used by the graph.

Range: $-2 \leq y \leq 4$.

For a function, each value in the domain has exactly one image in the range. It can help to see the domain and range if the portion of the graph under consideration is enclosed in a rectangle (red rectangle shown).

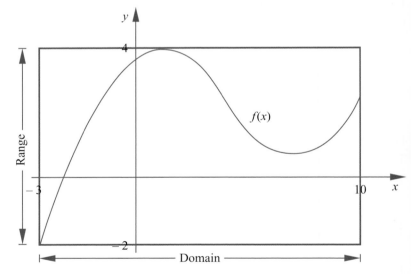

Graph test

A simple test can be performed on a graph to decide whether or not it represents a function within a given domain. If any vertical line cuts the graph at only one point, then the graph represents a function. If any vertical line cuts the graph at more than one point, then the graph does not represent a function.

Note: All mathematical graphs are read from left to right.

Graphing linear, quadratic and cubic functions

Linear functions

A **linear** function is usually given in the form $f : x \rightarrow ax + b$, where $a, b \in \mathbb{Q}, x \in \mathbb{R}$.
To graph a linear function, only two points are needed.

1. $a > 0$ 2. $a = 0$ 3. $a < 0$

Quadratic functions

A **quadratic** function is usually given by $f : x \rightarrow ax^2 + bx + c$, where $a, b, c \in \mathbb{Q}, x \in \mathbb{R}$ and $a \neq 0$.
Because of its shape, quite a few points are needed to graph a quadratic function.

1. $a > 0$ 2. $a < 0$

 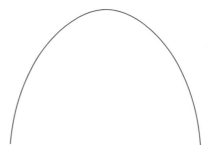

Cubic functions

A **cubic** function is usually given by $f : x \rightarrow ax^3 + bx^2 + cx + d$, where $a, b, c, d \in \mathbb{Z}, x \in \mathbb{R}$ and $a \neq 0$.
Because of its shape, quite a few points are needed to graph a cubic function.

1. $a > 0$ 2. $a < 0$

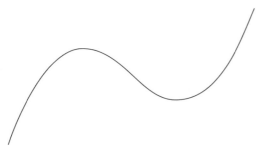

3. $a > 0$

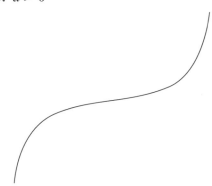

4. $a < 0$

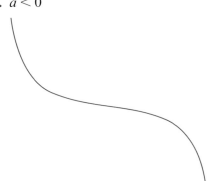

Using graphs

Once we have drawn the graph, we are usually asked to use it to answer some questions. Below are examples of the general types of problem where graphs are used.

Notes: 1. $y = f(x)$, so $f(x)$ can be replaced by y.
       2. In general, if given x find y, and vice versa.
       3. On the x-axis $y = 0$ ($y = 0$ is the equation of the x-axis).
       4. On the y-axis $x = 0$ ($x = 0$ is the equation of the y-axis).

Examples of the main types of problem, once the graph is drawn.

EXAMPLE 1

Find the values of x for which $f(x) = 0$.
This question is asking:
'Where does the curve meet the x-axis?'

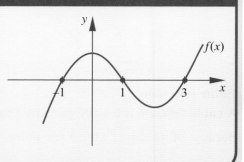

Solution:
Write down the values of x where the graph meets the x-axis.
From the graph: $x = -1$ or $x = 1$ or $x = 3$.

EXAMPLE 2

Find the values of x for which $f(x) = 6$.

This question is asking:

'When $y = 6$, what are the values of x?'

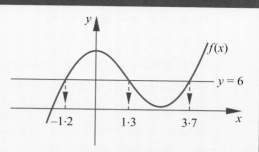

Solution:

Draw the line $y = 6$. Where this line meets the curve, draw broken perpendicular lines onto the x-axis.

Write down the values of x where these broken lines meet the x-axis.

From the graph:

When $y = 6$, $x = -1\cdot2$ or $x = 1\cdot3$ or $x = 3\cdot7$.

EXAMPLE 3

Find the value of $f(-1\cdot6)$.

This question is asking:

'When $x = -1\cdot6$, what is the value of y?'

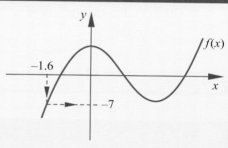

Solution:

From $x = -1\cdot6$ on the x-axis, draw a broken perpendicular line to meet the curve. From this draw a broken horizontal line to meet the y-axis.

Write down the value of y where this line meets the y-axis.

From the graph: $f(-1\cdot6) = -7$.

EXAMPLE 4

Local maximum and minimum points or the local maximum and minimum values

Often we are asked to find the local maximum and minimum points or the local maximum and minimum values. Consider the graph on the right. The local maximum and minimum points are where the graph turns, at $(1, 4)$ and $(4, -2)$, respectively. The local maximum and minimum values are

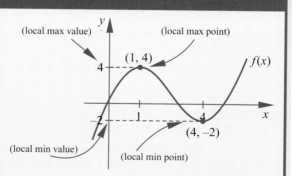

found by drawing a line from the turning points to the y-axis and reading the values where these lines meet the y-axis. The maximum and minimum values are 4 and -2, respectively.

EXAMPLE 5

Increasing and decreasing
Graphs are read from left to right.

Increasing: $f(x)$ is increasing where the graph is **rising** as we go from left to right.

Decreasing: $f(x)$ is decreasing where the graph is **falling** as we go from left to right.

Find the values of x for which:
(i) $f(x)$ is increasing
(ii) $f(x)$ is decreasing

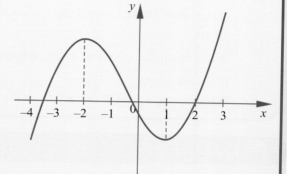

Solution:
(i) $f(x)$ increasing, graph rising from left to right.
   The values of x are
   $-4 \leq x < -2$ and $1 < x \leq 3$.
(ii) $f(x)$ decreasing, graph falling from left to right.
   The values of x are $-2 < x < 1$.

Note: At $x = -2$ and $x = 1$, the graph is neither increasing nor decreasing.

EXAMPLE 6

Positive and negative
Positive, $f(x) > 0$: Where the graph is **above** the x-axis.

Negative, $f(x) < 0$: Where the graph is **below** the x-axis.

Find the values of x for which:
(i) $f(x) > 0$ (ii) $f(x) < 0$.

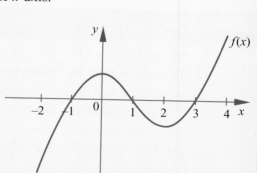

Solution:
(i) $f(x) > 0$, curve **above** the x-axis.
   The values of x are
   $-1 < x < 1$ and $3 < x \leq 4$.
(ii) $f(x) < 0$, curve **below** the x-axis.
   The values of x are
   $-2 \leq x < -1$ and $1 < x < 3$.
Note: If the question uses $f(x) \geq 0$ or $f(x) \leq 0$, then the values of x where the graph meets the x-axis must also be included.

EXAMPLE 7

Two functions graphed on the same axes and scales

The diagram shows the graph of two functions: $f(x)$, a curve, and $g(x)$, a line.

Find the values of x for which:

(i) $f(x) = g(x)$ **(ii)** $f(x) \leq g(x)$ **(iii)** $f(x) \geq g(x)$

Solution:

(i) $f(x) = g(x)$

(curve = line)

The values of x are 0·4, 1·4 and 3·1.

(ii) $f(x) \leq g(x)$

(curve equal to and below the line)

The values of x are

$-1 \leq x \leq 0\cdot4$ and $1\cdot4 \leq x \leq 3\cdot1$.

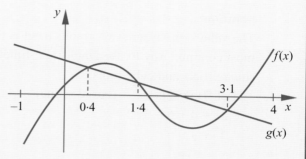

(iii) $f(x) \geq g(x)$

(curve equal to and above the line)

The values of x are:

$0\cdot4 \leq x \leq 1\cdot4$ and $3\cdot1 \leq x \leq 4$.

Note: If the question uses $f(x) < g(x)$ or $f(x) > g(x)$, then the values of x where the graphs meet (0·4, 1·4 and 3·1) are **not** included in the solution.

EXAMPLE 8

Graph above or below a constant value (an inequality)

Find the values of x for which: **(i)** $f(x) \geq 2$ **(ii)** $f(x) \leq 2$

These questions are asking:

'What are the values of x for which the curve, $f(x)$, is **(i)** 2 or above **(ii)** 2 or below?'

Solution:

Draw the line $y = 2$.

Write down the values of x for which the curve is:

(i) On or above the line $y = 2$

(ii) On or below the line $y = 2$

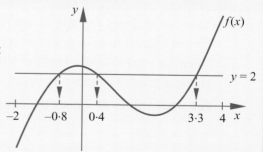

(i) $f(x) \geq 2$, curve on or above the line $y = 2$.

The values of x are:

$-0\cdot8 \leq x \leq 0\cdot4$ and $3\cdot3 \leq x \leq 4$.

(ii) $f(x) \leq 2$, curve on or below the line $y = 2$.

The values of x are:

$-2 \leq x \leq -0\cdot8$ and $0\cdot4 \leq x \leq 3\cdot3$.

Note: If the question uses $f(x) > 2$ or $f(x) < 2$, then the values of x where the curve meets the line $y = 2$ (−0·8, 0·4 and 3·3) are **not** included in the solution.

EXAMPLE 9

Using two graphs to estimate square roots and cube roots

The diagram shows graphs of the functions:

$f : x \rightarrow x^3 - 3x + 4$ and $g : x \rightarrow 6 - 3x$, in the domain $-2 \leq x \leq 3$.

Show how the graphs may be used to estimate the value of $\sqrt[3]{2}$.

Solution:

The values of x where two graphs meet is the most common way to use graphs to estimate square roots and cube roots.

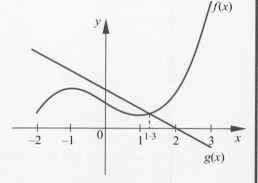

Let $f(x) = g(x)$.   (curve = line)

$$x^3 - 3x + 4 = 6 - 3x$$
$$x^3 + 4 = 6$$
$$x^3 = 2$$
$$x = \sqrt[3]{2}$$

Hence, where the two graphs meet can be used to estimate the value of $\sqrt[3]{2}$.

Where the two graphs intersect, draw a broken line to meet the x-axis.

This line meets the x-axis at 1·3.

Thus, using the graphs, we estimate the value of $\sqrt[3]{2}$ to be 1·3.

Note: A calculator gives $\sqrt[3]{2} = 1·25992104989$.

EXAMPLE 10

Number of times a graph meets the x-axis

The number of times a graph meets the x-axis gives the number of roots of its equation. Often we need to find a range of values of a constant, which shifts a graph up or down, giving a graph a certain number of roots. For example:

For what values of k does the equation $f(x) = k$ have three roots?

Solution:

The equation $f(x) = k$ will have three roots if the line $y = k$ cuts the graph three times. So we have to draw lines parallel to the x-axis that cut the graph three times. The range of values of k will be in between the lowest and highest values on the y-axis, so that the line $y = k$ cuts the graph three times.

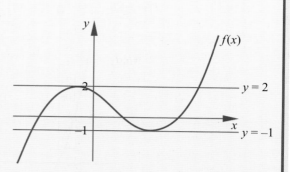

Question: Find the range of values of k for which $f(x) = k$ has three roots.

The range of values of k is found by finding the range of the equations of the lines parallel to the x-axis which cut the graph three times.

Any lines drawn parallel to the y-axis between $y = -1$ and $y = 2$ will cut the graph three times.

$\therefore$ k will lie between -1 and 2.

$\therefore$ $f(x) = k$ will have three roots for $-1 < k < 2$.

EXAMPLE 11

Graph the function $f : x \rightarrow 2 - 9x + 6x^2 - x^3$ in the domain $-1 \leq x \leq 5$, where $x \in \mathbb{R}$.
Use your graph to estimate:

  (i) The values of x for which $f(x) = 0$

  (ii) $f(-0\cdot5)$

  (iii) The values of x for which $f(x) > 0$ and is increasing

  (iv) The range of real values of k for which $f(x) = k$ has more than one solution

Solution:

Let $y = f(x) \Rightarrow y = 2 - 9x + 6x^2 - x^3$

x	$-x^3 +$	$6x^2 -$	$9x + 2$	y
-1	$+\ \ 1+$	6	$+\ 9\ +2$	18
0	$+\ \ 0+$	0	$+\ 0\ +2$	2
1	$-\ \ 1+$	6	$-\ 9\ +2$	-2
2	$-\ \ 8+$	24	$-18\ +2$	0
3	$-27+$	54	$-27\ +2$	2
4	$-64+$	96	$-36\ +2$	-2
5	$-125+$	150	$-45\ +2$	-18

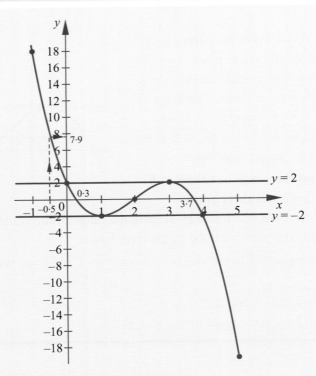

(i) **Estimate the values of x for which $f(x) = 0$.**

This question is asking, 'Where does the curve meet the x-axis?'

The curve meets the x-axis at 0·3, 2 and 3·7.

Therefore, the values of x for which $f(x) = 0$ are 0·3, 2 and 3·7.

Note: 'Find the values of x for which $2 - 9x + 6x^2 - x^3 = 0$' is another way of asking the same question.

(ii) **Estimate the value of $f(-0·5)$.**

This question is asking, 'When $x = -0·5$, what is the value of y?'

From $x = -0·5$ on the x-axis, draw a broken perpendicular line to meet the curve. From this draw a broken horizontal line to meet the y-axis.

This line meets the y-axis at 7·9.

Therefore, $f(-0·5) = 7·9$.

(iii) **Estimate the values of x for which $f(x) > 0$ and is increasing.**

This question is asking, 'Where is the curve above the x-axis and increasing as we go from left to right?' From the graph, the curve is above the x-axis and increasing between 2 and 3. Therefore, the values of x for which $f(x) > 0$ and are increasing are $2 < x < 3$.

Note: $x = 2$ is not included because at $x = 2$, $f(x) = 0$ and we are given $f(x) > 0$.

$x = 3$ is not included because at $x = 3$ there is a turning point and $f(x)$ is not increasing.

(iv) Estimate the range of real values of k for which $f(x) = k$ has more than one solution.

The range of values of k is found by drawing lines parallel to the x-axis that meet the graph more than once.

Any lines drawn parallel to the x-axis between -2 and 2 will meet the curve more than once. Therefore, k will lie between -2 and 2, including -2 and 2.

Therefore, $f(x) = k$ will have more than one solution when $-2 \leq k \leq 2$.

EXAMPLE 12

$f(x) = x^2 - 6x + 2$, where $x \in \mathbb{R}$.

  (i) Express $f(x)$ in the form $(x - a)^2 + b$.

 (ii) Hence, find the minimum point of $f(x)$.

(iii) Sketch $f(x)$ and state its range.

Solution:

(i) $x^2 - 6x + 2$ (half the coefficient of $x = -3$)

      $= x^2 - 6x + 9 + 2 - 9$ (add and subtract $(-3)^2 = 9$)

      $= (x - 3)(x - 3) - 7$ $(x^2 - 6x + 9 = (x - 3)(x - 3))$

      $= (x - 3)^2 - 7$ (in the form $(x - a)^2 + b$)

(ii) Minimum value of $(x - 3)^2 - 7$

occurs when $(x - 3) = 0$.

$x - 3 = 0$

    $x = 3$

$\therefore$ Minimum value $= -7$ and the minimum point is $(3, -7)$.

Note: $x = 3$ is an axis of symmetry of the graph of $f(x)$.

(iii)

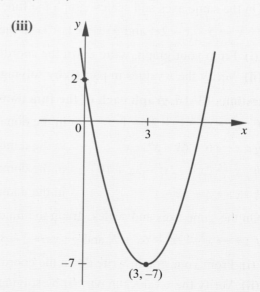

Range: $y \geq -7$, where $y \in \mathbb{R}$.

Exercise 12.1

In questions 1–6, graph each of the functions in the given domain.

1. $f : x \rightarrow 2x + 3$ in the domain $-2 \leq x \leq 3,$ where $x \in \mathbb{R}$.

2. $g : x \rightarrow -3x + 2$ in the domain $-3 \leq x \leq 2,$ where $x \in \mathbb{R}$.

3. $h : x \rightarrow 5$ in the domain $-1 \leq x \leq 4,$ where $x \in \mathbb{R}$.

4. $k : x \rightarrow -x$ in the domain $-3 \leq x \leq 3,$ where $x \in \mathbb{R}$.

5. $f : x \rightarrow \frac{1}{2}x$ in the domain $-2 \leq x \leq 4,$ where $x \in \mathbb{R}$.

6. $g : x \rightarrow \frac{1}{3}x + 1$ in the domain $-3 \leq x \leq 3,$ where $x \in \mathbb{R}$.

7. Using the same axes and scales, graph the functions:

$f : x \rightarrow 2x - 1$ and $g : x \rightarrow 2 - x$ in the domain $-2 \leq x \leq 3,$ $x \in \mathbb{R}$.

  (i) From your graph, write down the coordinates of the point of intersection of f and g.

  (ii) Verify your answer to part **(i)** by solving the simultaneous equations

     $2x - y = 1$ and $x + y = 2$.

In questions 8–11, graph each of the functions in the given domain.

8. $h : x \rightarrow x^2 - 2x - 8$ in the domain $-3 \leq x \leq 5,$ where $x \in \mathbb{R}$.

9. $k : x \rightarrow 5 + 4x - x^2$ in the domain $-2 \leq x \leq 6,$ where $x \in \mathbb{R}$.

10. $f : x \rightarrow 2x^2 - x - 4$ in the domain $-2 \leq x \leq 3,$ where $x \in \mathbb{R}$.

11. $g : x \rightarrow 3 + 5x - x^2$ in the domain $-2 \leq x \leq 7,$ where $x \in \mathbb{R}$.

12. On the same axes and scales, graph the functions

$f : x \rightarrow 5 - x - 2x^2$ and $g : x \rightarrow 1 - 3x$ in the domain $-3 \leq x \leq 3,$ $x \in \mathbb{R}$.

  (i) From your graph, write down the coordinates of the points of intersection of f and g.

  (ii) Verify the x values in part **(i)** by solving the equation $g(x) = f(x)$.

In questions 13–16, graph each of the functions in the given domain.

13. $f : x \rightarrow x^3 + x^2 - 2x - 1$ in the domain $-3 \leq x \leq 2,$ where $x \in \mathbb{R}$.

14. $g : x \rightarrow 6 + 6x - x^2 - x^3$ in the domain $-3 \leq x \leq 3,$ where $x \in \mathbb{R}$.

15. $h : x \rightarrow 2x^3 - 2x^2 - 3x + 10$ in the domain $-2 \leq x \leq 2,$ where $x \in \mathbb{R}$.

16. $k : x \rightarrow 3 + 5x - x^3$ in the domain $-3 \leq x \leq 3,$ where $x \in \mathbb{R}$.

17. On the same axes and scales, graph the functions

$f : x \rightarrow x^3 - 2x^2 - 6x + 2,$ and $g : x \rightarrow 2 - 3x$ in the domain $-2 \leq x \leq 4,$ where $x \in \mathbb{R}$.

  (i) From your graph, write down the coordinates of the points of intersection of f and g.

  (ii) Verify the x values in part **(i)** by solving the equation $f(x) = g(x)$.

18. On the same axes and scales, graph the functions

$f : x \rightarrow x^3 + 3x^2 - x - 3$ and $g : x \rightarrow 3 - 2x - x^2$ in the domain $-4 \le x \le 2$, where $x \in \mathbb{R}$.

(i) From your graph, write down the coordinates of the points of intersection of f and g.

(ii) Verify the x values in part (i) by solving the equation $f(x) = g(x)$.

19. For each of these graphs, state the domain and range.

(i)

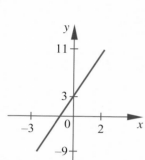

(ii)

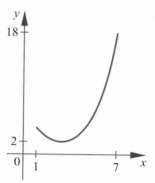

(iii)

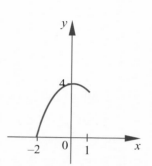

20. $f(x) = x^2 - 2x + 6$, where $x \in \mathbb{R}$.

(i) Express $f(x)$ in the form $(x - a)^2 + b$.

(ii) Hence, find the minimum value of $f(x)$ and state the range of $f(x)$.

21. $g(x) = 1 - 6x - x^2$, where $x \in \mathbb{R}$.

(i) Express $f(x)$ in the form $p - (x - q)^2$.

(ii) Hence, find the maximum point on $f(x)$ and state the range of $f(x)$.

22. Each of the following functions have domain $x \in \mathbb{R}$. In each case, find, by completing the square, the maximum point or the minimum point and distinguish between them. Hence, state the range of each function.

(i) $f(x) = x^2 + 4x + 7$ (ii) $g(x) = x^2 - 6x + 2$ (iii) $h(x) = x^2 + 2x$

(iv) $k(x) = -4 - 6x - x^2$ (v) $f(x) = 3 - 8x - x^2$ (vi) $g(x) = 4x - x^2$

23. $f(x) = \sqrt{x^2 - 9}$, where $x \in \mathbb{R}$. Find the domain of f.

24. The graph of the quadratic function

$g : x \rightarrow ax^2 + bx - 3$, where $x \in \mathbb{R}$, is shown.

(i) Write down the value of p.

(ii) Find the values of a and b.

(iii) Hence, calculate the values of h and k.

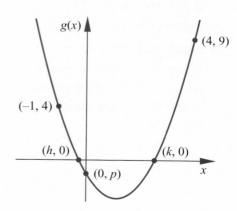

25. The graph of the quadratic function
$f : x \rightarrow x^2 + bx + c$, where $x \in \mathbb{R}$, is shown.

   (i) Find the values of b and c.

   (ii) Hence, find the values of k, l and m.

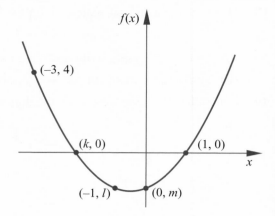

26. The graph of the function
$f : x \rightarrow ax^3 + bx^2 + cx + d$,
where $x \in \mathbb{R}$, is shown.

   (i) Write down the value
of d.

   (ii) Find the values of a, b
and c.

   (iii) Hence, calculate the
values of p, q and r.

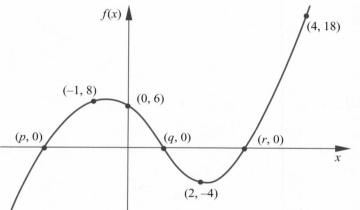

27. The diagram shows the sketches
of four functions, $f(x)$, $g(x)$,
$h(x)$ and $k(x)$, for $x \in \mathbb{R}$.

$f(x) = x^2(1 - x)$
$g(x) = (x^2 + 1)(2 - x)$
$h(x) = x(x - 1)(x - 2)$
$k(x) = (x^2 + 1)(x - 1)$

Match each function with its
graph and in each case find
the coordinates of the points
where each graph meets the
axes.

1.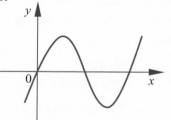

2.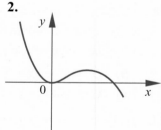

3.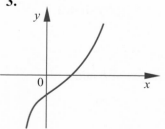

4.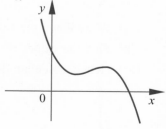

28. Below is a graph of the function $f : x \rightarrow x^3 - 3x^2 + 4$ in the domain $-2 \leq x \leq 4$, where $x \in \mathbb{R}$.

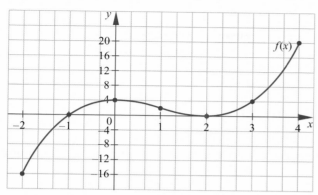

Use your graph to:

(i) Find the values of x for which $f(x) = 0$

(ii) Find the coordinates of the local maximum and minimum points of f

(iii) Find the local maximum and minimum values

(iv) Estimate the value of $f(3.5)$

(v) Find the values of x for which $f(x)$ is decreasing

(vi) Find the values of x for which $f(x)$ is increasing

(vii) Find the values of x for which $f(x) < 0$ and is increasing

(viii) Find the values of k for which $f(x) = k$ has three solutions

(ix) Estimate the values of x for which **(a)** $f(x) = 2$ **(b)** $f(x) \geq 2$

29. Let $f(x) = 2x^3 - 3x^2 - 12x + 4$ for $x \in \mathbb{R}$.

(i) Complete the table.

x	-2.5	-2	-1	0	1	2	3	3.5
$f(x)$	-16							11

(ii) Draw the graph of $f(x)$ in the domain $-2.5 \leq x \leq 3.5$, where $x \in \mathbb{R}$.

(iii) Write down the coordinates of the local maximum and the local minimum points.

(iv) Use your graph to find the values of x for which $f(x)$ is:

(a) increasing (b) decreasing (c) positive and increasing and $x < 0$.

(v) Estimate the values of x for which $f(x) = 0$.

30. On the same axes and scales, graph the functions

$f : x \rightarrow x^3 - 2x^2 - 6x + 4$ and $g : x \rightarrow 2x - 5$ in the domain $-2 \leq x \leq 4$, where $x \in \mathbb{R}$.

Use your graphs to find:

(i) The two values of x for which $f(x) = g(x)$

(ii) The range of values of x for which $f(x) \leq g(x)$

(iii) The range of values of x for which $f(x) \geq g(x)$

31. Let $f(x) = x^3 + 2x^2 - 7x - 2$ for $x \in \mathbb{R}$.

   (i) Complete the following table.

x	−4	−3	−2	−1	0	1	2	3
f(x)		10				−6		

   (ii) Draw the graph of f.
   (iii) Estimate the values of x for which $f(x) = 0$.
   (iv) Use the graph to find the least value of $f(x)$ in $0 \le x \le 3$.
   (v) If $g : x \rightarrow f(x) + k$, find the value of k when the x-axis is a tangent to the graph of g in $0 \le x \le 3$.
   (vi) By drawing an appropriate line, use both graphs to solve $x^3 + 2x^2 - 5x - 6 = 0$.

32. Factorise $x^3 - 4x$ and hence solve the equation $x^3 - 4x = 0$.
   Graph the function $f : x \rightarrow x^3 - 5x + 2$ in the domain $-3 \le x \le 3$, where $x \in \mathbb{R}$.

   (i) From your graph, estimate the three values of x for which $f(x) = 0$.
   (ii) From your graph, estimate the three values of x for which $f(x) = 2$ and hence estimate $\sqrt{5}$, giving a reason for your answer.

33. Graph the function $f : x \rightarrow x^3 - 3x + 2$ in the domain $-3 \le x \le 3$, where $x \in \mathbb{R}$.

   Use your graph to find the following.

   (i) The local maximum and minimum values.
   (ii) The coordinates of the local maximum and minimum points.
   (iii) The range of values of x for which $f(x)$ is:
       (a) decreasing   (b) negative and increasing   (c) positive and increasing.
   (iv) The range of real values of k for which the equation $x^3 - 3x + 2 = k$ has three real and distinct roots.
   (v) From your graph, estimate the values of x for which $f(x) = 2$.
   (vi) Hence, estimate $\sqrt{3}$, giving a reason for your answer.

Graphing exponential functions of the form ab^x

On our course an exponential function will be given in the form $f : x \rightarrow ab^x$, where $a, x \in \mathbb{R}$ and $b \in \mathbb{R}^+$ and $b > 0$ (b must be a positive real number) and $a \neq 0$.

Note: All mathematical graphs are read from left to right.

1. $a > 0, b > 1, f(x)$ is increasing

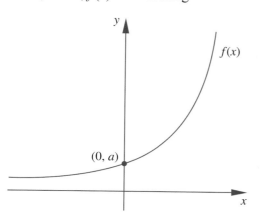

2. $a > 0, 0 < b < 1, g(x)$ is decreasing

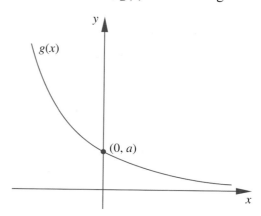

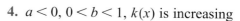

3. $a < 0, b > 1, h(x)$ is decreasing

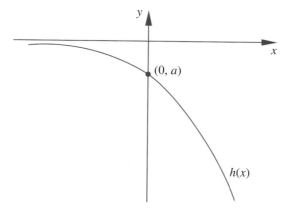

4. $a < 0, 0 < b < 1, k(x)$ is increasing

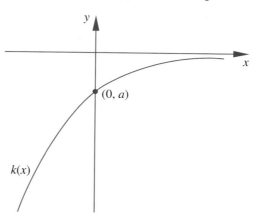

In each case, the curve intersects the y-axis at $(0, a)$ and is called the **focal point**.

Notes on exponential functions of the form:

1. When $a > 0$ the graph is totally **above** the x-axis and when $a < 0$ the graph is totally **below** the x-axis.
2. If $a > 0$ and $b > 1$ the graph will keep increasing away from the x-axis and if $a < 0$ and $b > 1$ the graph will keep decreasing away from the x-axis.
3. If $0 < b < 1$ the graph decreases towards, but never reaches, the x-axis. We say that the x-axis is a horizontal asympote of the graph.

Limits

$$\lim_{n \to \infty} (\text{proper fraction})^n = 0$$

$$\lim_{n \to \infty} \left(\tfrac{1}{2}\right)^n = 0 \qquad \lim_{n \to \infty} \left(-\tfrac{4}{5}\right)^n = 0$$

$n \to \infty$ means **as n approaches infinity**.

EXAMPLE 1

Graph the function $f : x \rightarrow 4(2)^x$ in the domain $-5 \leq x \leq 1$, where $x \in \mathbb{R}$.

Solution:

Let $y = f(x) = 4(2)^x$.

x	$4(2)^x$	y
-5	$4(2)^{-5}$	$0 \cdot 125$
-4	$4(2)^{-4}$	$0 \cdot 25$
-3	$4(2)^{-3}$	$0 \cdot 5$
-2	$4(2)^{-2}$	1
-1	$4(2)^{-1}$	2
0	$4(2)^{0}$	4
1	$4(2)^{1}$	8

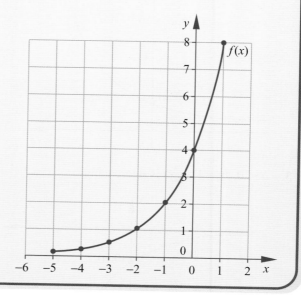

Note: $4(2)^x$ could also be written as $4(2^x)$ or 4×2^x.

$$2^{-x} = \frac{1}{2^x} = \left(\frac{1}{2}\right)^x$$

EXAMPLE 2

A colony of bacteria grows according to the model $P(t) = A(2)^t$, where $P(t)$ is the size of the population at time t hours. It is known that at the start of the observation the number of bacteria in the colony was 1,000.

  (i) Find the value of A.

 (ii) Find the size of the population after 6 hours.

(iii) Find the time, correct to the nearest hour, at which the population will exceed 1,000,000.

Solution:

(i)
$$P(t) = A(2)^t$$
Given: $P(0) = 1,000$

$\therefore$ $A(2)^0 = 1,000$

       $A(1) = 1,000$ $(2^0 = 1)$

          $A = 1,000$

(ii) $P(t) = 1,000(2)^t$

      $P(6) = 1,000(2)^6$

      $P(6) = 64,000$

After 6 hours the size of the population of bacteria is 64,000.

(iii) $P(t) = 1{,}000(2)^t$
   $1{,}000{,}000 = 1{,}000(2)^t$
   $1{,}000 = 2^t$ (divide both sides by 1,000)
   $2^t = 1{,}000$ (swap sides)
   $\ln 2^t = \ln (1{,}000)$ (take the ln of both sides)
   $t \ln 2 = \ln 1{,}000$ ($\log x^n = n \log x$)
   $t = \dfrac{\ln 1{,}000}{\ln 2}$ (divide both sides by ln 2)
   $t = 9{\cdot}965784285$ (calculator)

Thus, it takes about 10 hours for the population of bacteria to exceed 1,000,000.

Check: $P(10) = 1{,}000 \, (2)^{10} = 1{,}024{,}000 > 1{,}000{,}000.$

Note: Using logs to the base 10 would give the same answer.

Exercise 12.2

In questions 1–6, graph the function in the given domain.

1. $f : x \rightarrow 3^x$ in the domain $-2 \leq x \leq 3,$ where $x \in \mathbb{R}.$
2. $f : x \rightarrow 8(4)^x$ in the domain $-3 \leq x \leq 1,$ where $x \in \mathbb{R}.$
3. $f : x \rightarrow 2\left(\frac{1}{2}\right)^x$ in the domain $-2 \leq x \leq 3,$ where $x \in \mathbb{R}.$
4. $g : x \rightarrow 2(0{\cdot}4)^x$ in the domain $-2 \leq x \leq 3,$ where $x \in \mathbb{R}.$
5. $h : x \rightarrow 6(2{\cdot}5)^x$ in the domain $-4 \leq x \leq 1,$ where $x \in \mathbb{R}.$
6. $k : x \rightarrow 0{\cdot}5(1{\cdot}8)^x$ in the domain $-1 \leq x \leq 5,$ where $x \in \mathbb{R}.$

7. (i) On the same axes and scales, graph the functions
   $f : x \rightarrow \left(\frac{1}{2}\right)^x$ and $g : x \rightarrow 3^x$ in the domain $-3 \leq x \leq 2.$
   (ii) From you graph, write down the point of intersection of f and g.

8. (i) On the same axes and scales, graph the functions $f : x \rightarrow (0{\cdot}5)^x$ and $g(x) = -3x - 1$ in the domain $-4 \leq x \leq 2.$
   (ii) From your graphs, write down the points of intersection of f and g.
   (iii) Find the values of $x > -2$ for which $f(x) \geq g(x).$

9. Graph the function $f(x) = 2^x$ in the domain $-3 \leq x \leq 3.$

   (i) Use your graph to estimate (a) $2^{1 \cdot 8}$ (b) $2^{2 \cdot 3}$ (c) $\sqrt{2}.$
   On the same axes and scales, graph the function $g(x) = 2^{-x}.$

   (ii) What is the horizontal asymptote of $f(x)$ and $g(x)$?
   (iii) Describe how $f(x)$ and $g(x)$ are related.

10. The function $f(x) = ab^x$ passes through the following pairs of points. In each case, find the value of a and the value of b.

   (i) (0, 6) and (1, 12)   (ii) (1, 6) and (3, 54)
   (iii) (1, 4) and (2, 12)   (iv) (−1, 0·6) and (1, 3·75)

11. The function $f(x) = ab^x$ passes through the points (1, 2) and (3, 32).
   Express $f(x)$ in the form k^y, where $k \in \mathbb{N}$ and y is a function of x.

12. The number of infected cells in a body is expected to follow the formula $n = f(t) = ab^t$, where n is the number of cells at a time t hours from when the infection was introduced. The following table shows the result of an experiment in which attempts were made to estimate n for various values of t.

t	0	1	2	3	4
n	k	7·8	10·14	13·182	17·1367

   (i) Show that the readings do fit the proposed model and find the values of the constants a and b.
   (ii) Find the value of k, the initial number of infected cells in the body.

13. The velocity, V m/s, of a vehicle varies with time, t seconds, and is given as $V(t) = 100(2·7)^{-t}$ km/hr.

   (i) Calculate V when $t = 0$.
   (ii) Make a rough sketch of $V(t)$ in the domain $0 \le t \le 6$.
   (iii) What happens to V as $t \to \infty$?

14. When medication is taken by a patient, it is slowly used by their body. After t hours, the amount of drug remaining in the body is given by $D(t) = 120 \times (0·9)^t$ mg.

   (i) What was the original drug dose?
   (ii) Find $D(t)$ when $t = 0, 4, 8, 12, 16, 20, 24$ correct to the nearest whole number.
   (iii) Graph $D(t)$ against t for $t \ge 0$ and $t \in \mathbb{R}$ using the information from part (ii).
   (iv) Find the time, correct to two decimal places, when there is only 30 mg of the drug left in the patient.

15. In questions (i) to (vi), solve each for n, correct to two decimal places.

   (i) $2^n = 12$ (ii) $3^n = 11$ (iii) $4^n = 20$
   (iv) $(0·8)^n = 0·7$ (v) $(1·25)^n = 6$ (vi) $120(0·75)^n = 15$

16. The growth of the population of bacteria, $P(t)$, is modelled by $P(t) = A(1·047)^t$ where t is the time in minutes. How long, to the nearest minute, will it take for the size of the population to double?

17. A population of ants grows according to the model $P(t) = A(3)^t$, where $P(t)$ is the size of the population after t days. It is known that at the start of the observation the size of the population was 400.

(i) Find the value of A.

(ii) Find the size of the population after one week.

(iii) Find, correct to three decimal places, the time at which the size of the population will exceed 2×10^6 ants.

18. A liquid cools is such a way that at time n minutes its temperature, $T(n)°C$, can be modelled by the formula $T(n) = 80(2)^{-n}$.

(i) Write down the initial temperature.

(ii) Graph the function $T(n)$ in the domain $0 \le n \le 6$.

(iii) Use your graph to estimate the temperature of the liquid after 1·5 minutes.

(iv) Verify your answer by calculating $T(1·5)$.

(v) Find, correct to two decimal places, the time when the temperature of the liquid first reaches 4·6°C.

(vi) Evaluate $\lim_{n \to \infty} T(n)$.

19. In a thermodynamic system, we have the following relationship: $\log(P) + n \log(V) = \log(C)$ where P is the pressure, V is the volume and C is a constant.

(i) Show that $PV^n = C$.

(ii) When $n = 0$, express P in terms of C.

(iii) If $P = 500$, $V = 2$ and $C = 13{,}928·8$, find the value of n, correct to one decimal place.

20. The population of turtles in a lake decreases each year to 80% of the previous year. In 2010, there were 120 turtles in the lake.

(i) Find a model for the number of turtles, $T(n)$, in the lake n years after 2010. Your model should be in the form $T(n) = T_0(a)^n$.

(ii) Graph $T(n)$ for $n = 0, 3, 6, 9, 12, 15, 18$.

(iii) Using your model, how many turtles should be in the lake in 2020, correct to the nearest whole number?

(iv) If the population falls as low as five, conservationists will not be able to save the turtle colony. According to your model, when, correct to the nearest month, will this occur?

21. The formula $P(n) = A(1·05)^n$ models the population, $P(n)$, of the number of bacteria in a culture at time t hours.

(i) What does A represent?

(ii) A culture starts with 1,000 bacteria. Find the population after 24 hours.

(iii) What simplifying assumptions are made using this model?

(iv) Why might the model not be reliable in giving the population after 5 days?

Composite functions

When one function is followed by another function, the result is a **composite** function.

Applying function g after applying function f is written in three different ways:

1. $g \circ f(x)$ **2.** $g\,f(x)$ **3.** $g[f(x)]$

All are pronounced 'g after f' and means 'do f followed by g'.

Consider the two functions $f(x) = x + 3$ and $g(x) = x^2 + 1$, where the domain of f is $\{1, 2, 3, 4\}$ and the domain of g is the range of f.

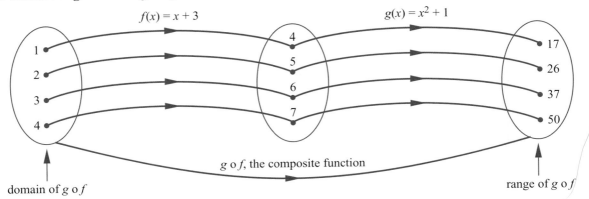

$$g \circ f = \{(1, 17), (2, 26), (3, 37), (4, 50)\}$$

We can work out a single **rule** for the composite function.

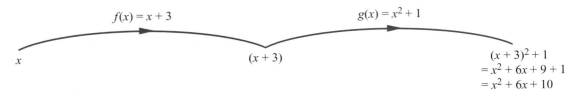

In this case, $g\,f(x) = x^2 + 6x + 10$.

Check: $g\,f(3) = (3)^2 + 6(3) + 10 = 9 + 18 + 10 = 37$ (same as before).

Note: $f \circ f(x)$ is usually written $f^2(x)$, $f \circ f \circ f$ is usually written $f^3(x)$, and so on.

EXAMPLE

$f(x) = 2x + 1$ and $g(x) = \dfrac{x}{3} + 2$, where $x \in \mathbb{R}$.

(i) Find **(a)** $f\,g(6)$ **(b)** $g\,f(-2)$.

(ii) Find an expression in x for $f\,g(x)$ and write your answer in the form $ax + b$.

Solution:

(i) $f(x) = 2x + 1$ and $g(x) = \dfrac{x}{3} + 2$

(a) $fg(6) = f\left(\dfrac{6}{3} + 2\right)$

$\qquad = f(2 + 2)$

$\qquad = f(4)$

$\qquad = 2(4) + 1$

$\qquad = 8 + 1$

$\qquad = 9$

(b) $gf(-2) = g[2(-2) + 1]$

$\qquad = g(-4 + 1)$

$\qquad = g(-3)$

$\qquad = \dfrac{-3}{3} + 2$

$\qquad = -1 + 2$

$\qquad = 1$

(ii)

$$g(x) = \tfrac{x}{3} + 2 \qquad\qquad f(x) = 2x + 1$$

$$x \qquad\qquad \left(\tfrac{x}{3} + 2\right) \qquad\qquad 2\left(\tfrac{x}{3} + 2\right) + 1$$

$$= \tfrac{2}{3}x + 4 + 1$$

$$= \tfrac{2}{3}x + 5$$

$fg(x) = \tfrac{2}{3}x + 5$

Check: $fg(6) = \tfrac{2}{3}(6) + 5 = 4 + 5 = 9$ (same as before)

Exercise 12.3

1. Given $f(x) = 2x + 3$, $g(x) = x^2 - 1$ and $h(x) = \dfrac{1}{x}$, evaluate the following.

   (i) $f(-1)$

   (ii) $g(3)$

   (iii) $h\left(\tfrac{1}{2}\right)$

   (iv) $gf(2)$

   (v) $fg(3)$

   (vi) $fh\left(\tfrac{1}{3}\right)$

   (vii) $h \circ f(1)$

   (viii) $g \circ f(-1 \cdot 5)$

   (ix) $f \circ f(-1)$

2. Given $f(x) = 3x + 2$, $g(x) = x^2$ and $h(x) = \dfrac{2}{x}$, find and simplify expressions for each of the following composite functions.

   (i) $f \circ g(x)$

   (ii) $g \circ f(x)$

   (iii) $h \circ f(x)$

   (iv) $f^2(x)$

   (v) $g \circ h(x)$

   (vi) $h \circ h(x)$

3. $f(x) = x^2 + 3$ and $g(x) = x + 5$, where $x \in \mathbb{R}$.

   (i) Find expressions for (a) $f[g(x)]$ (b) $g[f(x)]$.

   (ii) Solve $f[g(x)] = g[f(x)]$ and verify your answer.

4. $h(x) = x^2$ and $k(x) = 2x + 5$. Solve the following equations.

   (i) $k^2(x) = 7$ (ii) $k \circ h(x) = 23$ (iii) $h \circ k(x) = 9$

5. $p(x) = 2 - \dfrac{6}{x}$ and $q(x) = x + 3$, where $x \in \mathbb{R}$ and $x \neq 0$. Solve $pq(x) = 1$.

6. $f(x) = x^2$ and $g(x) = 2x - 5$, where $x \in \mathbb{R}$. Solve $f\,g(x) = 1$ and verify your solutions.

7. $f(x) = x^2 - 4x + 1$ and $g(x) = kx + 5$, where $x \in \mathbb{R}$ and $k \in \mathbb{Q}$. If $g\,f(1) = 2$, find the value of k.

8. Given that $f(x) = 2x + 5$, $g(x) = 4x + a$ and $f\,g(x) = g\,f(x)$, find the value of a.

9. Let $h(x) = x^2 + 3$, $k(x) = 2x + a$ and $h \circ k(x) = 4x^2 - 8x + 7$, where $x \in \mathbb{R}$ and $a \in \mathbb{Z}$. Calculate the value of a.

10. $f(x) = x + 2$ and $g(x) = ax^2 + b$, where $x \in \mathbb{R}$ and $a, b \in \mathbb{Z}$.
    If $g\,f(x) = 3x^2 + 12x + 2$, find the values of a and b.

11. $f(x) = x^2$ and $g(x) = 3x + 1$, where $x \in \mathbb{R}$.

    (i) Show that $f\,g(x) \neq g\,f(x)$.   (ii) Solve for x: $f\,g(x) = g\,f(x)$.

12. $g(x) = \dfrac{6}{x}$ and $h(x) = \dfrac{2}{x + 5}$, where $x \in \mathbb{Z}$, $x \neq 0, -5$. Explain why $g\,h(x)$ is always divisible by 3.

13. $f(x) = x^2$ and $g(x) = \cos x$, where $x \in \mathbb{R}$. Evaluate: (i) $f\,g(0)$ (ii) $f g\left(\dfrac{\pi}{3}\right)$

14. $h(x) = px + q$ and $k(x) = rx + s$, where $p, q, r, s, x \in \mathbb{R}$. If $h[k(x)] = k[h(x)]$, show that $s(p - 1) = q(r - 1)$.

15. $f(x) = x + 1$ and $g(x) = 2^x$

    (i) Show that $f(3) = g(2)$.

    (ii) Find (a) $g\,f(x)$ (b) $f\,g(x)$.
    (iii) Solve for x: $g\,f(x) = f\,g(x)$.

16. The function f and g are defined as follows:
    $f(x) = x^2$ where $0 \leq x \leq 4$ and $g(x) = x + 3$ where $x \in \mathbb{R}$. Find the composite function $g f(x)$ and state the range of this function.

17. $f(x) = \sqrt{x - 1}$ and $g(x) = x^2$, where $x \in \mathbb{R}$. Find the range of values of x for which
    (i) $f(x)$ and   (ii) $f\,g(x)$ exists.

18. The diagram shows the graph of $y = f(x)$. Use the graph to write down:

    (i) $f(2)$

    (ii) $f^2(2)$

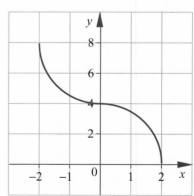

19. $g(x) = 10 - x$, where $x \in \mathbb{R}$.

 (i) Find **(a)** $g^2(x)$ **(b)** $g^3(x)$ **(c)** $g^4(x)$ **(d)** $g^5(x)$ **(e)** $g^{21}(x)$ **(f)** $g^{100}(x)$.

 (ii) Find an expression for $g^{2k}(x)$, where $k \in \mathbb{N}$.

20. $f(x) = \dfrac{x + 5}{2x - 1}$, where $x \in \mathbb{R}$ and $x \neq \frac{1}{2}$. Find:

 (i) $f^2(x)$ **(ii)** $f^3(x)$ **(iii)** $f^4(x)$ **(iv)** $f^{12}(x)$ **(v)** $f^{71}(x)$

 (vi) Find an expression for **(a)** $f^{2n}(x)$ **(b)** $f^{2n-1}(x)$ where $n \in \mathbb{N}$ and hence solve
 $f^{2n}(x) + f^{2n-1}(x) = -5$.

 (vii) Express $\displaystyle\sum_{n=1}^{40} f^{2n}(x)$ in the form kx, where $k \in \mathbb{N}$.

21. (i) Explain why $\dfrac{-12}{9x - 15} = \dfrac{12}{15 - 9x} = \dfrac{4}{5 - 3x}$.

 (ii) $f(x) = \dfrac{2x - 4}{x}$, where $x \in \mathbb{R}$ and $x \neq 0$. Find:

 (a) $f^2(x)$ **(b)** $f^3(x)$ **(c)** $f^4(x)$ **(d)** $f^5(x)$ **(e)** $f^6(x)$

 (iii) Find expressions for **(a)** $f^{3n-2}(x)$ **(b)** $f^{3n-1}(x)$ **(c)** $f^{3n}(x)$ for all $n \in \mathbb{N}$.

 (iv) Evaluate $\displaystyle\sum_{n=1}^{10} f^{3n}(x)$ when $x = 2$.

22. A gas meter indicates the amount of gas in cubic metres used by a consumer. The number of therms of heat from x cubic metres of gas is given by the function f where
 $f(x) = 36x$, where $x \geq 0$.

 A particular gas company's charge in € for t therms is given by the function g where
 $g(t) = 20 + 0.03t$.

 (i) How many therms of heat are produced from 120 cubic metres of gas?

 (ii) What is the cost of using 4,968 therms?

 (iii) Find the cost of using the following amounts of gas from this gas company.
 (a) 100 cubic metres **(b)** 150 cubic metres **(c)** 440 cubic metres

 (iv) Find the rule, in its simplest form, for the function gf where $gf(x)$ is the cost of using x cubic metres of gas and verify one answer from part **(iii)**.

 (v) Use your rule to find the cost of 550 cubic metres of gas.

23. The manager of a theatre found that when he raises the temperature on the heating thermostat, the sales of ice cream during the interval increases. By keeping records he discovered that the proportion of the audience buying ice cream can be modelled by the function $P(c)$ where

$$P(c) = 1 - \frac{8}{c}, \quad 10 \le c \le 25 \text{ and } c \text{ is the temperature in degrees Celsius, } °C.$$

   (i) What proportion of the audience buys ice cream when the temperature is 12°C?
   (ii) At what temperature will 60% of the audience buy ice cream?
   (iii) What is the range of $P(c)$?
   The function $F(t) = \frac{5}{9}(t - 32)$ gives the temperature in degrees Celsius where t is the temperature in degrees Fahrenheit.
   (iv) What proportion of the audience buys ice cream when the temperature is 59°F?
   (v) Find the rule for the composite function $P[F(t)]$ and use it to verify your answer to part (iv).
   (vi) One evening, 36% of the audience bought ice cream. What was the temperature in degrees Fahrenheit?
   (vii) Calculate an appropriate domain for the function $P[f(t)]$.

Injective, surjective and bijective functions

Consider a function f, such that $f : X \to Y$, where X is the domain and Y is the codomain.

Injective function
A function f is said to be injective from X to Y if every element in Y has at most one element in X.
An injective function is often called a **one-to-one mapping**.
On a coordinated graph, a horizontal line intersects the curve at most once.

Note: There can be elements in Y that are not busy.

Mathematically: For any $y \in Y$, there exists at most one $x \in X$, such that $f(x) = y$.

Surjective function
A function f is said to be surjective from X to Y if **every** element in Y has **at least one matching** element in X. A surjective function is often called a **many-to-one** or **onto map**.
On a coordinated graph, a horizontal line can intersect the curve at least once.

Note: Every element in Y is busy. In other words, **the range and the codomain are equal**.

Mathematically: For every $y \in Y$, there exists at least one $x \in X$, such that $f(x) = y$.

Bijective function
A function f is said to be bijective if it is both injective (one-to-one) **and** surjective (onto).
There is **perfect one-to-one corrspondence** between the elements of X and Y.

Note: A function f has an inverse if and only if f is bijective.

Mathematically: For every $y \in Y$, there is a unique $x \in X$, such that $f(x) = y$.

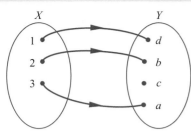

Injective (one-to-one),
not surjective
(c in codomain
is **not** busy)

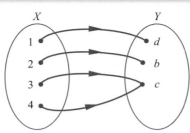

Surjective (many-to-one),
not injective
(not one-to-one)

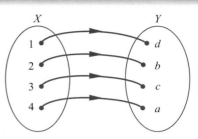

Bijective,
injective and surjective
(perfect one-to-one)

EXAMPLE

$f(x) = x^2$, where $x \in \mathbb{R}$.
(i) Explain why $f(x)$ is (a) a function (b) **not** injective.
(ii) What restriction can be placed on the domain to ensure that $f(x)$ is an injective function?

Solution:
(i) $f(x) = x^2$

    (a) Any vertical line cuts the graph
       only once.
       $\therefore f(x)$ is a function
       (each input always generates a
       unique output).

    (b) $f(2) = 4$ and $f(-2) = 4$,
       two different inputs in the
       domain have the same output in
       the range.
       $\therefore f(x)$ is **not** injective
       (not one-to-one).

(ii) If the domain was restricted to
    $x \in \mathbb{R}$ where $x \geq 0$, then $f(x)$ would
    be one-to-one (as shown).
    (Any $x \geq 0$ or $x \leq 0$ would ensure
    $f(x)$ is bijective.)
    If x is restricted to $x \geq 0$, then $f(x)$
    is injective.

    Note: There is no $f(-2)$.

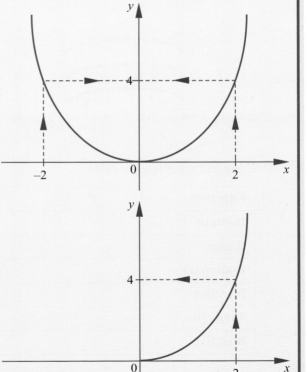

Note: The function $f : \mathbb{R} \rightarrow \mathbb{R} : x \rightarrow x^2$ is **not** surjective. There are elements in the codomain, $\mathbb{R}$, which are not used. For example, -1 is in the codomain but there is no real number x such that $x^2 = -1$.

However, with a restricted codomain we can ensure $f(x)$ is surjective. The function $f : \mathbb{R} \rightarrow \mathbb{R}^+ : x \rightarrow x^2$ is surjective because for each element y in the positive real codomain there is at least one real x in the domain such that $x^2 = y$.

Note: $\mathbb{R}^+$ means any real number greater than zero (zero not included).

Exercise 12.4

1. Consider the four functions, f, g, h and k.

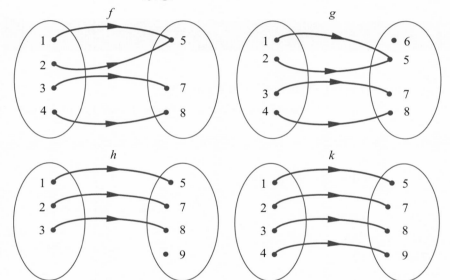

Copy and complete the table.

Function	f	g	h	k
Domain				
Range				
Codomain				
Injective				
Surjective				
Bijective				

2. For each of the curves graphed below, determine if the curve represents:
   (a) a function   (b) an injective function.

(i)

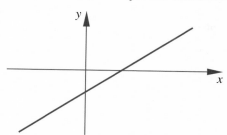

(ii)

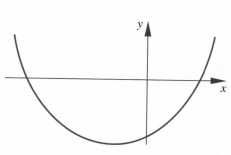

(iii)

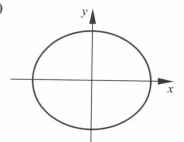

(iv)

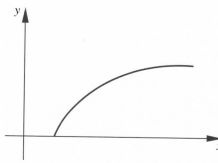

(v)

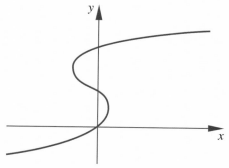

(vi)

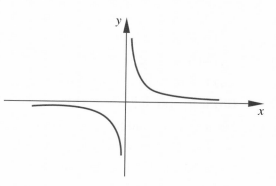

3. $f(x) = x^2 + 3$, where $x \in \mathbb{R}$. Make a sketch of f.

   (i) Explain why $f(x)$ is   (a) a function   (b) not injective   (c) not surjective.
   (ii) What restriction can be placed on the domain to ensure $f(x)$ is an injective?

4. The function g is defined by $g(x) = x^2 - 2x - 3$, where $x \in \mathbb{R}$.

   (i) Express $g(x)$ in the form $(x - a)^2 - b$ and hence write down the coordinates of the minimum point of $g(x)$.
   (ii) $x \geq k$ restricts the domain so that $f(x)$ is injective. What is the minimum value of k, where $k > 0$?

5. Graph the function $f : x \rightarrow x^3 - 3x + 2$ in the domain $-3 \leq x \leq 3$.
      (i) From your graph, find:
         (a) The values of x for which $f(x) = 2$
         (b) The local maximum and minimum points
      (ii) Is f (a) injective (b) surjective? Justify your answers.
      (iii) Give a restricted domain for which $f(x)$ is bijective.

6. $g(x) = (x - 2)^3$, where $x \in \mathbb{R}$. Make a sketch of g.
   Is g a bijective function? Justify your answer.

7. The function f is defined by $f(x) = ax + b$, where $x \in \mathbb{R}$ and $a, b \in \mathbb{Q}$ and $a \neq 0$.
   Is f a bijective function? Justify your answer.

8. $f : \mathbb{N} \rightarrow \mathbb{N} : x \rightarrow 2x + 1$. Explain why f is not surjective.

9. A method to show that the function $f(x)$ is injective is to show $f(a) = f(b)$ leads to $a = b$, where a, b are elements of the domain of f. Use this method to decide which of the functions below are injective, where $x \in \mathbb{R}$.

      (i) $f(x) = 3x - 2$ (ii) $f(x) = \dfrac{x + 2}{x}$ (iii) $f(x) = x^2$ (iv) $f(x) = x^3 + 1$

10. f is a function defined by $f : \mathbb{R} \rightarrow \mathbb{R}^+ : x \rightarrow 3(2)^x$. Is f a bijective function? Justify your answer.

11. $f(x) = x - 2$ and $g(x) = |x - 2|$, where $x \in \mathbb{R}$.

      (i) Make a sketch of (a) f (b) g.
      (ii) Is f bijective? Justify your answer.
      (iii) Is g (a) injective (b) surjective? Justify your answers.

12. Set $A = [0, \pi]$ and Set $B = [-1, 1]$, where $A, B \in \mathbb{R}$.
      $f : A \rightarrow B : x \rightarrow \cos x$ and $g : A \rightarrow B : x \rightarrow \sin x$.

      (i) Make a sketch of (a) f and (b) g.
      (ii) Is f a bijection? Justify your answer.
      (iii) Is g a bijection? Justify your answer.

13. $f(x) = \tan x$, where $-\dfrac{\pi}{2} < x < \dfrac{\pi}{2}$. Is f bijective? Justify your answer.

Inverse functions

A function, $f(x)$, must give exactly one unique output for each input. A function that 'reverses' or 'undoes' the result of $f(x)$ is called its inverse and is denoted by $f^{-1}(x)$. For an inverse function, $f^{-1}(x)$, to exist, the $f(x)$ must be bijective.

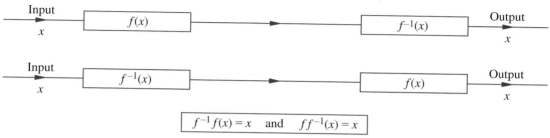

$$f^{-1}f(x) = x \quad \text{and} \quad ff^{-1}(x) = x$$

Note: A function that is not one-to-one (not injective), such as $f(x) = x^2$, can be arranged to be one-to-one by restricting its domain. If the domain of $f(x) = x^2$, where $x \in \mathbb{R}$ is restricted to $x \geq 0$, $f(x) = x^2$ will be injective and have an inverse for that domain.

> If f is a one-to-one function, the graphs of $y = f(x)$ and $y = f^{-1}(x)$ are reflections of each other in the line $y = x$.

The graphs of a function, $f(x)$, and its inverse, $f^{-1}(x)$, are reflections of each other in the line $y = x$. In general, if the point (a, b) is on $y = f(x)$, then the point (b, a) is on $y = f^{-1}(x)$.
For a function and its inverse, the roles of x and y are interchanged. The range of $f(x)$ is the domain of $f^{-1}(x)$ and the range of $f^{-1}(x)$ is the domain of $f(x)$. Any points of intersection will be on the line $y = x$.

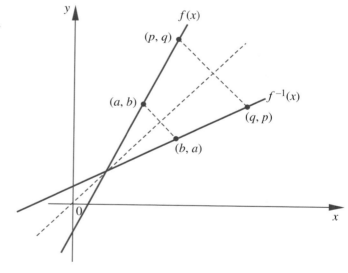

To find the inverse of a function, do the following.

> 1. Let $f(x) = y$.
> 2. Express x in terms of y (x on its own).
> 3. Rewrite as $f^{-1}(x)$, replacing y with x.

EXAMPLE 1

The function $f(x) = 3x - 5$, where $x \in \mathbb{R}$.

(i) Find $f^{-1}(x)$. (ii) Show that $f^{-1}f(x) = x$.

Solution:

(i) Let $f(x) = y$.

$$3x - 5 = y$$
$$3x = y + 5$$
$$x = \frac{y + 5}{3}$$
$$\therefore f^{-1}(x) = \frac{x + 5}{3}$$

(ii) $f^{-1}f(x)$
$$= f^{-1}(3x - 5)$$
$$= \frac{(3x + 5) - 5}{3}$$
$$= \frac{3x + 5 - 5}{3} = \frac{3x}{3} = x$$

EXAMPLE 2

$f(x) = \dfrac{1}{x + 1}$, where $x \in \mathbb{R}$ and $x \neq -1$, and $g(x) = \dfrac{1 - x}{x}$, where $x \in \mathbb{R}$ and $0 < x < 1$.

Show that $f(x)$ and $g(x)$ are inverse functions.

Solution:

(multiply top and bottom by x)

$$f g(x) = f\left(\frac{1 - x}{x}\right) = \frac{1}{\dfrac{1 - x}{x} + 1} = \frac{x}{1 - x + x} = \frac{x}{1} = x$$

(multiply top and bottom by $(x + 1)$)

$$g f(x) = g\left(\frac{1}{x + 1}\right) = \frac{1 - \dfrac{1}{x + 1}}{\dfrac{1}{x + 1}} = \frac{x + 1 - 1}{1} = \frac{x}{1} = x$$

Therefore, $f(x)$ and $g(x)$ are inverse functions.

Note: An alternative method is to find $f^{-1}(x)$ and $g^{-1}(x)$ and show that
$$f^{-1}(x) = g(x) \text{ and } g^{-1}(x) = f(x).$$

Sometimes we have to complete the square to find $f^{-1}(x)$.

EXAMPLE 3

$f(x) = x^2 - 6x + 7$, where $x \in \mathbb{R}$ and $x \geq 3$. Find $f^{-1}(x)$.

Solution:

Let $f(x) = y$.

$\therefore (x-3)^2 - 2 = y$

$(x-3)^2 = y + 2$

$x - 3 = \pm \sqrt{y+2}$

$x = 3 \pm \sqrt{y+2}$

$\therefore f^{-1}(x) = 3 \pm \sqrt{x+2}$

Complete the square.

$x^2 - 6x + 7$

$= x^2 - 6x + 9 + 7 - 9$

$= (x^2 - 6x + 9) + 7 - 9$

$= (x-3)(x-3) - 2$

$= (x-3)^2 - 2$

We are given $x \geq 3$, therefore we use the positive value.

$\therefore f^{-1}(x) = 3 + \sqrt{x+2}$

Note: If we were given $x \leq 3$, we would use the negative value, $3 - \sqrt{x+2}$.

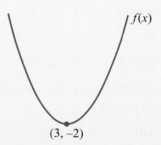

$(3, -2)$

Exercise 12.5

In question 1, assume $x \in \mathbb{R}$.

1. Find the inverse of each of the following functions.

   (i) $f(x) = 3x$

   (ii) $g(x) = x + 3$

   (iii) $h(x) = 3x + 1$

   (iv) $k(x) = 2x - 5$

   (v) $g(x) = 4x - 5$

   (vi) $f(x) = 3 - 5x$

   (vii) $k(x) = \dfrac{2}{x}, x \neq 0$

   (viii) $f(x) = \dfrac{2}{x-1}, x \neq 1$

   (ix) $h(x) = \dfrac{x+3}{x}, x \neq 0$

   (x) $h(x) = \dfrac{x}{1-x}$

   (xi) $g(x) = \dfrac{3x}{2x-1}, x \neq \frac{1}{2}$

   (xii) $k(x) = 1 + \dfrac{1}{x}, x \neq 0$

2. $f(x) = 3x - 2$, where $x \in \mathbb{R}$.

   (i) Find $f^{-1}(x)$.

   (ii) Find the coordinates of the point of intersection of $f(x)$ and $f^{-1}(x)$.

3. $f(x) = 2x + 5$, where $x \in \mathbb{R}$. Verify $f^{-1}f(x) = ff^{-1}(x) = x$.

4. $f(x) = \dfrac{x}{x-1}$, where $x \in \mathbb{R}$ and $x \neq 1$. Show that $f(x)$ is self inverse.

5. $f(x) = \dfrac{1}{x-2}$, where $x \in \mathbb{R}$ and $x \neq 2$. $g(x) = \dfrac{1+2x}{x}$, where $x \in \mathbb{R}$ and $x \neq 0$.

   Are $f(x)$ and $g(x)$ inverse functions? Justify your answer.

6. $f(x) = \dfrac{2}{2x+1} + \dfrac{3}{(x-1)(2x+1)}$, where $x > 1$.

   (i) Prove that $f(x) = \dfrac{1}{x-1}$.

   (ii) Find $f^{-1}(x)$.

7. $f(x) = 3 - \dfrac{2}{x}$, where $x \in \mathbb{R}$ and $x \neq 0$.

   (i) Find $f^{-1}(x)$ and find the value of x for which $f^{-1}(x)$ is undefined.

   (ii) Solve $f(x) = f^{-1}(x)$.

8. The function f is defined by $f(x) = \dfrac{2x+1}{x+2}$, where $x \in \mathbb{R}$ and $x > -2$.

   Find the coordinates of the points of intersection of $y = f(x)$ and $y = f^{-1}(x)$.

9. The function f is defined by $f(x) = 2x - 3$, where $x \in \mathbb{R}$ and $-1 \leq x \leq 4$.

   (i) Find $f^{-1}(x)$.

   (ii) Sketch the graphs of $y = f(x)$ and $y = f^{-1}(x)$ on the same axes and scales.

   (iii) Hence or otherwise, verify that $f^{-1}f(x) = x = ff^{-1}(x)$.

10. Functions f and g are defined by $f(x) = 3x + 1$ and $g(x) = x + 5$, where $x \in \mathbb{R}$.

    (i) Find $[fg(x)]^{-1}$.   (ii) Verify that $[fg(x)]^{-1} = g^{-1}f^{-1}(x)$.

11. $f(x) = x^3 + 5$, where $x \in \mathbb{R}$. (i) Find $f^{-1}(x)$.   (ii) Evaluate: (a) $f(2)$ (b) $f^{-1}(13)$.

12. $f(x) = \dfrac{2x+1}{k-x}$, where $x \in \mathbb{R}$ and $x \neq k$. If $f^{-1}(3) = 4$, find k, where $k \in \mathbb{N}$.

13. The diagram show a sketch of the function $y = g(x)$, where $x \in \mathbb{R}$ and $0 \leq x \leq 3$.

    (i) Write down the range of $g(x)$.

    (ii) Write down $g^{-1}(2)$ and $g^{-1}(4{\cdot}5)$.

    (iii) Copy the diagram and sketch $g^{-1}(x)$.

    (iv) Explain why $g^2(3)$ is not defined.

    (v) Find $g^{100}(2)$.

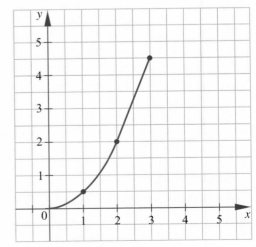

14. The diagram shows $y = f(x)$,
    where $x \in \mathbb{R}$ and $0 < x \le 3 \cdot 5$.

    (i) Find $ff(2\cdot5)$.
    (ii) Solve $f(x) = x$.
    (iii) Find $f^{-1}(0\cdot5)$.
    (iv) Explain why $f^3(2\cdot5)$ is not defined.

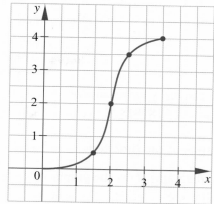

15. The function g is defined by $g(x) = (x - 2)^2$, where $x \in \mathbb{R}$ and $x \ge 2$.

    (i) Sketch $g(x)$.
    (ii) Find $g^{-1}(x)$ and sketch $g^{-1}(x)$ on the same axes and scales.

16. By completing the square, find the inverse of each of the following functions.

    (i) $f(x) = x^2 - 6x + 1$, $\quad x \ge 3$ (ii) $g(x) = x^2 + 4x - 2$, $\quad x \ge -2$
    (iii) $h(x) = 4 + 2x - x^2$, $\quad x \ge 1$ (iv) $k(x) = -x^2 - 16x - 61$, $\quad x \le -8$

17. The function f is defined by $f(x) = x^2 - 4x + 3$, where $x \in \mathbb{R}$ and $x \ge 2$.

    (i) Determine the range of f.
    (ii) Find $f^{-1}(x)$ and state its domain and range.
    (iii) On the same axes and scales, sketch the graphs of $f(x)$ and $f^{-1}(x)$.

Exponential and logarithmic functions

The exponential function e^x

Consider the value of $\left(1 + \dfrac{1}{n}\right)^n$, as n increases and $n > 0$.

n	1	2	5	10	100	10,000	...
$\left(1 + \dfrac{1}{n}\right)^n$	2	2·25	2·48832	2·59374246	2·704813827	2·718145927	...

As $n \to \infty$, $\left(1 + \dfrac{1}{n}\right)^n$ approaches (made as close to) a number called e.

Mathematically:
$$\lim_{n \to \infty}\left(1 + \frac{1}{n}\right)^n = e$$

The number e has proven to be of great importance to mathematics, with applications that include number theory, probability, biological and physical sciences, engineering and finance.

The word 'exponential' comes from the word '**exponent**', which is another word for power or index.
A function of the form $f(x) = a^x$, where $x \in \mathbb{R}$ and a is a positive constant, is called an exponential function.

> The exponential function is $f(x) = e^x$.

You can use your calculator to evaluate e^x for different values of x.
$e = e^1 = 2{\cdot}718281828, \quad e^2 = 7{\cdot}389056099, \quad \sqrt{e} = e^{\frac{1}{2}} = 1{\cdot}648721271.$

Graphs of the functions $y = e^x$ and $y = e^{-x} = \dfrac{1}{e^x}$

The diagrams show the graphs of $y = e^x$ and $y = e^{-x}$.
Both graphs meet the y-axis at $(0, 1)$.

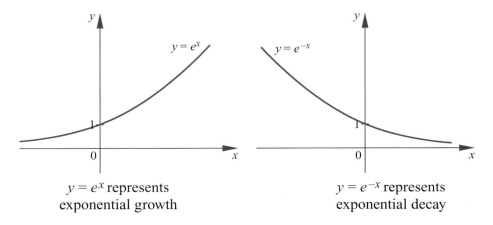

$y = e^x$ represents
exponential growth

$y = e^{-x}$ represents
exponential decay

For functions $y = e^x$ and $y = e^{-x}$, the domain is $x \in \mathbb{R}$ and the range is $y \in \mathbb{R}$ and $y > 0$. Where the graph of the function $y = e^x$ crosses the y-axis, the slope of the tangent at this point is 1. This is the only function of the form $y = a^x$ that has this property. In Chapter 14 on differential calculus we will find out more about the slope of a tangent to the curve $y = e^x$ at any point on the curve.

The logarithm function, ln x

From Chapter 6:

> $\log_b a = c \Longleftrightarrow a = b^c$

Logarithms to the base e are denoted by $\log_e x$ or $\ln x$.
First let's find the inverse function of $f(x) = e^x$.

$$\text{Let } e^x = y.$$

$$\log_e e^x = \log_e y \qquad \text{(take } \log_e \text{ of both sides)}$$
$$x \log_e e = \log_e y \qquad (\log_e x^n = n \log x)$$
$$x = \log_e y \qquad (\log_e e = 1)$$
$$\therefore f^{-1}(x) = \log_e x \quad \text{or} \quad \ln x \qquad \text{(replace } y \text{ with } x)$$

In actual fact, $f(x) = e^x$ and $f(x) = \ln x$ are inverses of each other. One 'undoes' the other.

$$e^{\ln x} = x \quad \text{and} \quad \ln e^x = x$$

For example: $e^{\ln 5} = 5$ and $\ln e^{3x+1} = 3x + 1$.

For e^x the domain is $x \in \mathbb{R}$ and the range is $y \in \mathbb{R}, y > 0$.

For the inverse function, $\ln x$, the domain is $x \in \mathbb{R}, x > 0$ and the range is $y \in \mathbb{R}$.

Note that the graphs of e^x and $\ln x$ are reflections of each other in $y = x$.

The x-axis is an asymptote to $y = e^x$.
The y-axis is an asymptote to $y = \ln x$.

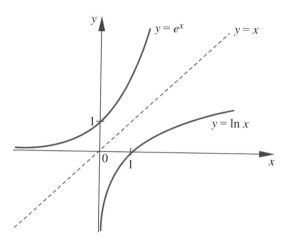

Note: The domain of e^x is the range of $\ln x$ and the range of e^x is the domain of $\ln x$.

EXAMPLE

   (i) If $\ln 4t = 2{\cdot}5$, find the value of t exactly.
   (ii) Solve, correct to three significant figures, $e^{2x-1} = 73$.

Solution:

(i) $\ln 4t = 2{\cdot}5$

      $\log_e 4t = 2{\cdot}5$ ($\ln x = \log_e x$)

          $4t = e^{2{\cdot}5}$ (if $\log_e x = y$, $x = e^y$)

          $t = \dfrac{e^{2{\cdot}5}}{4}$ or $\frac{1}{4}e^{2{\cdot}5}$ (divide both sides by 4)

(ii) $e^{2x-1} = 73$

       $\ln e^{2x-1} = \ln 73$ (take ln of both sides)

   $(2x - 1) \ln e = \ln 73$ ($\ln x^n = n \ln x$)

         $2x - 1 = \ln 73$ ($\ln e = 1$)

            $2x = 1 + \ln 73$ (add 1 to both sides)

              $x = \dfrac{1 + \ln 73}{2}$ (divide both sides by 2)

              $x = 2{\cdot}65$ (correct to three significant figures)

Exercise 12.6

1. Evaluate the following, correct to two decimal places.

    (i) e^3 (ii) $\dfrac{1}{e}$ (iii) $3e^2$ (iv) $\ln 2$ (v) $\ln \sqrt{3}$ (vi) $e^{-2.7}$ (vii) $\ln \left(\tfrac{1}{5}\right)$

2. Write down the exact value of each of the following.

    (i) $e^{\ln 4}$ (ii) $\ln e^3$ (iii) $e^{\ln 2.5}$ (iv) $\ln e^{-1.5}$

3. Simplify each of the following.

    (i) $e^{\ln(x+2)}$ (ii) $\ln e^{(5x-1)}$ (iii) $e^{\ln x^2}$ (iv) $\ln e^{\sqrt{x}}$

4. Solve for x, correct to three significant figures.

    (i) $e^x = 7.5$ (ii) $e^x = 16.8$ (iii) $2e^x - 1 = 81$

    (iv) $4e^{2x} = 170$ (v) $e^{-x} = 2$ (vi) $e^{-5x} + 4 = 5$

    (vii) $\ln 2x = 2$ (viii) $\ln 3x = 4$ (ix) $\ln 4x - 1 = 3$

5. (i) Copy and complete the table, giving each value correct to one decimal place, where necessary.

x	-2	-1	0	1	2	3
e^x						

    (ii) Graph the function $f(x) = e^x$, $x \in \mathbb{R}$ in the domain $-2 \le x \le 3$.

    (iii) From your graph, find the following, correct to two significant figures.

    (a) $e^{-0.3}$ (b) $e^{1.5}$ (c) $e^{2.4}$ (d) $e^{2.7}$

6. A species of animal has population growth modelled by $P(t) = 10 - 5e^{-t}$.

t	0	1	2	3	4	5
$P(t)$						

    (i) Copy and complete the table, giving all values of $P(t)$ correct to one decimal place, where necessary.

    (ii) What is the size of the population as t becomes very large?

7. (i) Graph the function $f(x) = 2 + 6e^{-x}$, where $x \in \mathbb{R}$ and $0 \le x \le 3$.

    (ii) Use your graph to find an approximate solution to the equation $2 + 6e^{-x} = 5$.

    (iii) Verify your answer by solving the equation $2 + 6e^{-x} = 5$, correct to two decimal places.

8. Find $f^{-1}(x)$ for each of the following.

    (i) $f(x) = e^{2x}$ (ii) $f(x) = e^{x-1} + 3$ (iii) $f(x) = \ln(x - 5)$ (iv) $f(x) = \ln(x + 2) - 5$

9. $f(x) = \ln(x - 3)$, $x > \tfrac{1}{2}$ and $g(x) = e^x + 3$, where $x \in \mathbb{R}$ are two functions. Show that $f(x)$ and $g(x)$ are inverse functions.

10. $f(x) = \ln(x - 1)$, $x > 1$ and $g(x) = e^{2x}$, where $x \in \mathbb{R}$ are two functions. Find the following.

    (i) $f^{-1}(x)$ (ii) $f^{-1}(0)$ (iii) $g\,f(3)$ (iv) $g\,f(x)$

11. (i) The curve $f(x) = Ae^x$ passes through $(0, 2)$. Find the value of A.

    (ii) Is the point $(e, e + 1)$ on the curve $y = x + \ln x$? Justify your answer.

12. The graphs of the functions $f(x) = e^{2x} + 1$ and $g(x) = 5$ meet at $(h, 5)$. Find h exactly.

13. A function is defined by $f(x) = 2e^{-x} - 1$, $x \in \mathbb{R}$.
    A sketch of $y = f(x)$ is shown.

    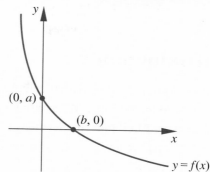

    (i) What is the value of a?

    (ii) Show that $b = \ln 2$.

    (iii) What is the range of f?

    (iv) Solve the equation $f(x) = 3$.

14. Benford's law states that for a set of numerical data, the proportion of numbers starting with the digit d is approximately modelled by $P(d) = \log_{10}\left(1 + \dfrac{1}{d}\right)$.

    (i) Show that Benford's law predicts that around:
       (a) 30% of numbers with start with 1   (b) 18% of numbers start with 2.

    (ii) What proportion of numbers does the law predict will start with 9?

15. A cup of coffee cools according to Newton's law of cooling, so that after t minutes its temperature, T°C, is given by $T(k) = 20 + 50^{-0.2t}$.

    (i) Find the initial temperature of the cup of coffee.

    (ii) How long, correct to the nearest minute, does it take the coffee to cool to half its initial temperature?

16. The number of bacteria in a particular culture is discovered to be $40\left(25 + e^{\frac{t}{50}}\right)$ where t is the time in days from the start of the experiment.

    (i) State the number of bacteria in the culture at the start of the experiment.

    (ii) Calculate the time it takes for the number of bacteria to reach 1,200.
        Give your answer to the nearest tenth of a day.

17. A radioactive substance is decaying in a cave. Initially 5 kg of the radioactive substance was present and four weeks later half of it remained. The mass, R kg, of radioactive substance at time t weeks can be modelled by $R(t) = R_0 e^{-kt}$, where $t \geq 0$.

    (i) State the value of R_0.

    (ii) Find the exact value of k.

    (iii) Sketch the graph of R against t, for $t \in \mathbb{R}$ and $0 \leq t \leq 16$.

    (iv) Find, correct to one decimal place, how long after it was placed in the cave 80% of the substance has decayed.

Introduction

Differentiation, or differential calculus, is the branch of mathematics measuring rates of change. This area of mathematics was discovered independently by two people. Both Sir Isaac Newton (in England) and Gottfried Leibnitz (in Germany) were each trying to solve a problem that involved calculating a rate of change at an instant rather than over a distance or period of time. Each solved the problem but it is not clear who did it first.

Slope of a line

On the right is part of the graph of the line $y = 3x$. There is a relationship between x and y. For every increase in x there is three times this increase in y.

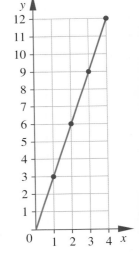

| Rate of change of y = 3 times rate of change of x. |

From coordinate geometry, the slope of the line $y = 3x$ is 3.

| Slope = 3 |

$\therefore$ | Rate of change = Slope |

The key word here is **slope**. The slope of a line will give **the rate of change** of the variable on the vertical axis with respect to (or compared to) the variable on the horizontal. Therefore, to find the rate of change we only need to find the slope.

Note: The y-axis is usually the vertical axis and the x-axis is the horizontal axis. Therefore, the slope of a line will give the rate of change of y with respect to (the change in) x.

Slope of a curve

Consider the curve below and the tangents that are constructed on it.

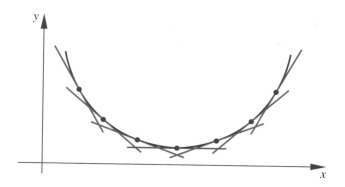

The slope of a curve at a point is equal to the slope of the tangent at that point. As we move along the curve, the slope of each tangent changes. In other words, the rate of change of y with respect to x changes. We need to find a method of finding the slope of the tangent at each point on the curve. The method of finding the slope of a tangent to a curve at any point on the curve is called **differentiation**.

Rates of change

Two well-known rates of change are slope (of a line) and speed. We have already met each of these and their respective formulae:

$$m = \frac{y_2 - y_1}{x_2 - x_1} \qquad \text{and} \qquad \text{speed} = \frac{\text{distance}}{\text{time}}$$

The problem is that the slope formula needs two points and therefore calculates a slope of a line. If we wish to calculate the changing slopes of a curve, then we may have a problem if we only have the one point of contact. Similarly, the method of calculating speed actually produces an *average speed* over the given distance and time. For example, when the space shuttle was launched it started at rest (speed = 0) and soon travelled at over 10 km per second. Given such a huge increase in speed, an average value would not reflect its speed during each of the first 60 seconds after launch. The method which gives us an expression for the *instantaneous speed* is another example of differentiation.

Note: At this level of mathematics, we will try to avoid using the term *speed*.
Velocity can be negative and therefore includes the *direction* of movement.

Estimating slope at a point

To estimate slope at a point P, we can take two points near P and calculate the slope of the line which passes through them. If the points are close enough, our estimate should be quite accurate.

EXAMPLE

Sketch the graph of $y = x^2$ for $-1 \leq x \leq 4$.
Mark the points $(1, 1)$, $(2, 4)$, $(3, 9)$ and $(4, 16)$ and use these points to estimate the slope of the tangent at $(1, 1)$.

Solution:

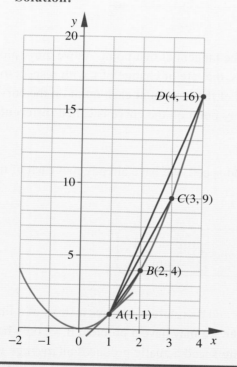

We will estimate the slope of the curve at $A(1, 1)$ by calculating a set of slopes which will hopefully suggest a pattern leading to an answer. The points B, C and D are also shown on the diagram.

Join A to each of B, C and D and calculate slopes:

$$m = \frac{y_2 - y_1}{x_2 - x_1}$$

$$m_{AD} = \frac{16 - 1}{4 - 1} = \frac{15}{3} = 5$$

$$m_{AC} = \frac{9 - 1}{3 - 1} = \frac{8}{2} = 4$$

$$m_{AB} = \frac{4 - 1}{2 - 1} = \frac{3}{1} = 3$$

That simple pattern suggests that the slope at A would be 2 (which we will show later to be true).

Note: While we often refer to the *slope of a curve* or the *slope of a curve at a point*, the correct term is **slope of the tangent to the curve at a point**.

Exercise 13.1

1.   (i) Sketch the graph of $y = x^2$ for $-1 \leq x \leq 5$.

    (ii) Join the points on the graph where $x = 1$ and $x = 5$ and calculate the slope of the line.

    (iii) Join the points on the graph where $x = 2$ and $x = 4$ and calculate the slope of the line.

    (iv) Do you have enough evidence to deduce the slope at the point where $x = 3$?

2. (i) Sketch the graph of $y = 8 - x^2$ for $-4 \leq x \leq 4$.
    (ii) Show the axis of symmetry of the curve.
    (iii) Show that $P(2, 4)$ is a point on the curve.
    (iv) Join the points on the graph where $x = 1$ and $x = 3$ and calculate the slope of the line.
    (v) Join the points on the graph where $x = 0$ and $x = 4$ and calculate the slope of the line.
    (vi) Deduce the slope at the point P.
    (vii) Show that $Q(-2, 4)$ is a point on the curve.
    (viii) Deduce the slope at the point Q.

3. (i) Sketch the curve $y = x^2 + 4x - 5$ in the domain $-3 \leq x \leq 3$.
    (ii) Devise a method to estimate the slope at the point $D(0, -5)$.
    (iii) Use your method to find the slope at D.

4. (i) Sketch the curve $y = x^3$ in the domain $0 \leq x \leq 4$.
    (ii) By joining $A(1, 1)$ to each of $(4, 64)$, $(3, 27)$ and $(2, 8)$, estimate the slope of the curve at A.

5. (i) Let $P(3, u)$ be a point on $y = x^2$. Find the value of u.
    (ii) Q is a point very close to P. t is a very tiny positive value.
        If the x-coordinate of Q is $3 + t$, find its y-coordinate in terms of t.
    (iii) Find the slope of PQ in terms of t.
    (iv) If t is zero, what will the slope of PQ now represent?
    (v) Why can't we let $t = 0$ *before* we do part (iii)?

Generalising the procedure

The work carried out by Newton and Leibnitz showed that there is a very simple rule for polynomials in x. They found, for example, that the formula for calculating slopes *for all points* on the curve $y = x^2$ is $2x$. It follows that at the point $(3, 9)$ on this curve, the slope would be $2x = 2(3) = 6$. Similarly, it was found that the slopes along the curve $y = x^3$ are represented by the expression $3x^2$.

The result is sometimes referred to as the **derivative**, as it is *derived* from the original function.

Notation

As we use two notations to describe functions, we must use the appropriate notation to indicate differentiation. Here are some examples:

Function	$y = x^2$	$f(x) = x^2$	$h = t^3$	$f(t) = t^3$
Differentiation	$\dfrac{dy}{dx} = 2x$	$f'(x) = 2x$	$\dfrac{dh}{dt} = 3t^2$	$f'(t) = 3t^2$
Pronunciation	dee y, dee x	f prime of x	dee h, dee t	f prime of t

Differentiation from first principles

Using the ideas of Newton and Leibnitz, we will now develop the method for finding the slope of the tangent to the curve $y = f(x)$ at any point $(x, f(x))$ on the curve.

To calculate the slope, a second point is needed that is *very close* to the first. For this, we should use the Δ notation. Δ ('delta') is the upper case version of the fourth letter of the Greek alphabet and means 'a small change in'. Thus, Δx represents a small change in x. This would allow us to set up the two points $(x, f(x))$ and $(x + \Delta x, f(x + \Delta x))$ which are, by definition, very close to each other. However, we will simplify the notation and use h in place of Δx.

Let the graph shown represent the function $y = f(x)$.
$(x, f(x))$ is a point on this curve and $(x + h, f(x + h))$ is a point further along the curve.

s is a line through these points.

t is a tangent to the curve at the point $(x, f(x))$.

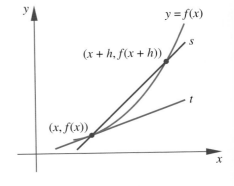

$$\text{Slope of } s = \frac{y_2 - y_1}{x_2 - x_1}$$
$$= \frac{f(x + h) - f(x)}{(x + h) - x}$$
$$= \frac{f(x + h) - f(x)}{h}$$

This would be a good approximation of the slope of the tangent t at the point $(x, f(x))$ if $(x + h, f(x + h))$ is *very close* to $(x, f(x))$. By letting h get smaller, the point $(x + h, f(x + h))$ moves closer to $(x, f(x))$.

The result is that the slope of s gets closer to the slope of t. In other words, as h approaches 0, the slope of s approaches the slope of t.

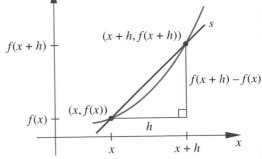

Mathematically speaking, we say that the slope of t is equal to the limit of the slope of s as h approaches 0. It is important to realise that h approaches 0, but *never* actually becomes equal to zero.

This is usually written $\lim\limits_{h \to 0} \dfrac{f(x + h) - f(x)}{h}$.

For neatness, this limit is written as $f'(x)$, pronounced 'f dash of x' or 'f prime of x'.

$$f'(x) = \lim_{h \to 0} \frac{f(x + h) - f(x)}{h}$$

When a functions is expressed in the form of $y = \ldots$, the limit is written as $\dfrac{dy}{dx}$.

$$\frac{dy}{dx} = \lim_{\Delta \to 0} \frac{\Delta y}{\Delta x}$$

$f'(x)$ or $\dfrac{dy}{dx}$ is called the

derivative or **differential coefficient** or **first derivative of y with respect to x.**

The process of finding this limiting value is called **differentiation**.

Definition

> The slope of the tangent to the curve $y = f(x)$ at any point on the curve is given by:
> $$\frac{dy}{dx} = f'(x) = \lim_{h \to 0} \frac{f(x + h) - f(x)}{h}$$

Note: It is important to understand that $\dfrac{dy}{dx}$ does not mean $dy \div dx$.

It means the derivative of y with respect to x.

The $\dfrac{d}{dx}$ is an operator. $\dfrac{d}{dx}$ means **the derivative with respect to x of.**

Thus, $\dfrac{dy}{dx}$ is often written $\dfrac{d}{dx}(y)$.

Procedure

Differentiation from first principles involves four steps:

1. $f(x + h)$ 2. $f(x + h) - f(x)$

3. $\dfrac{f(x + h) - f(x)}{h}$ 4. $\lim\limits_{h \to 0} \dfrac{f(x + h) - f(x)}{h}$

EXAMPLE 1

Differentiate $5x - 10$ from first principles.

Solution:

$$f(x) = 5x - 10$$
$$f(x + h) = 5(x + h) - 10$$
$$f(x + h) - f(x) = 5(x + h) - 10 - (5x - 10)$$
$$= 5x + 5h - 10 - 5x + 10$$
$$= 5h$$

$$\frac{f(x + h) - f(x)}{h} = 5 \qquad \text{(dividing both sides by } h\text{)}$$

$$\lim_{h \to 0} \frac{f(x + h) - f(x)}{h} = \lim_{h \to 0} (5)$$

$$f'(x) = 5$$

EXAMPLE 2

Differentiate x^2 from first principles.

Solution:

$$f(x) = x^2$$
$$f(x + h) = (x + h)^2$$

$$\overline{\begin{aligned} f(x + h) - f(x) &= (x + h)^2 - x^2 \\ &= x^2 + 2xh + h^2 - x^2 \\ &= 2xh + h^2 \end{aligned}}$$

$$\frac{f(x + h) - f(x)}{h} = 2x + h \qquad \text{(dividing both sides by } h\text{)}$$

$$\lim_{h \to 0} \frac{f(x + h) - f(x)}{h} = \lim_{h \to 0} (2x + h)$$

$$f'(x) = 2x$$

Exercise 13.2

In questions 1–12, differentiate the given expression from first principles.

1. $4x$
2. $8x + 3$
3. x
4. $6 - 3x$
5. $x^2 + 6$
6. $x^2 - 2x$
7. $x^2 + 11x$
8. $x^2 + 4x + 23$
9. $x^2 - 2x + 1$
10. $2x^2$
11. $2x^2 + 3x$
12. $3x^2 - 5x + 12$

13. Prove that the differentiation of $f(x) = kx$ is $f'(x) = k$ for all $k \in \mathbb{R}$.

14. (i) Prove that the differentiation of a constant is always zero.

    (ii) Sketch the line $y = 4$.

    (iii) What does your answer to (i) tell you about the line in part (ii)?

Differentiation by rule

Rather than repeat the work of Newton and Leibnitz, we will use the rules they discovered.

Rule 1: General rule

$$
\text{If} \quad y = x^n \quad \text{then} \quad \frac{dy}{dx} = nx^{n-1}
$$
$$
y = ax^n \quad \text{then} \quad \frac{dy}{dx} = nax^{n-1}
$$

In words:

Multiply by the power and reduce the power by 1.

EXAMPLE 1

Differentiate with respect to x.

(i) $y = x^5$ (ii) $y = -3x^2$ (iii) $y = 5x$ (iv) $y = \dfrac{8}{x^2}$

Solution:

(i) $y = x^5$ $\dfrac{dy}{dx} = 5 \times x^{5-1} = 5x^4$

(ii) $y = -3x^2$ $\dfrac{dy}{dx} = 2 \times -3x^{2-1} = -6x$

(iii) $y = 5x = 5x^1$ $\dfrac{dy}{dx} = 1 \times 5x^{1-1} = 5x^0 = 5$ $(x^0 = 1)$

(iv) $y = \dfrac{8}{x^2} = 8x^{-2}$ $\dfrac{dy}{dx} = -2 \times 8x^{-2-1} = -16x^{-3} = -\dfrac{16}{x^3}$

EXAMPLE 2

Differentiate with respect to x.

(i) $y = 6\sqrt{x}$ (ii) $y = \dfrac{2}{\sqrt{x}}$ (iii) $y = \dfrac{6}{x^{\frac{1}{3}}}$ (iv) $y = 7$

Solution:

(i) $y = 6\sqrt{x} = 6x^{\frac{1}{2}}$ $\dfrac{dy}{dx} = \frac{1}{2} \times 6x^{\frac{1}{2}-1} = 3x^{-\frac{1}{2}} = \dfrac{3}{x^{\frac{1}{2}}}$

(ii) $y = \dfrac{2}{\sqrt{x}} = 2x^{-\frac{1}{2}}$ $\dfrac{dy}{dx} = -\frac{1}{2} \times 2x^{-\frac{1}{2}-1} = -1x^{-\frac{3}{2}} = -\dfrac{1}{x^{\frac{3}{2}}}$

(iii) $y = \dfrac{6}{x^{\frac{1}{3}}} = 6x^{-\frac{1}{3}}$ $\dfrac{dy}{dx} = -\frac{1}{3} \times 6x^{-\frac{1}{3}-1} = -2x^{-\frac{4}{3}} = -\dfrac{2}{x^{\frac{4}{3}}}$

(iv) $y = 7 = 7x^0$ $\dfrac{dy}{dx} = 0 \times 7x^{0-1} = 0$

Part **(iv)** leads to the rule:

$$\boxed{\text{The derivative of a constant} = 0.}$$

Note: The line $y = 7$ is a horizontal line. Its slope is 0.

Therefore, its derivative (also its slope) equals 0.

In other words, the derivative of a constant always equals zero.

Sum or difference

If the expression to be differentiated contains more than one term, just differentiate, separately, each term in the expression.

EXAMPLE 3

Find $f'(x)$ for each of the following.

(i) $f(x) = x + \dfrac{1}{x^2}$ (ii) $f(x) = \dfrac{2}{\sqrt{x}} - \dfrac{1}{x^4} + 5$

Solution:

(i) $f(x) = x + \dfrac{1}{x^2}$

$\quad = x + x^{-2}$

$f'(x) = 1 - 2x^{-3}$

$f'(x) = 1 - \dfrac{2}{x^3}$

(ii) $f(x) = \dfrac{2}{\sqrt{x}} - \dfrac{4}{x^4} + 5$

$\quad = 2x^{-\frac{1}{2}} - x^{-4} + 5$

$f'(x) = -x^{-\frac{3}{2}} + 4x^{-5} + 0$

$\quad = -\dfrac{1}{x^{\frac{3}{2}}} + \dfrac{4}{x^5}$

Evaluating derivatives

Often we have to evaluate a derivative for a particular value. If the function is given as $y = f(x)$, then $\dfrac{dy}{dx}$ represents the derivative of the function and $\left.\dfrac{dy}{dx}\right|_{x=5}$ would represent the value of that derivative when $x = 5$.

Similarly, if $f(x)$ represents a function, then $f'(x)$ is its derivative and $f'(5)$ is the value of that derivative when $x = 5$.

EXAMPLE

(i) If $s = 3t^2 + 5t - 7$, find the value of $\dfrac{ds}{dt}$ when $t = 2$.

(ii) If $f(x) = \sqrt{x} + 3x$, evaluate $f'(4)$.

Solution:

(i)
$$s = 3t^2 + 5t - 1$$
$$\frac{ds}{dt} = 6t + 5$$
$$\left.\frac{ds}{dt}\right|_{t=2} = 6(2) + 5$$
$$= 12 + 5 = 17$$

(ii)
$$f(x) = \sqrt{x} + 3x$$
$$f(x) = x^{\frac{1}{2}} + 3x$$
$$f'(x) = \frac{1}{2}x^{-\frac{1}{2}} + 3$$
$$= \frac{1}{2\sqrt{x}} + 3$$
$$f'(4) = \frac{1}{2\sqrt{4}} + 3$$
$$= \frac{1}{4} + 3 = 3\frac{1}{4}$$

$\dfrac{ds}{dt}$ is the derivative of s with respect to t. $\dfrac{dA}{dr}$ is the derivative of A with respect to r.

Second derivatives

The derivative of $\dfrac{dy}{dx}$, that is, $\dfrac{d}{dx}\left(\dfrac{dy}{dx}\right)$, is denoted by $\dfrac{d^2y}{dx^2}$ and is called the **second derivative of y with respect to x**.

$\dfrac{d^2y}{dx^2}$ is pronounced 'dee two y, dee x squared'.

The derivative of $f'(x)$ is denoted by $f''(x)$ and is called the **second derivative of $f(x)$ with respect to x**.

Note: The second derivative, $\dfrac{d^2y}{dx^2}$, is **not** the same as the square of the first derivative, $\dfrac{dy}{dx}$.

In other words, $\dfrac{d^2y}{dx^2} \neq \left(\dfrac{dy}{dx}\right)^2$.

EXAMPLE 1

(i) If $f(x) = x + \dfrac{1}{x}$, find $f''(x)$ and $f''(2)$.

(ii) If $h = 10 + 30t^2 - 4t^3$, evaluate $\dfrac{d^2h}{dt^2}$ when $t = 3$.

Solution:

(i)
$$f(x) = x + \frac{1}{x}$$
$$f(x) = x + x^{-1}$$
$$f'(x) = 1 - x^{-2}$$
$$f''(x) = 2x^{-3}$$
$$= \frac{2}{x^3}$$
$$f''(2) = \frac{2}{2^3} = \frac{2}{8} = \frac{1}{4}$$

(ii)
$$h = 10 + 30t^2 - 4t^3$$
$$\frac{dh}{dt} = 60t - 12t^2$$
$$\frac{d^2h}{dt^2} = 60 - 24t$$
$$\left.\frac{d^2h}{dt^2}\right|_{t=3} = 60 - 24(3) = -12$$

EXAMPLE 2

If $y = x^4$, show that $\dfrac{4y}{3}\left(\dfrac{d^2y}{dx^2}\right) - \left(\dfrac{dy}{dx}\right)^2 = 0$.

Solution:

$$y = x^4$$
$$\frac{dy}{dx} = 4x^3$$
$$\frac{d^2y}{dx^2} = 12x^2$$

$$\frac{4y}{3}\left(\frac{d^2y}{dx^2}\right) - \left(\frac{dy}{dx}\right)^2$$
$$= \frac{4x^4}{3}(12x^2) - (4x^3)^2$$
$$= 16x^6 - 16x^6$$
$$= 0 \quad \text{as required}$$

Exercise 14.1

In questions 1–24, differentiate the expression with respect to x.

1. x^3
2. $3x^4$
3. $-5x^2$
4. $3x$
5. $-2x$

6. 5
7. -3
8. $\dfrac{1}{x^2}$
9. $\dfrac{2}{x^3}$
10. $-\dfrac{2}{x^5}$

11. $6x^{\frac{1}{3}}$
12. $\dfrac{1}{x}$
13. $\sqrt{x}$
14. $\dfrac{1}{\sqrt{x}}$
15. $\dfrac{1}{x^{\frac{2}{3}}}$

16. $x^3 - 5x$ **17.** $1 - x^2$ **18.** $x^2 - \dfrac{5}{x}$ **19.** $2x^2 - \dfrac{3}{x^4}$ **20.** $\dfrac{1}{x^2} + \dfrac{1}{x}$

21. $x^4 - \dfrac{2}{x^2}$ **22.** $6\sqrt{x} - \dfrac{2}{\sqrt{x}}$ **23.** $\dfrac{3}{x} + \dfrac{2}{x^2} + \dfrac{6}{x^{\frac{1}{3}}}$ **24.** $\dfrac{2}{x} - \dfrac{1}{\sqrt{x}} + \dfrac{3}{\sqrt[3]{x}}$

In questions 25–33, find $\dfrac{d^2y}{dx^2}$.

25. $y = 4x^3 + 6x^2$ **26.** $y = x^2 - x^4$ **27.** $y = 6x^3 - 12x^2 - 8x + 4$

28. $y = \dfrac{1}{x}$ **29.** $y = x^2 - \dfrac{8}{x}$ **30.** $y = \sqrt{x}$

31. $y = \dfrac{1}{\sqrt{x}} + \sqrt{x}$ **32.** $y = 8\sqrt{x} - \dfrac{1}{x^2}$ **33.** $y = 9x^{\frac{1}{3}} + \dfrac{18}{x^{\frac{1}{3}}}$

34. If $f(x) = 3x^2 - 4x - 7$, evaluate **(i)** $f'(2)$ **(ii)** $f''(-1)$.

35. If $f(x) = -4\sqrt{x}$, evaluate $f''(9)$.

36. If $A = 3r^2 - 5r$, find the value of $\dfrac{dA}{dr}$ when $r = 3$.

37. If $s = 3t - 2t^2$, find the value of **(i)** $\dfrac{ds}{dt}$ **(ii)** $\dfrac{d^2s}{dt^2}$ when $t = 2$.

38. If $V = 3h - h^2 - 3h^3$, find $\dfrac{dV}{dh}$ when $h = 1$.

39. If $A = \pi r^2$, find $\dfrac{dA}{dr}$ when $\dfrac{r}{5} = 1$.

40. If $V = \frac{4}{3}\pi r^3$, find $\dfrac{dV}{dr}$ when $2r - 5 = 0$.

41. $f(x) = 3x^2 - 4x$. If $f'(k) = 8$, find the value of k, $k \in \mathbb{R}$.

42. $f(x) = x^3 + 1$. If $f''(a) = 18$, find the value of a, $a \in \mathbb{R}$.

43. If $y = 3x^2 + 2x$, show that $y\dfrac{d^2y}{dx^2} - 3x\dfrac{dy}{dx} - 6x = 0$.

44. **(i)** If $y = 4x^3 - 6x^2$, show that $x^2\dfrac{d^2y}{dx^2} - 2x\dfrac{dy}{dx} - 12x = 0$.

(ii) Find the values of x for which **(a)** $\dfrac{dy}{dx} = 0$ **(b)** $\dfrac{d^2y}{dx^2} = 0$.

45. If $y = \dfrac{1}{x^2}$, show that $y\dfrac{d^2y}{dx^2} + \left(\dfrac{dy}{dx}\right)^2 - 10y^3 = 0$.

Product, quotient and chain rules

Rule 2: Product rule

> Suppose u and v are functions of x.
>
> $$\text{If } y = uv$$
>
> $$\text{then } \frac{dy}{dx} = u\frac{dv}{dx} + v\frac{du}{dx}.$$

In words:

> First by the derivative of the second + second by the derivative of the first.

EXAMPLE 1

If $y = (x^2 - 3x + 2)(x^2 - 2)$, find $\dfrac{dy}{dx}$.

Solution:

$$\text{Let } u = x^2 - 3x + 2 \qquad \text{and} \qquad \text{let } v = x^2 - 2.$$

$$\frac{du}{dx} = 2x - 3 \qquad\qquad\qquad \frac{dv}{dx} = 2x$$

$$\frac{dy}{dx} = u\frac{dv}{dx} + v\frac{du}{dx} \qquad\qquad \text{(product rule)}$$

$$\frac{dy}{dx} = (x^2 - 3x + 2)(2x) + (x^2 - 2)(2x - 3)$$

$$= x^3 - 6x^2 + 4x + 2x^3 - 3x^2 - 4x + 6$$

$$= 4x^3 - 9x^2 + 6$$

Rule 3: Quotient rule

> Suppose u and v are functions of x.
>
> $$\text{If } y = \frac{u}{v}$$
>
> $$\text{then } \frac{dy}{dx} = \frac{v\dfrac{du}{dx} - u\dfrac{dv}{dx}}{v^2}.$$

In words:

> $$\frac{\text{Bottom by the derivative of the top} - \text{Top by the derivative of the bottom}}{(\text{Bottom})^2}$$

Note: It is usual practice to simplify the top but not the bottom.

EXAMPLE 2

If $y = \dfrac{x^2}{x - 2}$, find $\dfrac{dy}{dx}$.

Solution:

$$\text{Let } u = x^2 \qquad \text{and} \qquad \text{let } v = x - 2.$$

$$\frac{du}{dx} = x - 2 \qquad\qquad \frac{dv}{dx} = 1$$

$$\frac{dy}{dx} = \frac{v\dfrac{du}{dx} - u\dfrac{dv}{dx}}{v^2} \qquad\qquad \text{(quotient rule)}$$

$$= \frac{(x - 2)(2x) - (x^2)(1)}{(x - 2)^2}$$

$$= \frac{2x^2 - 4x - x^2}{(x - 2)^2} \qquad\qquad \text{(do not expand the bottom)}$$

$$= \frac{x^2 - 4x}{(x - 2)^2}$$

Function of a function

When we write, for example, $y = (x + 5)^3$, we say that y is a function of x.
If we let $u = (x + 5)$, then $y = u^3$, where $u = (x + 5)$.
We say that y is a function of u, and u is a function of x.
The new variable, u, is the **link** between the two expressions.

Rule 4: Chain rule

> Suppose u is a function of x.
> If $y = u^n$
> then $\dfrac{dy}{dx} = nu^{n-1}\dfrac{du}{dx}$.

The chain rule should be done in **one** step.
In words:

> The result using the general rule times the differentiation of the expression.

EXAMPLE 3

Find $\dfrac{dy}{dx}$ for each of the following.

(i) $y = (x^2 - 3x)^4$ (ii) $y = \dfrac{3}{2x + 5}$ (iii) $y = \sqrt{4x - 3}$ (iv) $y = \left(x^2 + \dfrac{1}{x}\right)^3$

Solution:

(i) $y = (x^2 - 3x)^4$

$\dfrac{dy}{dx} = 4(x^2 - 3x)^3 \times (2x - 3)$

$= 4(2x - 3)(x^2 - 3x)^3$

(ii) $y = \dfrac{3}{2x + 5}$

$= 3(2x + 5)^{-1}$

$\dfrac{dy}{dx} = -3(2x + 5)^{-2} \times 2$

$= -\dfrac{6}{(2x + 5)^2}$

(iii) $y = \sqrt{4x - 3}$

$y = (4x - 3)^{\frac{1}{2}}$

$\dfrac{dy}{dx} = \tfrac{1}{2}(4x - 3)^{-\frac{1}{2}} \times 4$

$= \dfrac{2}{(4x - 3)^{\frac{1}{2}}}$

$= \dfrac{2}{\sqrt{4x - 3}}$

(iv) $y = \left(x^2 + \dfrac{1}{x}\right)^3$

$= (x^2 + x^{-1})^3$

$\dfrac{dy}{dx} = 3(x^2 + x^{-1})^2 \times (2x - x^{-2})$

$= 3\left(x^2 + \dfrac{1}{x}\right)^2 \left(2x - \dfrac{1}{x^2}\right)$

Often we have to deal with a combination of the product, quotient or chain rules.

EXAMPLE 4

Find $\dfrac{dy}{dx}$ if: (i) $y = x\sqrt{9 - x^2}$ (ii) $y = \sqrt{\dfrac{1 - x}{1 + x}}$

Solution:

(i) $y = x\sqrt{9 - x^2}$

$y = x(9 - x^2)^{\frac{1}{2}}$

$\dfrac{dy}{dx} = (x)\left[\tfrac{1}{2}(9 - x^2)^{-\frac{1}{2}} \times (-2x)\right] + (9 - x^2)^{\frac{1}{2}}(1)$ (product rule and chain rule)

$\uparrow$

(chain rule here)

$= -x^2(9 - x^2)^{-\frac{1}{2}} + (9 - x^2)^{\frac{1}{2}}$

$= -\dfrac{x^2}{\sqrt{9 - x^2}} + \sqrt{9 - x^2}$

(ii) $y = \sqrt{\dfrac{1-x}{1+x}}$

$y = \left(\dfrac{1-x}{1+x}\right)^{\frac{1}{2}}$

$\dfrac{dy}{dx} = \dfrac{1}{2}\left(\dfrac{1-x}{1+x}\right)^{-\frac{1}{2}}\left[\dfrac{(1+x)(-1)-(1-x)(1)}{(1+x)^2}\right]$

$\qquad = \dfrac{1}{2}\left(\dfrac{1+x}{1-x}\right)^{\frac{1}{2}}\left[\dfrac{-1-x-1+x}{(1+x)^2}\right]$

$\qquad = \dfrac{(1+x)^{\frac{1}{2}}}{2(1-x)^{\frac{1}{2}}} \times \dfrac{-2}{(1+x)^2}$

$\qquad = -\dfrac{1}{2(1-x)^{\frac{1}{2}}(1+x)^{\frac{3}{2}}}$

$\left(\begin{array}{l}\text{chain rule}\\\text{followed by the}\\\text{quotient rule}\end{array}\right)$

$\left(\left(\dfrac{a}{b}\right)^{-n} = \left(\dfrac{b}{a}\right)^{n}\right)$

Exercise 14.2

In questions 1–6, use the product rule to find $\dfrac{dy}{dx}$.

1. $y = (2x+3)(x-4)$
2. $y = (x+5)(x^2-3x+2)$
3. $y = (3x-4)(x^2-2x+3)$
4. $y = (x+3)(x^2-6x+8)$
5. $y = (5x^2-3x)(x^2-5x)$
6. $y = (3x^3-2x^2+4)(2x-1)$

In questions 7–12, use the quotient rule to find $\dfrac{dy}{dx}$.

7. $y = \dfrac{3x+2}{x+1}$
8. $y = \dfrac{2x-1}{x+3}$
9. $y = \dfrac{3x-1}{x^2-2}$
10. $y = \dfrac{x^2-1}{x^2+1}$
11. $y = \dfrac{1-x}{2x-x^2}$
12. $y = \dfrac{x^2-x-6}{x^2+x-6}$

In questions 13–18, use the chain rule to find $\dfrac{dy}{dx}$.

13. $y = (3x+2)^4$
14. $y = (x^2+2x)^3$
15. $y = (2x^2+1)^5$
16. $y = \sqrt{4x+2}$
17. $y = \dfrac{1}{2x-5}$
18. $y = \dfrac{1}{\sqrt{2x^2-4x}}$

In questions 19–24, find $\dfrac{dy}{dx}$.

19. $y = x^2(x+3)^4$
20. $y = 3x(x+2)^3$
21. $y = 3x^2(2x+3)^2$
22. $y = x^2\sqrt{2x+1}$
23. $y = x\sqrt{1+x^2}$
24. $y = \sqrt{\dfrac{x+1}{x}}$

25. If $f(x) = \sqrt{\dfrac{x}{x+3}}$, find the value of $f'(1)$.

26. If $f(x) = \sqrt{\dfrac{x-1}{x+1}}$, find the value of $f'(\tfrac{5}{4})$.

Differentiation of trigonometric functions

The basic rules for differentiating trigonometric functions are in the booklet of formulae and tables on page 25, but they are shown only for x. For more complex functions, use the chain rule.

Therefore, if you are using the tables, replace x with u and **always** multiply by $\dfrac{du}{dx}$.

Note: Powers of trigonometrical functions, such as $\sin^2 x$, are usually written without parentheses. When differentiating such expressions, always put in the parentheses. Thus, we write $\sin^2 x$ as $(\sin x)^2$.

Basic rule (page 25 of tables)	
$f(x)$	$f'(x)$
$\cos x$	$-\sin x$
$\sin x$	$\cos x$
$\tan x$	$\sec^2 x$

Chain rule	
$f(u)$	$f'(u) \times \dfrac{du}{dx}$
$\cos u$	$-\sin u \times \dfrac{du}{dx}$
$\sin u$	$\cos u \times \dfrac{du}{dx}$
$\tan u$	$\sec^2 u \times \dfrac{du}{dx}$

EXAMPLE 1

Find the derivatives of the following functions.

(i) $\cos 3x$　(ii) $\tan^3 5x$　(iii) $x \sin x$　(iv) $\sqrt{\cos x}$

Solution:

(i)　$y = \cos 3x$

$\dfrac{dy}{dx} = -\sin 3x \times 3$

$= -3\sin 3x$

(ii)　$y = \tan^3 5x$

$y = (\tan 5x)^3$

$\dfrac{dy}{dx} = 3(\tan 5x)^2 \times \sec^2 5x \times 5$

PTA : (power)(trig function)(angle)

$= 15 \tan^2 5x \sec^2 5x$

(iii) $y = x \sin x$

(use the product rule)

$$\frac{dy}{dx} = (x)(\cos x) + (\sin x)(1)$$

$$= x \cos x + \sin x$$

(iv) $y = \sqrt{\cos x}$

$y = (\cos x)^{\frac{1}{2}}$

$$\frac{dy}{dx} = \frac{1}{2}(\cos x)^{-\frac{1}{2}} \times (-\sin x)$$

(use the chain rule)

$$= -\frac{\sin x}{2\sqrt{\cos x}}$$

EXAMPLE 2

If $f(x) = \dfrac{x^2}{x + \cos x}$, evaluate $f'\left(\dfrac{\pi}{2}\right)$.

Solution:

$$f(x) = \frac{x^2}{x + \cos x}$$

$$f'(x) = \frac{(x + \cos x)(2x) - (x^2)(1 - \sin x)}{(x + \cos x)^2} \qquad \text{(quotient rule)}$$

$$f'\left(\frac{\pi}{2}\right) = \frac{\left(\dfrac{\pi}{2} + \cos\dfrac{\pi}{2}\right)\left(2\left(\dfrac{\pi}{2}\right)\right) - \left(\dfrac{\pi}{2}\right)^2\left(1 - \sin\dfrac{\pi}{2}\right)}{\left(\dfrac{\pi}{2} + \cos\dfrac{\pi}{2}\right)^2} \qquad \left(\begin{array}{l}\text{don't simplify:} \\[4pt] \text{put in } x = \dfrac{\pi}{2}\end{array}\right)$$

$$= \frac{\left(\dfrac{\pi}{2} + 0\right)(\pi) - \left(\dfrac{\pi^2}{4}\right)(1 - 1)}{\left(\dfrac{\pi}{2} + 0\right)^2} \qquad \left(\cos\dfrac{\pi}{2} = 0, \sin\dfrac{\pi}{2} = 1\right)$$

$$= \frac{\left(\dfrac{\pi}{2}\right)(\pi) - \left(\dfrac{\pi^2}{4}\right)(0)}{\left(\dfrac{\pi}{2}\right)^2}$$

$$= \frac{\dfrac{\pi^2}{2}}{\left(\dfrac{\pi^2}{4}\right)} = \frac{2\pi^2}{\pi^2} = 2$$

Exercise 14.3

In questions 1–18, find $\dfrac{dy}{dx}$.

1. $y = \sin 4x$
2. $y = \cos 3x$
3. $y = \tan 2x$

4. $y = \sin(2x - 3)$
5. $y = \tan(3x + 2)$
6. $y = 2 \tan x + \cos x$

7. $y = x^2 \sin x$
8. $y = 3x \tan x$
9. $y = x^2 \cos 2x$

10. $y = \dfrac{\sin x}{x}$
11. $y = \dfrac{1}{2 - \sin x}$
12. $y = \dfrac{1 + \sin x}{\cos x}$

13. $y = \cos^3 x$
14. $y = \sin^2 4x$
15. $y = \tan^4 3x$

16. $y = (1 + \sin^2 x)^3$
17. $y = \sqrt{\sin x}$
18. $y = \sqrt{\cos 2x}$

19. $f(x) = \dfrac{\cos x + \sin x}{\cos x - \sin x}$. Show that $f'(x) = \dfrac{2}{1 - \sin 2x}$.

20. If $y = \cos 3x$, show that $\dfrac{d^2y}{dx^2} = -9y$.

21. If $y = 3\cos x + \sin x$, show that:

    (i) $\cos x \left(\dfrac{dy}{dx} \right) + y \sin x - 1 = 0$

    (ii) $\dfrac{d^2y}{dx^2} - 3\left(\dfrac{dy}{dx} \right) + 2y - 10 \sin x = 0$

22. If $f(x) = \sin x \cos x$, evaluate $f'\left(\frac{\pi}{4} \right)$.

23. If $y = \cos 2x + 2\sin x$, evaluate $\dfrac{dy}{dx}$ at $x = \dfrac{\pi}{6}$.

24. $f(x) = \dfrac{\sin x}{1 + \tan x}$. Evaluate $f'(0)$.

Differentiation of inverse trigonometric functions

The basic rules for differentiating trigonometric functions are in the booklet of formulae and tables on page 25, but they are shown only for $\dfrac{x}{a}$. This is ideal for functions such as $\sin^{-1} \dfrac{x}{4}$ but not for $\sin^{-1} 5x$ or $\sin^{-1} \dfrac{3}{x}$.

For more complex functions, use the chain rule. Replace a with 1, x with u and multiply by $\dfrac{du}{dx}$.

Basic rule (page 25 of tables)	
$f(x)$	$f'(x)$
$\sin^{-1}\dfrac{x}{a}$	$\dfrac{1}{\sqrt{a^2 - x^2}}$
$\tan^{-1}\dfrac{x}{a}$	$\dfrac{a}{a^2 + x^2}$

Chain rule	
$f(u)$	$f'(u) \times \dfrac{du}{dx}$
$\sin^{-1} u$	$\dfrac{1}{\sqrt{1 - u^2}} \times \dfrac{du}{dx}$
$\tan^{-1} u$	$\dfrac{1}{1 + x^2} \times \dfrac{du}{dx}$

Note: The derivative of $\cos^{-1} u$ is **not** in the syllabus.

EXAMPLE 1

If $y = \tan^{-1}\left(\dfrac{x}{1 + x}\right)$, show that $\dfrac{dy}{dx} = \dfrac{1}{2x^2 + 2x + 1}$, $x \neq -1$.

Solution:

$y = \tan^{-1}\left(\dfrac{x}{1 + x}\right)$

(quotient rule)

$\dfrac{dy}{dx} = \dfrac{1}{1 + \left(\dfrac{x}{1 + x}\right)^2} \times \dfrac{(1 + x)(-1) - (x)(1)}{(1 + x)^2}$

$\boxed{\begin{array}{l} y = \tan^{-1} u \\ \dfrac{dy}{dx} = \dfrac{1}{1 + u^2} \times \dfrac{du}{dx} \end{array}}$

$= \dfrac{1}{1 + \dfrac{x^2}{(1 + x)^2}} \times \dfrac{1 + x - x}{(1 + x)^2}$

$= \dfrac{(1 + x)^2}{(1 + x)^2 + x^2} \times \dfrac{1}{(1 + x)^2}$

$\left(\begin{array}{l}\text{multiply the top and bottom} \\ \text{of the first fraction by } (1 + x)^2\end{array}\right)$

$= \dfrac{1}{(1 + x)^2 + x^2}$

$= \dfrac{1}{1 + 2x + x^2 + x^2}$

$= \dfrac{1}{2x^2 + 2x + 1}$

Given $y = \sin^{-1}(3x - 1)$, calculate the value of $\dfrac{dy}{dx}$ at $x = 5$.

Solution:

$$y = \sin^{-1}(3x - 1)$$

$$\frac{dy}{dx} = \frac{1}{\sqrt{1 - (3x - 1)^2}} \times 3$$

$$= \frac{3}{\sqrt{1 - (3x - 1)^2}}$$

$$\boxed{\begin{aligned} y &= \sin^{-1} u \\ \frac{dy}{dx} &= \frac{1}{\sqrt{1 - u^2}} \times \frac{du}{dx} \end{aligned}}$$

$$\frac{dy}{dx}\bigg|_{x=\frac{1}{3}} = \frac{3}{\sqrt{1 - \left(3\left(\frac{1}{3}\right) - 1\right)^2}}$$

$$= \frac{3}{\sqrt{1 - (1 - 1)^2}} = \frac{3}{\sqrt{1}} = 3$$

Exercise 14.4

In questions 1–12, find $\dfrac{dy}{dx}$.

1. $y = \sin^{-1} 2x$

2. $y = \tan^{-1} 3x$

3. $y = \sin^{-1}(x - 1)$

4. $y = \tan^{-1}(2x + 1)$

5. $y = \tan^{-1} x^2$

6. $y = \sin^{-1} 2x^3$

7. $y = (\sin^{-1} 5x)^2$

8. $y = \tan^{-1}\left(\dfrac{x}{3}\right)$

9. $y = \sin^{-1}\left(\dfrac{x}{2}\right)$

10. $y = \sin^{-1}(\cos x)$

11. $y = x \sin^{-1} x$

12. $y = 6x \tan^{-1} 2x$

13. Given $y = \sin^{-1}(4x - 1)$, calculate the value of $\dfrac{dy}{dx}$ at $x = \dfrac{1}{4}$.

14. Given $y = \tan^{-1}\left(\dfrac{1}{x}\right)$, show that $\dfrac{dy}{dx} = -\dfrac{1}{1 + x^2}$.

15. Given $y = \tan^{-1}(\cos x)$, calculate the value of $\dfrac{dy}{dx}$ at $x = \dfrac{\pi}{6}$.

16. If $y = \tan^{-1}\left(\dfrac{x}{a}\right)$, show that $\dfrac{dy}{dx} = \dfrac{a}{a^2 + x^2}$.

17. If $y = \tan^{-1} x$, show that $\dfrac{d^2y}{dx^2}(1 + x^2) + 2x\dfrac{dy}{dx} = 0$.

18. **(i)** Explain why $p\sqrt{1-q} = \sqrt{p^2 - p^2 q}$, $\quad p, q \in \mathbb{R}$.

    (ii) If $y = \sin^{-1}\left(\dfrac{x}{a}\right)$, show that $\dfrac{dy}{dx} = \dfrac{1}{\sqrt{a^2 - x^2}}$.

19. $f(x) = \dfrac{1}{x}\sin^{-1}\left(\dfrac{1}{x}\right)$. Show that $f'(\sqrt{2}) = -\dfrac{1}{2} - \dfrac{\pi}{8}$.

20. **(i)** If $u = \dfrac{1+x}{1-x}$, show that $\dfrac{du}{dx} = \dfrac{2}{(1-x)^2}$.

    (ii) Hence, if $y = \tan^{-1}\left(\dfrac{1+x}{1-x}\right)$, find $\dfrac{dy}{dx}$.

    (iii) Verify that $2x\left(\dfrac{dy}{dx}\right)^2 + \dfrac{d^2y}{dx^2} = 0$.

21. **(i)** Explain why $\sqrt{a} = \dfrac{a}{\sqrt{a}}$, $a \in \mathbb{R}$, $a > 0$.

    (ii) Given $y = \sin^{-1} x + x\sqrt{1-x^2}$, show that $\dfrac{dy}{dx} = 2\sqrt{1-x^2}$.

22. Given that $y = x + \sin^{-1} x$, show that $(1 - x^2)\dfrac{d^2y}{dx^2} - x\dfrac{dy}{dx} + x = 0$.

Differentiation of exponential functions

Exponent is another word for index or power. A function such as $y = 2^x$, in which the variable occurs as an index, is called **an exponential function**.

The function $y = e^x$ is called **the exponential function** or **natural exponential function**.

e is an irrational constant whose value is $2 \cdot 71828$ correct to six significant figures.

e^x is the only basic function which is its own derivative. That is:

$$\text{If } y = e^x, \qquad \frac{dy}{dx} = e^x.$$

Note: The positive number e behaves just like other positive numbers such as 2 or 5. e^x obeys all the usual laws of indices or exponents.

Using the chain rule

$$\text{Suppose } u \text{ is a function of } x.$$
$$\text{If } \quad y = e^u$$
$$\text{then } \quad \frac{dy}{dx} = e^u \times \frac{du}{dx}.$$

EXAMPLE 1

Find $\dfrac{dy}{dx}$ if: (i) $y = e^{x^2-3x}$ (ii) $y = \dfrac{2}{e^{3x}}$ (iii) $y = e^{\sin 2x}$ (iv) $y = \dfrac{x}{e^{2x}}$

Solution:

(i) $y = e^{x^2-3x}$

$\dfrac{dy}{dx} = e^{x^2-3x} \times (2x - 3)$

$\quad = (2x - 3)e^{x^2-3x}$

(ii) $y = \dfrac{2}{e^{3x}} = 2e^{-3x}$

$\dfrac{dy}{dx} = 2e^{-3x} \times (-3)$

$\quad = -6e^{-3x} = -\dfrac{6}{e^{3x}}$

(iii) $y = e^{\sin 2x}$

$\dfrac{dy}{dx} = e^{\sin 2x} \times (\cos 2x) \times 2$

$\quad = 2(\cos 2x)e^{\sin 2x}$

(iv) $y = \dfrac{x}{e^{2x}} = xe^{-2x}$

(use the product rule)

$\dfrac{dy}{dx} = (x)(e^{-2x}(-2)) + (e^{-2x})(1)$

$\quad = -2xe^{-2x} + e^{-2x}$

$\quad = e^{-2x}(1 - 2x)$

$\quad = \dfrac{1 - 2x}{e^{2x}}$

Note: The quotient rule could also be used in parts **(ii)** and **(iv)**.

EXAMPLE 2

If $y = xe^{-x}$, show that $\dfrac{d^2y}{dx^2} + 2\dfrac{dy}{dx} + y = 0$.

Solution:

$y = xe^{-x}$

$\dfrac{dy}{dx} = (x)(e^{-x}(-1)) + (e^{-x})(1)$ (product rule)

$\quad = -xe^{-x} + e^{-x}$

$\quad = e^{-x}(1 - x)$

$$\frac{d^2y}{dx^2} = (e^{-x})(-1) + (1-x)(e^{-x}(-1)) \qquad \text{(product rule, again)}$$

$$= -e^{-x} + (1-x)(-e^{-x})$$

$$= -e^{-x} - e^{-x} + xe^{-x}$$

$$= -2e^{-x} + xe^{-x}$$

$$= e^{-x}(x-2)$$

$$\underbrace{\frac{d^2y}{dx^2}}_{} \quad + \underbrace{2\frac{dy}{dx}}_{} \quad + \underbrace{y}_{}$$

$$= e^{-x}(x-2) + 2[e^{-x}(1-x)] + xe^{-x}$$

$$= xe^{-x} - 2e^{-x} + 2e^{-x} - 2xe^{-x} + xe^{-x}$$

$$= e^{-x}(x - 2 + 2 - 2x + x)$$

$$= e^{-x}(0)$$

$$= 0$$

Exercise 14.5

In questions 1–20, find $\dfrac{dy}{dx}$.

1. $y = e^{4x}$

2. $y = 2e^{3x}$

3. $y = e^{x^2}$

4. $y = e^{x^2 - 5x}$

5. $y = e^{4x^2}$

6. $y = e^{-x}$

7. $y = \dfrac{5}{e^{2x}}$

8. $y = \dfrac{2}{e^{x^2}}$

9. $y = e^{\sin x}$

10. $y = e^{\cos 2x}$

11. $y = e^{4\tan x}$

12. $y = e^{x \sin x}$

13. $y = xe^x$

14. $y = x^2 e^{5x}$

15. $y = e^{2x} \cos x$

16. $y = e^{-x^2} \sin x$

17. $y = \dfrac{x^2}{e^{2x}}$

18. $y = (3 + e^{x^2})^4$

19. $y = \dfrac{1}{3 - e^{2x^2}}$

20. $y = \sqrt{1 - 2e^{4x}}$

21. If $f(x) = \dfrac{1 + e^x}{1 - e^x}$, show that $f'(x) = \dfrac{2e^x}{(1 - e^x)^2}$.

22. If $f(\theta) = e^{1 + \sin \theta}$, evaluate   (i) $f'(0)$ (ii) $f''\left(\frac{\pi}{2}\right)$.

23. If $y = e^{2x}$, show that $\dfrac{d^2y}{dx^2} - 3\dfrac{dy}{dx} + 2y = 0$.

24. If $y = xe^{-2x}$, show that $\dfrac{d^2y}{dx^2} + 4\dfrac{dy}{dx} + 4y = 0$.

25. If $y = e^x \sin x$, show that $\dfrac{d^2y}{dx^2} - 2\dfrac{dy}{dx} + 2y = 0$.

26. If $y = e^{kx}$, find the values of $k \in \mathbb{R}$ for which $\dfrac{d^2y}{dx^2} - 3\dfrac{dy}{dx} + 2y = 0$.

27. If $y = e^{-nx} \cos kx$, $n, k \in \mathbb{R}$, show that $\dfrac{d^2y}{dx^2} + 2n\dfrac{dy}{dx} + (n^2 + k^2)y = 0$.

Differentiation of natural logarithmic functions

Logarithms to the base e are called **natural logarithms**.

The notation $\ln x$ is used as an abbreviation of $\log_e x$.

The function $y = \ln x$ is the inverse function of $y = e^x$
(exponents and logs are inverse functions of each other).

Note: $\log_e x$ or $\ln x$ is defined only for $x > 0$.

Natural logarithms obey the same laws as logarithms to any other base.

Laws of logs

$$\ln ab = \ln a + \ln b \qquad \ln \frac{a}{b} = \ln a - \ln b \qquad \ln a^n = n \ln a$$

Using the laws of logs before differentiating can simplify the work.

The following is worth remembering when evaluating the derivatives of natural logarithmic functions:

$$\ln e^k = k, \quad \text{for any } k \in \mathbb{R}.$$

For example,

$$\ln 1 = \ln e^0 = 0, \qquad \ln e = \ln e^1 = 1, \qquad \ln e^2 = 2, \qquad \ln \sqrt{e} = \ln e^{\frac{1}{2}} = \frac{1}{2}.$$

The rules for differentiating also apply to natural logarithmic functions.

Suppose u is a function of x.

If $\quad y = \ln u$

then $\dfrac{dy}{dx} = \dfrac{1}{u} \times \dfrac{du}{dx}$.

EXAMPLE

Find $\dfrac{dy}{dx}$ if: (i) $y = \ln(x^2 + 1)$ (ii) $y = \ln(\sin x)$ (iii) $y = \ln \sqrt{x^2 - 3}$ (iv) $y = x \ln x$

Solution:

(i) $y = \ln(x^2 + 1)$

$$\frac{dy}{dx} = \frac{1}{x^2 + 1} \times 2x$$

$$= \frac{2x}{x^2 + 1}$$

(ii) $y = \ln(\sin x)$

$$\frac{dy}{dx} = \frac{1}{\sin x} \times \cos x$$

$$= \frac{\cos x}{\sin x}$$

(iii) $y = \ln \sqrt{x^2 - 3}$

$$= \ln (x^2 - 3)^{\frac{1}{2}}$$

$$= \frac{1}{2} \ln(x^2 - 3) \qquad \text{(using log law)}$$

$$\frac{dy}{dx} = \frac{1}{2} \times \frac{1}{x^2 - 3} \times 2x$$

$$= \frac{x}{x^2 - 3}$$

(iv) $y = x \ln x$

(use the product rule)

$$\frac{dy}{dx} = (x)\left(\frac{1}{x}\right) + (\ln x)(1)$$

$$= 1 + \ln x$$

Exercise 14.6

In questions 1–12, find $\dfrac{dy}{dx}$.

1. $y = \ln 5x$

2. $y = \ln(2x + 3)$

3. $y = \ln(x^2 + 3)$

4. $y = \ln(\cos x)$

5. $y = \ln\left(\dfrac{1}{x}\right)$

6. $y = \ln(e^x + 2)$

7. $y = \ln(\sin 2x)$

8. $y = \ln(\tan 3x)$

9. $y = \ln(e^{2x})$

10. $y = x \ln x^2$

11. $y = x^3 \ln(x + 1)$

12. $y = x^2 \ln 4x$

In questions 13–18, use the rules of logarithms, or otherwise, to find $\dfrac{dy}{dx}$.

13. $y = \ln \left(\dfrac{2x}{x + 1}\right)$

14. $y = \ln(2x + 3)^2$

15. $y = \ln\left(\dfrac{1}{e^x}\right)$

16. $y = \ln \sqrt{1 + x^2}$

17. $y = \ln\sqrt{\sin x}$

18. $y = \ln \sqrt{\dfrac{x}{1 + x}}$

19. If $f(x) = \ln(e^x \cos x)$, show that $f'(x) = 1 - \tan x$.

20. If $f(x) = x^2 \ln x$, evaluate (i) $f'(e)$ (ii) $f'(1)$.

21. If $f(x) = \ln(\ln x)$, evaluate $f'(e)$.

22. If $f(x) = \ln\left(\dfrac{e^x}{1 + e^x}\right)$, evaluate $f'(0)$.

23. (i) If $y = \dfrac{\ln x}{x}$, show that $\dfrac{dy}{dx} = \dfrac{1 - \ln x}{x^2}$.

    (ii) Evaluate $\dfrac{d^2y}{dx^2}$ at $x = e$.

24. Given $f(x) = e^x \ln x$, $x > 0$, evaluate $f''(1)$.

25. Given $y = x \ln(x^2)$, show that $x\dfrac{dy}{dx} - 2x = y$.

26. Using $\ln \dfrac{a}{b} = \ln a - \ln b$, or otherwise, show that if $y = \ln\left(\dfrac{1 + x}{1 - x}\right)$:

    (i) $(1 - x^2)\dfrac{dy}{dx} = 2$ (ii) $\left(\dfrac{2x}{1 - x^2}\right)\dfrac{dy}{dx} - \dfrac{d^2y}{dx^2} = 0$.

27. (i) Factorise $a^x + a^{2x}$.

    (ii) If $y = \ln(1 + e^x)$, show that $\dfrac{d^2y}{dx^2} + \left(\dfrac{dy}{dx}\right)^2 = \dfrac{dy}{dx}$.

28. If $y = \ln\left(e^{-x}\sqrt{\dfrac{1 + 2x}{1 - 2x}}\right)$, show that $\dfrac{dy}{dx} = \dfrac{1 + 4x^2}{1 - 4x^2}$.

    Find the value of $\dfrac{dy}{dx}$ at $x = -1$.

    (Hint: $\ln \dfrac{ab}{c} = \ln a + \ln b - \ln c$)

Finding the equation of a tangent to a curve at a point on the curve

$\dfrac{dy}{dx}$ = the slope of a tangent to a curve at any point on the curve.

To find the equation of a tangent to a curve at a given point, (x_1, y_1), on the curve, do the following.

Step 1: Find $\dfrac{dy}{dx}$.

Step 2: Evaluate $\dfrac{dy}{dx}\Big|_{x=x_1}$ (this gives m, the slope of the tangent).

Step 3: Use m (from step 2) and the given point (x_1, y_1) in the equation $y - y_1 = m(x - x_1)$.

Note: Sometimes only the value of x is given. When this happens, substitute the value of x into the original function to find y for step 3.

EXAMPLE 1

Find the equation of the tangent to the curve $y = 3 + \sin x$ at the point $(0, 3)$.

Solution:

$$y = 3 + \sin x$$
$$\frac{dy}{dx} = \cos x$$
$$\frac{dy}{dx}\Big|_{x=0} = \cos (0) = 1$$

∴ At the point $(0, 3)$ the slope $= 1$. Equation of the tangent at the point $(0, 3)$:
$$y - 3 = 1(x - 0)$$
$$y - 3 = x$$
$$x - y + 3 = 0$$

413

Sometimes we are given the value of $\dfrac{dy}{dx}$ and asked to find unknown coefficients.

EXAMPLE 2

The slope of the tangent to the curve $y = ax^3 + bx + 4$ is 21 at the point $(2, 14)$ on the curve.

Find the value of a and the value of b.

Solution:

$$y = ax^3 + bx + 4$$

$$\dfrac{dy}{dx} = 3ax^2 + b \qquad \text{(slope)}$$

$$\text{slope} = 21 \qquad \text{(when } x = 2\text{)}$$

$$3a(2)^2 + b = 21 \qquad \text{(put in } x = 2\text{)}$$

$$12a + b = 21 \qquad ①$$

Given: $(2, 14)$ is on the curve.

Thus, $\quad 14 = a(2)^3 + b(2) + 4$

$$14 = 8a + 2b + 4$$

$$8a + 2b = 10$$

$$4a + b = 5 \qquad ②$$

Solving the simultaneous equations ① and ② gives $a = 2$ and $b = -3$.

Exercise 15.1

In questions 1–8, find the equation of the tangent to the curve.

1. $y = 3 + 2x - x^2$ at $(2, 3)$

2. $y = x^3 - 2x^2 - 4x + 1$ at $(-1, 2)$

3. $y = (2x + 3)^3$ at $(-1, 1)$

4. $y = \dfrac{6x - 3}{4x + 2}$ at $\left(1, \tfrac{1}{2}\right)$

5. $y = 2x + \dfrac{1}{x}$ at $x = \dfrac{1}{2}$

6. $y = \ln x$ at $x = 1$

7. $y = 2\cos x + \sin x$ at $(0, 2)$

8. $y = \tan^{-1} x$ at $x = 0$

9. Find the equation of the tangent to the curve $y = x + e^{2x}$ at the point where $x = 0$.

10. (i) Find the coordinates of the points on the curve $y = \dfrac{x}{1 + x}$ at which the tangents to the curve are parallel to the line $x - y + 8 = 0$.

    (ii) Find the equations of the two tangents at these points.

11. The slope of the tangent to the curve $y = x^4 - 1$ at the point P is 32. Find the coordinates of P.

12. The slope of the tangent to the curve $y = ax^2 + bx + 6$ at the point $(2, 4)$ is 3. Find the value of a and the value of b.

13. The slope of the tangent to the curve $y = px^2 + 1$ at the point $(1, q)$ is 6. Find the value of p and the value of q.

14. (i) Show that there is only one point on the curve $y = 6x^3 + 6x^2 + 2x - 1$ where the slope is zero.

    (ii) Find the equation of the tangent at this point.

15. The curve $y = \dfrac{p + qx}{x(x + 2)}$, $p, q \in \mathbb{R}$, $x \neq 0$, $x \neq -2$, has zero slope at the point $(1, -2)$. Find the value of p and the value of q.

16. A curve is represented by $y = ax^2 + bx + c$, where a, b and c are constants. The curve passes through $(1, 8)$ and $(0, -7)$. At the point $(1, 8)$ the slope is 17.

    (i) Find the values of a, b and c.

    (ii) Find the coordinates of the two points where the curve cuts the x-axis.

    (iii) Hence, sketch the curve.

17. The equation of a curve is $y = ax^3 + bx^2 + cx + d$ where a, b, c and d are constants. The curve passes through $(0, 8)$ and $(1, 6)$. At these points the slopes are 2 and -5, respectively.

    (i) Find the values of a, b, c and d.

    (ii) Show that the curve crosses the x-axis at the point $(4, 0)$.

    (iii) Find the coordinates of the other two points where the curve cuts the x-axis.

    (iv) Hence, sketch the curve.

Increasing and decreasing

$\dfrac{dy}{dx}$, being the slope of a tangent to a curve at any point on the curve, can be used to determine if, and where, a curve is increasing or decreasing.

Note: Graphs are read from left to right.

Where a curve is increasing, the tangent to the curve will have a positive slope. Therefore, where a curve is increasing, $\dfrac{dy}{dx}$ will be positive.

Where a curve is decreasing, the tangent to the curve will have a negative slope. Therefore, where a curve is decreasing, $\dfrac{dy}{dx}$ will be negative.

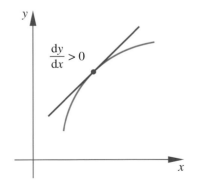

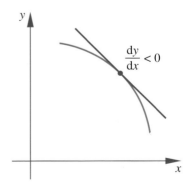

EXAMPLE

If $y = \dfrac{2x}{1 - x}$, show that $\dfrac{dy}{dx} > 0$ for all $x \neq 1$.

Solution:

$$y = \frac{2x}{1 - x}$$

$$\frac{dy}{dx} = \frac{(1 - x)(2) - (2x)(-1)}{(1 - x)^2} \qquad \text{(quotient rule)}$$

$$= \frac{2 - 2x + 2x}{(1 - x)^2}$$

$$\frac{dy}{dx} = \frac{2}{(1 - x)^2}$$

Since $2 > 0$ and $(1 - x)^2 > 0$ for all $x \neq 1$, it follows that $\dfrac{2}{(1 - x)^2} > 0$ for all $x \neq 1$.

$\therefore \dfrac{dy}{dx} > 0$ for all $x \neq 1$.

Note: (any real number)^2 will always be a positive number unless the number is zero.

$\therefore (1 - x)^2$ must always be positive, unless $x = 1$, which gives $0^2 = 0$.

Exercise 15.2

1. Let $f(x) = x^2 - 2x - 8$. Find the values of x for which $f(x)$ is (i) decreasing (ii) increasing.

2. Let $f(x) = x^3 + 4x + 2$.

   (i) Show that $f'(x) > 0$ for all $x \in \mathbb{R}$.

   (ii) Explain why this function is bijective.

3. Let $y = \dfrac{x + 2}{x + 1}$.

   (i) Show that $\dfrac{dy}{dx} < 0$ always.

   (ii) Explain why this function is bijective.

4. Let $y = 10 - 3x + 3x^2 - x^3$. Show that $\dfrac{dy}{dx} \leq 0$ for all $x \in \mathbb{R}$.

5. Let $f(x) = x^3 - 3x^2 - 9x + 2$. Find the values of x for which $f'(x) < 0$.

6. Let $f(x) = \dfrac{x^2 + 3}{x + 1}$, $x \neq -1$. Find the values of x for which $f'(x) > 0$.

7. Let $f(x) = x - \sin x$. Show that $f'(x) > 0$ for $0 < x < \dfrac{\pi}{2}$.

8. An artificial ski slope is described by the function

$$h = 165 - 120s + 60s^2 - 10s^3,$$

where s is the horizontal distance and h is the height of the slope. Show that the ski slope never rises.

9. Let $f(x) = x \ln x$, $x > 0$. Find the values of x for which $f'(x) > 0$.

10. $f(x) = \dfrac{\sin x + \cos x}{\sin x - \cos x}$. Show that $f(x)$ is decreasing for all

$x \in \mathbb{R}$, $\tan x \neq 1$.

11. Prove that the curve $y = \dfrac{px + q}{rx + s}$, $x \neq -\dfrac{s}{r}$, is increasing for all x as long as $ps - qr > 0$.

Local maximum point, local minimum point and point of inflection

Local maximum point

To the left of P	At P	To the right of P
$\dfrac{dy}{dx} > 0$	$\dfrac{dy}{dx} = 0$	$\dfrac{dy}{dx} < 0$

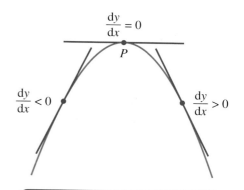

As the curve passes through the point P, $\dfrac{dy}{dx}$ changes from

positive to negative, i.e. $\dfrac{dy}{dx}$ is decreasing.

Thus, the rate of change of $\dfrac{dy}{dx}$ is negative, i.e. $\dfrac{d^2y}{dx^2} < 0$ for

a maximum point.

For a local maximum point:

$$\dfrac{dy}{dx} = 0 \text{ and } \dfrac{d^2y}{dx^2} < 0$$

Local minimum point

To the left of Q	At Q	To the right of Q
$\dfrac{dy}{dx} < 0$	$\dfrac{dy}{dx} = 0$	$\dfrac{dy}{dx} > 0$

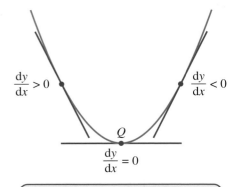

As the curve passes through the point Q, $\dfrac{dy}{dx}$ changes

from negative to positive, i.e. $\dfrac{dy}{dx}$ is increasing.

Thus, the rate of change of $\dfrac{dy}{dx}$ is positive, i.e. $\dfrac{d^2y}{dx^2} > 0$

for a minimum point.

For a local minimum point:
$$\frac{dy}{dx} = 0 \text{ and } \frac{d^2y}{dx^2} > 0$$

Note: Local maximum points or local minimum points are also called **turning points**. They are called **local maximum points** or **local minimum points** as the terms 'maximum' and 'minimum' values apply only in the vicinity of (or close to) the turning points, and not to the values of y in general.

Point of inflection

This is a point at which the curvature of a curve changes. In other words, at a point of inflection, a curve stops bending in one direction and starts bending the other way. At a point of inflection, the tangent to the curve cuts the curve at that point.

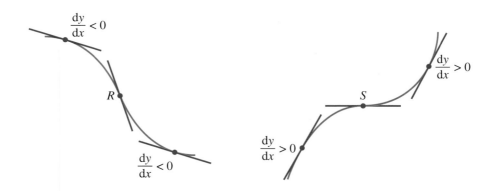

The points R and S are points of inflection.

Note: The point S is called a **horizontal point of inflection** or **saddle point**.

The slope of the tangent, $\dfrac{dy}{dx}$, does **not** change sign as a curve passes through a point of inflection.

> For a point of inflection:
> $$\frac{d^2y}{dx^2} = 0$$

Summary of conditions for a function $y = f(x)$

1.	Increasing	$\dfrac{dy}{dx} > 0$
2.	Decreasing	$\dfrac{dy}{dx} < 0$
3.	Maximum point	$\dfrac{dy}{dx} = 0$ and $\dfrac{d^2y}{dx^2} < 0$
4.	Minimum point	$\dfrac{dy}{dx} = 0$ and $\dfrac{d^2y}{dx^2} > 0$
5.	Point of inflection	$\dfrac{d^2y}{dx^2} = 0$

Note: Points on a curve where $\dfrac{dy}{dx} = 0$ are called **stationary points**. At a stationary point, the tangent to the curve is horizontal. Local maximum turning points, local minimum turning points and horizontal points of inflection (saddle points) are stationary points.

EXAMPLE 1

Find the coordinates of the local maximum point, the local minimum point and the point of inflection of the curve $y = x^3 - 3x^2 + 5$.

Draw a rough graph of the curve $y = x^3 - 3x^2 + 5$.

Solution:

$$y = x^3 - 3x^2 + 5$$

$$\frac{dy}{dx} = 3x^2 - 6x$$

$$\frac{d^2y}{dx^2} = 6x - 6$$

For a maximum or a minimum:

$$\frac{dy}{dx} = 0$$

$$\therefore 3x^2 - 6x = 0$$

$$x^2 - 2x = 0$$

$$x(x - 2) = 0$$

$$x = 0 \text{ or } x = 2$$

$$\left.\frac{d^2y}{dx^2}\right|_{x=0} = 6(0) - 6 = -6 < 0$$

$\therefore$ Local maximum at $x = 0$.

$x = 0;\quad y = (0)^3 - 3(0)^2 + 5 = 5$

$\therefore$ Local maximum point is $(0, 5)$.

$$\left.\frac{d^2y}{dx^2}\right|_{x=2} = 6(2) - 6 = 6 > 0$$

$\therefore$ Local minimum at $x = 2$.

$x = 2;\quad y = (2)^3 - 3(2)^2 + 5 = 1$

$\therefore$ Local minimum point is $(2, 1)$.

For a point of inflection:

$$\frac{d^2y}{dx^2} = 0$$

$$6x - 6 = 0$$

$$6x = 6$$

$$x = 1$$

$x = 1;\quad y = (1)^3 - 3(1)^2 + 5 = 3$

$\therefore$ Point of inflection is $(1, 3)$.

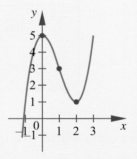

EXAMPLE 2

Let $f(x) = xe^{-ax}$, $x \in \mathbb{R}$, a constant and $a > 0$.

Show that $f(x)$ has a local maximum and express the coordinates of this local maximum point in terms of a.

Find, in terms of a, the coordinates of the point at which the second derivative of $f(x)$ is zero.

Solution:

For a maximum: 1. $f'(x) = 0$ and 2. $f''(x) < 0$.

$$f(x) = xe^{-ax}$$
$$f'(x) = x(e^{-ax})(-a) + e^{-ax}(1)$$
$$= -axe^{-ax} + e^{-ax}$$
$$= e^{-ax}(1 - ax)$$

$$f'(x) = 0$$
$$e^{-ax}(1 - ax) = 0$$
$$\therefore 1 - ax = 0$$
$$ax = 1$$
$$x = \frac{1}{a}$$

Note: $e^{-ax} \neq 0$ for any value of x.

$$f''(x) = ae^{-ax}(-a) + (1 - ax)(e^{-ax})(-a)$$
$$= -ae^{-ax} - ae^{-ax} + a^2xe^{-ax}$$
$$= ae^{-ax}(-1 - 1 + ax)$$
$$= ae^{-ax}(ax - 2)$$

$$f(x) = xe^{-ax}$$
$$f'\left(\frac{1}{a}\right) = ae^{-a\left(\frac{1}{a}\right)}\left[a\left(\frac{1}{a}\right) - 2\right]$$
$$= ae^{-1}(1 - 2)$$
$$= -ae^{-1}$$
$$= -\frac{a}{e} < 0 \qquad (\text{as } a > 0)$$

Local maximum occurs at $x = \frac{1}{a}$.

$$f(x) = xe^{-ax}$$

$$f\left(\frac{1}{a}\right) = \frac{1}{a}e^{-a\left(\frac{1}{a}\right)} = \frac{1}{a}e^{-1} = \frac{1}{a} \times \frac{1}{e} = \frac{1}{ae}$$

Thus, the coordinates of the local maximum point are $\left(\frac{1}{a}, \frac{1}{ae}\right)$.

$$f''(x) = 0$$
$$ae^{-ax}(ax - 2) = 0$$
$$\therefore ax - 2 = 0$$
$$ax = 2$$
$$x = \frac{2}{a}$$

Note: $ae^{-ax} \neq 0$ for any value of x.

$$f(x) = xe^{-ax}$$
$$f\left(\frac{2}{a}\right) = \frac{2}{a}e^{-a\left(\frac{2}{a}\right)}$$
$$= \frac{2}{a}e^{-2}$$
$$= \frac{2}{a} \times \frac{1}{e^2}$$
$$= \frac{2}{ae^2}$$

Thus, the coordinates of the point at which $f''(x) = 0$ are $\left(\frac{2}{a}, \frac{2}{ae^2}\right)$.

Exercise 15.3

In questions 1–3, find the coordinates of the turning point of each of the given functions and determine if each turning point is a local maximum or local minimum.

1. $y = x^2 - 2x + 5$
2. $y = 3x^2 + 6x - 5$
3. $y = 1 - 12x - 2x^2$

In questions 4–7, find the coordinates of the local maximum point, the local minimum point and the point of inflection of the function. Draw a rough graph of the function.

4. $y = x^3 - 6x^2 + 9x - 5$
5. $y = 12x - x^3$
6. $y = x^3 - 9x^2 + 15x + 10$
7. $y = 2 - 3x^2 - x^3$

8. (i) Let $f(x) = x + \dfrac{1}{x}$, $x \neq 0$. Find the coordinates of the local maximum and the local minimum of $f(x)$.

   (ii) Verify that $f(x)$ has no points of inflection.

9. If $f(x) = x^4 - 4x^3$, find the coordinates of any points of inflection.

10. (i) $f(x) = x^4 - 2x^2$. Verify that $f(x)$ has one local maximum and two local minimum points and calculate the coordinates of these points.

    (ii) Find the coordinates of the two points of inflection of $f(x)$.

11. Let $f(x) = \dfrac{4x - 3}{x^2 + 1}$.

    Calculate the coordinates of the local maximum point and the local minimum point of $f(x)$.

In questions 12–19, find the coordinates of any turning points of each of the following and determine whether they are local maximum points or local minimum points.

12. $y = x^3 - 45x^2 + 600x + 20$
13. $y = \frac{1}{4}x^4 - x^3 - 5x^2 + 1$

14. $y = x \ln x - 2x$, $x > 0$
15. $y = \dfrac{\ln x}{x}$, $x > 0$

16. $y = e^{x^2}$
17. $y = xe^x$

18. $y = x^2 e^{-x}$
19. $y = (1 - \ln x)^2$, $x > 0$

20. Let $f(x) = xe^{-x}$. Find:

    (i) $f'(x)$

    (ii) $f''(x)$

    (iii) The coordinates of the turning point and determine if it is a maximum or a minimum

    (iv) The coordinates of the point of inflection

21. **(i)** Given that the curve $y = ax^2 + 12x + 1$ has a turning point at $x = 2$, calculate the value of a.

   (ii) Is the point a maximum or a minimum?

22. The curve $y = px^2 + qx + r$ has a maximum turning point at $(2, 18)$. If $(0, 10)$ is a point on the curve, find the value of p, q and r.

23. The curve $y = e^x (px^2 + q)$ has a local minimum point at $(1, -4e)$. Find the value of p and the value of q.

24. **(i)** Given that $y = e^{2x} \cos 2x$, find $\dfrac{dy}{dx}$ and $\dfrac{d^2y}{dx^2}$.

   (ii) Verify that $e^{2x} \cos 2x$ has a maximum value at $x = \dfrac{\pi}{8}$ and write down this maximum value.

25. **(i)** $y = e^{2x} - 2e^x$ has one turning point. Find its coordinates.

   (ii) Determine if it is a local maximum or a local minimum point.

26. Let $f(x) = e^{2x} - ae^x$, $x \in \mathbb{R}$ and a constant, $a > 0$.

   Show that $f(x)$ has a local minimum and find its coordinates in terms of a.

27. Consider the function $y = \frac{1}{3}x^3 + kx^2 + 36$ where $k > 0$.

   (i) Show that one of the turning points is independent of k and the other is dependent on k.

   (ii) Find the value of k for which the equation $y = 0$ has a repeated root.

   (iii) Find the range of values of k for which the equation $y = 0$ has only one real root.

28. **(i)** Let $f(x) = ax^3 + bx^2 + cx + d$, $a \neq 0$. Verify that $f'''(x) \neq 0$.

   (ii) If $b^2 = 3ac$, show that $f(x)$ has only one turning point.

29. Let $f(x) = 2x^3 - kx^2 + \dfrac{10k^3}{27}$, $x \in \mathbb{R}$ and $k > 0$. Find the coordinates of the local minimum and the local maximum points in terms of k.

Maximum and minimum problems

The technique of finding the local maximum or local minimum of a function can be applied to many real and practical problems, such as manufacturers wanting to maximise profits, farmers trying to minimise costs, speculators attempting to minimise risk, etc. These types of problem often require the construction of an appropriate function. We can then use our knowledge of differentiation to find the maximum or minimum.

Maximum and minimum problems can be solved with the following steps.

1. Draw a diagram (if necessary). Label the diagram with the variables and constants.

2. Write down an equation in terms of the variables in the diagram for the quantity to be maximised or minimised. (If the quantity to be maximised or minimised is expressed in terms of one variable, go to step 5.)

3. If the quantity to be maximised or minimised is expressed in terms of two variables (for example, $P = 2l + 2b$, $A = \pi r^2 + 2\pi rh$, $V = \pi r^2 h$), then read the question again to find the **constant** expression **linking** the two variables. From this constant expression, write one variable in terms of the other.

4. Using a substitution from step 3, write the quantity to be maximised or minimised in terms of one variable.

5. Differentiate the quantity to be maximised or minimised with respect to the single variable in step 4. Put this derivative equal to zero and solve the equation.

6. Reject values that don't make sense. Check, if necessary, that the value gives a maximum or minimum by using the second derivative.

   (i) $\dfrac{d^2y}{dx^2} < 0$ for a maximum value   (ii) $\dfrac{d^2y}{dx^2} > 0$ for a minimum value

7. Answer the question (for example, 'find the radius' or 'calculate the volume').

EXAMPLE 1

A rectangular area is enclosed by a three-sided fence with 100 metres of fencing, using a ditch as the fourth side. Find the dimensions of the rectangle if the area is to be a maximum, and find the maximum area.

Solution:

1.

Ditc

Let the dimensions be x m and y m and let the area be A m^2.

2. Maximise the area, A:
$$A = xy$$
(two variables, x and y)
Thus we need a link between x and y.

3. Link between x and y:
Given: Length of fence is constant $= 100$ m
Link: $2x + y = 100$
$$y = (100 - 2x)$$

4. Area in terms of one variable:
$$A = xy$$
$$A = x(100 - 2x)$$
$$A = 100x - 2x^2$$

5. $A = 100x - 2x^2$

$\dfrac{dA}{dx} = 100 - 4x = 0$ (max/min)

$-4x = -100$

$x = 25$

6. $\dfrac{dA}{dx} = 100 - 4x$

$\dfrac{d^2A}{dx} = -4 < 0$

$\therefore$ a maximum value

7. The dimensions:

$x = 25$

$y = 100 - 2x = 100 - 50 = 50$

Thus, $x = 25$ m and $y = 50$ m
are the required dimensions.

$A_{max} = xy$

$= 25 \times 50 = 1250$

Thus, the maximum area is 1250 m².

EXAMPLE 2

A rectangular sheet of cardboard is 24 cm by 15 cm. Four equal squares are cut from each corner and the flaps are turned up to form an open box. Find the length of the side of the square that makes the volume of the box as large as possible. Find this largest volume.

Solution:

1. Let the length of the side of each square be x cm, and let V cm³ be the volume of the box.

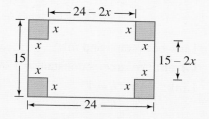
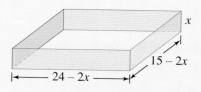

2. Maximise the volume, V:

$V = 1 \times b \times h$

$V = (24 - 2x)(15 - 2x)(x)$

$V = 4x^3 - 78x^2 + 360x$

(one variable, $\therefore$ skip steps 3 and 4)

5. $V = 4x^3 - 78x^2 + 360x$

$\dfrac{dV}{dx} = 12x^2 - 156x + 360 = 0$ (max/min)

$x^2 - 13x + 30 = 0$

$(x - 3)(x - 10) = 0$

$x = 3$ or $x = 10$

$x = 10$ is rejected, as the length of the side of the square must be less than half the breadth of the rectangle.

6.
$$\frac{dV}{dx} = 12x^2 - 156x + 360$$
$$\frac{d^2V}{dx^2} = 24x - 156$$

$$\left.\frac{d^2V}{dx^2}\right|_{x=3} = 24(3) - 156 = -84 < 0$$

∴ a maximum value.

Thus, $x = 3$ is the solution.

7. Maximum volume of the box:

height $= h = x = 3$
length $= l = (24 - 2x) = 24 - 6 = 18$
breadth $= b = (15 - 2x) = 15 - 6 = 9$

$$V_{max} = l \times b \times h$$
$$= 18 \times 9 \times 3$$
$$= 486 \text{ cm}^3$$

EXAMPLE 3

A closed cylindrical can is made so that its volume is 128π cm³. Find the dimensions of the can if the surface area is to be a minimum.

Solution:

1. Let the radius be r cm, the height be h cm and the surface area be A cm².

Surface Area

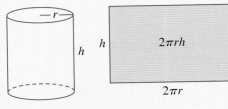 +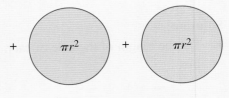

2. Minimise the surface area, A:

$$A = 2\pi r^2 + 2\pi rh$$

(two variables, r and h)

Thus we need a link between r and h.

3. Link between r and h:

Given: Volume is constant $= 128\pi$ cm³

Link:
$$\pi r^2 h = V$$
$$\pi r^2 h = 128\pi$$
$$r^2 h = 128$$
$$h = \frac{128}{r^2}$$

4. Surface area in terms of one variable:

$$A = 2\pi r^2 + 2\pi rh$$

$$A = 2\pi r^2 + 2\pi r\left(\frac{128}{r^2}\right) \qquad \left(\text{put in } h = \frac{128}{r^2}\right)$$

$$A = 2\pi r^2 + \frac{256\pi}{r}$$

$$A = 2\pi r^2 + 256\pi r^{-1} \qquad \left(\frac{1}{r} = r^{-1}\right)$$

5. $A = 2\pi r^2 + 256\pi r^{-1}$

$$\frac{\mathrm{d}A}{\mathrm{d}r} = 4\pi r - 256\pi r^{-2} = 0 \qquad \text{(max/min)}$$

$$4\pi r - \frac{256\pi}{r^2} = 0$$

$$4\pi r^3 - 256\pi = 0 \qquad \text{(multiple both sides by } r^2\text{)}$$

$$r^3 - 64 = 0$$

$$r^3 = 64$$

$$r^3 = 4$$

6. $\qquad \dfrac{\mathrm{d}A}{\mathrm{d}r} = 4\pi r - 256\pi r^{-2}$

$$\frac{\mathrm{d}^2 A}{\mathrm{d}r^2} = 4\pi + 512\pi r^{-3}$$

$$\frac{\mathrm{d}^2 A}{\mathrm{d}r^2} = 4\pi + \frac{512\pi}{r^3}$$

$$\left.\frac{\mathrm{d}^2 A}{\mathrm{d}r^2}\right|_{r=4} = 4\pi + \frac{512\pi}{64} > 0$$

$\therefore$ a minimum value.

7. $r = 4$

$$h = \frac{128}{r^2}$$

$$h = \frac{128}{16} = 8$$

Thus, $r = 4$ cm and $h = 8$ cm are the required dimensions.

EXAMPLE 4

a is the point $(0, 1)$.

$p(x, y)$ is a point on the curve $y = x^2$, where $x > 0$.

(i) Express $|ap|$ in terms of x.

(ii) Given that there is only one value of x
for which $|ap|$ is a minimum, find this value of x.

(iii) Hence, find the minimum value of $|ap|$.

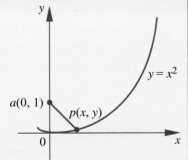

Solution:

1. $|ap|$ is the distance between the points $a(0, 1)$ and $p(x, y)$.

$$\begin{aligned}
|ap| &= \sqrt{(x - 0)^2 + (y - 1)^2} \\
&= \sqrt{(x - 0)^2 + (x^2 - 1)^2} \qquad (y = x^2) \\
&= \sqrt{(x^2 + x^4 - 2x^2 + 1)} \\
&= \sqrt{x^4 - x^2 + 1} \\
&= (x^4 - x^2 + 1)^{\frac{1}{2}}
\end{aligned}$$

(ii) Let $|ap| = l$

$$l = (x^4 - x^2 + 1)^{\frac{1}{2}}$$ (apply the chain rule)

$$\frac{dl}{dx} = \tfrac{1}{2}(x^4 - x^2 + 1)^{-\frac{1}{2}}(4x^3 - 2x) = 0$$ (max/min)

$$\frac{4x^3 - 2x}{2(x^4 - x^2 + 1)} = 0$$

$$4x^3 - 2x = 0$$ (multiply both sides by $2(x^4 - x^2 + 1)$)

$$2x^2 - 1 = 0 \qquad x > 0$$

$$2x^2 = 1$$

$$x^2 = \frac{1}{2}$$

$$x = \frac{1}{\sqrt{2}} \qquad \left(\text{reject } \frac{1}{\sqrt{2}} \text{ as } x > 0\right)$$

(iii) $|ap| = \sqrt{x^4 - x^2 + 1}$

$$|ap|_{\min} = \sqrt{\left(\frac{1}{\sqrt{2}}\right)^4 - \left(\frac{1}{\sqrt{2}}\right)^2 + 1} \qquad \left(\text{put in } x = \frac{1}{\sqrt{2}}\right)$$

$$= \sqrt{\frac{1}{4} - \frac{1}{2} + 1}$$

$$= \sqrt{\frac{3}{4}} = \frac{\sqrt{3}}{\sqrt{4}} = \frac{\sqrt{3}}{2}$$

⬤ EXAMPLE 5

Find the area of the rectangle of maximum area
that can be drawn inside a circle of radius r.
(There is no need to test for a maximum.)

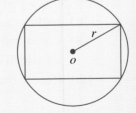

Solution:

1. Let the dimensions of the rectangle be $2x$
    and $2y$ and let the area of the rectangle be A.

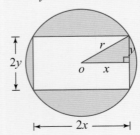

2. Maximise the area, A:

    $$A = 2x \times 2y$$
    $$A = 4xy$$

    (two variable, x and y)
    Thus we need a link between
    x and y.

3. Link between x and y:
    Given: radius of circle is constant $= r$
    Link: $x^2 + y^2 = r^2$ (Pythagora's theorem)
    $$y^2 = r^2 - x^2$$
    $$y = \sqrt{r^2 - x^2}$$

4. Area in terms of one variable
    $$A = 4xy$$
    $$A = 4x\sqrt{r^2 - x^2}$$
    $$A = \sqrt{16x^2}\sqrt{r^2 - x^2}$$
    $$A = \sqrt{16x^2(r^2 - x^2)}$$
    $$A = \sqrt{16r^2x^2 - 16x^4}$$

5. $A = \sqrt{16r^2x^2 - 16x^4}$
    $A = (16r^2x^2 - 16x^4)^{\frac{1}{2}}$ (apply the chain rule)
    $\dfrac{dA}{dx} = \frac{1}{2}(16r^2x^2 - 16x^4)^{-\frac{1}{2}}(32r^2x - 64x^3) = 0$ (max/min)

    $$\frac{32r^2x - 64x^3}{2(16r^2x^2 - 16x^4)^{\frac{1}{2}}} = 0$$
    $32r^2x - 64x^3 = 0$ (multiply both sides by $2(16r^2x^2 - 16x^4)^{\frac{1}{2}}$)
    $$64x^3 = 32xr^2$$
    $$2x^2 = r^2 \quad (x > 0)$$
    $$x^2 = \frac{r^2}{2}$$
    $$x^2 = \frac{r}{\sqrt{2}}$$

(No need for step 6.)

7. $x = \dfrac{r}{\sqrt{2}}$

    $$y = \sqrt{r^2 - x^2} = \sqrt{r^2 - \frac{r^2}{2}} = \sqrt{\frac{r^2}{2}} = \frac{r}{\sqrt{2}}$$

    $$A_{max} = 4xy = 4 \times \frac{r}{\sqrt{2}} \times \frac{r}{\sqrt{2}} = 4\frac{r^2}{2} = 2r^2$$

Notes: 1. Letting the dimensions of the rectangle be $2x$ and $2y$ rather than x and y avoids fractions.
     2. Writing $4x\sqrt{r^2 - x^2} = \sqrt{16x^2(r^2 - x^2)}$ avoids having to use a combination of the product and chain rule when differentiating.

Exercise 15.4

1. $x + y = 10$

   (i) Express y in terms of x.

   (ii) If $A = xy$, find the maximum value of A and the values of x and y which give this maximum.

2. Let $x + y = 12$. If $A = x^2 + y^2$, calculate the minimum value of A.

3. Let $x + y = 13$, where $x, y > 0$. If $W = 2x + 3y + xy$, write W as a quadratic in x. Calculate the maximum value of W.

4. The length of a rectangle is $(x + 6)$ m and its width is $(18 - x)$ m. Calculate the value of x that gives the rectangle of maximum area. What is this maximum area?

5. A garden is to be L-shaped, as shown. Its perimeter is 36 m.

   (i) Express y in terms of x.

   (ii) Express the area of the garden in terms of x.

   (iii) Find the value of x and the value of y that maximise the area of the garden.

   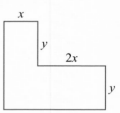

6. A piece of wire 32 cm long is bent into the shape of a rectangle. Show that for the rectangle to have maximum area, the rectangle will be a square.

7. The cost of running a machine is given by $C = 17V(V - 5) + 80$, where C = cent per hour and V is the number of revolutions per second. Find the number of revolutions per second that will minimise the cost.

8. A new slide is to be built for a children's playground. A long strip of metal, 80 cm wide, is to be used for the chute by bending up the sides.

   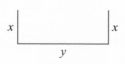

For safety reasons, the area of the cross-section should be a maximum.

(i) Write down an equation expressing y in terms of x.

(ii) Find an expression for A, the area of the cross-section, in terms of x.

(iii) Find the dimensions of the cross-section which makes the slide as safe as possible.

9. At a speed of x km/hr, a motorbike can cover y km on 1 litre of petrol, where

$$y = 5 + \frac{1}{2}x + \frac{1}{30}x^2 - \frac{1}{450}x^3.$$

Calculate the maximum distance that the motorbike can travel on 16 litres of petrol.

10. A box has a square base, x cm by x cm, and a height h cm, where $h + x = 12$.

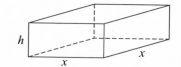

(i) Express h in terms of x.

(ii) Find the maximum volume of the box.

11. (i) A closed rectangular box is made of metal of negligible thickness. Its length is three times its width.

The volume of the box is 288 cm³. If its width is x cm, show that its surface area, A, is given by $A = \left(\dfrac{768}{x} + 6x^2 \right)$ cm².

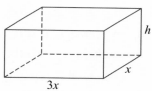

(ii) If the surface area of the box is to be a minimum, find the dimensions of the box.

12. A farmer wishes to fence in a rectangular enclosure of 162 m². One part of the enclosure is formed by a wall. The length of the rectangle is y m and the width is x m.

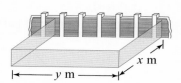

(i) Express y in terms of x.

(ii) What is the least possible length of fencing required for the other three sides?

13. The diagram shows a block with a base measuring $2x$ cm by x cm and a height of h cm. The total surface area of the block is 300 cm².

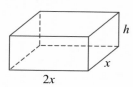

(i) Show that $h = \dfrac{150 - 2x^2}{3x}$.

(ii) Express the volume of the block in terms of x.

(iii) Find the value of x that gives the block of maximum volume and calculate this maximum volume.

14. A rectangular sheet of cardboard measures 40 cm by 25 cm. Four equal squares are cut from each corner and the flaps are turned up to form an open box. Find the length of the side of the square which makes the volume of the box as large as possible. Find this largest volume.

15. The width and length of a page in a book are x cm and y cm, respectively.

    (i) If the area of the page is 96 cm², express y in terms of x.

    (ii) It is necessary to leave a margin of 2 cm at each side of the text and 3 cm at the top and bottom (as shown).

        (a) Express, in terms of x and y, the area of the page available for text.

        (b) Express, in terms of x, the area of the page available for text.

        (c) Find the dimensions of the page if the area available for text is a maximum.

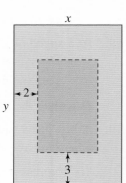

16. A rectangular sheet of cardboard measures 16 cm by 10 cm. Four equal squares are cut from each corner and the flaps are turned up to form an open box.

    (i) Find the length of the side of the square which makes the volume of the box as large as possible.

    (ii) Find this largest volume.

17. A display box needs to be 12 cm high and have a base area of 800 cm². It will be cut from a rectangular piece of cardboard as shown.

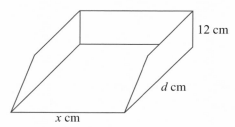
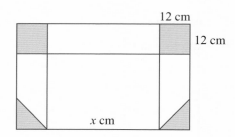

The width of the box is x cm and its depth from front to back is d cm.

    (i) Express d in terms of x.

    (ii) Show that the total area of the cardboard piece, A cm², is given by
    $$A = 1{,}088 + 12x + \frac{19{,}200}{x}.$$

(iii) Find the minimum value of A and hence find the dimensions of the cardboard piece which yields this minimum.

18. The diagram shows a minor sector OAB of a circle of radius r cm and angle θ radians. The perimeter of the sector is 12 cm and its area is A cm^2.

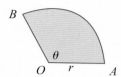

   (i) Express θ in terms of r.

   (ii) Show that $A = 6r - r^2$.

   (iii) Find the maximum value of A and the corresponding value of θ.

19. A closed cylinder has a base radius of r cm and a perpendicular height of h cm. Its total surface area is 96π cm^2.

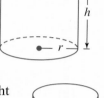

   (i) Express h in terms of r.

   (ii) If the volume of the cylinder is to be a maximum, find the dimensions of the cylinder.

   (iii) Find the maximum volume in terms of π.

20. An open cylindrical can, with no lid, has a base radius of r cm and a height of h cm. The total outer surface area of the can is 300π cm^2.

   (i) Express h in terms of r.

   (ii) Show that the volume V cm^3 is given by:

   $$V = 150\pi r - \tfrac{1}{2}\pi r^3.$$

   (iii) Find the dimensions of the can that gives a maximum volume. Calculate this maximum volume.

21. A cylinder with an open top has a capacity of 512π cm^3.

   (i) Find the total outer surface area in terms of its radius.

   (ii) If the surface area is to be a minimum, what will be the dimensions of the cylinder?

22. Closed cylindrical tins are to have a volume of one litre (1,000 cm^3). The curved surface area (the walls of the tin) are to be made from rectangular sheets of length $2\pi r$ cm and width h cm, without any waste. However, stamping out each circular end of πr^2 cm^2 requires a square piece of tin of length $2r$ cm and some tin is wasted.

   (i) Express h in terms of r.

   (ii) Express the area of the tin used in terms of r and h.

   (iii) Express the area of the tin in terms of r.

   (iv) Tin plate costs 0·03c per cm^2. Find the radius, height and cost of the tin which will manufacture the tin most cheaply.

23. The shape of a playing field is a rectangle with semicircular ends. The rectangle has dimensions of x m by $2r$ m.

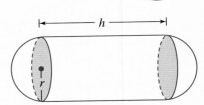

   (i) If the area of the rectangle is $3{,}200\pi$ m^2, express r in terms of x.

   (ii) Show that the perimeter, P m, is given by:

   $$P = 2x + \frac{3{,}200\pi^2}{x}.$$

   (iii) Find the minimum value of P.

24. A fuel storage tank is in the shape of a cylinder with a hemisphere at each end, as shown. The cylindrical part has a length of h m and the hemispheres each have an exterior radius of r m.

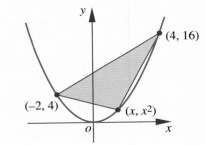

   The volume of the tank is 36π m^3. Show that:

   (i) $h = \dfrac{108 - 4r^3}{3r^2}$

   (ii) The total exterior surface area is given by $A = \dfrac{4}{3}\pi r^2 + \dfrac{72\pi}{r}$

   (iii) The minimum value of A is 36π cm^2

25. $(-2, 4)$, (x, x^2) and $(4, 16)$ are three points on the curve $y = x^2$.

   If these three points are the vertices of a triangle as shown, calculate the value of x so that the area enclosed by the triangle is a maximum, where $-2 < x < 4$, and find this maximum area.

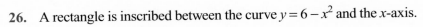

26. A rectangle is inscribed between the curve $y = 6 - x^2$ and the x-axis.

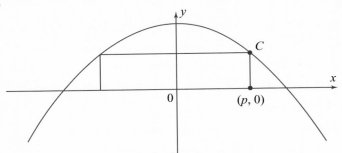

   (i) Find the coordinates of C in terms of p.

   (ii) Write an expression for the area enclosed by the rectangle in terms of p.

   (iii) Hence, find the value of p which makes the rectangle with the largest area.

27. o is the origin, $(0, 0)$. $p(x, y)$ is a point on the curve $y = \dfrac{4}{x}$, where $x > 0$. $|op|$ is the distance from the origin to p.

   (i) Express $|op|$ in terms of x.

   (ii) Given that there is one value of x for which $|op|$ is a minimum, find this value of x.

   (iii) Hence, find the minimum value of $|op|$.

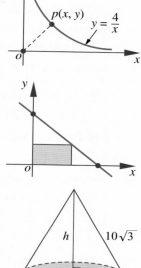

28. A rectangle is bounded by the positive x-axis, the positive y-axis and the line with equation $y = mx + c$.

   Find, in terms of m and c, the area of the rectangle of largest possible area.

29. A right circular cone with a base radius of r cm and a perpendicular height of h cm has a slant height of $10\sqrt{3}$ cm.

   (i) Express r^2 in term of h^2.

   (ii) If the volume of the cone is to be a maximum, find:

      (a) the perpendicular height   (b) the radius.

30. The slant height of a right circular cone is 12 cm. Find the maximum volume of the cone in terms of π.

31. A cylinder is inscribed within a sphere of radius 3. The cylinder has a radius r and a height $2h$.

   (i) Express r^2 in terms of h.

   (ii) Find the value of r when the volume of the cylinder is a maximum.

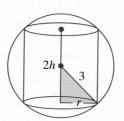

32. A window is in the shape of a rectangle surmounted by a semicircle (called a 'Roman arc').

   The perimeter of the window is $(12 + 3\pi)$ m.

   What width should the window be in order to maximise the area of the window?

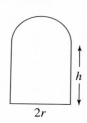

33. *PQRS* is a rectangular field 155 m long and 60 m wide. *PQ* is a path and the field has recently been ploughed. A woman can run at an average speed of 260 m per minute along the path and 100 m per minute on the field. She wants to reach the point *R* as quickly as possible. She runs to a point *U* along the path and then from *U* to *R*.

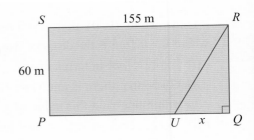

(i) If $|UQ| = x$ m, express, in terms of x:

    (a) $|PU|$ (b) $|UR|$ (c) the time taken to reach *R*.

(ii) Find the value of x for which the time is a minimum and calculate this time in seconds.

34. Two cars, *P* and *Q*, are approaching an intersection, *O*, as shown. At the same instant, *P* is 100 m from *O* and travelling east at a steady speed of 10 m/s, while *Q* is 300 m from *O* and travelling north at a steady speed of 20 m/s.

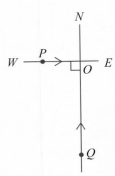

(i) Write down, in terms of t, the distances that *P* and *Q* will each have travelled after t seconds,

(ii) Write down, in terms of t, the distances that *P* and *Q* will be from *O* after t seconds.

(iii) Show that the distance between *P* and *Q* after t seconds is given by:

$$d = 10\sqrt{5t^2 - 140t + 1{,}000}.$$

(iv) Hence or otherwise, find after how many seconds *P* will be closest to *Q*.

35. The diagram shows a right circular cone of base radius 4 cm and perpendicular height 12 cm. A cylinder of base radius r cm and perpendicular height h cm stands inside the cone such that the cylinder touches the curved surface of the cone, as shown.

The cylinder has a volume of V cm^3.

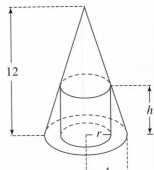

(i) Using similar triangles, or otherwise, show that $h = 12 - 3r$.

(ii) Show that $V = 12\pi r^2 - 3\pi r^3$.

(iii) Find the maximum value of V.

Graphs of slope of a curve

EXAMPLE

The functions $f : x \rightarrow x^2 + 6x - 3$ and $g : x \rightarrow (x + 3)^2$ are defined for $x \in \mathbb{R}$.

(i) Show that $f'(x) = g'(x)$.

(ii) Which of the following represents the graph of $f'(x)$?

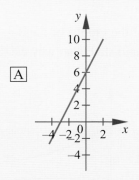
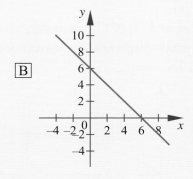
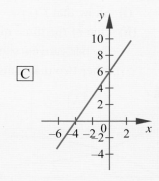

Solution:

(i)

$$f(x) = x^2 + 6x - 3$$
$$f'(x) = 2x + 6$$

$$g(x) = (x + 3)^2$$
$$g'(x) = 2(x + 3)^1 \times 1$$
$$= 2x + 6$$

$$\therefore f'(x) = g'(x)$$

(ii) Writing the expression for $f'(x)$ as $y = 2x + 6$, we know it's a line with slope $+2$ so graph $\boxed{B}$ is excluded, as it has a negative slope.

Next, we hope the y-intercept will be helpful, but with $y = 2x + 6$, the intercept should be at $+6$ and *all* the graphs pass through $(0, 6)$.

Instead, we can find the x-intercept by letting $y = 0$. If $2x + 6 = 0$, then $x = -3$, which indicates that graph $\boxed{A}$ is the one which represents $f'(x)$.

Exercise 15.5

1. (i) Sketch the graph of $f(x) = x^2 - 6x + 8$ in the domain $0 \le x \le 6$.
   (ii) Find $f'(x)$ and using the same axes and scales, sketch $f'(x)$.
   (iii) Explain the connection between the x-intercept of $f'(x)$ and minimum point of $f'(x)$.

2. (i) Sketch the graph of $g(x) = 4 + 3x - x^2$ in the domain $-2 \le x \le 5$.
   (ii) Find $g'(x)$ and using the same axes and scales, sketch $g'(x)$.
   (iii) Explain the connection between the x-intercept of $g'(x)$ and maximum point of $g(x)$.

3. (i) Sketch the graph of $f(x) = x^3 - 6x^2 + 11x - 6$ in the domain $0 \le x \le 4$.
   (ii) Find $f'(x)$ and using the same axes and scales, sketch $f'(x)$.

(iii) If P and Q are the x-intercepts of $f'(x)$, estimate the coordinates of P and Q to one decimal place of accuracy.

(iv) Hence, estimate the local maximum and local minimum of $f(x)$.

(v) Find $f''(x)$.

(vi) Sketch $f''(x)$ and use it to find the coordinates of the point of inflection of $f(x)$.

4. Let $f(x) = \tan^{-1}\left(\frac{x}{3}\right)$ and $g(x) = \tan^{-1}\left(\frac{3}{x}\right)$ for $x > 0$.

   (i) Show that $f'(x) = -g'(x)$.

   (ii) One of the three diagrams A, B or C, represents parts of the graphs of f and g. Using the derivatives, state which diagram is the correct one, and state also why each of the other two diagrams is incorrect.

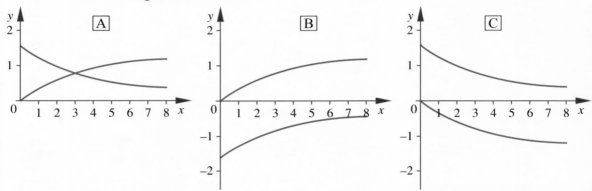

5. The functions f and g are defined on the domain $\mathbb{R}\backslash\{-1, 0\}$ as follows:

$$f : x \rightarrow \tan^{-1}\left(\frac{-x}{x+1}\right) \text{ and } g : x \rightarrow \tan^{-1}\left(\frac{x+1}{x}\right).$$

(i) Show that $f'(x) = \dfrac{-1}{2x^2 + 2x + 1}$.

(ii) It can be shown that $f'(x) = g'(x)$.

   One of the three diagrams, A, B or C, represents parts of the graphs of f and g. Based only on the derivatives, state which diagram is the correct one and also state why each of the other two diagrams is incorrect.

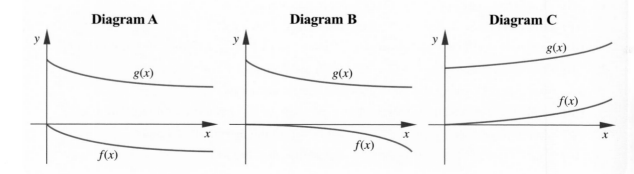

Rates of change 1

Displacement (position), velocity and acceleration

The derivative $\dfrac{dy}{dx}$ is the **rate of change of y with respect to x.**

It shows how changes in y are related to changes in x.

If $\dfrac{dy}{dx} = 5$, then y is increasing five times as fast as x increases.

If $\dfrac{dy}{dx} = -3$, then y decreases three times as fast as x increases.

In mechanics, for example, letters other than x and y are used.

If s denotes the displacement (position) of a particle from a fixed point, at time t, then:

> **1.** Velocity $= v = \dfrac{ds}{dt}$,
> the rate of change of position with respect to time.
>
> **2.** Acceleration $= a = \dfrac{dv}{dt} = \dfrac{d^2s}{dt^2}$,
> the rate of change of velocity with respect to time.

EXAMPLE

A particle moves along a straight line such that, after t seconds, the distance moved, s metres, is given by $s = t^3 - 9t^2 + 15t - 3$. Find:

  (i) The velocity and acceleration of the particle in terms of t

  (ii) The values of t when its velocity is zero

 (iii) The acceleration after $3\frac{1}{2}$ seconds

 (iv) The time at which the acceleration is 6 m/s^2 and the velocity at this time

Solution:

(i)

$$s = t^3 - 9t^2 + 15t - 3$$

$$v = \frac{ds}{dt} = 3t^2 - 18t + 15 \qquad \text{(velocity at any time } t\text{)}$$

$$a = \frac{d^2s}{dt^2} = 6t - 18 \qquad \text{(acceleration at any time } t\text{)}$$

(ii) Velocity = 0

$$\therefore \frac{ds}{dt} = 0$$

$$3t^2 - 18t + 15 = 0$$

$$t^2 - 6t + 5 = 0$$

$$(t - 1)(t - 5) = 0$$

$$t = 1 \text{ or } t = 5$$

Thus, the particle stopped after 1 second and again after 5 seconds.

(iv) Acceleration = 6m/s^2

$$\therefore \frac{d^2s}{dt^2} = 6$$

$$6t - 18 = 6$$

$$6t = 24$$

$$t = 4$$

After 4 seconds, the acceleration is 6 m/s^2.

(iii)

$$\frac{d^2s}{dt^2} = 6t - 18$$

$$\therefore \frac{d^2s}{dt^2}\Big|_{t=3\frac{1}{2}} = 6\left(3\frac{1}{2}\right) - 18$$

$$= 21 - 18$$

$$= 3\text{m/s}^2$$

Thus, after $3\frac{1}{2}$ seconds the acceleration is 3 m/s^2.

Velocity after 4 seconds:

$$\frac{ds}{dt}\Big|_{t=4} = 3(4)^2 - 18(4) + 15$$

$$= 48 - 72 + 15$$

$$= -9 \text{ m/s}$$

After 4 seconds, the velocity is −9 m/s. The negative value means that after 4 seconds it is going in the opposite direction to when it started.

Exercise 15.6

1. If $s = t^3 - 2t^2$, evaluate $\dfrac{ds}{dt}$ at $t = 3$.

2. If $\theta = 3t^2 - \frac{1}{3}t^3$, evaluate $\dfrac{d\theta}{dt}$ at $t = 2$.

3. If $V = \frac{4}{3}\pi r^3$, evaluate $\dfrac{dV}{dr}$ at $r = 5$.

4. A ball is thrown upwards and its vertical height above level ground after t seconds is given by
    $$h = 1{\cdot}5 + 29{\cdot}4t - 4{\cdot}9t^2 \text{ metres.}$$

    (i) How high was the ball above ground when it was thrown?

    (ii) Find $\dfrac{dh}{dt}$ and state what it represents.

    (iii) What is the maximum height reached by the ball?

    (iv) Find the velocity of the ball **(a)** when thrown **(b)** when $t = 3$ **(c)** when $t = 5$.
    (d) Why is the answer to **(c)** negative?

    (v) Show that the ball hits the ground within 7 seconds of being thrown.

5. A particle is moving in a straight line. Its distance, s metres, from a fixed point O after t seconds is given by $s = t^3 - 9t^2 + 15t + 2$. Calculate the following.
   (i) Its velocity at any time t.
   (ii) Its velocity after 6 seconds.
   (iii) The distance of the particle from O when it is instantly at rest.
   (iv) Its acceleration after 4 seconds.

6. A car, starting at $t = 0$ seconds, travels a distance of s metres in t seconds where $s = 30t - \frac{9}{4}t^2$
   (i) Find the speed of the car after 2 seconds.
   (ii) After how many seconds is the speed of the car equal to zero?
   (iii) Find the distance travelled by the car up to the time its speed is zero.

7. Marco's height h cm at age a years can be modelled by the equation

$$h = -\frac{a^4}{576} + (a - 1)^2 + 60 \qquad \text{for } 11 \leq a \leq 16.$$

   Find Marco's rate of growth when he is aged (i) 12 and (ii) 16.

   Give your answer correct to one place of decimals where appropriate.

8. The air resistance, R, to a body moving with speed v metres per second is given by $R = \dfrac{v^2}{100}$.
   (i) Find the rate of change of the air resistance with respect to the speed.
   (ii) Calculate this rate of change when $v = 16$ m/s.

9. After sugar is added to a cup of coffee and stirred, the concentration of sugar, measured in g/l, is given by

$$c = \frac{t^2}{200}(100 - t^2)^2 \qquad \text{for } 0 \leq t \leq 10,$$

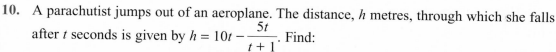

   where t is the time in seconds after the sugar is added.
   (i) Find the rate at which the concentration increases after 5 seconds.
   (ii) Show that the rate of change of concentration is zero after 10 seconds.

10. A parachutist jumps out of an aeroplane. The distance, h metres, through which she falls after t seconds is given by $h = 10t - \dfrac{5t}{t + 1}$. Find:
    (i) The distance she falls in the first second
    (ii) Her velocity after two seconds

11. The height of a tree is given by $H = 4 - \dfrac{9}{t+5}$ metres, where t is the number of years after the tree is ready to be planted in a garden.

   (i) How high was the tree when it was planted?

   (ii) Find an expression for $\dfrac{dH}{dt}$.

   (iii) Find its rate of growth when $t = 0$, $t = 4$ and $t = 10$ years.

   (iv) Explain why $\dfrac{dH}{dt} > 0$ for all values of t. What does this mean in practical terms?

12. A swimming pool is being drained such that the volume of water remaining after t minutes is given by $V = 100(40 - t)^2 \text{ m}^3$.

   (i) What was the volume of the water just as the draining began?

   (ii) How much water remained after 5 minutes?

   (iii) What was the average rate at which the water was being drained in the first 5 minutes?

   (iv) What was the exact rate at which the water was being drained when $t = 5$?

13. A particle moves in a straight line so that its distance, s metres, from a fixed point O at time t is given by $s = 1{\cdot}5t^3 - 10{\cdot}5t^2 - 4t + 10$.

   (i) If its velocity after k seconds is $3{\cdot}5$ m/s, find the value of k.

   (ii) If its acceleration after q seconds is 6 m/s^2, find the value of q.

14. The position, x metres, of a particle moving on the x-axis is given by $x = \cos 4t$ where t is in seconds. Find the velocity and the acceleration of the particle at $t = \frac{\pi}{4}$ seconds.

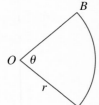

15. A piece of wire of length 20 cm is shaped to enclose a sector of a circle.

   (i) If the radius is r cm and the angle in the sector is θ radians, express θ in terms of r.

   (ii) Show that the area of the sector, A cm^2, is given by $A = 10r - r^2$.

16. A shrub's growth, measured in centimetres, can be represented by $H = 20\ln(3t + 1) + 30$ cm, where t is the number of years since it was planted.

   (i) How high was it when it was planted?

   (ii) Find an expression for the rate of growth of the plant.

   (iii) Find its rate of growth after (a) 1 year (b) 3 years (c) 8 years.

17. The distance, s metres, travelled by a car in t seconds after the brakes are applied is given by $s = 10t - t^2$.

   (i) Show that its acceleration is constant.

   (ii) Find the speed of the car when the brakes are applied.

   (iii) Find the distance the car travels before it stops.

18. The distance, s metres, of an object from a fixed point in t seconds is given by $s = \dfrac{t+1}{t+3}$.

   (i) What is the speed of the object, in terms of t, at t seconds?

   (ii) After how many seconds will the speed of the object be less than 0.02 m/s?

19. The equation $\theta = 3\pi + 20t - 2t^2$ gives the angle θ, in radians, through which a wheel turns in t seconds. Find:

   (i) The rate of change of θ with respect to time t

   (ii) The time the wheel takes to come to rest

   (iii) The angle turned through in the last second of motion

20. A plane is travelling at a steady speed horizontally at a height of 2,000 m above the ground.

A parachutist jumps from the plane and descends for 8 seconds without opening his parachute. The function which represents his height above the ground is

$$f : t \rightarrow 2{,}000 - 4t - 16t^2$$

where t is the time in seconds and $t \leq 8$.

After 8 seconds he opens his parachute and descends to the ground. This part of the descent is represented by

$$g : t \rightarrow 1{,}200 - 4t^2$$

where t is the time in seconds and $t > 8$.

   (i) Copy and complete a table of values for the descent using 2-second intervals ending with $t = 18$.

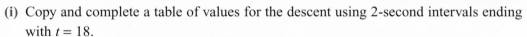

t	0	2	4	6	8		10	12	14	16	18
$f(t)$						$g(t)$					

   (ii) Using the same axes and scales, draw the graphs of $f(t)$ and $g(t)$ using appropriate scales for t on the horizontal axis and for $f(t)$ and $g(t)$ on the vertical axis.

   (iii) Use your graph to estimate how many seconds it takes the parachutist to reach the ground.

   (iv) Find $f'(6)$.

   (v) Find $g'(11)$.

   (vi) Compare the rate of change of $f(t)$ at 6 seconds and that of $g(t)$ at 11 seconds. Explain the physical difference between the two values.

Rates of change 2

Related rates of change

By convention, unless specified otherwise, the phrase 'rate of change' refers to the rate at which a variable is changing **with respect to time**. For example, if we are told the rate of change of h is 10, this means 'the rate of change of h with respect to time is 10'. In other words, we are given $\dfrac{dh}{dt} = 10$. Related rates of change, using differentials, can be related using the chain rule.

$$\frac{dy}{dt} = \frac{dy}{dx} \times \frac{dx}{dt}$$

$$\frac{dV}{dr} = \frac{dV}{dt} \times \frac{dt}{dr}$$

For example:In many rate of change problems we will deal with three things:

1. What we **want** to find.
2. What we are **given**.
3. What we **need** to complete the fraction (look for a link connecting the variables).

$$\textbf{Find} = (\textbf{Given}) \times \left(\begin{array}{c} \text{What we } \textbf{need} \text{ to} \\ \text{complete the fraction} \end{array} \right)$$

Note: cm/s means centimetres per second.

EXAMPLE 1

The radius of a circle increases at 4 cm/s.
What is the rate of increase of the area when the radius is 5 cm?

Solution:

The radius increases at 4 cm/s.

Thus, we are given $\dfrac{dr}{dt} = 4$ and asked to find $\dfrac{dA}{dr}$ when $r = 5$.

Let the surface area $= S$.

$$\text{Find} = \text{Given} \times \text{Need}$$
$$\frac{dA}{dt} = \frac{dr}{dt} \times \frac{dA}{dr}$$
$$= 4 \times 2\pi r$$
$$\frac{dA}{dr} = 8\pi r$$

$$\left. \frac{dA}{dt} \right|_{r=5} = 8\pi(5) = 40 \text{ cm}^2\text{/s}$$

Link connecting A and r:
$$A = \pi r^2$$
$$\frac{dA}{dr} = 2\pi r$$

EXAMPLE 2

Air is pumped into a spherical balloon at the rate of 300 cm³/s. When the radius of the balloon is 15 cm, calculate:

 (i) The rate at which its radius is increasing

(ii) The rate at which its surface area is increasing

Solution:

(i) Air is pumped in at a rate of 300 cm³/s.

We are given $\dfrac{dV}{dt} = 300$ and asked to find $\dfrac{dr}{dt}$.

$$\text{Find} = \text{Given} \times \text{Need}$$

$$\frac{dr}{dt} = \frac{dV}{dt} \times \frac{dr}{dV}$$

$$= 300 \times \frac{1}{4\pi r^2}$$

$$= \frac{300}{4\pi r^2} = \frac{75}{\pi r^2}$$

$$\left.\frac{dr}{dt}\right|_{r=15} = \frac{75}{\pi(15)^2} = \frac{75}{225\pi} = \frac{1}{3\pi} \text{ cm/s}$$

Link connecting V and r:

$$V = \frac{4}{3}\pi r^3$$

$$\frac{dV}{dr} = 3 \times \frac{4}{3}\pi r^2$$

$$\frac{dV}{dr} = 4\pi r^2$$

$$\therefore \frac{dr}{dV} = \frac{1}{4\pi r^2}$$

(ii) Let the surface area = S.

$$\text{Find} = \text{Given} \times \text{Need}$$

$$\frac{dS}{dt} = \frac{dr}{dt} \times \frac{dS}{dr}$$

$$= \frac{1}{3\pi} \times 8\pi r$$

$$\frac{dS}{dt} = \frac{8r}{3}$$

$$\left.\frac{dS}{dt}\right|_{r=15} = \frac{8(15)}{3} = 40 \text{ cm}^2/\text{s}$$

We are given $\dfrac{dr}{dt} = \dfrac{1}{3\pi}$ and asked to find $\dfrac{dS}{dt}$ when $r = 15$.

Link connecting S and r:

$$S = 4\pi r^2$$

$$\frac{dS}{dr} = 8\pi r$$

Exercise 15.7

In questions 1–6, complete the following derivatives using the chain rule.

1. $\dfrac{dy}{dx} = \dfrac{dy}{du} \times \underline{\quad}$

2. $\dfrac{dV}{dt} = \dfrac{dr}{dt} \times \underline{\quad}$

3. $\dfrac{dS}{dr} = \dfrac{dS}{dt} \times \underline{\quad}$

4. $\dfrac{dA}{dt} = \dfrac{dr}{dt} \times \underline{\quad}$

5. $\dfrac{dh}{dt} = \dfrac{dV}{dt} \times \underline{\quad}$

6. $\dfrac{dA}{dr} = \dfrac{dA}{dt} \times \underline{\quad}$

7. If $\dfrac{dx}{dt} = 5$ and $y = 2x^2 - 3x + 4$, find $\dfrac{dy}{dt}$ in terms of x.

8. If $y = (x^2 - 3x)^3$, find $\dfrac{dy}{dt}$ when $x = 2$, given $\dfrac{dx}{dt} = \dfrac{1}{2}$.

9. If $y = \left(\dfrac{x-1}{x}\right)^2$, find $\dfrac{dx}{dt}$ when $x = 2$, given $\dfrac{dy}{dt} = 4$.

10. The path of a projectile is given by
$$y = 2x - \dfrac{x^2}{20}, \quad x \geq 0.$$

    If $\dfrac{dx}{dt} = 4$, for all t, find $\dfrac{dy}{dt}$ when $x = 5$.

11. A stone dropped into a still pond causes a circular ripple whose radius increases at a rate of 1 metre per second.

    How rapidly is the area enclosed by the ripple increasing after 5 seconds?

12. The radius of a circle is increasing at a rate of $\dfrac{1}{\pi}$ cm/s. Find the rate of increase of the circumference.

13. (i) The area of a square, of side x cm, is increasing at the rate of 8 cm^2/s. Find an expression in term of x for the rate of increase of the length of a side.

    (ii) Find this rate of increase when $x = 16$ cm.

14. If $\dfrac{dV}{dt} = \dfrac{\pi}{2}$ and $V = \dfrac{4}{3}\pi r^3$, evaluate $\dfrac{dr}{dt}$ at $r = 2$.

15. A spherical snowball melts at the rate of 20 cm³/h.

    (i) What is the rate of change of the radius when
       (a) the radius is r (b) the radius is 2 cm?

    (ii) What is the rate of change of the surface area when the radius is
       5 cm?

16. A metallic cube, of side length x cm, is being heated in a furnace. The side lengths are expanding at the rate of 0·2 cm/s. Find the rates at which the cube's surface area and the cube's volume are changing when $x = 5$ cm.

17. If a hemispherical bowl of radius 6 cm contains water to a depth of h cm, the volume of the water is $\frac{1}{3}\pi h^2(18 - h)$. Water is poured into the bowl at a rate of 4 cm³/s. Find the rate at which the water level is rising when the depth is 2 cm.

18. A vessel is shaped such that when the depth of water is h cm, the volume is given by
$V = \sqrt{5 + h^2}$.

    If the height of the water is increasing at 18 cm/s, calculate the rate at which V is increasing when $h = 2$ cm.

ANSWERS

Exercise 1.1

2. $12x^3$ 3. $2x^2$ 4. 0   5. b^2 6. $x(x+3)$ 7. $3y(x-2y)$ 8. $ab(a+b)$

9. $(3x+4y)(3x-4y)$ 10. $(11p-q)(11p+q)$ 11. $(1-5a)(1+5a)$ 12. $(x-4)(x+2)$

13. $(3x-2)(x+5)$ 14. $(2x-3)(3x-1)$ 15. $(3a+2b)(9a^2-6ab+4b^2)$

16. $(1-4x)(1+4x+16x^2)$ 17. $(5-2p)(25+10p+4p^2)$ 18. $(1+5x)(1-5x+25x^2)$

19. $(6-x)(36+6x+x^2)$ 20. $(10x+y)(100x^2-10xy+y^2)$ 21. $a+4$ 22. $\dfrac{x}{x+2}$

23. $a+b$ 24. 1   25. $a+4$ 26. $\dfrac{x}{y}$ 27. $\dfrac{2a}{b}$ 28. (i) 8,052   (ii) 2,240   (iii) 604

29. (i) $(x+y)(a+b)$ (ii) $(a+4)(m-n)$ (iii) $(x-3)(x+y)$ (iv) $(b+c)(a-2)$

(v) $(p-2)(x-y)$ (vi) $(x-1)(p+q)$ (vii) $(a+b)(3-2a)$ (viii) $(n-5)(a+b)$

(ix) $(p+1)(p-2q)$ (x) $(a-3)(a-b)$ 30. $x+12$

31. (i) (a) xy (b) x^2 (c) xy (d) y^2 (ii) $(x+y)^2$

32. (i) $x(3x-2)$ (ii) $2(2x-3y)(2x+3y)$ (iii) $3x(2-3x)$ (iv) $(7x-5y)(7x+5y)$ (v) $4(3x^2+4)$

(vi) $2x(x^2+3a^2)$

33. (i) $\dfrac{3x+2}{x+7}$ (ii) $2(x+5)$ (iii) $\dfrac{x(x+4)}{x-1}$ (iv) $\dfrac{x-1}{3x-4}$ (v) n^2-2n+4

34. (i) $\dfrac{2x}{x^2-1}$ (ii) $\dfrac{2}{x^2-1}$ (iii) $\dfrac{x+10}{(x+1)(x+4)}$ (iv) $\dfrac{12(x+1)}{x(x+2)}$ (v) $\dfrac{6-x}{(2x-3)(x+3)}$

(vi) $\dfrac{6}{(2x-3)(2x+3)}$

36. (i) $\dfrac{3}{4}$ (ii) $\dfrac{4}{7}$ (iii) $\dfrac{7}{11}$ (iv) $\dfrac{A}{B} \rightarrow \dfrac{B}{A+B}$ $\therefore \dfrac{11}{11+7} = \dfrac{11}{18}$

37. (i) $\dfrac{x}{x+1}$ (ii) $\dfrac{x+1}{2x+1}$ (iii) $\dfrac{2x+1}{3x+2}$ (iv) $\dfrac{3x+2}{5x+3}$

38. (i) $\dfrac{2x}{(x+3)(x-2)}$ (ii) $\dfrac{1}{x+1}$ (iii) $\dfrac{3}{2x-3}$ (iv) $\dfrac{a-b}{ab}$ (v) $\dfrac{x^2-2x+3}{x-1}$ (vi) $\dfrac{x+3}{x+4}$

39. (i) 1   (ii) 2   (iii) 1   (iv) 3   (v) 0   40. (i) xy (ii) $a+b$ (iii) 4   (iv) $x+2$

(v) $\dfrac{2}{x-2}$ 42. $(a-b)^5$ 43. $(2)^2(2p+1)(2p-1)$ 44. 1   45. $a=1, b=-2$

Exercise 1.2

1. $\dfrac{b + 3c}{2}$ 2. $\dfrac{t}{p - r}$ 3. $\dfrac{b^2}{a - bd}$ 4. $\dfrac{q^2 - qr}{2r}$

5. (i) $P = 2x + 2y,\ \dfrac{1}{2}(P - 2y) = x$ (ii) $A = 6K^2,\ \sqrt{\dfrac{A}{6}} = K$

6. $2S - a - c$ 7. $\dfrac{2A}{h} - a$ 8. $\dfrac{x - 1}{x - 2}$ 9. (i) (a) $x - 2$ (b) $\dfrac{1}{3}y$ (ii) $3x - 6 = y$

10. $4u - p - r - s$ 11. $\sqrt{300 - h^2}$ 12. $\dfrac{b^2 + c^2 - a^2}{2bc}$ 13. $\sqrt{r^2 - x^2}$

14. (i) $2\pi r$ (ii) πr^2 (iii) $(3 - 2\pi r)$ 15. (i) $\pm\sqrt{\dfrac{1}{m^2 + 8p}}$ (ii) $\pm 0{\cdot}2$ 16. (i) $2a + a^2$ (ii) 0

17. (i) $\dfrac{p + 2q^2}{q^2}$ 18. $\dfrac{x^2 + 1}{x^2 - 1}$ 19. $\dfrac{uv}{u + v}$ 20. $\dfrac{gt^2}{k^2}$ 21. $\dfrac{p^2 + 4}{p^2}$ 22. (i) $\dfrac{a + b}{p + q}$ 23. $y^3 - 1$

Exercise 1.3

1. $a = 4,\ b = 2$ 2. (i) $2a + b = 4,\ 3a - 4b = 17$ (ii) $a = 3,\ b = -2$ 3. $a = 2,\ b = -10$

4. $p = 5,\ q = -2,\ r = -3$ 5. $8, -6, -8$ 6. (i) $a = 5,\ b = 7$ (ii) $k = -3,\ t = 9$

7. $3, -4$ 8. $3, -5$ 9. $3, -4, 5$ 10. $2,\ \dfrac{5}{4}, \dfrac{23}{8}$ 11. $2, 3$ 12. $2, 3, 5$

13. $a = 2,\ b = -3$ 14. (i) $(x - p)(x^2 + px + p^2)$ 15. $-1,\ -\dfrac{1}{2},\ -\dfrac{1}{4}$ 16. $1, 3, -3$ 21. (i) $6, 7, 2$

22. -4 23. (i) $x + 3$ (ii) $3, -56$ 24. (i) $3, -1, -12, 4$ (ii) $14, -4, -8$ 25. $\dfrac{6}{x + 1}$

Exercise 1.4

1. (i) $2\sqrt{3}$ (ii) $3\sqrt{2}$ (iii) $2\sqrt{5}$ (iv) $6\sqrt{2}$ (v) $4\sqrt{3}$ (vi) $3\sqrt{5}$ (vii) $5\sqrt{5}$ (viii) $3\sqrt{7}$

(ix) $10\sqrt{5}$ (x) $2\sqrt{5}$ (xi) $2\sqrt{3}$ (xii) $3\sqrt{3}$

2. (i) $\dfrac{2}{3}$ (ii) $\dfrac{6}{7}$ (iii) $\dfrac{10}{9}$ (iv) $\dfrac{3}{2}$ (v) $\dfrac{5}{4}$ (vi) $\dfrac{11}{5}$

3. (i) $4\sqrt{3}$ (ii) $3\sqrt{2}$ (iii) $3\sqrt{5}$ (iv) $4\sqrt{7}$ (v) $2\sqrt{2}$ (vi) $3\sqrt{5}$

4. (i) $\dfrac{5\sqrt{2}}{2}$ (ii) $\dfrac{4\sqrt{3}}{3}$ (iii) $\dfrac{3\sqrt{2}}{2}$ (iv) $\dfrac{3\sqrt{5}}{2}$ (v) $\dfrac{4\sqrt{2}}{3}$ (vi) $\dfrac{5\sqrt{5}}{3}$

5. (i) 6 (ii) 4 (iii) $2\sqrt{11}$ 6. (i) $\sqrt{12}$ (ii) $\sqrt{12}$ (iii) $\dfrac{1}{\sqrt{3}}$ (iv) $\sqrt{10}$ (v) $2\sqrt{5}$

(vi) $\sqrt{12}$ 7. (i) $6\sqrt{2}$ (ii) $2\sqrt{2}$ (iii) $12\sqrt{2}$ (iv) $\dfrac{1}{12}\sqrt{2}$

8. (i) -1 (ii) 98 (iii) 18 (iv) -109 10. 4 11. $7 - 4\sqrt{3}$ 12. $28\sqrt{5}$

13. $\dfrac{1}{60}\sqrt{5}$ **14. (i)** $\sqrt{3}-2$ **(ii)** $2\sqrt{2}-3$ **15.** $b=3$ **16.** $\dfrac{13}{2}-\sqrt{3}$ **17.** $2\sqrt{2}$

18. 70   **19.** 3   **20.** $x^4+\dfrac{1}{x^4}$ **21. (i)** $\dfrac{b-a}{ab}$ **(ii)** $-2\sqrt{2}$ **22.** $n=12$

Exercise 2.1

1. $-4,\dfrac{3}{2}$ **2.** 0, 3   **3.** $-2, 2$ **4.** $-4, -\dfrac{2}{3}$ **5.** $-3,\dfrac{1}{5}$ **6.** 3   **7.** $0,\dfrac{3}{2}$

8. $-\dfrac{1}{2},\dfrac{2}{3}$ **9.** $\dfrac{2}{3}$ **10.** $-\dfrac{3}{2},\dfrac{3}{4}$ **11.** $-\dfrac{2}{3},\dfrac{3}{5}$ **12.** $-\dfrac{5}{2},\dfrac{5}{2}$ **13.** $-3+\sqrt{5}, -3-\sqrt{5}$

14. $2+\sqrt{3}, 2-\sqrt{3}$ **15.** $4+\sqrt{3}, 4-\sqrt{3}$ **16.** $1+\sqrt{3}, 1-\sqrt{3}$ **17.** $2+3\sqrt{2}, 2-3\sqrt{2}$

18. $-5+4\sqrt{3}, -5-4\sqrt{3}$

Exercise 2.2

1. 3 m, 9 m   **2.** 12 m, 16 m   **3.** $2\sqrt{61}$ **4. (i)** 6 cm, 8 cm   **(ii)** 24 cm^2 **5.** 1.5 m

6. 2.5 m   **7.** 3 m   **8.** 5 cm, 9 cm   **9.** 11   **10.** 11 cm   **11.** 9 cm, 11 cm

12. 2 sec, 5 sec   **13.** 1 sec, 3 sec   **14.** 0.55 sec, 5.45 sec   **15.** 5, 6   **16.** 11, 13

17. 11, 13   **18.** $-3, -2, -1$ and $-4, -3, -2$

Exercise 2.3

1. 2, 3   **2.** $\dfrac{2}{3}, 1$ **3.** $-1, 2$ **4.** $-2, 3$ **5.** $-1, 3$ **6.** $-4, 8$ **7.** $-\dfrac{5}{7}, 6$ **8.** $-2, 3$

9. $-1,\dfrac{8}{5}$ **10.** -14 m, 3 m   **11.** $4+2\sqrt{5}, 4-2\sqrt{5}$ **12.** $1\pm\sqrt{7}$ **13.** $\dfrac{2x+5}{12}$

14. $\dfrac{2x-10}{15}$ **15. (i)** $x+8$ **(ii)** 12 **(iii)** $\dfrac{12}{20}$ **16. (i)** $\dfrac{72}{x}$ **(ii)** $\dfrac{70}{(x-2)}$ **(iii)** 12

17. (i) $\dfrac{100}{x}$ **(ii)** $\dfrac{100}{(x-5)}$ **(iii)** 25   **18. (i)** $\dfrac{x}{10}+\dfrac{(x+4)}{8}$ **(ii)** 20 km   **19.** 40 km/hr

20. 4 km/hr   **21.** 4 km/hr and 6 km/hr   **22.** 7   **23.** 30   **24.** 8, 9   **25.** 9   **26.** 20

Exercise 2.4

1. $x=-4, 5; k=-1,\dfrac{1}{2}, 2$ **2.** $x=-6,\dfrac{2}{3}; k=-\dfrac{7}{3}, 1, 3, -1$ **3.** $x=-4, 6; x=-2, 3+\sqrt{5}, 3-\sqrt{5}$

4. $x=2, 4; x=1, 2+\sqrt{3}, 2-\sqrt{3}$ **5.** $x=-9, 6; y=-8, -1, 2, 4$ **6.** $x=3, 8; x=-2, -1, 3, 4$

7. $x=4, 5; y=16, 25$ **8.** $x=0, 7; x=1, 2$ **9.** $x=-2, 7; x=-1, 2$

10. (i) $x=-3, -2, 2, 3$ **(ii)** $x=-4, -1, 1, 4$

Exercise 2.5

1. $-3, 5$ **2.** $-1, 5$ **3.** $-8, 2$ **4.** $-1, 2$ **5.** $-1,\dfrac{5}{3}$ **6.** $-\dfrac{1}{2},\dfrac{5}{2}$ **7.** $\dfrac{1}{2}$ **8.** $-2, 0$

9. $\dfrac{1}{3}, 1$ **10.** 1, 3   **11.** $0,\dfrac{2}{5}$ **12.** $\dfrac{1}{3}, 3$ **13.** $-\dfrac{5}{3}, 1$ **14.** $-4, -\dfrac{2}{5}$ **15.** $\dfrac{4}{3}, 4$

16. $-1, 5$ **17.** $-3, \dfrac{1}{5}$ **18.** $-\dfrac{4}{5}, 0$ **19.** $1, 4$ **20.** 3 **21.** $4, 9$ **22.** 5 **23.** 3

24. 5 **25.** $2, 3$ **26.** 6 **27.** $2, 5$ **28.** $-18, 8$ **29.** $-1, 7$ **30.** $\dfrac{1}{3}, 3$

Exercise 2.6

1. $(x + 1)^2$ **2.** $(x + 3)^2$ **3.** $(x - 4)^2$ **4.** $(x - 5)^2$ **5.** $(x + 2)^2$ **6.** $(x - 8)^2$

7. $(2x - 1)^2$ **8.** $(2x - 5)^2$ **9.** $(3x + 2)^2$ **10.** $(x - 3)^2 + 2; \ x = 3; \ 2$

11. $(x + 1)^2 + 5; \ x = -1; \ 5$ **12.** $(x + 4)^2 - 2; \ x = -4; \ -2$ **13.** $(x - 5)^2 - 6; \ x = 5; \ -6$

14. $(x + 6)^2 - 33; \ x = -6; \ -33$ **15.** $(x - 2)^2 + 3; \ x = 2; \ 3$ **16.** $(x - 3)^2 - 2 = 0; \ 3 \pm \sqrt{2}$

17. $(x - 5)^2 - 3; \ 5 \pm \sqrt{3}$ **18.** $(x + 1)^2 - 7 = 0; \ -1 \pm \sqrt{7}$ **19.** $(x + 2)^2 - 5 = 0; \ -2 \pm \sqrt{5}$

20. $(x + 2)^2 - 7 = 0; \ -2 \pm \sqrt{7}$ **21.** $(x + 1)^2 - 3 = 0; \ -1 \pm \sqrt{3}$ **22.** $(x - 1)^2 - 5 = 0; \ 1 \pm \sqrt{5}$

23. $(x + 6)^2 - 20 = 0; \ -6 \pm 2\sqrt{5}$ **24.** $(x - 4)^2 - 12 = 0; \ 4 \pm 2\sqrt{3}$ **25.** $2^2 - (x - 3)^2; \ x = 3; \ 4$

26. $3^2 - (x + 1)^2; \ x = -1; \ 9$ **27.** $4^2 - (x + 5)^2; \ x = -5; \ 16$ **28.** $5^2 - (x + 3)^2; \ x = -3; \ 25$

29. $4^2 - (x - 4)^2; \ x = 4; \ 16$ **30.** $7^2 - (x + 2)^2; \ x = -2; \ 49$ **31.** $2[(x + 3)^2 + 4^2]; \ 32$

32. $3[(x - 5)^2 - 2]$ **(i)** -6 **(ii)** $5 \pm \sqrt{2}$

Exercise 2.7

1. $(-2, 0); (-5, 0); (0, 10)$ **2.** $(-4, 0); (1, 0); (0, -4)$ **3.** $(3, 0); (-3, 0); (0, -18)$

4. $(2, 0); (5, 0); (0, -10)$ **5.** $(1, 0); \left(\dfrac{-10}{3}, 0\right); (0, 10)$ **6.** $(2, 0); \left(\dfrac{-7}{2}, 0\right); (0, -14)$

7. $(4, 0); (0, 16)$ **8.** $(2, 0); (7, 0); (0, -14)$ **9.** $(-1, 0); (4, 0); (0, 8)$ **10.** $x^2 - 3x - 10 = 0$

11. $x^2 + 7x + 12 = 0$ **12.** $2x^2 - 7x + 3 = 0$ **13.** $6x^2 + x - 1 = 0$ **14.** $6x^2 - 13x - 5 = 0$

15. $10x^2 + x - 2 = 0$ **16.** $f(x) = x^2 + 2x - 8$ **17.** $f(x) = x^2 - 16$ **18.** $f(x) = x^2 - 6x$

19. $f(x) = -x^2 + 4x - 4$ **20.** $a = -2; \ p = -2$ **21.** $a = -7; \ p = 7$ **22.** 8 cm   **23.** 10 m

24. 6 m   **25.** 30 m   **26.** **(i)** $100 - 2x$ **(ii)** $100x - 2x^2$ **(iv)** $w = 25$ m; $l = 50$ m

27. **(i)** $\theta = \dfrac{8 - 2r}{r}$ **(iv)** $A = 4$ m^2; $r = 2$ m^2 **28.** **(i)** $\theta = \dfrac{100 - 2r}{r}$ **(iii)** 625 m^2

(iv) $r = 25$ m, $\theta = 2$ rad   **29.** **(i)** $\dfrac{20x - x^2}{2}$ **(ii)** 50 cm^2 **30.** **(i)** $5A - A^2$ **(ii)** $A = 2{\cdot}5$

31. **(i)** $y = \dfrac{8 - x}{2}$ **(ii)** $A = \dfrac{8x - x^2}{2}$ **(iii)** 8 cm^2 **(iv)** $x = 4, y = 2$

Exercise 2.8

1. $(x + 1)(x + 2)$ **2.** $(x + 1)(x + 5)$ **3.** $(x + 2)(3x - 1)$ **4.** $(x - 2)(x - 4)$

6. $k = 19; \ (2x + 3)(3x - 1)$ **7.** $k = 7; \ (x + 1)(x + 2)$ **8.** $k = 4; \ (x + 1)(x - 3)$ **9.** $(2x - 1)$

10. $p = 2$; $q = -10$ 11. $a = 5$; $b = 19$ 12. $a = 9$; $b = 7$ 13. $h = 5$; $k = 3$

14. $(x + 3)(x - 2)$; $p = 3$, $q = 12$ 15. $p = -5$; $q = 19$ 16. $p = -12$; $q = 16$

Exercise 2.9

1. $a = 2$; $b = 3$ 6. (ii) $x = p, \pm\sqrt{q}$ 7. (ii) $x = -p, p$

8. $a = -1$, $b = -4$ or $a = 2$, $b = 2$ 9. $a = 6$, $b = 3$ or $a = -6$, $b = -3$

Exercise 2.10

1. (i) $(x + 4)$, $(x - 2)$, $(x - 3)$ (ii) $-4, 2, 3$ 2. (i) $(x + 3)$, $(x - 1)$, $(x - 4)$ (ii) $-3, 1, 4$

3. (i) $(x + 1)$, $(2x - 1)$, $(x - 1)$ (ii) $-1, \dfrac{1}{2}, 1$ 4. (i) $(x + 1)$, $(2x - 1)$, $(x - 2)$ (ii) $-1, \dfrac{1}{2}, 2$

5. (i) $x^3 + 6x^2 + 8x = 192$ (ii) $4, 6, 8$ 6. $x^3 - 5x^2 - 4x + 20 = 0$ 7. $x^3 + 6x^2 + 5x - 12 = 0$

8. $2x^3 - 11x^2 + 17x - 6 = 0$ 9. $30x^3 - x^2 - 6x + 1 = 0$ 10. $24x^3 - 58x^2 - 7x + 5 = 0$

11. $30x^3 - 17x^2 - 8x + 4 = 0$ 12. $f(x) = x^3 + 5x^2 + 2x - 8$ 13. $f(x) = x^3 + 2x^2 - 11x - 12$

14. $f(x) = x^3 + x^2 - 8x - 12$ 15. $f(x) = x^3 + 2x^2 - 7x + 4$ 16. $a = -11$, $p = -3$, $q = 2$

17. $a = 3$, $p = -8$, $q = 4$ 18. $x = -1, 3$ 19. $x = -3 + 2\sqrt{2}, -3 - 2\sqrt{2}$

20. (i) $k = 7$ (ii) $x = 2, 3$ 21. (i) $a = 2$, $b = 9$ (ii) $k = \dfrac{3}{2}$ 22. $k = -4, \dfrac{1}{2}$

23. $p = -1$, $q = 14$, $r = -8$; $x = 1, 2, 4$ 24. $-4p, -p, 2p$ 25. (i) $v = 2h^3 + 2h^2$ (ii) $h = 5$ cm

(iii) $l = 10$ cm, $w = 6$ cm   26. (i) $v = \pi(h^3 + 4h^2 + 4h)$ (ii) $h = 3$ cm   (iii) $r = 5$ cm

27. (i) $r^2 = 52 - h^2$ (ii) $h = 2$ cm or 6 cm

Exercise 3.1

1. $x = 1, y = 3$ 2. $x = 6, y = 2$ 3. $x = 5, y = 4$ 4. (ii) €895, €565

5. (i) (a) $2x + 2y = 29$ (b) $4x + 2y = 48$ or $2x + y = 24$ (iii) (a) $\dfrac{95}{2}$ (b) 80

6. (i) $x - y = 13$; $2x + 19y = 110$ (ii) $x = 17, y = 4$ 7. (ii) $x + y = 26, 2x + 4y = 74$

(iii) $x = 15, y = 11$ 8. (i) $3x + 2y = 125$; $2x + 3y = 115$ (ii) €29 adult, €19 child

9. (i) $x + y = 400$, $1{\cdot}5x - 1{\cdot}5y = -78$ (ii) $174, 226$ 10. (i) $x + y = 36$; $2x + 5y = 141$ (ii) $13, 23$

11. (i) $14x + 10y = 555$; $12x + 5y = 390$ (ii) €22·50, €24   12. $-3, 8$ 13. $9, 4$

14. $3, 4$ 15. $10, 5$ 16. $15, 4$ 17. $\dfrac{4}{5}, -\dfrac{6}{5}$ 18. (i) $\left(\dfrac{3 - k}{2}, 6 - k\right)$ (ii) $\left(\dfrac{5}{k}, -3\right)$

(iii) $\left(k - 1, \dfrac{5 - 4k}{k}\right)$ (iv) $(0, 10)$ 19. $2, -1, 4$ 20. $2, 4, 6$ 21. $2, -3, 4$

22. $-2, 3, 5$ 23. $-2, -1, 4$ 24. $1, -2, -1$ 25. €5·80, €1·80, €7·20

26. $a = 2$, $b = -3$, $c = 5$ 27. $p = 2$, $q = -1$, $r = -3$ 28. $a = -10$, $b = -2$, $c = 1$

29. (i) $3, -2, -1$ (ii) $5, -7, -2$ 30. (ii) $30, 24, 28$ 31. (i) $x + y + z = 12$; $x + 4y = 19$;

$3x + y + 2z = 23$ (ii) $x = 3, y = 4, z = 5$

32. (i) $x + y + z = 52$, $\dfrac{1}{2}x + \dfrac{1}{5}y + \dfrac{1}{10}z = €14{\cdot}30$ (ii) $\dfrac{1}{2}y + \dfrac{1}{5}z + \dfrac{1}{10}x = €14{\cdot}30$

(iii) $x = 18$, $y = 19$, $z = 15$ **33.** (i) $x + y + z = 30$, $4x - 2y + z = 54$, $(x - 1) + (y - 3) + 2z = 30$

(ii) $x = 17$, $y = 9$, $z = 4$ (iii) 60   **34.** (i) $4, -1, 5$ (ii) $\pm 2, 1, 3$ **35.** $1, 3, 2$ and $-2, \dfrac{7}{3}, \dfrac{1}{2}$

36. (i) $a = 3$, $b = 4$, $c = 5$ (ii) $\dfrac{3}{5}$ (iii) $P(n) = \dfrac{n + 1}{n}$

Exercise 3.2

Degree one: 4, 5, 10, 13

Degree two: All other questions

Exercise 3.3

1. $(-3, 9)$ and $(1, 1)$ **2.** $(2, 2)$ and $(5, 11)$ **3.** $(-2, 6)$ **4.** $(2, -1)$ and $\left(-\dfrac{1}{3}, -\dfrac{17}{3}\right)$

5. $(3, 1)$ and $\left(\dfrac{9}{5}, -\dfrac{13}{5}\right)$ **6.** $(4, -3)$ and $(-3, 4)$ **7.** $(-3, -3)$ and $(1, 1)$

8. $(7, 6)$ and $(-6, -7)$ **9.** $(3, 1)$ **10.** $(5, 2)$ and $(4, 1)$ **11.** $(2, 3)$ and $\left(\dfrac{-4}{3}, \dfrac{-11}{3}\right)$

12. $\left(\dfrac{1}{4}, -\dfrac{1}{4}\right)$ and $\left(0, -\dfrac{1}{3}\right)$ **13.** $(1, -8)$ and $(5, 4)$ **14.** $(4, 2)$ **15.** $(1, 1)$ and $(2, -1)$

16. $(4, -1)$ **17.** $(7, 3)$ **18.** $(-2, -4)$ and $\left(1, \dfrac{7}{2}\right)$ **19.** $\left(-1, -\dfrac{2}{3}\right)$ and $\left(-\dfrac{7}{2}, 1\right)$

20. (i) $16 - 20 < 0$ (ii) $144 - 224 < 0$ (iii) $1 - 64 < 0$ (iv) $36 - 52 < 0$

21. only one point of contact $(-2, 4) \Rightarrow$ gas will not ignite

22. two points of intersection $(-2{\cdot}4, -1{\cdot}2)$ and $(-3, 0) \Rightarrow$ craft must change course

23. $b^2 - 4ac = 6{,}724 - 8{,}100 < 0 \Rightarrow$ paths will not cross   **24.** $49{\cdot}19$ m

25. (i) $21{\cdot}6$ m   (ii) $37{\cdot}5$ m   **26.** A only. $3 - 1 = \sqrt{3 + 1}$, $2 = \sqrt{4}$; $0 - 1 \neq \sqrt{0 + 1}$, $-1 \neq 1$

Exercise 4.1

1. $x \leq 3$ **2.** $x \leq 5$ **3.** $x \leq 1$ **4.** $x \geq 3$ **5.** $x < -2$ **6.** $x \leq -4$ **7.** $x < -2$

8. $x < 5$ **9.** $x > -6$ **10.** $x \leq 2$ **11.** $-2 \leq x \leq 4$ **12.** $-3 < x \leq 5$

13. $-1 < x \leq 2$ **14.** $-4 \leq x \leq -1$ **15.** $-1 < x < 4$ **16.** $0 < x < 2$ **17.** (i) $x \leq 6$

(ii) $x > -4$ (iii) $-4 < x \leq 6$ **18.** (i) $x \leq 2$ (ii) $x \geq -3$ (iii) $-3 \leq x \leq 2$ **19.** (i) $x \geq -2$

(ii) $x \leq 5$ (iii) $a = -2$, $b = 5$ **20.** (i) $x \leq 4$ (ii) $x > 1$ (iii) $1 < x \leq 4$ **21.** 7   **22.** 3

23. $x \leq 4$, $x \geq 5$; no intersection   **24.** $x = 3$ **25.** $\dfrac{4}{3} < x < 4$ **26.** 3, 4, 5

27. (i) $2 < x < 5$ (ii) $10 < A < 55$ **28.** $(10, 7)$

Exercise 4.2

1. $-2 < x < 1$ 2. $x < -1$ or $x > 3$ 3. $-4 \leq x \leq 3$ 4. $x \leq -2$ or $x \geq 2$

5. $-5 \leq x \leq 5$ 6. $0 < x < 3$ 7. $x < -4$ or $x > 0$ 8. $-1 \leq x \leq 2$ 9. $-2 \leq x \leq 4$

10. $x \leq -2$ or $x \geq 3$ 11. $\dfrac{1}{2} < x < 5$ 12. $x \leq -2$ or $x \geq 5$ 13. $0 \leq x \leq 3$

14. $x \leq -4$ or $x \geq 0$ 15. $0 \leq x \leq \dfrac{3}{2}$ 16. $-3 \leq x \leq 3$ 17. $x \leq -5$ or $x \geq 5$

18. $-\dfrac{3}{2} \leq x \leq \dfrac{3}{2}$ 19. $x < -3$ or $x > 5$ 20. $x < -4$ or $x > \dfrac{3}{2}$ 21. $x \leq \dfrac{1}{2}$ or $x \geq \dfrac{5}{2}$

22. (i) $x = -2, y = 9$ or $x = 4, y = -3$ (ii) $x < -2$ or $x > 4$ 23. $-1, 0, 1, 2, 3$

24. (i) $x^2 - 6x + 5$ (ii) $1 \leq x \leq 5$ 25. $1 < x < 2$ 26. $2 < x < 5$ 27. $x < -1$ or $x > 0$

28. $x < 1$ or $x > 2$ 29. $x < -3$ or $x > 4$ 30. $-2 < x < 1$ 31. $x < 0$ or $x > 1$

32. $x \leq -3$ or $x \geq 5$ 33. $-3 < x < 3$ 34. $x < -9$ or $x > 5$ 35. $-2 < x < 0$

36. $-1 < x < 1$ 38. $x < 1$ or $x > 3$ 39. (i) $\dfrac{x+3}{x+1}$ (ii) $x < -1$ or $x > 1$

40. (ii) $1 < x < 2$ 41. (i) 2 (ii) $x < 2$ or $x > 4$ 42. $1 \leq x \leq 3$ 43. no

44. (i) $\pm\sqrt{\dfrac{x}{1 - x^2}}$ (ii) $-1 < x < 1$ 45. (ii) $0 < x < 4$ 46. $5 \leq x \leq 8$

47. $10, 11, 12, 13, 14, 15$ 48. $7 < x < 10$ 49. (i) rectangle would not exist   (ii) $x > 4$

50. (i) 7 m   (ii) 9 seconds   (iii) $2 < t < 6$ 51. (i) $6\sqrt{2}$; $10\sqrt{2}$ (ii) $9, 10, 11, 12, 13, 14$

52. $2 < x < 5$ 53. (iii) otherwise the rectangle would not exist   (iv) (a) $5 \leq x \leq 9$

(b) $0 < x < 5$ or $9 < x < 14$

Exercise 4.3

1. $-7 \leq x \leq 3$ 2. $1 < x < 7$ 3. $-10 \leq x \leq 4$ 4. $x < -5$ or $x > 3$ 5. $x \leq 3$ or $x \geq 7$

6. $x < -7$ or $x > -1$ 7. $-1 \leq x \leq 3$ 8. $x < -4$ or $x > 8$ 9. $2 < x < 4$ 10. $-1 \leq x \leq 2$

11. $x \leq -4$ or $x \geq 1$ 12. $\dfrac{1}{3} < x < 1$ 13. $x \leq \dfrac{3}{2}$ or $x \geq 2$ 14. $-1 < x < \dfrac{1}{5}$

15. $-\dfrac{8}{3} < x < -1$ 16. $-\dfrac{5}{4} \leq x \leq \dfrac{1}{4}$ 17. $-\dfrac{1}{6} < x < \dfrac{5}{6}$ 18. $x \leq \dfrac{8}{15}$ or $x \geq \dfrac{2}{15}$

19. $-3, -2, -1, 0, 1$ 20. $-6 < x < 8$ 21. 2 22. (i) $-2 \leq x \leq 4$ (ii) $-2 \leq x \leq 4$

23. (i) $A(1, 2), B(5, 2), C(3, 0), D(0, 3)$ (ii) $1 < x < 5$ 24. (i) $A(-1, 0), B(0, 1)$

(ii) $(-5, 4), (3, 4)$ (iii) (a) $-5 \leq x \leq 3$ (b) $x < -5$ or $x > 3$ 25. (i) $(1, -1), (3, -1)$

(ii) (a) $1 < x < 3$ (b) $x \leq 1$ or $x \geq 3$

Exercise 5.1

1. 9   2. 32   3. 16   4. $\dfrac{1}{7}$ 5. $\dfrac{1}{4}$ 6. 1,000   7. $\dfrac{7}{2}$ 8. $\dfrac{27}{8}$ 9. $\dfrac{1}{9}$

10. $\dfrac{1}{8}$ 11. $\dfrac{1}{2}$ 12. $\dfrac{9}{8}$ 13. $\dfrac{4}{3}$ 14. $\dfrac{1}{32}$ 15. 32   16. $n = 3$ 17. $n = 2$

18. $n = -1$ 19. $n = \dfrac{4}{3}$ 20. $a = 2, b = 5$ 21. $x - y$ 22. x 23. $x + 1$ 24. $\dfrac{x + 1}{x(x - 1)}$

25. (i) 0   26. (i) 0; 0 (ii) 0   27. (i) 4; 4 (ii) 4

28. (i) 4; 4 (ii) 4   29. $k = 6$ 30. $k = 2$

Exercise 5.2

1. $\dfrac{5}{2}$ 2. 4   3. 2, 4   4. $-\dfrac{3}{7}$ 5. 7   6. 7   7. $\dfrac{5}{4}$ 8. 3   9. $\dfrac{13}{2}$

10. $\dfrac{3}{2}$ 11. 1, 3   12. $-\dfrac{1}{3}, 2$ 13. (i) 3^3 (ii) 2^5 (iii) $x = 2, y = -1$ 14. $x = 1, y = 1$

15. $x = 21, y = 6$ 16. $x = 1, y = 0$ 17. $x = 2, y = -1$ 18. $x = 1, y = 3$ 19. $x = 4, y = -2$

20. (i) 2 (ii) 1 (iii) 0 (iv) −2 (v) −1 (vi) no solution (vii) no solution (viii) −3

Exercise 5.3

1. (i) (a) y^2 (b) $2y$ (ii) $x = 1, 3$ 2. (i) (a) y^2 (b) $2y^2$ (ii) $x = 3$

3. (i) (a) y^2 (b) $3y^2$ (ii) $x = -1$ 4. $x = 2$ 5. 0, 2   6. 0, 1   7. 1, 2

8. 2, 3   9. −1, 1   10. 1, 2   11. −1, 0   12. 1, 2   13. −2, 2   14. (i) $k = 7$ (ii) $x = 5$

Exercise 5.4

1. (i) (a) $u_{n+1} = 2(2^n) + 3(3^n)$ (b) $u_{n+2} = 4(2^n) + 9(3^n)$

2. (i) (a) $u_{n+1} = 15(3^n) + 4(4^n)$ (b) $u_{n+2} = 45(3^n) + 16(4^n)$

3. (i) (a) $u_{n+1} = 6(3^n) - 10(2^n)$ (b) $u_{n+2} = 18(3^n) - 20(2^n)$

4. (i) (a) $f(n + 1) = 10(5^n) - 2(-1)^n$ (b) $f(n + 2) = 50(5^n) + 2(-1)^n$ 6. (ii) $n < 22$ 7. (ii) $n < 6$

Exercise 6.1

1. (i) $16 = 2^4$ (ii) $81 = 3^4$ (iii) $1{,}000 = 10^4$ (iv) $125 = 5^3$ (v) $36 = 6^2$ (vi) $2 = 4^{\frac{1}{2}}$

(vii) $3 = 27^{\frac{1}{3}}$ (viii) $8 = 4^{\frac{3}{2}}$

2. (i) $\log_{10}100 = 2$ (ii) $\log_2 8 = 3$ (iii) $\log_3 27 = 3$ (iv) $\log_7 49 = 2$ (v) $\log_{16}4 = \dfrac{1}{2}$

(vi) $\log_{27}9 = \dfrac{2}{3}$ (vii) $\log_4 4 = 1$ (viii) $\log_8 1 = 0$

3. (i) 3 (ii) 2 (iii) 4 (iv) 3 (v) 4 (iv) 5 (vii) 1 (viii) 0 (ix) −1 (x) −2

(xi) $\dfrac{5}{2}$ (xii) $\dfrac{3}{4}$ (xiii) $\dfrac{3}{2}$ (xiv) 1 (xv) $-\dfrac{1}{3}$ (xvi) $\dfrac{3}{2}$

4. (i) 2   (ii) 3   (iii) 4   (iv) 81   (v) 0   **5.** (i) (a) 2   (b) 4   (c) -2 (d) 1   (ii) 16

6. 0   **7.** (i) (a) $\dfrac{4}{3}$ (b) $\dfrac{3}{5}$ (ii) 1   **8.** $p = 2q^3$ **9.** $y = \dfrac{x^2}{5}$

Exercise 6.2

1. 4   **2.** 8   **3.** ± 10 **4.** 3   **5.** 8   **6.** 10   **7.** 6   **8.** 7   **9.** $\dfrac{2}{7}$ **10.** 4, 6

11. 18   **12.** 2   **13.** 3   **14.** $-\dfrac{1}{2}$ **15.** $x = 2, y = 1$ **16.** $x = 3, y = 2$ **17.** $x = 2, y = \dfrac{5}{2}$

18. $x = 1, y = 1$ or $x = -3, y = 9$ **19.** $x = 1, y = 4$ **20.** $x = 4, y = -1$ **21.** 3   **22.** 2, 4

23. 3, 27   **24.** 4, 16   **25.** $125, \dfrac{1}{25}$ **26.** $2, \dfrac{1}{16}$ **27.** 10   **28.** $p = \sqrt{q}; \dfrac{3}{4}$ **29.** $\dfrac{a}{2}, 2a$

30. $x = 8, y = 2$ or $x = 2, y = 8$ **31.** (i) $2k$ (ii) $2k + 1$ (iii) $\dfrac{1}{2}k$ (iv) $\dfrac{1}{k}$ (v) $-\left(\dfrac{1}{k}\right)$

32. 7·122   **33.** 4·052   **34.** 2·161   **35.** 4·954   **36.** 3·878   **37.** 4·358   **38.** 1·756

39. 1·635   **40.** (i) 1   (ii) 3   (iii) -2 (iv) $\dfrac{1}{2}$ **42.** (i) $\ln 2$ (ii) $\ln 5$ (iii) no solution

(iv) $-\ln 3$ or $\ln \dfrac{1}{3}$ (v) no solution   (vi) $\dfrac{1}{2}\ln 3$ or $\ln \sqrt{3}$ (vii) e (viii) e^2

(ix) $\sqrt{e}$ or $e^{\frac{1}{2}}$ (x) e^{-1} or $\dfrac{1}{e}$ (xi) e^{-3} or $\dfrac{1}{e^3}$ (xii) $e^{-\frac{1}{2}}$ or $\dfrac{1}{e^{\frac{1}{2}}}$ or $\dfrac{1}{\sqrt{e}}$

43. (i) $\ln 2, \ln 3$ (ii) $\ln 3, \ln 5$ (iii) $\ln 4$ (iv) $-\ln 3, \ln 2$

44. (i) $y^2 + (k - 2)y + (-3k - 2) = 0$ (ii) $-2, -6$ (iii) $\ln 2, \ln 4$

45. (i) e, e^2 (ii) $\sqrt{e}, e^3$

Exercise 6.3

1. 34·7 years   **2.** 9.9%   **3.** 12·3 years   **4.** 2·8 years   **5.** $k = 0·305$ **6.** 6·7 years

7. 11 years   **8.** 0·231   **9.** (i) 28,747   (ii) 31.44 years   **10.** 12 days

11. (i) $a = 2·920, b = 0·100$ (iv) $k = 6·93$

Exercise 7.1

2. 6 square units   **3.** A and D **4.** (i) $\sqrt{40}$ or $2\sqrt{10}$ (ii) $M(3, 1)$

(iii) $3 : 3x - y - 8 = 0$ (iv) $r = -14$ (v) $x + 3y - 6 = 0$ (vi) $h = 6, k = 2$ **5.** $Q(-8, 3)$

6. (i) $c = -3$ (ii) $2x + 5y - 4 = 0$ **7.** (i) $k = -4$ (ii) $t = 8$ **10.** $a = 5$

11. $k = 2$ **12.** (i) $x - y - 5 = 0$ (ii) $x + y + 1 = 0$ **13.** (i) $Q(2, -1)$ (ii) $5x + 2y - 8 = 0$

(iv) $R(0, 4)$ **14.** (i) $\dfrac{1}{2}$ m per year   (ii) 13 m   (iii) $x - 2y - 1,994 = 0$

15. (ii) $\dfrac{5}{2}, 1, \dfrac{1}{2}, \dfrac{3}{4}, -\dfrac{4}{3}, -\dfrac{2}{3}, -\dfrac{1}{2}, -\dfrac{3}{5}$ (iii) the roads go *down* the hill   (iv) sections $P_2 - P_4$ and $P_6 - P_8$

16. $h = 2$, $k = -1$ **17.** $a = 4$, $b = 2$ or $a = 6$, $b = -2$ **18.** $5x - 2y - 19 = 0$

19. (i) $3x - 2y - 24 = 0$ (ii) $3x - 2y + 18 = 0$ **20.** $(8, 3)$ **21.** $x - y - 2 = 0$, $x + y - 6 = 0$

22. (i) $x - 3y + 1 = 0$ (ii) $2x + y - 12 = 0$ (iii) $Q(5, 2)$, $S(1, 3)$ **23.** (i) $P\left(-\dfrac{c}{a}, 0\right)$, $Q\left(0, -\dfrac{c}{b}\right)$

(ii) $\sqrt{\dfrac{c^2}{a^2} + \dfrac{c^2}{b^2}}$ or $\left|\dfrac{c}{ab}\right|\sqrt{a^2 + b^2}$ (iii) $\dfrac{1}{2}\left|\dfrac{c^2}{ab}\right|$ or $\dfrac{c^2}{2}\left|\dfrac{1}{ab}\right|$ **24.** (i) (a) $-\dfrac{1}{100}$ (b) $\dfrac{1}{16,700}$ (c) $\dfrac{1}{120}$

(ii) $x - 16,700y - 756,000 = 0$ (iii) $92,800$ m   **25.** (i) $-\dfrac{1}{2}$; $-\dfrac{7}{10}$; -1

(ii) $y = -\dfrac{1}{2}x + 21$; $y = -\dfrac{7}{10}x + 21$; $y = -x + 21$ (iii) $W(30, 0)$ **26.** (i) $2\cdot 5$

(ii) $5x - 2y = 0$ (iii) yes   **27.** $ax + \dfrac{y}{a} = 2b$ or $a^2x + y - 2ab = 0$ **28.** $t = \pm 2$

29. $k = -2$ or 14 **30.** $x = 5$ or 15 **31.** $x = 1$ or 7 **32.** (i) $P(3, 2)$

(ii) $c : 5x - y - 13 = 0$ (iii) yes   (iv) any $t \in \mathbb{R}$

Exercise 7.2

1. 7   **2.** 13   **3.** 24   **4.** 20   **5.** $\dfrac{11}{2}$ or $5\dfrac{1}{2}$ **6.** 12   **7.** 10   **8.** 12   **9.** 6

10. 7   **11.** 9   **12.** 37   **13.** 36   **14.** 72   **16.** $k = -8$ or 4 **17.** $t = \pm 2$

18. $k = \pm 2$ **19.** $k = 5$ **20.** P is $(-29, 0)$ or $(3, 0)$

Exercise 7.3

1. $(7, 3)$ **2.** $(4, -3)$ **3.** $(0, 1)$ **4.** $(-11, 6)$ **5.** $(7, -17)$ **6.** $(8, -10)$

7. $P(2, -3)$ **8.** $R(7, -1)$ **9.** $B(-3, 11)$ **10.** $C(24, 16)$ **11.** $A(21, 0)$, $B(0, -14)$

12. (i) $(8h, -9k)$ (ii) $(32h, -57k)$

Exercise 7.4

1. $(3, 2)$ **2.** $(4, 1)$ **3.** $(1, 0)$ **4.** $(-2, 1)$ **5.** $p = 4$; $q = 9$ **6.** $h = -25$; $q = -51$

7. $(2, -4)$ **8.** $(5, -9)$ **9.** $(3, -1)$ **10.** $(1, -2)$ **11.** $(3, 2)$ **12.** $(-2, -1)$

13. $(-3, 12)$ **14.** $(2, 10)$ **15.** (i) (a) $\left(\dfrac{5}{3}, -\dfrac{1}{3}\right)$ (b) $(2, -1)$ (c) $(1, 1)$

(ii) $\left(\dfrac{5}{3}, -\dfrac{1}{3}\right)$ is on $2x + y - 3 = 0$ **16.** (i) $B(4, 0)$; $R(4, 6)$ (ii) $x = 4$ (iv) (a) $(4, 2)$

(b) $\left(4, \dfrac{8}{3}\right)$ (c) $\left(4, \dfrac{2}{3}\right)$

Exercise 7.5

1. 5   **2.** 1   **3.** 2   **4.** 2   **5.** $\sqrt{5}$ **6.** $\dfrac{8}{\sqrt{2}}$ or $4\sqrt{2}$ **8.** 1   **9.** 1

10. $\dfrac{15}{13}$ **11.** $\dfrac{3}{2}$ **12.** $\sqrt{5}$ **13.** (i) $\dfrac{4}{3}$ (ii) $4x - 3y = 0$ (iii) 3 km

14. (i) $\dfrac{12}{5}$ (ii) $12x - 5y = 0$ (iii) 12 km   (iv) 32 km   **16.** different sides

17. only (30, 16) is on the same side as (0, 0)   18. $a = 0$ or 4   19. $k = -25$ or 35

20. $3x - 4y - 9 = 0$, $3x - 4y + 11 = 0$ 21. $mx - y + 2m + 1 = 0$; $y - 1 = 0$, $4x + 3y + 5 = 0$

22. $7x + y - 29 = 0$, $x - y - 3 = 0$ 23. $3x - 2y - 18 = 0$, $3x - 2y + 8 = 0$

Exercise 7.6

1. $45°$, $135°$ 2. $42°$, $138°$ 3. $18°$, $162°$ 4. $71°$, $109°$ 5. 3   6. $45°$ 7. $135°$

8. $45°$ 10. (i) $mx - y + 3 - 2m = 0$ (ii) $3x - y - 3 = 0$, $x + 3y - 11 = 0$

11. $5x + 7y - 41 = 0$, $7x - 5y - 13 = 0$ 12. (i) $90°$ (ii) $30°$ (iii) $45°$

13. $x - 2y + 2 = 0$, $11x + 2y - 2 = 0$ 14. (i) -3 (ii) $45°$ (iii) 2; $-\dfrac{1}{2}$ (iv) $Q(0, 2)$, $S(6, 4)$

15. -7 or 1   16. (i) 8 m, 16 m   (ii) $l_1 : 4x - 5y = 0$, $l_3 : 8x - 5y = 0$ (iii) yes

(iv) $l_2 : 6x - 5y = 0$; yes   (v) $38·66°$, $50·19$, $57·99$; no

Exercise 8.1

1. $x^2 + y^2 = 4$ 2. $x^2 + y^2 = 9$ 3. $x^2 + y^2 = 25$ 4. $x^2 + y^2 = 13$ 5. $x^2 + y^2 = 5$

6. $x^2 + y^2 = 12$ 7. $x^2 + y^2 = \dfrac{1}{4}$ or $4x^2 + 4y^2 = 1$ 8. $x^2 + y^2 = \dfrac{5}{2}$ or $2x^2 + 2y^2 = 5$

9. $x^2 + y^2 = 25$ 10. $x^2 + y^2 = 169$ 11. $x^2 + y^2 = 26$ 12. $x^2 + y^2 = 9$ 13. $x^2 + y^2 = 2$

14. $x^2 + y^2 = 29$ 15. 4   16. 10   17. 1   18. $\sqrt{13}$ 19. $\sqrt{5}$ 20. $\sqrt{29}$

21. $\dfrac{3}{2}$ 22. $\dfrac{5}{3}$ 23. $\dfrac{1}{4}$ 24. $x^2 + y^2 = 25$ 25. $x^2 + y^2 = 37$ 26. $(-6, 3)$

27. 40π square units   28. $x^2 + y^2 = 5$ 29. $x^2 + y^2 = 17$ 30. $x^2 + y^2 = 10$

31. $x^2 + y^2 = 26$ 32. $x^2 + y^2 = 8$ 33. $x^2 + y^2 = 20$

Exercise 8.2

1. $(x - 2)^2 + (y - 3)^2 = 16$ 2. $(x - 1)^2 + (y - 4)^2 = 25$ 3. $(x - 2)^2 + (y + 1)^2 = 4$

4. $(x + 5)^2 + (y - 2)^2 = 1$ 5. $(x + 4)^2 + (y + 3)^2 = 17$ 6. $(x + 3)^2 + y^2 = 13$

7. $x^2 + (y - 2)^2 = 5$ 8. $(x + 2)^2 + (y + 6)^2 = 29$ 9. $(x + 1)^2 + (y + 1)^2 = 10$

10. $(x + 4)^2 + (y - 2)^2 = 12$ 11. $(x - 1)^2 + (y - 2)^2 = 10$ 12. $(x - 2)^2 + (y + 1)^2 = 41$

13. $(x - 4)^2 + (y + 3)^2 = 80$ 14. $(x + 2)^2 + (y + 5)^2 = 50$ 15. $(x - 1)^2 + (y + 1)^2 = 26$

16. $(x + 4)^2 + (y + 2)^2 = 20$ 17. $(3, 2)$; 4   18. $(-4, -5)$; 3   19. $(1, -3)$; 5   20. $(3, 5)$; 2

21. $(2, 2)$; 7   22. $(8, 7)$; 1   23. $(5, -2)$; $\sqrt{20}$ or $2\sqrt{5}$ 24. $(1, -5)$; $\sqrt{32}$ or $4\sqrt{2}$

25. $(0, 2)$; 8   26. $(3, 0)$; 2   27. $(x - 3)^2 + (y - 3)^2 = 5$ 28. $(x + 1)^2 + (y - 2)^2 = 13$

29. (ii) $(x - 2)^2 + (y - 9)^2 = 25$ 30. $(x - 1)^2 + (y - 3)^2 = 25$ or $x^2 + y^2 - 2x - 6y - 15 = 0$

31. $(x + 6)^2 + (y - 1)^2 = 8$ or $x^2 + y^2 + 12x - 2y - 29 = 0$

32. $s_2 : (x - 6)^2 + y^2 = 16$; $s_4 : (x - 18)^2 + y^2 = 16$; $s_5 : (x - 24)^2 + y^2 = 16$

33. (i) $(0, 0)$ (ii) $(3, 3)$ (iii) $x - y = 0$ 34. (i) $(0, 0)$; 5   (ii) $A(5, 0)$ (iii) $B(5, 5)$

(iv) $(x - 5)^2 + (y - 5)^2 = 25$, $(x + 5)^2 + (y - 5)^2 = 25$, $(x + 5)^2 + (y + 5)^2 = 25$, $(x - 5)^2 + (y + 5)^2 = 25$

35. (i) $(x - 4)^2 + y^2 = 16$ (ii) $B(8, 0)$ (iii) $C(12, 0)$ (iv) 12   (v) $(6, 0)$ (vi) $(x - 6)^2 + y^2 = 36$

(viii) $(x - 10)^2 + y^2 = 100$

Exercise 8.3

1. $x^2 + y^2 - 2x - 4y - 4 = 0$ 2. $x^2 + y^2 + 4x - 6y - 12 = 0$ 3. $x^2 + y^2 + 6x + 10y + 17 = 0$

4. $x^2 + y^2 - 4x - 6 = 0$ 5. $x^2 + y^2 + 6y + 1 = 0$ 6. $x^2 + y^2 - x + y - \dfrac{9}{2} = 0$

   or $2x^2 + 2y^2 - 2x + 2y - 9 = 0$ 7. $x^2 + y^2 + 2x - 6y - 10 = 0$ 8. $x^2 + y^2 + 6x + 4y - 12 = 0$

9. $(3, 4)$; 6   10. $(2, 3)$; 4   11. $(1, -2)$; 3   12. $(5, -1)$; $\sqrt{20}$ or $2\sqrt{5}$ 13. $(-4, 3)$; 5

14. $(-1, 5)$; 6   15. $(-3, 0)$; 4   16. $(0, 2)$; $\sqrt{8}$ or $2\sqrt{2}$ 17. $\left(\dfrac{1}{2}, \dfrac{3}{2}\right)$; 3   18. $\left(\dfrac{1}{3}, -3\right)$; 2

19. $(-1, 3)$; 4   20. $(0, -4)$; $\sqrt{13}$ 21. on   22. inside   23. outside   24. inside

25. on   26. outside   27. $k = -6, 4$ 28. $p = 1, 7$ 29. $k = -6$

30. (i) $(k, -2)$; $\sqrt{k^2 + 11}$ (ii) $k = \pm5$ 31. $t = \pm3$ 32. $k = 11$; $\sqrt{117}$ or $3\sqrt{13}$

33. (i) (a) $5k^2 + 8k + 4$ (b) $5k^2 - 28k + 40$

(ii) $k = 1$; $(x - 2)^2 + (y - 1)^2 = 17$ or $x^2 + y^2 - 4x - 2y - 12 = 0$

Exercise 8.4

1. $(-3, -1)$, $(3, 1)$; not a tangent   2. $(-1, 3)$, $(3, 1)$; not a tangent

3. $(-1, 2)$, $(2, 1)$; not a tangent   4. $(4, -1)$; tangent   5. $(1, 0)$, $(2, 1)$; not a tangent

6. $(-1, -1)$, $(3, 1)$; not a tangent   7. $(-4, 0)$; tangent   8. $(-2, 1)$, $(7, 4)$; not a tangent

9. $(3, 2)$; tangent   10. $(-2, -2)$; tangent   11. $(1, -4)$, $(4, 1)$; not a tangent

12. $(6, 1)$; tangent   13. $4\sqrt{5}$ 14. (i) $A(-1, 0)$, $B(5, 2)$ (ii) yes

15. (i) $(0, 0)$; $\sqrt{52}$ km   (ii) $A(-6, 4)$, $B(-4, 6)$ (iii) no   (iv) $C(-5, 5)$ (v) no   16. (ii) yes

Exercise 8.5

1. $x^2 + y^2 - 6x - 10y + 24 = 0$ 2. $x^2 + y^2 - 4x - 2y - 45 = 0$ 3. $x^2 + y^2 - 4x + 8y = 0$

4. $x^2 + y^2 - 12x - 10y - 4 = 0$ 5. $x^2 + y^2 - 2x - 9 = 0$ 6. $x^2 + y^2 + 2x + 6y + 5 = 0$

Exercise 8.6

1. $(x - 2)^2 + (y - 3)^2 = 10$ or $x^2 + y^2 - 4x - 6y + 3 = 0$

2. $(x + 1)^2 + (y + 2)^2 = 10$ or $x^2 + y^2 + 2x + 4y - 20 = 0$ 3. $g = -2$, $f = 1$, $c = -15$

4. $(x - 1)^2 + (y - 2)^2 = 10$ or $x^2 + y^2 - 2x - 4y - 15 = 0$

5. $(x - 2)^2 + (y - 2)^2 = 10$ or $x^2 + y^2 - 4x - 4y - 2 = 0$ 6. $g = -2$, $f = 3$, $c = -7$

Exercise 8.7

1. $x^2 + y^2 - 2x + 6y + 6 = 0$, $x^2 + y^2 - 2x - 2y - 2 = 0$

2. $x^2 + y^2 + 8x - 8y + 12 = 0$, $x^2 + y^2 - 4x + 4y - 12 = 0$

3. $x^2 + y^2 + 12x - 6y + 35 = 0$, $x^2 + y^2 + 4x - 2y - 5 = 0$

4. $x^2 + y^2 + 4x - 6y = 0$, $x^2 + y^2 - 4x + 6y = 0$

5. (i) $R(2, 1)$; $x - 2y = 0$ (ii) 5   (iii) $x^2 + y^2 - 12x - 6y + 20 = 0$, $x^2 + y^2 + 4x + 2y - 20 = 0$

6. $x^2 + y^2 + 4x - 2y - 5 = 0$, $x^2 + y^2 - 4x - 10y + 19 = 0$

Exercise 8.8

1. $3x + y - 10 = 0$
2. $2x - 5y + 29 = 0$
3. $7x + y + 50 = 0$
4. $8x - 6y - 25 = 0$
5. $3x - y - 25 = 0$
6. $5x - 2y - 19 = 0$
7. $2x + 3y + 22 = 0$
8. $x + 2y - 7 = 0$
9. $3x + 4y - 43 = 0$
10. $x + y - 2 = 0$
17. 10
18. 8
19. 4
20. 5
21. $\sqrt{20}$ or $2\sqrt{5}$
22. $\sqrt{50}$ or $5\sqrt{2}$
23. $k = 31$
24. $x - 2y - 23 = 0$

Exercise 8.9

1. $k = \pm 5$
2. $k = -12, 8$
3. $k = -12, -2$
4. $t = \dfrac{1}{9}, 3$
5. $k = -2, \dfrac{1}{2}$
6. $k = \pm 4$
7. $4x - 3y - 25 = 0, 4x - 3y + 25 = 0$
8. $3x - y - 10 = 0, 3x - y + 10 = 0$
9. $2x - y - 4 = 0, 2x - y + 6 = 0$
10. $x + 4y - 12 = 0, x + 4y + 22 = 0$
11. $3x - 4y - 12 = 0, 3x - 4y + 38 = 0$
12. $m = -7, 1$
13. $x - 2y - 5 = 0, x + 2y - 5 = 0$
14. $2x - y + 10 = 0, x - 2y - 10 = 0$
15. $y = 0, 4x - 3y = 0$
16. $x + 2y + 1 = 0, 2x + y - 4 = 0$
17. $x + y - 1 = 0, x - y + 1 = 0$
18. $x - 3y + 5 = 0, 3x - y - 1 = 0$

19. (ii) $\left(\dfrac{6}{5}, \dfrac{8}{5}\right)$

Exercise 8.10

1. $(x - 2)^2 + (y - 5)^2 = 25$ or $x^2 + y^2 - 4x - 10y + 4 = 0$
2. $(x + 3)^2 + (y - 4)^2 = 9$ or $x^2 + y^2 + 6x - 8y + 16 = 0$
4. (ii) $(x - 5)^2 + (y - 4)^2 = 16$ or $x^2 + y^2 - 10x - 8y + 25 = 0$
5. (ii) $(x - 5)^2 + (y - 2)^2 = 25$ or $x^2 + y^2 - 10x - 4y + 4 = 0$
6. $(x - 2)^2 + (y - 2)^2 = 4$ or $x^2 + y^2 - 4x - 4y + 4 = 0$
7. (iii) $(x - 3)^2 + (y - 3)^2 = 9$ or $x^2 + y^2 - 6x - 6y + 9 = 0$; $(x - 15)^2 + (y - 15)^2 = 225$
   or $x^2 + y^2 - 30x - 30y + 225 = 0$
8. $(x - 1)^2 + (y - 1)^2 = 1$ or $x^2 + y^2 - 2x - 2y + 1 = 0$;
   $(x - 5)^2 + (y - 5)^2 = 25$ or $x^2 + y^2 - 10x - 10y + 25 = 0$

Exercise 8.11

1. $3 + 2 = 5$
2. $8 + 5 = 13$
3. $11 - 1 = 10$
4. $4\sqrt{5} - \sqrt{5} = 3\sqrt{5}$
5. $5 + 5 = 10; (5, 5)$
6. $10 + 5 = 15; (-1, -3)$
7. $\sqrt{2} + 4\sqrt{2} = 5\sqrt{2}; (2, -1)$
8. $4\sqrt{2} - \sqrt{2} = 3\sqrt{2}; (2, 1)$
9. $2\sqrt{2} + \sqrt{2} = 3\sqrt{2}; (-2, 2)$
10. $(x - 12)^2 + (y - 5)^2 = 81$ or $x^2 + y^2 - 24x - 10y + 88 = 0$
11. $k = -19$
12. (ii) $(7, 2)$ (iii) $(x - 5)^2 + (y - 2)^2 = 36$ or $x^2 + y^2 - 10x - 4y - 7 = 0$

Exercise 8.12

1. $(-5, 0), (1, 0); (0, -1), (0, 5)$
2. $P(2, 0); Q(8, 0)$
3. (i) $(x + 2)^2 + (y - 1)^2 = 20$ (ii) 8
4. (i) $(1, 2); \sqrt{13}$ (ii) $(x - 1)^2 + (y - 2)^2 = 13$ or $x^2 + y^2 - 2x - 4y - 8 = 0$ (iii) $(-2, 0), (4, 0)$
5. (i) $(-2, 0), (8, 0)$ (ii) $(0, -8), (0, 2)$ 6. 6 7. 8 8. $x - y - 3 = 0; x + y - 1 = 0$
9. $x - y + 1 = 0$ 10. $x + 3y + 2 = 0$ 11. $x - 2y = 0; A(4, 2); B(8, 4)$
12. $A(-3, 4); B(-5, 2)$ 13. $P(-3, 2)$ 14. $h = -15; k = 45$
15. $c : (x - 5)^2 + (y - 3)^2 = 29$ or $c : x^2 + y^2 - 10x - 6y + 5 = 0$

16. $s : (x - 2)^2 + y^2 = 13$ or $s : x^2 + y^2 - 4x - 9 = 0$

17. $(x - 4)^2 + (y - 5)^2 = 25$ or $x^2 + y^2 - 8x - 10y + 16 = 0$

18. $(x - 4)^2 + (y - 2)^2 = 16$ or $x^2 + y^2 - 8x - 4y + 4 = 0$

19. (i) $\sqrt{50}$ or $5\sqrt{2}$ (ii) $k = -10$ 20. (i) $(-2, 1)$ (ii) $3\sqrt{2}$ (iii) $\sqrt{26}$; $k = -21$

21. $(x - 4)^2 + (y - 1)^2 = 8$ or $x^2 + y^2 - 8x - 2y + 9 = 0$

Exercise 9.1

1. $42°$ 2. $55°$ 3. $7°$ 4. $17°$ 5. $63°$ 6. $53°$ 7. $44°$ 8. $18°$

9. (i) $\dfrac{3}{5}, \dfrac{3}{4}$ (iii) $37°$ 10. (i) $\dfrac{8}{17}, \dfrac{15}{17}$ (iii) $28°$ 11. (i) $\dfrac{24}{25}, \dfrac{7}{24}$ 12. $k = 20$

13. (i) $45°$ (ii) $52°$ (iii) $34°$ 14. (i) $9·4$ (ii) $28·8$ (iii) $26·4$ 15. (i) $2·5$ (ii) $37°$

16. (i) 5 (ii) $39°$ 17. (i) 34 cm (ii) 64 cm (iii) $14°$ 20. (i) 13 m (ii) $1{,}265$ cm

(iii) 566 cm   21. $10·7$ m   22. $15·89$ m   23. 426 m   24. (i) 84 m (ii) $19°$

25. (ii) 7 m   26. (i) 128 cm

Exercise 9.2

1. $180°$ 2. $30°$ 3. $45°$ 4. $120°$ 5. $108°$ 6. $240°$ 7. $225°$ 8. $80°$

9. $50°$ 10. $330°$ 11. $\dfrac{\pi}{6}$ 12. $\dfrac{\pi}{4}$ 13. $\dfrac{\pi}{3}$ 14. $\dfrac{\pi}{2}$ 15. $\dfrac{2\pi}{3}$ 16. $\dfrac{5\pi}{6}$

17. $\dfrac{7\pi}{6}$ 18. $\dfrac{4\pi}{3}$ 19. $\dfrac{3\pi}{4}$ 20. $\dfrac{5\pi}{2}$ 21. $\dfrac{13\pi}{6}$ 22. $\dfrac{2\pi}{5}$ 23. $\dfrac{8\pi}{5}$ 24. $\dfrac{7\pi}{12}$

25. $\dfrac{\pi}{8}$ 26. (i) 8 cm (ii) 40 cm^2 27. (i) $4·8$ cm (ii) $9·6$ cm^2

28. (i) 10π cm (ii) 60π cm^2 29. (i) 2 (ii) $1·5$ (iii) 1 (iv) $2·4$ 30. 12 cm

31. 5 cm   32. $\dfrac{7}{4}$ 33. $\dfrac{5\pi}{4}$; 90π cm^2 34. $\dfrac{2}{3}$ 35. 2π cm   36. 30 cm^3 37. $6{,}600$ cm^2

38. (i) $r\theta = 12$; $r^2\theta = 96$ (ii) $r = 8$ cm and $\theta = \dfrac{3}{2}$ 39. (ii) (a) 10 cm (b) 2

40. (i) $\dfrac{2}{3}$ (ii) $2 : 3$ 41. (i) $2·5$ (ii) $5 : 3$ (iii) $27 : 29$ 42. (i) $l = r$ (ii) $r = 4$ cm

43. $1{,}789\ l$ 44. (i) 36θ cm^2 (ii) $18 \tan \theta$ 45. (i) $\dfrac{6\pi}{5}$ (ii) (a) $r = 6$ cm (b) $h = 8$ cm

46. (i) l (ii) $\dfrac{2\pi r}{l}$ 47. (i) 20 cm

Exercise 9.3

1. $\dfrac{1}{2}$ 2. 1 3. $\dfrac{\sqrt{3}}{2}$ 4. $\sqrt{3}$ 5. $\dfrac{1}{2}$ 6. $\dfrac{1}{\sqrt{2}}$ 7. 3 8. 1 9. 1 10. $\dfrac{5}{4}$

11. 1 12. -5 13. 0 14. $\dfrac{13}{12}$ 15. (i) $\dfrac{2}{\sqrt{13}}, \dfrac{3}{\sqrt{13}}$ (iii) $34°$

16. (i) (a) $\dfrac{1}{\sqrt{5}}$ **(b)** 2 **(iii)** 63·43° **17.** $\dfrac{m}{\sqrt{m^2+n^2}}$; $\dfrac{n}{\sqrt{m^2+n^2}}$; $\dfrac{mn}{m^2+n^2}$

18. (i) (a) $(a+b)^2$ **(b)** $(x^2-y^2)^2$ **(ii)** $\dfrac{|p^2-1|}{p^2+1}$; $\dfrac{2p}{|p^2-1|}$

Exercise 9.4

1. 60° **2.** 45° **3.** 30° **4.** 30° **5.** 20° **6.** 40° **7.** $\dfrac{\pi}{6}$ **8.** $\dfrac{\pi}{3}$

9. $\dfrac{1}{2}$ **10.** $\dfrac{1}{\sqrt{2}}$ **11.** $-\sqrt{3}$ **12.** $\dfrac{1}{\sqrt{3}}$ **13.** $-\dfrac{1}{2}$ **14.** $\dfrac{1}{\sqrt{2}}$ **15.** $-\dfrac{1}{\sqrt{3}}$

16. $-\dfrac{\sqrt{3}}{2}$ **17.** $\dfrac{\sqrt{3}}{2}$ **18.** $\sqrt{3}$ **19.** $-\dfrac{1}{\sqrt{2}}$ **20.** $-\dfrac{1}{2}$ **21.** $-\dfrac{1}{2}$ **22.** $-\sqrt{3}$

23. $\dfrac{\sqrt{3}}{2}$ **24.** $-\dfrac{\sqrt{3}}{2}$ **25.** $\dfrac{1}{4}$ **26.** $-\dfrac{\sqrt{3}}{2}$ **27.** -3 **28.** 120° **29.** 135°

30. 315°

Exercise 9.5

1. (i) 30° + *n* (360°) or 150° + *n* (360°) for *n* ∈ ℤ **(ii)** 30°, 150°

2. (i) 30° + *n* (360°) or 330° + *n* (360°) for *n* ∈ ℤ **(ii)** 30°, 330°

3. (i) 135° + *n* (360°) or 315° + *n* (360°) for *n* ∈ ℤ. Alternatively, 135° + *n* (180°) for *n* ∈ ℤ
  (ii) 135°, 315°

4. (i) $\dfrac{\pi}{3} + 2n\pi$ or $\dfrac{4\pi}{3} + 2n\pi$ for *n* ∈ ℤ. Alternatively, $\dfrac{\pi}{3} + n\pi$ for *n* ∈ ℤ **(ii)** $\dfrac{\pi}{3}, \dfrac{4\pi}{3}$

5. (i) $\dfrac{5\pi}{4} + 2n\pi$ or $\dfrac{7\pi}{4} + 2n\pi$ for *n* ∈ ℤ **(ii)** $\dfrac{5\pi}{4}, \dfrac{7\pi}{4}$

6. (i) $\dfrac{5\pi}{6} + 2n\pi$ or $\dfrac{7\pi}{6} + 2n\pi$ for *n* ∈ ℤ **(ii)** $\dfrac{5\pi}{6}, \dfrac{7\pi}{6}$

7. (i) 30° + *n*(180°) or 150° + *n*(180°) for *n* ∈ ℤ **(ii)** 30°, 150°, 210°, 330°

8. (i) 80° + *n*(120°) or 100° + *n*(120°) for *n* ∈ ℤ **(ii)** 80°, 100°, 200°, 220°, 320°, 340°

9. (i) 10° + *n*(120°) or 70° + *n*(120°) for *n* ∈ ℤ. Alternatively, 10° + *n* (60°) for *n* ∈ ℤ
  (ii) 10°, 70°, 130°, 190°, 250°, 310°

10. (i) $\dfrac{5\pi + 8n\pi}{12}$ or $\dfrac{7\pi + 8n\pi}{12}$ for *n* ∈ ℤ **(ii)** $\dfrac{5\pi}{12}, \dfrac{7\pi}{12}, \dfrac{13\pi}{12}, \dfrac{15\pi}{12}, \dfrac{21\pi}{12}, \dfrac{23\pi}{12}$

11. (i) $\dfrac{\pi + 8n\pi}{20}$ or $\dfrac{5\pi + 8n\pi}{20}$ for *n* ∈ ℤ. Alternatively, $\dfrac{\pi + 4n\pi}{20}$ for *n* ∈ ℤ

  (ii) $\dfrac{\pi}{20}, \dfrac{\pi}{4}, \dfrac{9\pi}{20}, \dfrac{13\pi}{20}, \dfrac{17\pi}{20}, \dfrac{21\pi}{20}, \dfrac{5\pi}{4}, \dfrac{29\pi}{20}, \dfrac{33\pi}{20}, \dfrac{37\pi}{20}$

12. (i) $\dfrac{2\pi + 6n\pi}{9}$ or $\dfrac{4\pi + 6n\pi}{9}$ for *n* ∈ ℤ **(ii)** $\dfrac{2\pi}{9}, \dfrac{4\pi}{9}, \dfrac{8\pi}{9}, \dfrac{10\pi}{9}, \dfrac{14\pi}{9}, \dfrac{16\pi}{9}$

13. (i) $n(360°)$ or $180° + n(360°)$ for $n \in \mathbb{Z}$ (ii) $0°$, $180°$ $360°$
14. (i) $90° + n(360°)$ for $n \in \mathbb{Z}$ (ii) $90°$ **15.** (i) $90° + n(360°)$ or $270° + n(360°)$ for $n \in \mathbb{Z}$
(ii) $90°$, 270 **16.** (i) $2n\pi$ for $n \in \mathbb{Z}$ (ii) 0, 2π **17.** (i) $2n\pi$ or $\pi + 2n\pi$ for $n \in \mathbb{Z}$.
Alternatively, $n\pi$ for $n \in \mathbb{Z}$ (ii) 0, π, 2π **18.** (i) $\pi + 2n\pi$ for $n \in \mathbb{Z}$ (ii) π
19. (i) $\dfrac{\pi + 4n\pi}{4}$ or $\dfrac{3\pi + 4n\pi}{4}$ for $n \in \mathbb{Z}$ (ii) $\dfrac{\pi}{4}$, $\dfrac{3\pi}{4}$, $\dfrac{5\pi}{4}$, $\dfrac{7\pi}{4}$
20. (i) $\dfrac{3\pi + 4n\pi}{6}$ for $n \in \mathbb{Z}$ (ii) $\dfrac{\pi}{2}$, $\dfrac{7\pi}{6}$ $\dfrac{11\pi}{6}$
21. (i) $\dfrac{n\pi}{2}$ or $\dfrac{\pi + 2n\pi}{4}$ for $n \in \mathbb{Z}$. Alternatively, $\dfrac{n\pi}{4}$ for $n \in \mathbb{Z}$ (ii) 0, $\dfrac{\pi}{4}$, $\dfrac{\pi}{2}$, $\dfrac{3\pi}{4}$, π, $\dfrac{5\pi}{4}$, $\dfrac{3\pi}{2}$, $\dfrac{7\pi}{4}$, 2π
22. (i) $11\cdot5° + n(360°)$ or $168\cdot5° + n(360°)$ for $n \in \mathbb{Z}$ (ii) $11\cdot5°$, $168\cdot5°$
23. (i) $36\cdot3° + n(180°)$ or $143\cdot7° + n(180°)$ for $n \in \mathbb{Z}$ (ii) $36\cdot3°$, $143\cdot7°$, $216\cdot3°$, $323\cdot7°$
24. (i) $20\cdot9° + n(120°)$ or $80\cdot9° + n(120°)$ for $n \in \mathbb{Z}$. Alternatively, $20\cdot9° + n(60°)$ for $n \in \mathbb{Z}$
  (ii) $20\cdot9°$, $80\cdot9°$, $140\cdot9°$, $200\cdot9°$, $260\cdot9°$, $320\cdot9°$

Exercise 9.6

1. $67\cdot62$ cm^2 **2.** $18\cdot13$ cm^2 **3.** $31\cdot01$ cm^2 **4.** $16\cdot67$ cm^2 **5.** $47\cdot55$ cm^2
6. $21\cdot46$ cm^2 **7.** 9 cm^2 **8.** 3 cm^2 **9.** 15 cm^2 **10.** $19\cdot03$ cm^2 **11.** $18\cdot39$ cm^2
12. (i) 3 cm (ii) $2\cdot16$ cm^2 (iii) $4\cdot98$ cm^2 **13.** 27 cm^2 **14.** 14 cm   **15.** 16 cm
16. 7 cm   **17.** 4 cm^2 **18.** $30°$, $150°$ **19.** $65°$, $115°$ **20.** (i) 10 (ii) 6 (iii) $\dfrac{3}{5}$
(iv) (a) 48 (b) 48 (c) 48 **21.** (ii) 8 cm (iii) (a) $\dfrac{4}{5}$ (b) $\dfrac{8}{17}$ (v) $16\cdot8$ cm
22. (i) 219 m (ii) $86{,}000$ m^2 **23.** 5 **24.** 2 **25.** (i) 22 cm   **26.** (iii) $108\sqrt{2}$
28. (i) $1{,}327$ cm (ii) $1{,}659$ cm   **29.** $(60\pi - 36)$ cm^2 **30.** $3(4\pi - 3\sqrt{3})$ cm^2 **31.** (i) $\dfrac{3\pi}{4}$
(ii) $8(3\pi - 2\sqrt{2})$ cm^2 **33.** $18(2\sqrt{3} - \pi)$ **34.** (i) $\dfrac{\pi}{3}$ (ii) $60\sqrt{3}$ cm
(iii) $(110\pi + 120\sqrt{3})$ cm   **36.** (i) $\sqrt{2}\,r$ **37.** (i) πx^2

Exercise 9.7

1. $13\cdot5$ **2.** $4\cdot9$ **3.** $37\cdot8°$ **4.** $53\cdot6°$ **5.** $8\cdot9$ **6.** $27\cdot4°$ **7.** $9\cdot2$ **8.** $15\cdot7$
9. $10\cdot2$ **10.** $41\cdot4°$ **11.** $57\cdot1°$ **12.** $94\cdot8°$ **13.** (i) $23°$ (ii) 103 m (iii) 93 m
16. $21\cdot8°$ **18.** $72\cdot7°$ or $107\cdot3°$ **19.** $75°$ or $105°$ **20.** (i) $45°$ or $135°$ (ii) $8\cdot9$ cm or $14\cdot3$ cm
21. 4 cm   **22.** (i) $30°$ or $150°$ (ii) $4\cdot1$ cm and $13\cdot5$ cm   **23.** (ii) $1\cdot5$ cm   **24.** $16\sqrt{6}$ cm^2
27. 204 cm   **28.** $13°$ **29.** (i) 46 m   **30.** (i) $37\cdot2°$ (ii) $23\cdot72$ km   **31.** (i) $65{,}449$ m
(ii) $15{:}03$ **32.** (i) Tom (ii) $12\cdot8$ m^2 **33.** (i) $60°$ (ii) $1\cdot885$ m (iii) $10\cdot37$ m
(iv) $3\cdot96$ m   **34.** (i) $3\cdot66$ m (ii) $20\cdot3$ m

Exercise 9.8

1. (i) 6 m   (ii) 15 m   (iii) 22·5 m²   (iv) 20·42 m   2. (i) 18·75 cm   (ii) 40·5°

3. (i) 74 seconds   (ii) yes   (iii) 4·3°   4. (i) 8 cm   (ii) 53·13°   5. (i) 59°   (ii) 96 cm²

6. (i) 65 m   (ii) 120°   7. (i) 5 cm   (ii) 13 cm   (iii) 45°   8. (i) $p = h, q = \sqrt{3}\,h$

(ii) $q^2 = p^2 + 2{,}500$ (iii) $25\sqrt{2}$ 9. (i) 25·99 m   (ii) 18·87 m   (iii) 49·92°   10. (i) 20 m

(ii) 30·6 m   11. (i) $300\sqrt{3}$ m   (ii) 1,000 m

Exercise 9.9

1. (i), (ii)

(iii) $x = 45° \le x \le 315°$

2. (i), (ii)

$x = 53°$ or $127°$

3. (i)

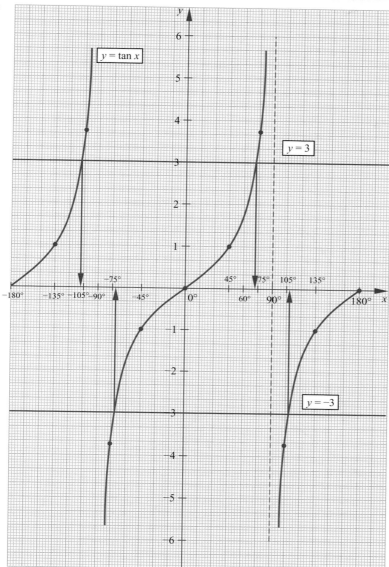

(ii) $-180° \leq x \leq -108°$, $-72° \leq x \leq 72°$ or $72° \leq x \leq 180°$

4.

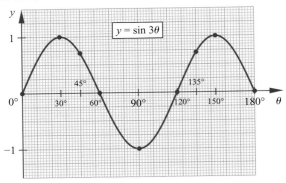

5.

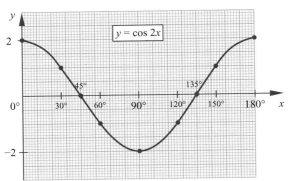

6. (i)

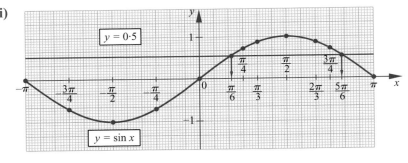

(ii) $x = \dfrac{\pi}{6}$ or $\dfrac{5\pi}{6}$

7.

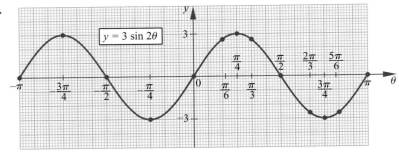

8. (i)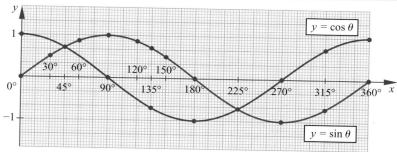

9. (i)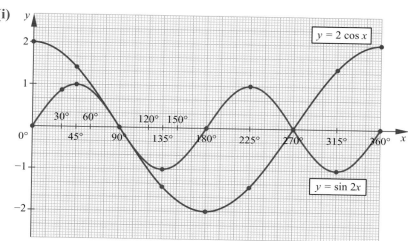

(ii) $x = 90°$ or $270°$

12. (i)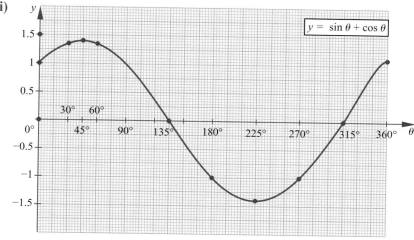

(ii) $360°$; $[-\sqrt{2}, \sqrt{2}]$

13. (i)

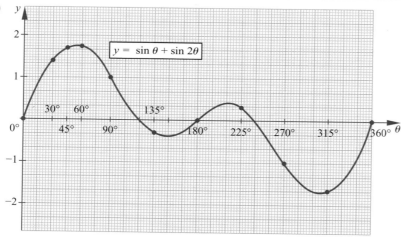

$y = \sin\theta + \sin 2\theta$

(ii) 360°; [−1.76, 1·76]

Exercise 9.10

1. $y = \sin\theta$, $0° \le \theta \le 360°$; 360°; [−1, 1]   **2.** $y = \cos x$, $0° \le x \le 360°$; 360°; [−1, 1]

3. $y = 2\sin x$, $0° \le x \le 360°$; 360°; [−2, 2]   **4.** $y = 2\cos 2\theta$, $0° \le \theta \le 360°$; 180°; [−2, 2]

5. $y = \cos 3\theta$, $0° \le \theta \le 360°$; 120°; [−1, 1]   **6.** $y = \sin 4x$, $0° \le x \le 360°$; 90°; [−1, 1]

7. (i) 180° **(ii)** $a = 2$; [−2, 2] **(iii)** $90° + n180°$ **8. (i)** 240° **(ii)** $b = -1$; [−1, 1]

(iii) $180° + n240°$ **9. (i)** $p = 30$ **(ii)** $q = 4$ **(iii)** $\dfrac{\pi}{2}$; [−30, 30] **(iv)** $\dfrac{\pi}{4} + \dfrac{n\pi}{2}$

Exercise 9.11

1. (i)

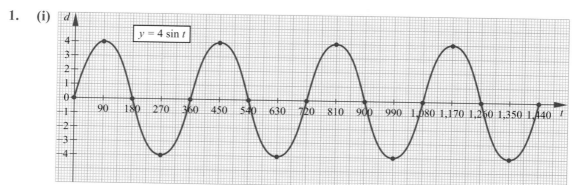

$y = 4 \sin t$

(ii) [−4, 4]   **(iii) (a)** 360 minutes **(b)** 6 hours   **(iv)** 8 m

2. (ii) 2 secs; [−1, 1]   **(iii)** $a = 2$; $b = 180$ **(iv)** $0 \le t \le 1$; $2 \le t \le 3$; $4 \le t \le 5$

(v) 10 cm

3. (i) 12 days; [17, 21]   **(ii)** cosine   **(iii)** 7 days

4. (i) 6 hours; [0, 300]   (ii) $05:30 \leq h \leq 20:30$ (iii) 50–100
5. (i) minimum 15 cm, maximum 35 cm

(ii)

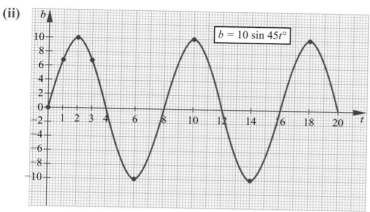

(iii) $\dfrac{8}{10}$ or $\dfrac{4}{5}$ of a second   (iv) 100 cm or 1 m   (v) 5   (vi) $b = 10 \sin 36t°$

6. (i) 12 months; [20, 50]   (ii) $a = 15$; $b = 30$ (iii) 4   (iv) 3

7. (i) ① 125 m/sec; [−1, 1]   ② 200 m/sec; [−0·75, 0·75]   ③ 400 m/sec; [−0·5, 0·5]
   (ii) ① 1; 8Hz   ② 0·75, 5Hz   ③ 0·5, 2·5 Hz

8. (i) (a) 12   (b) 4πm   (c) 48πm^2 (d) 36 m   (e) 164°

   (ii) (a) 0 m   (b) 6 secs   (c) $4\pi \sin\left(\dfrac{\pi}{6}t\right)$

(d)

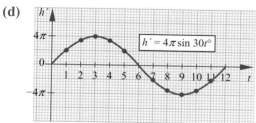

   (e) 3 seconds or 9 seconds

Exercise 9.12

1. (i) $\dfrac{5}{13}$ (ii) $\dfrac{12}{5}$ (iii) $\dfrac{3}{5}$ (iv) $\dfrac{3}{4}$ (v) $\dfrac{63}{65}$ (vi) $-\dfrac{16}{65}$ (vii) $-\dfrac{63}{16}$ (viii) $\dfrac{120}{169}$

3. (i) (a) $\dfrac{840}{841}$ (b) $\dfrac{41}{841}$ (c) $\dfrac{840}{41}$ (ii) $-\dfrac{3}{5}$ 4. $\dfrac{\sqrt{3}-1}{2\sqrt{2}}$

5. $\dfrac{\sqrt{3}+1}{2\sqrt{2}}$ 6. $2 + \sqrt{3}$ 7. $\dfrac{\sqrt{3}+1}{2\sqrt{2}}$ 8. $\dfrac{\sqrt{3}-1}{2\sqrt{2}}$ 9. $2 - \sqrt{3}$ 10. $\dfrac{1}{21}$

11. (i) $\dfrac{9}{2}$ (ii) $\dfrac{36}{85}$ **12.** $45°$ **19.** $\pm\dfrac{5}{7}$ **20.** $\pm\dfrac{1}{5}$ **21.** (iii) $-\dfrac{1}{9}$

23. (i) $\dfrac{5}{3}\sin\beta$ (ii) $\dfrac{\sqrt{11}}{5}$ **24** (i) $2\cos\theta$ **25.** (i) (a) $\dfrac{4}{7}$ (b) $\dfrac{3}{11}$ (ii) 1

Exercise 9.13

1. $2\sin 3\theta\cos\theta$ **2.** $2\cos 6\theta\cos\theta$ **3.** $-2\sin 5\theta\sin 3\theta$ **4.** $2\cos 4\theta\sin\theta$

5. $-2\sin 4\theta\sin 2\theta$ **6.** $2\cos 4\theta\cos 3\theta$ **7.** $2\sin 2\theta\cos\theta$

8. $2\cos 3\theta\cos 2\theta$ **9.** $-2\cos 5\theta\sin 3\theta$ **10.** $\sin 8\theta+\sin 4\theta$

11. $\cos 4\theta+\cos 2\theta$ **12.** $\cos 5\theta+\cos 3\theta$ **13.** $\sin 9\theta-\sin 3\theta$

14. $\cos 5\theta-\cos 3\theta$ **15.** $\sin 13\theta-\sin\theta$ **16.** $\dfrac{1}{2}[\sin 6x+\sin 4x]$

17. $\dfrac{1}{2}[\cos A-\cos 3A]$ **18.** $\dfrac{1}{2}[\sin 4A-\sin 2A]$ **19.** $\dfrac{1}{\sqrt{2}}$ or $\dfrac{\sqrt{2}}{2}$

20. $-\dfrac{\sqrt{3}}{\sqrt{2}}$ or $-\dfrac{\sqrt{6}}{2}$ **21.** $-\dfrac{\sqrt{3}}{\sqrt{2}}$ or $-\dfrac{\sqrt{6}}{2}$ **22.** $\dfrac{2+\sqrt{3}}{2}$ or $1+\dfrac{\sqrt{3}}{2}$

23. $\dfrac{1}{2}$ **24.** $\dfrac{\sqrt{2}-1}{4}$ or $\dfrac{2-\sqrt{2}}{4\sqrt{2}}$ **25.** (i) 2 (ii) 2 **26.** (i) $\dfrac{4}{5}; -\dfrac{4}{3}$ (ii) $-\dfrac{11}{2}$

Exercise 9.14

19. (ii) $105°+n180°,\ 165°+n180°$ **20.** (ii) $15°+n180°,\ 75°+n180°$

23. (i) $\sin 2x$ (ii)

(iii) $15°+n180°,\ 75°+n180°$

24. (ii)

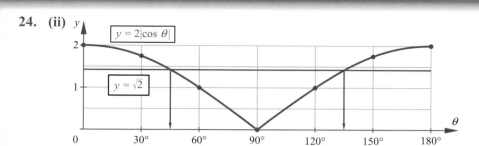

(iii) $180°$; $[0, 2]$ **(iv)** $45°$, $135°$

Exercise 9.15

1. $0°$, $30°$, $150°$, $180°$, $360°$ **2.** $60°$, $180°$, $300°$ **3.** $0°$, $60°$, $180°$, $240°$, $360°$

4. $0°$, $90°$, $270°$ **5.** $0°$, $135°$, $180°$, $315°$, $360°$ **6.** $90°$, $210°$, $330°$ **7.** $\dfrac{\pi}{3}, \dfrac{\pi}{2}, \dfrac{3\pi}{2}, \dfrac{5\pi}{3}$

8. $0, \dfrac{\pi}{2}, \pi, 2\pi$ **9.** $0, \dfrac{\pi}{3}, \dfrac{5\pi}{3}, 2\pi$ **10.** $0°$, $120°$, $180°$, $240°$, $360°$

11. (i) $0, \dfrac{\pi}{4}, \pi, \dfrac{7\pi}{4}, 2\pi$ **(ii)** where $n \in \mathbb{Z}$; $2n\pi, \dfrac{\pi}{4} + 2n\pi, \pi + 2n\pi, \dfrac{7\pi}{4} + 2n\pi, 2\pi + 2n\pi$ or

$2\pi(1 + n)$ **12. (i)** $\dfrac{\pi}{6}, \dfrac{5\pi}{6}, \dfrac{3\pi}{2}$ **(ii)** where $n \in \mathbb{Z}$; $\dfrac{\pi}{6} + 2n\pi, \dfrac{5\pi}{6} + 2n\pi, \dfrac{3\pi}{2} + 2n\pi$

13. $0°$, $30°$, $180°$, $330°$, $360°$ **14. (i)** $\dfrac{\pi}{3}, \dfrac{2\pi}{3}, \dfrac{4\pi}{3}, \dfrac{5\pi}{3}$ **(ii)** $\dfrac{\pi}{6}, \dfrac{5\pi}{6}, \dfrac{7\pi}{6}, \dfrac{11\pi}{6}$

15. (i) $\dfrac{\pi}{4}, \dfrac{3\pi}{4}, \dfrac{5\pi}{4}, \dfrac{7\pi}{4}$ **(ii)** where $n \in \mathbb{Z}$; $\dfrac{\pi}{4} + 2n\pi, \dfrac{3\pi}{4} + 2n\pi, \dfrac{5\pi}{4} + 2n\pi, \dfrac{7\pi}{4} + 2n\pi$

16. (i) $\dfrac{\sin A}{\cos A}$ **(ii)** $\dfrac{\pi}{4}; \dfrac{5\pi}{4}$ **17. (i)** max value of $\sin \theta = 1$ **(ii) (a)** $\dfrac{\pi}{3}; \dfrac{5\pi}{3}$ **(b)** where $n \in \mathbb{Z}$;

$\dfrac{\pi}{3} + 2n\pi, \dfrac{5\pi}{3} + 2n\pi$ **18.** $30°$, $150°$, $199°$, $341°$ **19. (i)** $\dfrac{5}{2}$ **(ii)** $\dfrac{\pi}{6}, \dfrac{5\pi}{6}, \dfrac{7\pi}{6}, \dfrac{11\pi}{6}$

20. (i) $a = 2$, $b = 3$ **(ii)** $0°$, $60°$, $300°$, $360°$ **21. (ii)** $0, \dfrac{\pi}{3}, \dfrac{2\pi}{3}, \pi, \dfrac{4\pi}{3}, \dfrac{5\pi}{3}, 2\pi$

22. (i) $15° + n(120°)$; $75° + n(120°)$ or $15° + n(60°)$, where $n \in \mathbb{Z}$

(ii) $15°$, $75°$, $135°$, $195°$, $255°$, $315°$ **23. (i)** $2 \cos 3x \sin x$ **(ii)** $0°$, $30°$, $90°$, $185°$, $180°$

24. $30°$, $60°$, $90°$, $150°$, $210°$, $240°$, $270°$, $330°$ **25.** $10°$, $70°$, $130°$, $190°$, $250°$, $310°$

Exercise 9.16

9. (ii) $\cos \alpha = \dfrac{d^2 + p^2 - c^2}{2pd}$; $\cos \beta = \dfrac{d^2 + q^2 - b^2}{2qd}$ (iii) $\alpha = 180° - \beta$

Exercise 10.1

1. 30   2. (i) 30   (ii) 4   3. (i) 1,263,600   (ii) 421,200   4. (i) 0000   (ii) 9999
(iii) 10,000   5. (i) 4,536   (ii) (a) 650   (b) poor   6. (i) 120   (ii) 24   (iii) 6
7. (i) 24   (ii) 120   8. (i) 5,040   (ii) (a) 720 too few   (b) 40,320 too many   (c) just right
9. (i) 234   10. 1,213,056 > 1 million   11. 120   12. (i) 5!   (ii) $2 \times 4!$ (iii) $5! - 2 \times 4!$
13. (i) 8!   (ii) $5! \times 3!$ (iii) $8! - (5! \times 3!)$ 14. (i) 6!   (ii) 4!   (iii) (a) $4! \times 2!$ (b) $6! - (4! \times 2!)$
15. 48   16. (i) 8!   (ii) 6,720   17. (i) 5!   (ii) 60   18. 18   19. 42
20. (i) 48   (ii) 100   21. (i) 1,296   (ii) 180   (iii) 216   (iv) 24   22. 18
23. (i) 108   (ii) 36   24. (i) 85   (ii) 34   (iii) 60   25. (i) (a) 125   (b) 100   (c) 674
(ii) (b) 50 : 50   (c) slightly fewer seniors

Exercise 10.2

1. 10   2. 45   3. 126   4. 10   5. 190   6. 4,060   7. 93   8. −126   9. 0
10. 3   11. 3   12. 35   13. (i) 210   (ii) 84   (iii) 126   (iv) 70   14. (i) 35   (ii) 20
(iii) 15   (iv) 10   (v) 6   15. (i) 252   (ii) 196   16. (i) 20   (ii) 6   17. (i) 126
(ii) 15   (iii) 111   18. (i) 126   (ii) 105   19. 56   20. (i) 780   (ii) 9,880
21. 22   22. (i) 35   (ii) 70   (iii) 120   23. (i) 30   (ii) 18   (iii) 8   24. 6,300

Exercise 10.3

1. (i) 56   (ii) 24   2. (i) 330   (ii) 150   3. (i) 24   4. (i) 126   (ii) 60   5. (i) 210
(ii) 90   (iii) 170   6. (i) 10   (ii) 20   (iii) 5   7. (i) 35   (ii) 13   8. (i) 40
(ii) 74   (iii) 50   9. 148   10. 281   11. 245   12. 180   13. (i) 72
(ii) double counting

Exercise 10.4

1. 4   2. 5   3. 6   4. 8   5. 10   6. 5   7. 25   8. 6   9. 8

Exercise 10.5

1. (i) $\dfrac{1}{3}$ (ii) $\dfrac{5}{12}$ (iii) $\dfrac{1}{12}$ (iv) $\dfrac{1}{6}$ (v) $\dfrac{5}{8}$ 2. (i) $\dfrac{1}{52}$ (ii) $\dfrac{1}{2}$ (iii) $\dfrac{1}{4}$ (iv) $\dfrac{1}{13}$ (v) $\dfrac{3}{13}$
(vi) $\dfrac{3}{26}$ (vii) $\dfrac{5}{13}$ (viii) $\dfrac{12}{13}$ (ix) 0   3. (i) $\dfrac{2}{5}$ (ii) 4   4. (i) (a) $\dfrac{1}{8}$ (b) $\dfrac{1}{4}$ (c) $\dfrac{1}{2}$
(ii) *B, B*   5. (i) $\dfrac{1}{5}$ (ii) $\dfrac{2}{5}$ 6. $\dfrac{3}{10}$ 7. (ii) (a) $\dfrac{2}{5}$ (b) $\dfrac{3}{5}$ (c) $\dfrac{3}{10}$ (d) $\dfrac{2}{5}$ (iii) $\dfrac{2}{3}$
(iv) $\dfrac{1}{5}$ 8. (i) (a) $\dfrac{2}{5}$ (b) $\dfrac{3}{5}$ (c) $\dfrac{3}{20}$ (d) $\dfrac{1}{2}$ (e) $\dfrac{1}{20}$ (ii) $\dfrac{1}{8}$ (iii) (a) $\dfrac{2}{3}$ (b) $\dfrac{7}{17}$

9. (i) (a) $\dfrac{7}{15}$ (b) $\dfrac{7}{30}$ (c) $\dfrac{18}{25}$ (d) $\dfrac{4}{25}$ (e) $\dfrac{1}{5}$ (ii) $\dfrac{1}{3}$ (iii) (a) $\dfrac{1}{4}$ (b) $\dfrac{9}{10}$ (iv) 230 (a) $\dfrac{7}{23}$

(b) $\dfrac{11}{46}$ (c) $\dfrac{88}{115}$ **10.** (i) 2 (ii) 3 (iii) 7

Exercise 10.6

1. 125   **2.** (i) $\dfrac{63}{100}$ (ii) 50   **3.** (i) 160 (ii) 120   **4.** (i) $\dfrac{13}{60}$ (ii) $\dfrac{1}{6}$

5. (i) $\dfrac{4}{7}$ (ii) 8   **6.** (i) 0·1 (ii) 0·5 (iii) (a) 240 (b) 400   **7.** (i) Nora (ii) Margaret

9. (i) Hard Rock (ii) 50, 73, 61, 56, 68, 52 (iii) $\dfrac{13}{90}$ **10.** (ii) (a) $\dfrac{13}{25}$

11. (i) 0·1 (ii) (a) 42 (b) 12   **12.** (i) 20 (ii) (a) 0·05 (b) 0·3

Exercise 10.7

1. (i) $\dfrac{1}{2}$ (ii) $\dfrac{1}{2}$ (iii) $\dfrac{5}{6}$ **2.** (i) $\dfrac{1}{2}$ (ii) $\dfrac{1}{4}$ (iii) $\dfrac{2}{3}$ (iv) $\dfrac{1}{3}$

3. (i) $\dfrac{1}{3}$ (ii) $\dfrac{1}{5}$ (iii) $\dfrac{7}{15}$ (iv) $\dfrac{8}{15}$ **4.** (i) $\dfrac{1}{9}$ (ii) $\dfrac{2}{9}$ (iii) $\dfrac{4}{9}$ (iv) $\dfrac{2}{3}$ (v) $\dfrac{1}{3}$

5. (i) $\dfrac{1}{3}$ (ii) $\dfrac{2}{3}$ (iii) $\dfrac{3}{4}$ (iv) $\dfrac{1}{4}$ **6.** (i) $\dfrac{7}{20}$ (ii) $\dfrac{11}{20}$ (iii) $\dfrac{3}{4}$ (iv) $\dfrac{17}{20}$

7. (i) $\dfrac{1}{2}$ (ii) $\dfrac{7}{13}$ (iii) $\dfrac{7}{26}$ (iv) $\dfrac{19}{26}$ **8.** (i) $\dfrac{2}{9}$ (ii) $\dfrac{11}{36}$ **9.** (i) $\dfrac{5}{8}$ (ii) $\dfrac{3}{8}$ (iii) $\dfrac{3}{4}$ (iv) $\dfrac{1}{4}$

10. (i) $\dfrac{1}{2}$ (ii) $\dfrac{1}{4}$ (iii) $\dfrac{2}{3}$ (iv) $\dfrac{3}{4}$ (v) $\dfrac{2}{3}$ (vi) $\dfrac{1}{3}$

11. (i) $A \cap B = \{6\}$ not mutually exclusive
(ii) $A \cup B = \{2, 3, 4, 6\}$ not exhaustive

12. (i) (a) $\dfrac{1}{2}$ (b) $\dfrac{9}{16}$ **14.** (i) 10 (ii) (a) $\dfrac{14}{25}$ (b) $\dfrac{16}{25}$ (c) $\dfrac{6}{25}$ (iii) part (b)

15. (i) $\dfrac{3}{10}$ (ii) none   **16.** (i) 1 (ii) exhaustive   **17.** $\dfrac{7}{30}$ **18.** (i) 0·7 (ii) 0·3

(iii) 0·1   **19.** (i) 0 (ii) $\dfrac{7}{10}$ **20.** (i) yes (ii) no   **21.** (i) 0 (ii) $\dfrac{22}{35}$ **22.** (i) 1

(ii) $\dfrac{5}{12}$ **23.** (i) 0 (ii) $\dfrac{1}{5}$ **24.** 0·6   **25.** $\dfrac{3}{4}$

Exercise 10.8

1. $\dfrac{1}{5}$ **2.** $\dfrac{4}{5}$ **3.** $\dfrac{13}{20}$ **4.** $\dfrac{17}{20}$ **5.** (i) 90% (ii) 18%   **6.** 0·65   **7.** (i) $\dfrac{1}{5}$ (ii) $\dfrac{3}{20}$

8. (iii) $\dfrac{1}{8}$ **9.** $\dfrac{11}{20}$ **10.** $\dfrac{2}{9}$ **11.** (i) $\dfrac{1}{10}$ (ii) $\dfrac{3}{10}$ **12.** (i) 0·16 (ii) 0·6 (iii) 0·4

13. (i) $\dfrac{1}{15}$ (ii) $\dfrac{4}{5}$ (iii) $\dfrac{1}{5}$ **14.** (i) $\dfrac{5}{42}$ (ii) $\dfrac{3}{7}$ **15.** (i) $\dfrac{17}{20}$ (ii) $\dfrac{3}{20}$ **16.** (i) $\dfrac{5}{21}$

(ii) $\dfrac{2}{3}$ (iii) $\dfrac{5}{12}$ **18.** (i) (a) $4x$ (b) $5x$ (ii) $\dfrac{1}{16}$

Exercise 10.9

1. (ii) (a) $\dfrac{11}{20}$ (b) $\dfrac{3}{8}$ (c) $\dfrac{8}{11}$ **2.** (i) $\dfrac{1}{35}$ (ii) $\dfrac{11}{35}$ **3.** (i) (a) 0.03 (b) 0.34

4. (i) (a) $\dfrac{2}{15}$ (b) $\dfrac{8}{15}$ (ii) no; $P(E\,|\,F) \ne P(E)$ **5.** (i) (a) $\dfrac{3}{20}$ (b) $\dfrac{3}{8}$ (c) $\dfrac{1}{3}$

6. (ii) E_2 and E_3 (iii) yes, $\dfrac{12}{36} \times \dfrac{6}{36} = \dfrac{2}{36}$ **7.** (ii) $\dfrac{4}{7}$ **8.** (i) $\dfrac{1}{3}$ (ii) $\dfrac{37}{45}$

(iii) $P(E)\,P(F) = \dfrac{1}{3} = P(E \cap F)$, $\therefore$ independent (iv) not **10.** $\dfrac{7}{16}$ **11.** (i) $\dfrac{11}{15}$ (ii) $\dfrac{2}{3}$

Exercise 10.10

1. $\dfrac{1}{6}$ **2.** (i) $(B, B)\,(B, G)\,(G, B)\,(G, G)$ (ii) (a) $\dfrac{1}{4}$ (b) $\dfrac{1}{2}$ **3.** $\dfrac{88}{16{,}575}$ **5.** (i) $\dfrac{1}{12}$

(ii) $\dfrac{5}{12}$ (iii) $\dfrac{7}{12}$ **6.** (i) (a) $\dfrac{5}{8}$ (b) $\dfrac{2}{3}$ (ii) $\dfrac{10}{23}$ **7.** (i) $\dfrac{25}{144}$ (ii) $\dfrac{25}{72}$ (iii) $\dfrac{5}{48}$ (iv) $\dfrac{5}{18}$

8. (i) $\dfrac{3}{8}$ (ii) $\dfrac{2}{13}$ (iii) $\dfrac{27}{110}$ (iv) $\dfrac{13}{25}$ **9.** (i) $\dfrac{11}{25}$ (ii) $\dfrac{1}{23}$ **10.** (ii) $\dfrac{25}{102}$

11. (i) 0.24 (ii) 0.7 **12.** (i) $\dfrac{7}{24}$ (ii) $\dfrac{1}{120}$ (iii) $\dfrac{21}{40}$ **13.** (i) 0.95 (ii) 0.095

14. (i) 0.3 (ii) 0.8 **15.** (i) (a) 0.16 (b) 0.48 (c) 0.64 (ii) $\dfrac{3}{8}$

16. (i) (a) 0.09 (b) 0.33 (ii) $\dfrac{3}{11}$ **17.** (i) $324{,}632$ (ii) 150 (iii) $4{,}350$

18. (i) $\dfrac{1}{6}$ (ii) $\dfrac{19}{36}$ (iii) $\dfrac{5}{18}$ **19.** (i) $\dfrac{1}{2}$ (ii) $\dfrac{17}{48}$ **20.** (i) $\dfrac{7}{20}$ (ii) $\dfrac{1}{40}$ (iii) $\dfrac{19}{24}$

21. (i) $\dfrac{3}{10}$ (ii) $\dfrac{11}{12}$ (iii) $\dfrac{11}{12}$ (iv) $\dfrac{1}{20}$ **22.** (i) (a) 0.1 (b) 0.24 (ii) 0.5 (iii) 0.35 (iv) $\dfrac{1}{4}$

23. (ii) 0.056 (iii) $\dfrac{5}{28}$ **24.** (i) 0.98 (ii) (a) 0.019 (b) 0.0288 (iii) 0.66

(iv) $3{,}300$ **25.** (i) $\dfrac{1}{10}$ (ii) $\dfrac{9}{20}$ (iii) $\dfrac{3}{20}$ **26.** (i) $\dfrac{1}{(30)^6}$ (ii) $\dfrac{2{,}639}{5{,}625}$ **27.** (i) $\dfrac{1}{13}$

(ii) $\dfrac{28}{65}$ (iii) $\dfrac{16}{65}$ **28.** (i) $\dfrac{30x}{(6 + x)(5 + x)(4 + x)}$ (ii) 7 **29.** (i) $\dfrac{r(r - 1)}{(w + r)(w + r - 1)}$

(ii) $r = 3$ (iii) $w = 6,\ r = 15$ **30.** (i) $\dfrac{8}{35}$ (ii) $\dfrac{18}{35}$ (iii) $\dfrac{3}{35}$

Exercise 10.11

1. (i) 0·205 (ii) 0·185 (iii) 0·041 (iv) 0·000 2. (i) (ii) and (iv) 4. (i) $\dfrac{3}{8}$ (ii) $\dfrac{3}{8}$ (iii) $\dfrac{1}{8}$

(iv) $\dfrac{7}{8}$ 5. 0·4096 6. (i) 0·002 (ii) 0·024 7. (i) $\dfrac{1}{4,096}$ (ii) $\dfrac{81}{4,096}$ (iii) $\dfrac{9}{2,048}$ (iv) $\dfrac{4,077}{4,096}$

8. (i) 0·0005 (ii) 0·128 (iii) 0·737 9. (i) $\left(\dfrac{4}{5}\right)^9$ (ii) 0·302 (iii) 0·564 10. (i) 0·016

(ii) 0·896 11. (i) 0·032 (ii) 0·019 (iii) 0·011 12. (i) 0·2048 (ii) 0·26272

13. (i) 0·267 (ii) 0·367 14. (i) $\dfrac{1}{2^6}$ (ii) $\dfrac{1}{2^6}$ (iii) $1 - \dfrac{1}{2^5}$ 15. $\dfrac{1}{32}, \dfrac{5}{32}, \dfrac{10}{32}, \dfrac{10}{32}, \dfrac{5}{32}, \dfrac{1}{32}$

17. (i) $\dfrac{3}{8}$ (ii) $\dfrac{3,375}{16,384}$ 18. 0·06561 19. (i) $\dfrac{25}{216}$ (ii) $\dfrac{2,821}{7,776}$ (iii) $\dfrac{6}{11}$

Exercise 10.12

1. (i) 0·9332 (ii) 0·1587 (iii) 0·2119 (iv) 0·8054 2. 0·8849 3. 0·7881 4. 0·9893

5. 0·0287 6. 0·1056 7. 0·2483 8. 0·1587 9. 0·0548 10. 0·017 11. 0·2417

12. 0·6826 13. 0·8673 14. 1·2 15. 1·83 16. −0·44 17. (i) 0·8413 (ii) 0·0062

18. (i) 0·9332 (ii) 0·0228 19. (i) 0·5328 (ii) 0·1359 20. (i) 0·6455 (ii) 0·3721

21. (i) 1 (ii) −2 (iii) 1·5 (iv) −2·5 22. (i) 112 (ii) 90·4 23. 0·5646 24. 212

25. (i) (a) 0·0668 (b) 0·7888 (ii) 316 26. (i) 25% (ii) 67 28. (i) 5 (ii) 65

29. (i) 4 (ii) 60 30. 9% 31. (i) 0·1587 (ii) 63 32. (i) 0·9938 (ii) (a) 0·9876

(b) 0·00004 (iii) 0·0123 33. (i) 0·2119 (ii) 146·6 cm (iii) 143·5, 176·5

34. (i) (a) 0·2743 (b) 0·0359 (c) 0·6898 (iii) 0·4758 35. (i) 0·0668 (ii) 0·00030

Exercise 10.13

1. $P = 0·3$, $E(x) = 1$ 2. $P = 0·4$, $E(x) = 2·7$ 3. $P = 0·2$, $E(x) = 4·4$ 4. $P = 0·5$, $E(x) = 6$,

$\sigma(x) = 2·2$ 5. $P = 0·2$, $E(x) = 5$, $\tau(x) = 1·1$ 6. (i) 0·1 (ii) 2 (iii) (a) 1·5 (b) 1·12

7. $a = 0·2$, $b = 0·3$ 8. $a = 0·3$, $b = 0·1$

9. (i)

x	0	1	2
$P(x)$	$\dfrac{1}{3}$	$\dfrac{8}{15}$	$\dfrac{2}{15}$

(iii) $\dfrac{4}{5}$ (iv) 800 10. (i) $\dfrac{7}{36}$ (ii) $\dfrac{53}{6}$ 12. (i) 0 (ii) $\dfrac{2}{5}$

13. (i) (a) $\dfrac{1}{10,000}$ (b) $\dfrac{1}{500}$ (c) $\dfrac{9,979}{10,000}$ (iii) 3 14. (i) (a) 0·2 (b) 12 (c) 21 (ii) 0·5

(iii) €5 15. father $E(x) = 10$; mother $E(x) = 10·5$ 16. (ii) (a) $\dfrac{1}{30}$ (b) $\dfrac{2}{15}$ (c) $\dfrac{1}{6}$

(d) $\dfrac{2}{3}$ 17. (i) $E(x) = 5$ (ii) one possible solution is to change €10 to €4 18. (i) 0·101

(ii) 0·086 (iii) €616·91 (iv) €520·39 (v) male €1,071·09; female €503·61 (vi) €448

Exercise 11.1

1. 3   2. 8   3. 5   4. 0   5. 5   6. $\frac{1}{3}$ 7. 4   8. 2   9. 12   10. $\frac{1}{8}$

11. 12   12. $\frac{1}{27}$ 13. 2   14. 6   15. 1   16. −4   17. 9   18. 3   19. 27

20. 3   21. $-\frac{1}{2}$ 22. 2   23. 2   24. $\frac{4}{3}$ 25. $\frac{2}{3}$ 26. $\frac{4}{5}$ 27. $\frac{3}{2}$ 28. 0

29. 0   30. 0   31. no limit   32. 0   33. no limit   34. 0   35. 0   36. no limit

37. **(i)**

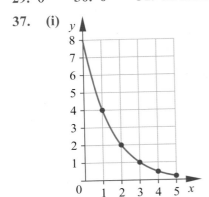

(ii) the curve lowers towards zero $(y \to 0)$

(iii) 0

38. **(i)**

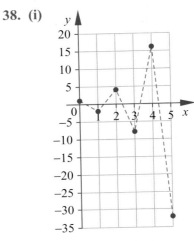

(ii) y is tending to both ∞ and $-\infty$. As neither of these is a number, there is no limit.

Exercise 11.2

1. 3   2. 5   3. $\frac{1}{2}$ 4. $\frac{1}{4}$ 5. $\frac{3}{4}$ 6. $\frac{3}{2}$ 7. 8   8. 3   9. $\frac{1}{2}$ 10. $\frac{1}{3}$ 11. 1

12. $\frac{4}{3}$ 13. 6   14. 6   15. $\frac{3}{4}$ 16. 0   17. 6   18. $\frac{2}{3}$ 19. 1   20. 1   21. 2

Exercise 12.1

7. **(i)** (1, 1)   **(ii)** (1, 1)   12. **(i)** (−1, 4), (2, −5)   **(ii)** (−1, 4), (2, −5)

17. **(i)** (−1, 5), (0, 2), (3, −7)   **(ii)** (−1, 5), (0, 2), (3, −7)   18. **(i)** (−3, 0), (−2, 3), (1, 0)

(ii) (−3, 0), (−2, 3), (1, 0)   19. **(i)** D: $-3 \le x \le 2$; R: $-9 \le y \le 11$ **(ii)** D: $1 \le x \le 7$;

R: $2 \le y \le 18$ **(iii)** D: $-2 \le x \le 1$; R: $0 \le y \le 4$ 20. **(i)** $(x-1)^2 + 5$ **(ii)** 5; $y \ge 5$

21. **(i)** $10 - (x+3)^2$ **(ii)** (−3, 10); $y \le 10$ 22. **(i)** min (−2, 3); $y \ge 3$ **(ii)** min (3, −7); $y \ge -7$

(iii) min (−1, −1); $y \ge -1$ **(iv)** max (−3, 5); $y \le 5$ **(v)** max (−4, 19); $y \le 19$ **(vi)** max (2, 4); $y \le 4$

23. $x \le -3$ or $x \ge 3$ **24.** (i) $p = -3$ (ii) $a = 2, b = -5$ (iii) $h = -\dfrac{1}{2}, k = 3$

25. (i) $b = 1, c = -2$ (ii) $k = -2, h = -2, m = -2$ **26.** (i) 6 (ii) $a = 1, b = -2, c = -5$

(iii) $-2, 1, 3$ **28.** (i) $-1, 2, 2$ (ii) max $(0, 4)$; min $(2, 0)$

(iii) local max value $= 4$ and local min value $= 0$ (iv) $10 : 25$

(v) $0 < x < 2$ (vi) $-2 \le x < 0$ or $2 < x \le 4$ (vii) $-2 \le x < -1$ (viii) $0 \le k \le 4$

(ix) (a) $-0.7, 1, 2.7$ (b) $-0.7 \le x \le 1$ or $2.7 \le x \le 4$ **29.** (iii) max $(-1, 11)$, min $(2, -16)$

(iv) (a) $-2.5 \le x < -1$ or $2 < x \le 3.5$ (b) $-1 < x < 2$ (c) $-2 < x < -1$ **30.** (i) $1, 3.5$

(ii) $1 \le x \le 3.5$ (iii) $-2 \le x \le 1$ or $3.5 \le x \le 4$ **31.** (iii) $-3.7, -0.3, 2$ (iv) -6 (v) 6

(vi) $-3, -1, 2$ (line is $4 - 2x$)   **32.** $x(x^2 - 4)$; $-2, 0, 2$ (i) $-2.4, 0.4, 2$ (ii) $-2.2, 0, 2.2$; 2.2

$f(x) = 2 \Rightarrow x^3 - 5x + 2 = 2 \Rightarrow x^3 - 5x = 0 \Rightarrow x(x^2 - 5) = 0 \Rightarrow x = 0$ or $x = \pm\sqrt{5}$

33. (i) local max value $= 4$ and local min $= 0$ (ii) max $(-1, 4)$, min $(1, 0)$ (iii) (a) $-1 < x < 1$

(b) $-3 \le x \le -2$ (c) $-2 < x < -1$ or $1 < x \le 3$ (iv) $0 < k < 4$ (v) $-1.7, 0, 1.7$

(vi) $f(x) = 2 \Rightarrow x^3 - 3x + 2 = 2 \Rightarrow x^3 - 3x = 0 \Rightarrow x(x^2 - 3) = 0$ $x = 0$ or $x = \pm\sqrt{3}$

Exercise 12.2

7. (ii) $(0, 1)$ **8.** (ii) $(-3, 8), (-1, 2)$ (iii) $-1 \le x \le 2$ **9.** (i) (a) 3.5 (b) 4.9 (c) 1.4

(ii) $y = 0$ (x-axis)   (iii) reciprocals of each other   **10.** (i) $a = 6, b = 2$ (ii) $a = 2, b = 3$

(iii) $a = \dfrac{4}{3}, b = 3$ (iv) $a = 1.5, b = 2.5$ **11.** 2^{2x-1} **12.** (i) $a = 6, b = 1.3$ (ii) 6

13. (i) 100 (iii) $V \to 0$ **14.** (i) 120 mg   (ii) $120, 78.7, 51.7, 33.9, 22.2, 14.6, 9.6$

(iv) 13.16 hours   **15.** (i) 3.58 (ii) 2.18 (iii) 2.16 (iv) 1.00 (v) 8.03 (vi) 7.23

16. 15 mins   **17.** (i) 400 (ii) $874,800$ (iii) 7.753 **18.** (i) $80°C$ (iii) $28°C$

(v) 4.12 mins   (vi) $0°C$ **19.** (ii) $p = c$ (iii) 4.8 **20.** (i) $T(n) = 120(0.8)^n$ (iii) 13

(iv) 14 years 3 months   **21.** (i) initial population   (ii) $3,225$ (iii) no bacteria die, all

reproduce at the same rate   (iv) some bacteria die

Exercise 12.3

1. (i) 1 (ii) 8 (iii) 2 (iv) 48 (v) 19 (vi) 9 (vii) $\dfrac{1}{5}$ or 0.2 (viii) -1 (ix) 5

2. (i) $3x^2 + 2$ (ii) $9x^2 + 12x + 4$ (iii) $\dfrac{2}{3x + 2}$ (iv) $9x + 8$ (v) $\dfrac{4}{x^2}$ (vi) x

3. (i) (a) $x^2 + 10x + 28$ (b) $x^2 + 8$ (ii) -2 **4.** (i) -2 (ii) ± 3 (iii) $-4, -1$ **5.** 3

6. $2, 3$ **7.** $\dfrac{3}{2}$ **8.** 15 **9.** -2 **10.** $a = 3, b = -10$

11. (i) $9x^2 + 6x + 1 \ne 3x^2 + 1$ (ii) $-1, 0$ **12.** $3(x + 5)$ is always devisable by 3 for $x \in \mathbb{Z}$

13. (i) 1   (ii) $\dfrac{1}{4}$ or 0·25   15. (i) $4 = 4$ (ii) (a) 2^{x+1} (b) $2^x + 1$ (iii) 0

16. $x^2 + 3; 3 \le gf(x) \le 19$ 17. (i) $x \ge 1$ (ii) $x \le -1$ or $x \ge 1$ 18. (i) 0   (ii) 4

19. (i) (a) x (b) $10 - x$ (c) x (d) $10 - x$ (e) $10 - x$ (f) x

(ii) $10 - x$ if k is odd and x if k is even   20. (i) x (ii) $\dfrac{x+5}{2x-1}$ (iii) x

(iv) x (v) $\dfrac{x+5}{2x-1}$ (vi) (a) x (b) $\dfrac{x+5}{2x-1}; -5, 0$ 21. (i) multiply each term on top and

bottom by -1 and then devide each term on top and bottom by 3   (ii) (a) $\dfrac{4}{2-x}$ (b) x (c) $\dfrac{2x-4}{x}$

(d) $\dfrac{4}{2-x}$ (e) x (iii) (a) $\dfrac{2x-4}{x}$ (b) $\dfrac{4}{2-x}$ (c) x (iv) 20   22. (i) 4,320   (ii) €169·04

(iii) (a) €128   (b) €182   (c) €495·20   (iv) $20 + 1·08x$ (v) €614   23. (i) $\dfrac{1}{3}$ (ii) 20°C

(iii) $\dfrac{1}{5} \le p(c) \le \dfrac{17}{25}$ (iv) $\dfrac{7}{15}$ (v) $1 - \dfrac{8}{\dfrac{5}{9}(t-32)}$ or $1 - \dfrac{72}{5(t-32)}$ or $1 - \dfrac{72}{5t-160}$ or $\dfrac{5t-232}{5t-160}$

(vi) 54·5°F   (vii) $50 \le t \le 77$

Exercise 12.4

1.

Function	f	g	h	k
Domain	1, 2, 3, 4	1, 2, 3, 4	1, 2, 3	1, 2, 3, 4
Range	5, 7, 8	5, 7, 8	5, 7, 8	5, 7, 8, 9
Codomain	5, 7, 8	5, 6, 7, 8	5, 7, 8, 9	5, 7, 8, 9
Injective	✗	✗	✓	✓
Surjective	✓	✗	✗	✓
Bijective	✗	✗	✗	✓

2. (i) (a) function   (b) injective   (ii) (a) function   (b) not injective   (iii) (a) not a function
(iv) (a) not a function. However, if the domain was restricted to values of x greater than or equal to
the value of x where the curve cuts the x-axis, then this would be an injective function   (v) (a) not a
function   (vi) (a) not a function, as input $x = 0$ has no output. However, would be an injective
function if $x \in \mathbb{R} \backslash 0$ 3. (i) (a) any vertical line will cut the graph of $f(x) = x^2 + 3$ once, therefore
$f(x)$ is a function   (b) $f(1) = 4$ and $f(-1) = 4$, two different inputs have the same output or a
horizontal can intersect the curve more than once   (c) not surjective, some horizontal lines will not
intersect the curve, for example $f(x) = 2$ (ii) $x \ge 0$ or $x \le 0$ 4. (i) $(x-1)^2 - 4$ (ii) $k = 1$
5. (i) (a) $-1·7, 0, 1·7$ (b) max $(-1, 4)$, min $(1, 0)$ (ii) (a) not injective; horizontal line can
intersect the curve more than once   (b) surjective; horizontal line will intersect the curve at least
once   (iii) $-3 \le x \le -1$ or $-1 \le x \le 1$ or $1 \le x \le 3$

6.

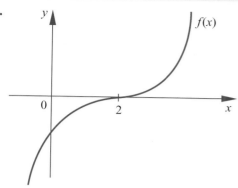

Bijective function
Any vertical or horizontal line will intersect the curve once only.

7. yes, any vertical or horizontal line will intersect the curve (line), ╱ or ╲, once only
8. all even numbers in the range have no inputs in the domain   **9. (i)** injective **(ii)** injective
(iii) not injective **(iv)** injective   **10.** yes; any vertical or horizontal line will intersect the curve once only
11. (i) (a)

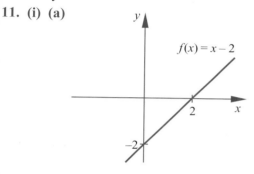

(b)

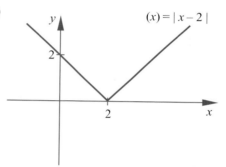

(ii) f is bijective; any vertical or horizontal line will intersect the curve once only
(iii) (a) g is not injective; a horizontal line can intersect the curve more than once. Alternatively,
$g(1) = g(3) = 1$, different inputs have the same output, therefore not injective **(b)** not surjective;
some horizontal lines will not intersect the curve, for example $g(x) = -1$.
12. (i) (a)

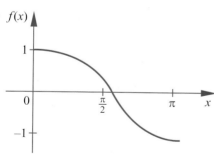

(b)

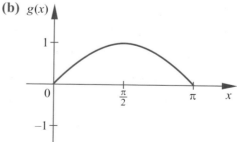

(ii) yes, any vertical or horizontal line will intersect the curve once in the given domain
(iii) not surjective, therefore not bijective, as a horizontal line can intersect the curve more than once
13. every vertical or horizontal line will intersect the graph once only in the given domain

Exercise 12.5

1. (i) $\dfrac{x}{3}$ (ii) $x-3$ (iii) $\dfrac{x-1}{3}$ (iv) $\dfrac{x+5}{2}$ (v) $\dfrac{x+5}{4}$ (vi) $\dfrac{3-x}{5}$ (vii) $\dfrac{2}{x}$ (viii) $\dfrac{x+2}{2}$

(ix) $\dfrac{3}{x-1}$ (x) $\dfrac{x}{1+x}$ (xi) $\dfrac{x}{2x-3}$ (xii) $\dfrac{1}{x-1}$ **2.** (i) $\dfrac{x+2}{3}$ (ii) $(1, 1)$

5. yes; $f\,g(x) = g\,f(x)$ **6.** (ii) $\dfrac{1+x}{x}$ **7.** (i) $\dfrac{2}{3-x}$; 3 (ii) 1, 2 **8.** $(-1, -1), (1, 1)$

9. (i) $\dfrac{x+3}{2}$ **10.** (i) $\dfrac{x-16}{3}$ **11.** (i) $(x-5)^3$ or $\sqrt[3]{x-5}$ (ii) (a) 13 (b) 2 **12.** 7

13. (i) $0 \le y \le 4{\cdot}5$ (ii) 2; 3 (iv) $f^2(3) = f(4{\cdot}5)$, which is outside the domain $0 \le x \le 3$ (v) 2

14. (i) 4 (ii) 2 (iii) 1·5 (iv) $f^3(2{\cdot}5) = f^2(4)$, which is outside the domain $0 \le x \le 3{\cdot}5$

15. (ii) $g^{-1}(x) = 2 + \sqrt{x},\ x \in \mathbb{R}$ and $x \ge 0$

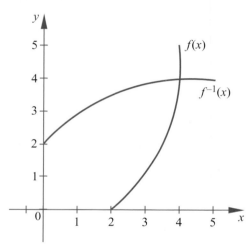

16. (i) $3 + \sqrt{x+8};\ x \ge -8$ (ii) $-2 + \sqrt{x+6};\ x \ge -6$

(iii) $1 + \sqrt{5-x};\ x \le 5$ (iv) $-8 - \sqrt{3-x};\ x \le 3$

17. (i) $y \ge -1$ (ii) $2 + \sqrt{x+1}$ (iii)

$x \ge -1,\ y \ge 2$

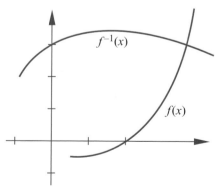

Exercise 12.6

1. (i) 20·09   (ii) 0·37   (iii) 22·17   (iv) 0·69   (v) 0·55   (vi) 0·07   (vii) −1·61
2. (i) 4   (ii) 3   (iii) 2·5   (iv) −1·5   3. (i) $x + 2$ (ii) $5x − 1$ (iii) x^2 (iv) $\sqrt{x}$
4. (i) 2·01   (ii) 2·82   (iii) 3·71   (iv) 1·87   (v) −0·693   (vi) 0   (vii) 3·69   (viii) 18·2   (ix) 13·6
5. (i)

x	−2	−1	0	1	2	3
e^x	0·1	0·4	1	2·7	7·4	20·1

(ii)

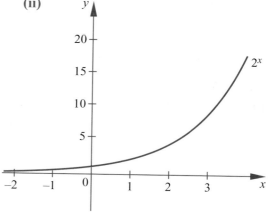

(iii) (a) 0·7   (b) 4·5   (c) 11   (d) 14·9

6. (i)

t	0	1	2	3	4	5
$P(t)$	5	8·2	9·3	9·8	9·9	10

(ii) as $t \to \infty$, $10 − 5e^{-t} \to 10$

7. (i)

x	0	1	2	3
$f(x)$	8	4·2	2·8	2·3

(ii) 0·7   (iii) 0·69

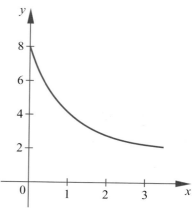

8. (i) $\frac{1}{2}\ln x$ (ii) $1 + \ln(x − 3)$ (iii) $5 + e^x$ (iv) $e^{x+5} − 2$ 10. (i) $1 + e^x$ (ii) 2   (iii) 4
(iv) $(x − 1)^2$ 11. (i) 2   12. $\ln 2$ 13. (i) $a = 1$ (iii) $y \geq −1$ (iv) $−\ln 2$ 14. (ii) 5%
15. (i) 70°C   (ii) 6 mins   16. (i) 1,040   (ii) 80·5 days   17. (i) 5   (ii) $\frac{1}{4}\ln 2$ (iv) 9·3 weeks

Exercise 13.1

1. (ii) 6   (iii) 6   2. (iv) −4   (v) −4   (vi) −4   (viii) 4   3. (iii) 4   4. (ii) 3
5. (i) 9   (ii) $(3 + t)^2$ or $9 + 6t + t^2$ (iii) $6 + t$ (iv) the slope of the tangent at P

Exercise 13.2

1. 4   2. 8   3. 1   4. −3   5. $2x$ 6. $2x - 2$ 7. $2x + 11$ 8. $2x + 4$

9. $2x - 2$ 10. $4x$ 11. $4x + 3$ 12. $6x - 5$ 14. (iii) the slope of $y = 4$ is zero

Exercise 14.1

1. $3x^2$ 2. $12x^3$ 3. $-10x$ 4. 3   5. −2   6. 0   7. 0   8. $-2x^{-3}$ or $-\dfrac{2}{x^3}$

9. $-6x^{-4}$ or $-\dfrac{6}{x^4}$ 10. $10x^{-6}$ or $\dfrac{10}{x^6}$ 11. $2x^{-\frac{2}{3}}$ or $\dfrac{2}{x^{\frac{2}{3}}}$ 12. $-x^{-2}$ or $-\dfrac{1}{x^2}$ 13. $\dfrac{1}{2}x^{-\frac{1}{2}}$ or $\dfrac{1}{2x^{\frac{1}{2}}}$

14. $-\dfrac{1}{2}x^{-\frac{3}{2}}$ or $-\dfrac{1}{2x^{\frac{3}{2}}}$ 15. $-\dfrac{2}{3}x^{-\frac{5}{3}}$ or $-\dfrac{2}{3x^{\frac{5}{3}}}$ 16. $3x^2 - 5$ 17. $-2x$

18. $2x + 5x^{-2}$ or $2x + \dfrac{5}{x^2}$ 19. $4x + 12x^{-5}$ or $4x + \dfrac{12}{x^5}$ 20. $-2x^{-3} - x^{-2}$ or $-\dfrac{2}{x^3} - \dfrac{1}{x^2}$

21. $4x^3 - 4x^{-3}$ or $4x^3 - \dfrac{4}{x^3}$ 22. $3x^{-\frac{1}{2}} + x^{-\frac{3}{2}}$ or $\dfrac{3}{\sqrt{x}} + \dfrac{3}{x^{\frac{3}{2}}}$

23. $-3x^{-2} - 4x^{-3} - 2x^{-\frac{4}{3}}$ or $-\dfrac{3}{x^2} - \dfrac{4}{x^3} - \dfrac{2}{x^{\frac{4}{3}}}$ 24. $-2x^{-2} + \dfrac{1}{2}x^{-\frac{3}{2}} - x^{-\frac{4}{3}}$ or $-\dfrac{2}{x^2} - \dfrac{1}{2x^{\frac{3}{2}}} - \dfrac{1}{x^{\frac{4}{3}}}$

25. $24x + 12$ 26. $2 - 12x^2$ 27. $36x - 24$ 28. $2x^{-3}$ or $\dfrac{2}{x^3}$ 29. $2 - 16x^{-3}$ or $2 - \dfrac{16}{x^3}$

30. $-\dfrac{1}{4}x^{-\frac{3}{2}}$ or $-\dfrac{1}{4x^{\frac{3}{2}}}$ 31. $\dfrac{3}{4}x^{-\frac{5}{2}} - \dfrac{1}{4}x^{-\frac{3}{2}}$ or $\dfrac{3}{4x^{\frac{5}{2}}} - \dfrac{1}{4x^{\frac{3}{2}}}$ 32. $2x^{-\frac{3}{2}} - 6x^{-4}$ or $-\dfrac{2}{x^{\frac{3}{2}}} - \dfrac{6}{x^4}$

33. $-2x^{-\frac{5}{3}} + 8x^{-\frac{7}{3}}$ or $-\dfrac{2}{x^{\frac{5}{3}}} + \dfrac{8}{x^{\frac{7}{3}}}$ 34. (i) 8   (ii) 6   35. $\dfrac{1}{27}$ 36. 13   37. (i) −5   (ii) −4

38. −8   39. 10π 40. 25π 41. $k = 2$ 42. $a = 3$ 44. (ii) (a) 0, 1   (b) $\dfrac{1}{2}$

Exercise 14.2

1. $4x - 5$ 2. $3x^2 + 4x - 13$ 3. $9x^2 - 20x + 17$ 4. $3x^2 - 6x - 10$

5. $20x^3 - 84x^2 + 30x$ 6. $24x^3 - 21x^2 + 4x + 8$ 7. $\dfrac{1}{(x + 1)^2}$ 8. $\dfrac{7}{(x + 3)^2}$

9. $\dfrac{-3x^2 + 2x - 6}{(x^2 - 2)^2}$ 10. $\dfrac{4x}{(x^2 + 1)^2}$ 11. $\dfrac{-x^2 + 2x - 2}{(2x - x^2)^2}$ 12. $\dfrac{2(x^2 + 6)}{(x^2 + x - 6)^2}$ 13. $12(3x + 2)^3$

14. $6(x + 1)(x^2 + 2x)^2$ 15. $20x(2x^2 + 1)^4$ 16. $2(4x + 2)^{\frac{1}{2}}$ or $\dfrac{2}{\sqrt{4x + 2}}$

17. $-2(2x - 5)^{-2}$ or $-\dfrac{2}{(2x - 5)^2}$ 18. $\dfrac{2(1 - x)}{(2x^2 - 4x)^{\frac{3}{2}}}$ 19. $6x(x + 1)(x + 3)^3$

20. $6(2x + 1)(x^2 + 2x)^2$ 21. $6x(2x + 3)(4x + 3)$ 22. $\dfrac{x^2}{\sqrt{2x + 1}} + 2x\sqrt{2x + 1}$

23. $\dfrac{x^2}{1 + x^2} + \sqrt{1 + x^2}$ 24. $-\dfrac{1}{2x^2}\sqrt{\dfrac{x}{x + 1}}$ 25. $\dfrac{3}{16}$ 26. $\dfrac{16}{27}$

Exercise 14.3

1. $4\cos 4x$ **2.** $-3\sin 3x$ **3.** $2\sec^2 2x$ **4.** $2\cos(2x-3)$ **5.** $3\sec^2(3x+2)$

6. $\sec^2 x - \sin x$ **7.** $x^2\cos x + 2x\sin x$ **8.** $3x\sec^2 x + 3\tan x$ **9.** $-2x^2\sin 2x + 2x\cos 2x$

10. $\dfrac{x\cos x - \sin x}{x^2}$ **11.** $\dfrac{\cos x}{(1-\sin x)^2}$ **12.** $\dfrac{\cos^2 x - \sin^2 x + \sin x}{\cos^2 x}$ **13.** $-3\sin x\cos^2 x$

14. $8\sin 4x\cos 4x$ **15.** $12\tan^3 3x\sec^2 3x$ **16.** $6\sin x\cos x(1+\sin^2 x)^2$ **17.** $\dfrac{\cos x}{2\sqrt{\sin x}}$

18. $-\dfrac{\sin 2x}{\sqrt{\cos 2x}}$ **22.** 0 **23.** $\sqrt{3}$ **24.** 1

Exercise 14.4

1. $\dfrac{2}{\sqrt{1-4x^2}}$ **2.** $\dfrac{3}{1+9x^2}$ **3.** $\dfrac{1}{\sqrt{2x-x^2}}$ **4.** $\dfrac{1}{2x^2+2x+1}$ **5.** $\dfrac{2x}{1+x^4}$ **6.** $\dfrac{6x^2}{\sqrt{1-4x^6}}$

7. $\dfrac{10\sin^{-1}5x}{\sqrt{1-25x^2}}$ **8.** $\dfrac{3}{x^2+9}$ **9.** $\dfrac{1}{2\sqrt{1-\dfrac{x^2}{4}}}$ or $\dfrac{1}{\sqrt{4-x^2}}$ **10.** -1 **11.** $\dfrac{x}{\sqrt{1-x^2}}+\sin^{-1}x$

12. $\dfrac{12x}{1+4x^2}+6\tan^{-1}2x$ **13.** 4 **15.** $-\dfrac{2}{7}$ **20. (ii)** $\dfrac{1}{1+x^2}$

Exercise 14.5

1. $4e^{4x}$ **2.** $6e^{3x}$ **3.** $2xe^{x^2}$ **4.** $(2x-5)e^{x^2-5x}$ **5.** $8xe^{4x^2}$ **6.** $-e^{-x}$ or $-\dfrac{1}{e^x}$

7. $-10e^{-2x}$ or $\dfrac{-10}{e^{2x}}$ **8.** $-4xe^{-x^2}$ or $\dfrac{-4x}{e^{x^2}}$ **9.** $\cos xe^{\sin x}$ **10.** $-2\sin 2xe^{\cos 2x}$

11. $4\sec^2 xe^{4\tan x}$ **12.** $(x\cos x+\sin x)e^{x\sin x}$ **13.** $e^x(1+x)$ **14.** $xe^{5x}(5x+2)$

15. $e^{2x}(2\cos x-\sin x)$ **16.** $e^{-x^2}(\cos x-2x\sin x)$ or $\dfrac{\cos x-2x\sin x}{e^{x^2}}$

17. $2xe^{-2x}(1-x)$ or $\dfrac{2x(1-x)}{e^{2x}}$ **18.** $8xe^{x^2}(3+e^{x^2})^3$ **19.** $\dfrac{4xe^{2x^2}}{(3-e^{2x^2})^2}$ **20.** $\dfrac{-4e^{4x}}{\sqrt{1-2e^{4x}}}$

22. (i) e **(ii)** $-e^2$ **26.** $1, 2$

Exercise 14.6

1. $\dfrac{1}{x}$ **2.** $\dfrac{2}{2x+3}$ **3.** $\dfrac{2x}{x^2+3}$ **4.** $-\tan x$ **5.** $-\dfrac{1}{x}$ **6.** $\dfrac{e^x}{e^x+2}$

7. $\dfrac{2\cos 2x}{\sin 2x}$ or $2\cot 2x$ **8.** $\dfrac{3\sec^2 3x}{\tan 3x}$ **9.** 2 **10.** $2+2\ln x$ **11.** $\dfrac{x^3}{x+1}+3x^2\ln(x+1)$

12. $x+2x\ln 4x$ **13.** $\dfrac{1}{x(x+1)}$ **14.** $\dfrac{4}{2x+3}$ **15.** -1 **16.** $\dfrac{x}{x^2+1}$

17. $\dfrac{1}{2 \tan x}$ or $\dfrac{1}{2} \cot x$ 18. $\dfrac{1}{2x(1 + x)}$ 20. (i) $3e$ (ii) 1 21. $\dfrac{1}{e}$ 22. $\dfrac{1}{2}$

23. (ii) $-\dfrac{1}{e^3}$ 24. e 27. (i) $a^x(1 + a^x)$ 28. $-\dfrac{5}{3}$

Exercise 15.1

1. $2x + y - 7 = 0$ 2. $3x - y + 5 = 0$ 3. $6x - y + 7 = 0$ 4. $4x - 6y - 1 = 0$

5. $2x + y - 4 = 0$ 6. $x - y - 1 = 0$ 7. $x - y + 2 = 0$ 8. $x - y = 0$ 9. $3x - y + 1 = 0$

10. (i) $(-2, 2), (0, 0)$ (ii) $x - y + 4 = 0, x - y = 0$ 11. $(2, 15)$ 12. $a = 2; b = -5$

13. $p = 3; q = 4$ 14. (ii) $9y + 11 = 0$ 15. $p = 2; q = -8$

16. (i) $a = 2; b = 13; c = -7$ (ii) $(-7, 0); \left(\dfrac{1}{2}, 0\right)$

(iii)

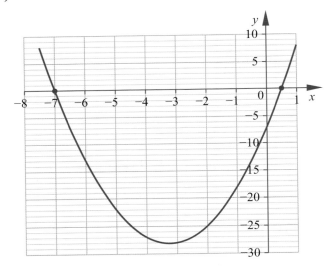

17. (i) $a = 1$; $b = -5$; $c = 2$; $d = 8$ **(iii)** $(-1, 0)$; $(2, 0)$

(iv)

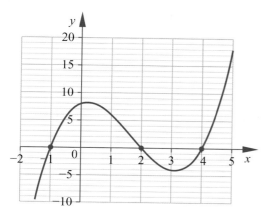

Exercise 15.2

1. (i) $x < 1$ **(ii)** $x > 1$ **2. (ii)** the graph is always increasing

3. (ii) the graph is always decreasing

5. $-1 < x < 3$ **6.** $x < -3$ or $x > 1$ **9.** $x > \dfrac{1}{e}$

Exercise 15.3

1. min $(1, 4)$ **2.** min $(-1, -8)$ **3.** max $(-3, 19)$

4. max $(1, -1)$, min $(3, -5)$, POI $(2, -3)$ **5.** max $(2, 16)$, min $(-2, 16)$, POI $(0, 0)$

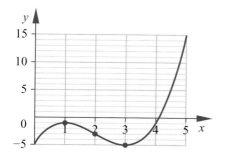

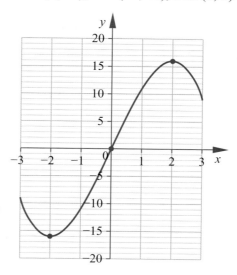

6. max (1, 17), min (5, −15), POI (3, 1)   7. max (0, 2), min (−2, −2), POI (−1, 0)

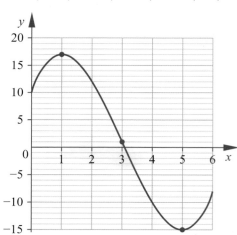

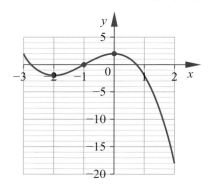

8. (i) max (−1, −2), min (1, 2)   9. (0, 0), (2, −16)

10. (i) max (0, 0), min (1, −1), min (−1, −1)   (ii) POI $\left(\dfrac{1}{\sqrt{3}}, -\dfrac{5}{9}\right)$, POI $\left(-\dfrac{1}{\sqrt{3}}, -\dfrac{5}{9}\right)$

11. max (2, 1), min $\left(-\dfrac{1}{2}, -4\right)$ 12. max (10, 2,520), min (20, 2,020)

13. min (−2, −7), max (0, 1), min $\left(5, -\dfrac{371}{4}\right)$ 14. min (e, −e)   15. max $\left(\dfrac{1}{e}, -e\right)$

16. min (0, 1)   17. min $\left(-1, -\dfrac{1}{e}\right)$ 18. max $\left(2, \dfrac{4}{e^2}\right)$, min (0, 0)   19. min (e, 0)

20. (i) $e^{-x}(1 - x)$ (ii) $e^{-x}(x - 2)$ (iii) max $\left(1, \dfrac{1}{e}\right)$ (iv) $\left(2, \dfrac{2}{e^2}\right)$ 21. (i) $a = -3$ (ii) max

22. (i) $p = -2$; $q = 8$; $r = 10$ 23. $p = 2$; $q = -6$

24. (i) $2e^{2x}(\cos 2x - \sin 2x)$; $-8e^{2x} \sin 2x$ (ii) $\dfrac{e^{\frac{\pi}{4}}}{\sqrt{2}}$ or $\dfrac{e^{\frac{\pi}{4}}\sqrt{2}}{2}$ 25. (i) (0, −1)   (ii) min

26. $\left(\ln\left(\dfrac{a}{2}\right), f\left(\ln\dfrac{a}{2}\right)\right)$ 27. (i) max (0, 36); min $\left(2k, 36 - \dfrac{4k^3}{3}\right)$ (ii) $k = 3$ (iii) $0 < k < 3$

29. min $\left(\dfrac{k}{3}, \dfrac{k^3}{9}\right)$, max $\left(0, \dfrac{10k^3}{27}\right)$

Exercise 15.4

1. (i) $y = 10 - x$ (ii) 25; 5; 5   2. 18   3. $x = 6$; 144 m^2 4. (i) $y = \dfrac{18 - 3x}{2}$

(ii) $36x - 6x^2$ (iii) $x = 3$; $y = \dfrac{9}{2}$ 6. $\dfrac{5}{2}$ revs/s   7. (i) $80 - 2x$ (ii) $80x - 2x^2$

(iii) 40 cm by 20 cm   8. 200 km   9. (i) $12 - x$ (ii) 256 cm^3

10. 4 cm by 6 cm by 12 cm **11. (i)** $y = \dfrac{162}{x}$ **(ii)** 36 cm **12. (ii)** $\dfrac{2}{3}(150x - 2x^3)$

(iii) 5; $\dfrac{1,000}{3}$ cm^3 **13.** 5 cm; 2,250 cm^3 **14. (i)** $y = \dfrac{96}{x}$ **(ii) (a)** $(x-4)(y-6)$

(b) $(x-4)\left(\dfrac{96}{x} - 6\right)$ **(c)** 8 cm by 12 cm **15.** 2 cm; 144 cm^3 **16. (i)** $d = \dfrac{800}{x}$

(iii) 2,048; 64 cm by 20 cm **17. (i)** $\theta = \dfrac{12 - 2r}{r}$ **(iii)** 9; 2 **18. (i)** $h = \dfrac{48 - r^2}{r}$

(ii) $r = 4$ cm; $h = 8$ cm **(iii)** 128π cm^3 **19. (i)** $h = \dfrac{300 - r^2}{2r}$

(iii) $r = h = 10$ cm; $V = 1,000\pi$ cm^3 **20. (i)** $A = \pi r^2 + \dfrac{1,024\pi}{r}$

(ii) $r = h = 8$ cm **21. (i)** $h = \dfrac{1,000}{\pi r^2}$ **(ii)** $A = 2\pi rh + 8r^2$ **(iii)** $A = \dfrac{2,000}{r} + 8r^2$

(iv) $r = 5$ cm; $h = \dfrac{40}{\pi}$ cm; 18c **22. (i)** $r = \dfrac{1,600\pi}{x}$ **(iii)** 160π **24.** $x = 1$; 27 units^2

25. (i) $(p, 6 - p^2)$ **(ii)** $A = 2p(6 - p^2)$ **(iii)** $\sqrt{2}$ **26. (i)** $\sqrt{x^2 + \dfrac{16}{x^2}}$ **(ii)** $x = 2$

(iii) $2\sqrt{2}$ **27.** $-\dfrac{c^2}{4m}$ (m is negative) **28. (i)** $r^2 = 300 - h^2$ **(ii) (a)** 10 cm

(b) $10\sqrt{2}$ cm **29.** 128π cm^3 **30. (i)** $9 - h^2$ **(ii)** $\sqrt{6}$ **31.** 6 m

32. (i) (a) $(155 - x)$ m **(b)** $\sqrt{3,600 + x^2}$ m **(c)** $\left(\dfrac{155 - x}{260} + \dfrac{\sqrt{3,600 + x^2}}{100}\right)$ mins **(ii)** 25; 69 s

33. (i) $10t$ m; $20t$ m **(ii)** $|100 - 10t|$ m; $|300 - 20t|$ m **(iv)** 14 s **34. (iii)** $\dfrac{256\pi}{9}$ cm^3

Exercise 15.5

1. (i)

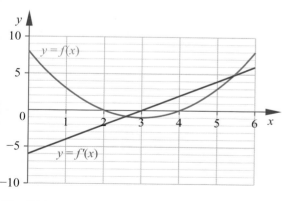

(ii) $f'(x) = 2x - 6$

2. (i)

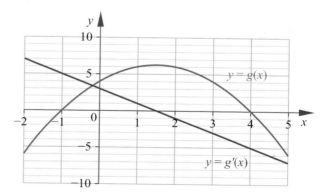

(ii) $g'(x) = 3 - 2x$

3. (i)

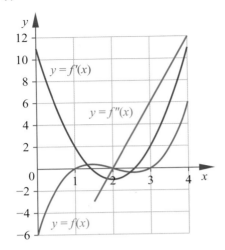

(ii) $f'(x) = 3x^2 - 12x + 11$ **(iii)** $P(1\cdot4, 0)$; $Q(2\cdot6, 0)$ **(iv)** min $(1\cdot4, 0\cdot4)$; max $(2\cdot6, -0\cdot4)$

(v) $f'(x) = 6x - 12$ **(vi)** $(2, 0)$ **4. (ii)** A **5. (ii)** A

Exercise 15.6

1. 15 **2.** 8 **3.** 100π

4. (i) $1\cdot5$ m **(ii)** $\dfrac{ds}{dt} = 29\cdot4 - 9\cdot8t$; the (upward) velocity of the ball **(iii)** $45\cdot6$ m

(iv) (a) $29\cdot4$ m/s **(b)** 0 m/s **(c)** $-19\cdot6$ m/s **(d)** the ball is falling

5. (i) $(3t^2 - 18t + 15)$ m/s **(ii)** 15 m/s **(iii)** 9 m; 23 m **(iv)** 6 m/s²

6. (i) 21 m/s **(ii)** $6\dfrac{2}{3}$ s **(iii)** 100 m **7. (i)** 10 cm/yr **(ii)** $1\cdot6$ cm/yr **8. (i)** $\dfrac{v}{50}$ **(ii)** $\dfrac{8}{25}$

9. (i) $93\cdot75$ g/ls **10. (i)** $7\cdot5$ m **(ii)** $9\dfrac{4}{9}$ m/s **11. (i)** $2\cdot2$ m **(ii)** $\dfrac{9}{25}$ m/yr; $\dfrac{1}{9}$ m/yr; $\dfrac{1}{25}$ m/yr

(iii) $\dfrac{9}{(t+5)^2}$ **12. (i)** $160{,}000$ m³ **(ii)** $122{,}500$ m³ **(iii)** $7{,}500$ m³/min

(iv) $7{,}000$ m³/min **13. (i)** $k = 5$ **(ii)** $q = 3$ **14.** 0 m/s; 16 m/s **15. (i)** $\theta = \dfrac{20 - 2r}{r}$

16. (i) 30 cm **(ii)** $\dfrac{60}{3t+1}$ **(iii) (a)** 15 m/yr **(b)** 6 m/yr **(c)** $2\dfrac{2}{5}$ m/yr **17. (ii)** 10 m/s

(iii) 25 m **18. (i)** $\dfrac{2}{(t+3)^2}$ m/s **(ii)** 7 s **19. (i)** $\dfrac{d\theta}{dt} = (20 - 4t)$ rads/s **(ii)** 5 s **(iii)** 2 rads

20. (i)

t	0	2	4	6	8		10	12	14	16	18
$f(t)$	2,000	1,928	1,728	1,400	944	$g(t)$	800	624	416	176	−96

(ii)

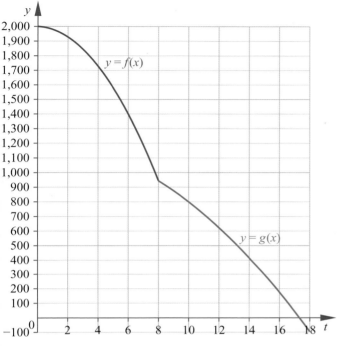

(iii) 17 s   **(iv)** −196 m/s   **(v)** −88 m/s

Exercise 15.7

1. $\dfrac{du}{dx}$ **2.** $\dfrac{dV}{dr}$ **3.** $\dfrac{dt}{dr}$ **4.** $\dfrac{dA}{dr}$ **5.** $\dfrac{dh}{dV}$ **6.** $\dfrac{dt}{dr}$ **7.** $5(4x - 3)$ **8.** 6   **9.** 16

10. 6   **11.** 10π m²/s   **12.** 2 cm/s   **13. (i)** $\dfrac{dx}{dt} = \dfrac{4}{x}$ cm/s   **(ii)** $\dfrac{1}{4}$ cm/s   **14.** $\dfrac{1}{32}$

15. (i) (a) $-\dfrac{5}{\pi r^2}$ cm/hr   **(b)** $-\dfrac{5}{4\pi r^2}$ cm/hr   **(ii)** -8 cm²/hr   **16.** $\dfrac{dA}{dt} = 12$ cm²/s; $\dfrac{dV}{dt} = 15$ cm³/s

17. $\dfrac{1}{5\pi}$ cm/s   **18.** 12 cm³/s